ENDS OF MAGIC

ALEXANDER OLSON

Antimage

Ends of Magic

Book One

Alexander Olson

Timeless
Wind

First published by Timeless Wind Publishing LLC 2023

First edition

Editing by Silas Sontag and Lorne Ryburn.

Cover art by Miblart.

For my mom, who read me Sherlock Holmes as a bedtime story.

North
Deadwatch
Woodsden
Pilriden
Thop
Wilsden
Stonefall
Honsy
Sheepcall
Farfield
Riverbank
Bridgeguard
Firewatch
Gemore
Tenby
Agmon
Kulketh
Nadrang
Grasmere
Grimsby
Woodhurst
Cromer
Blackburn
Tarren
Surfeld
Litcliff

Skargess
Lerwik
Halsmet
Giantsrest
Azamar
Ardglass
Map of
Davrar

Chapter 1

A Long Trip

Nathan twisted the key to his apartment and felt the heavy bolt clunk back. He took three steps into the darkened single-room studio, swinging the door closed and shucking his backpack into the center of the bright carpet that took up most of the open floor space. Then, he flopped into the overstuffed armchair that was the largest piece of furniture in the place, aside from the bed.

It had been a nightmare getting the chair up the stairs and into the apartment, but Nathan's friends had earned their pizza for helping him move out of the graduate student dorms a few years ago. Besides, he'd found the comfortable chair marked "up for grabs" on the street. On a graduate student's stipend it was hard to turn down comfortable furniture for the low price of *free.*

Sighing, Nathan twisted in the chair to fish his phone from underneath his wallet and keys, pulling up the meditation app. He'd started doing mindfulness meditation almost a year ago to help deal with the anxiety of graduate school. To his surprise, it had helped.

I'm definitely better about not just sitting in this chair and feeling bad about everything I should be doing. Instead, I can meditate and feel productive about not doing anything!

Nathan started the session, listening to the soothing voice through his earbuds as he relaxed deeper into the cushions. He let his mind go still, silencing his inner voice and focusing on the sensations of breathing, of gravity pulling his body into the chair.

Time passed, and Nathan didn't focus on anything. He didn't make plans, and he especially didn't worry about the fellowship application due soon. Or tomorrow's experiment that would cap off the last two months of work. If that experiment worked, it would be a big step forward towards his doctorate. If it didn't... well. It depended on how it didn't work. Nathan realized he was spiraling, and with a moment of attention, the worries dissipated like smoke.

Some more time passed, and another thought intruded on Nathan's mind.

[A kinnar avi, nukol ad kayikxrokko, dlan avail-xalark da dhak!]

He was confused.

The words had emerged clearly in his consciousness in a deep, booming voice, but he didn't understand where they'd come from or the language itself. They hadn't come from the earbuds – the words had seemed to inject themselves directly into his brain.

He was about to stop meditating early and start making dinner when it happened again, the words more forceful this time. They pressed against the inside of his head, grinding and overwhelming.

[A KINNAR AVI. DANO DA NO JAILROAV UDLAKK DHO XAAK. A KINNAR AVI]

Nathan's eyes snapped open and he tore off his earbuds, exhaling with frustration.

I don't need this now! Can't it wait until after the cytometry experiment? Just gimme a 24-hour rain check.

He started to stand, but the voice crashed into his skull for a third time. It wiped out all thought.

[DANO DA NO]

Nathan didn't feel the chair under him anymore, or the clothes on his skin. His eyes were open and saw nothing but black. Air tore itself from his open mouth, and his ears spiked in pain.

This must be what being in vacuum feels like. Why aren't there any stars?

Nathan flailed, accomplishing nothing but feeling the vacuum pulling on his lungs and eyes and the spit in his mouth boiling away. He tumbled in absolute darkness, with no reference point and no sense of anything other than himself.

After what must have been mere seconds but felt much longer, he tumbled into brightness, landing on his butt on smooth stone. With vision tunneling, he heaved deep breaths, paying attention to nothing but pumping air in and out of his abused lungs. After a minute of slowing breaths, he looked around the room.

Why am I naked?

He was sitting in a shallow bowl of cold stone in the center of a large room. The entire place was made of the same smooth, pale stone that was under his butt, all lit evenly by a grid of bright lights in the ceiling. It looked like a clean-room done in tan marble.

The bowl was only a foot deep and several feet wide, so he could see out easily. The room around him was decorated with several pedestals capped with orbs shining in muted purples, yellows and blues. They were linked together by a complex grid of glowing metal that looked like multiple overlapping circuit boards. The metal dimmed in color before his eyes, losing some of its blinding radiance.

The formation wasn't centered on Nathan, but rather right behind him. He scooted around, sitting on his hands to protect his butt from the cold stone. There was a metal filigree arch supporting a horizontal disk of exquisitely carved stone eight feet across. Multicolored lights emanated from a series of enormous gemstones inlaid into the arch and the stone. Over the disc hovered a horizontal portal into darkness. The portal rapidly shrank until it vanished with a tiny pop.

Nathan stared blankly at the disk, losing himself in the fractal-like carvings for a moment.

Whatever that is, it's beautiful. It's like an arcane language or art, all carved with mathematical precision. Magic?

Nathan's attention was drawn by something moving beyond the arch. There was a man on a low dais at the edge of the room, and it looked like he was concluding a victory dance. The man pumped his fists and bounced on his feet like somebody who had just won the lottery, his orange robe flapping. Just behind him were a pair of humanoid statues with eerie levels of detail, flanking the door out of the room.

The orange-robed man saw Nathan looking at him, and held out his palm, the semi-universal gesture for "stop" as he mouthed a word that didn't look like "stop" at all. He busied himself at a wide control panel, complete with flashing lights. The grid of equipment surrounding Nathan dimmed even faster, quickly turning into a mix of shiny metal in steel, copper and gold tones. The shining orbs lost their glow, many of them cracking apart with a faint tinkling sound that sounded expensive.

The man hopped down from the dais, nearly skipping over to Nathan's bowl. He kept his attention fixed on Nathan, not sparing a second glance at the complicated apparatus that he threaded his bulk through with a deftness bourne of familiarity.

Nathan found the man's single-minded focus unnerving and looked around for anything to cover himself with. He settled for simply putting a hand in front of his genitals before looking up to observe the man who was approaching Nathan's bowl.

He looked to be a man of average height in late-middle age, fairly pudgy, with a full head of black hair and a wide, stubbly face. His eyes glowed orange (*what?*), and his face was full of excitement as he stopped in front of Nathan. He clapped his hands together and spoke in a low, fast voice. "Dhak ak ka odadark!"

It sounded like the same deep voice Nathan had heard in his head earlier, and Nathan looked up at him dumbly and spoke with a raw throat. "Excuse me, sorry, but what?" The man slapped one hand across each eye in a gesture of self-admonishment, before stepping forward and laying a hand on Nathan's forehead.

[Ankiko Rurkiuko]

Orange light emitted from the man's mouth with the words – and from the hand on Nathan's forehead. Nathan's head spiked in pain, a pressure and tightness squeezing down behind both temples like a concussion combined with the worst migraine Nathan had ever had. His eyes slammed shut and Nathan collapsed sideways. Both hands flew to his head, modesty forgotten.

After a brief moment, he heard the man's voice again, and Nathan felt the language was more familiar than before. Cold and unyielding hands slid underneath him, lifting Nathan gently off the floor as he tried to curl into a ball around the pain in his head.

Whatever held him felt more like a statue than a person. Nathan felt its steps carry him across the room, down a staircase and through a hallway. The pain in his head receded rapidly, and he blinked teary eyes open. He was being carried by a humanoid statue made of the same sand-colored marble as the walls. A multicolored opalescence shone from its eyes. Then, a blue box flashed in Nathan's vision, front and center.

Welcome to Davrar

Davrar will help you survive

Adapting you to the local biosystem

Davrar is calibrating to your understanding and determining your capabilities

Please, be patient, this will not take long

What.

Nathan desperately wanted to figure out what any of that meant, but the box vanished as soon as he parsed what it said. The man in orange hovered next to him and when he saw Nathan open his eyes, he heaved a relieved sigh and started to talk quickly. "Hail the Giant, you must be so confused. Be patient for just a moment and all will be explained." Each word caused another pulse of pain, but they were just faint wisps compared to the earlier migraine.

Hang on, that wasn't English or Spanish. And neither was the text in the box. How did I understand that? Was that magic? I'm being carried by a statue?

The man had distinctly spoken in the same language as before, but this time Nathan understood all the words and the grammar. His head was sore, his breathing uncertain, and too many questions and observations swirled in his mind, so he let the statue carry him down another flight of stairs and to a metal door.

Beyond the door was a small stone room in the same seamless pale marble, complete with a bed, table and two chairs in light wood. In one corner of the room, a trough of water smoothly ran underneath a hollowed-out seat. The statue (*or golem? Animated object?*) gently set Nathan down in one of the chairs on one side of the table. The orange-robed man smoothly slid into the seat across the table, and his orange eyes focused on Nathan's face like two search-lights. Given that they were faintly glowing, it wasn't too bad of a comparison.

"I will explain. I am Grand Dimension Archmage Taeol dho Droxol, seventh finger and third researcher of the Ascendant Academy of Giantsrest. I have summoned you here in a grand quest for Insights and power. I scried across dimensions to find..."

He was interrupted by Nathan loudly coughing into his elbow, his lungs scraped raw. Taeol's eyes widened briefly, and he took in Nathan's teary eyes and naked body. "Oh, a *gauntlet* of apologies. You have had a long journey." His lips curved into a self-satisfied smile. "A very long journey".

Taeol sized up Nathan, then gestured to the golem. "Fetch an extra-large apprentice robe, a bowl of porridge and one spoon". The mobile statue immediately turned and left the room, closing the door gently behind it. Taeol leaned across the table, catching Nathan's left hand in his right, even as Nathan flinched away. He spoke again in that resonant voice that Nathan had heard before Taeol had taught him a language with a touch.

[Moderate Curing]

Nathan's residual headache lessened dramatically, his breathing evened out and the ringing in his ears reduced to background noise. He shook his head out, amazed at how good he felt all of a sudden. As if by magic.

Actually by magic. He used magic on me! And called himself an archmage! There's magic here and I *can probably learn it!*

Excitement quickly replaced the pain. Nathan knew he should probably be scared, he should probably ask what the hell had just happened to bring him here. But instead, his mouth spoke the words at the forefront of his mind. "Can I learn magic?"

Taeol smiled again, teeth white and eyes glittering. "Yes, my boy. You will give me the secrets of your world, and I will teach you magic. Together, we will grasp Davrar and bring it to our breast!"

CHAPTER 2

NEW SYSTEMS

Nathan shared a grin with Taeol, excitement flooding through him. He'd wanted to do magic ever since he was little, when his parents had read fantasy stories to him in bed. The wish had only grown stronger as he grew older and started reading on his own. Every birthday when he blew out the candles, his wish had been the same.

I wish I could do magic.

Then – nothing fantastic had ever happened to him. No magic had appeared. So Nathan had turned to the closest thing available – Science. If you couldn't discover arcane secrets and bend reality around you with magic spells, then at least you could discover secrets of the natural world and bend reality with normal tools.

That motivation had gotten harder to rely on over the years. It could be hard to convince yourself that understanding the signaling pathways of stem cell differentiation was plumbing the deep secrets of reality. Especially if your last few experiments failed to even let you know if you were on the right track.

But none of that matters now! Wherever I am, magic is real and I can learn it!

Taeol leaned back in his chair, adjusting his bulk and steepling his fingers. "I am glad you are a willing helper in this. It is easier than if you were unwilling, and presents fewer knots to slice. But ah, here – food and clothes have arrived. I will allow you some time to dress and eat. Soon I shall return to discuss what you will tell me."

As he spoke, the door opened and the golem of pale stone walked through, holding a steaming bowl. It placed the bowl in front of Nathan, then put a spoon next to it and laid a folded robe of gray cloth and a pair of slippers on the bed. Taeol pushed himself up from the table and followed the golem out of the door. There came the thud of a bar being placed across the door.

Should I be concerned about that? Hard to know.

Nathan sat in the chair for a moment, too many thoughts crowding his mind. His excitement warred with his worry and anxiety about everything that had just happened.

What are my priorities? Clothes first, I'm cold.

He picked up the robe and put it on with only a bit of fumbling. It consisted of a t-shirt-like undershirt that fell past Nathan's hips. Draped over and attached to that garment was an enveloping robe that touched the floor, flowing around Nathan's legs like a bathrobe. There was a separate pair of underwear, like thick boxers with a drawstring. All of the material was soft and warm against his bare skin. Had his body changed at all? Nothing obvious. Pale, tall, a little bit more fat than he'd prefer. He eyed a lock of lanky blonde hair.

Wish I'd gotten that cut last week. Hard to plan for portal shenanigans.

He put on the slippers and looked at the bowl. He'd been about to eat back on Earth, but food was at the bottom of his list after the events of the last... hour? Half hour? Nathan had no idea.

It's possible to eat and think. You don't want to be distracted by hunger when it's time to learn magic! Or learn more about what's going on here.

Nathan sat and started to mechanically eat. It was bland, but that was okay. He was excited about magic, obviously. But he couldn't let that overwhelm everything else. And he *was* being overwhelmed. Nathan took a minute to just sit, close his eyes and breathe, clearing his mind for a moment so he could focus on one thing at a time.

What had happened, and what did it mean? Taeol had summoned him here intentionally... what had he said? He wanted knowledge, science and technology? But where was here? Another reality? A parallel dimension or universe? Another world in the same universe as Earth, but far away and magical? It probably didn't matter – likely the only way to get back would be magic, the same way he'd arrived.

Something to think about. I'm not raring to go back immediately. There's magic here!

Magic was an opportunity he'd only dreamed of. Nathan didn't have people waiting for him that trumped that – he definitely didn't want to see his ex-girlfriend again. His parents were distant and divorced, and he'd drifted apart from most of his friends over the last few years of intensive research. Nathan wondered if his labmates would notice he had stopped coming into work before his few friends noticed he hadn't scheduled their next D&D session.

I don't want to forget about the idea of going home, but I definitely want to learn more about this place. Is the world called Davrar? That's how the... box thing identified it, and Taeol said it too.

Why were the people here humans? Taeol certainly *looked* human. That suggested either a parallel universe or... something else going on. Magic or something that made everybody look like what he expected, to put him at ease. Nathan had read a sci-fi short story like that.

Don't jump to conclusions. What do you know?

Nathan grimaced. Taeol had mental magic, didn't he? That spell had *taught Nathan a language.* If you could add something to a brain, you could probably take something away.

Would Taeol use mental magic on somebody without their consent? He kind of already had, and hadn't made a good first impression on Nathan. Taeol reminded Nathan of some really arrogant professors he'd met, the ones who thought their positions and authority made them unquestionable beacons of knowledge, and god help the poor grad student who disagreed with their ideas.

He also implied that if I didn't cooperate it would just make things harder. "More knots to slice." I don't like that phrasing at all.

Nathan finished the porridge. He looked down at the empty bowl and the metal spoon he was holding. With a flash of inspiration, he looked around the room for somewhere inconspicuous. The corner of the room with a trough of water running underneath a chair looked best.

On closer inspection, the chair was almost exactly like a toilet seat, with waste intended to fall into the shallow trough of running water. It also seemed intended as a source of drinking water – there was an empty stone cup next to the seat. Mixing sewage and drinking water was a terrible idea, but maybe they relied on the water to sweep away everything?

Maybe cleaning or healing magic makes that a non-issue. I wouldn't want to tempt fate with that, I bet bacteria can evolve magic resistance. They can figure out how to resist just about everything else, after all.

Regardless, it was the perfect spot for Nathan's plan. An inconspicuous part of the room that he would often return to, even if someone messed with his mind. Using the base of the metal spoon he'd used to eat, Nathan scratched a symbol into the stone wall next to the toilet. It was something he was confident he'd recognize as coming from himself – nobody else here should know the chemical structure of caffeine. Then, after another moment of thought, he added a single tick mark next to it.

Okay, maybe if he got mind-wiped this would help him realize what had happened. What was next? That weird blue box?

As if summoned by the thought, a larger blue box popped up.

Davrar has recognized you, Nathan Lark.

You have become fully integrated into Davrar, and are ready to begin!

As you have no Talents, classes or skills despite being of mature age, Davrar has deemed you to be at a **Disadvantage.**

Therefore, Davrar will provide more explanations than usual. Your class, Talent and skill gain will be accelerated until you are no longer at a **Disadvantage**.

Davrar is here to help you survive and prosper. It will offer you Talents and utility skills according to your innate talents and abilities, and allow you to choose a class to suit your needs.

Talents and utility skills can Develop every 10 ranks, but require Insight to do so.

Each class will grant different and unique class skills according to the theme of the class.

To unlock classes, reach level 9 and choose from the presented list. Classes Develop at levels 27, 81, 243 and so on. There are ways to acquire more than one class; good luck discovering them!

To level up, overcome challenges. The more dire the challenge, the more you will be rewarded.

Davrar hopes you will survive and prosper.

Nathan read through the box to be certain, but he knew what it said as soon as it appeared. As if he'd always known, and was just now remembering the information. He felt anxiety build in the pit of his stomach as the strangeness of this place mounted. The box knew his full name, and *more* information had been inserted into his head. Those weren't even his biggest concerns!

The contents of the box imply that my survival is in question.

Davrar – the world and the origin of the boxes? – seemed to be offering him an RPG-like progression system. And how was it appearing to him? More mental magic? Nathan turned his head, and the box turned with him. He wished it would move to the corner of his vision – and it did.

It's definitely integrated with my thoughts somehow. Don't like not knowing anything about that.

He closed the box with another thought, and tried to open it up again. It took a second, only opening when Nathan prompted it with the first sentence of the box.

I gotta figure out what's going on with these things. Toss it on the pile of stuff to figure out with everything else.

Honestly, it seemed like something he should just ask Taeol about. Was there any reason to hide it from the mage? Maybe Nathan should ask about it circumspectly. Nathan was mulling it over when another box opened up.

Status of Nathan Lark
Talent 1: Pending
Talent 2: None
Talent 3: None

Class: None, level 1

Utility skills: None

That was pretty bare-bones. The Pending Talent was listed underneath the status.

Pending Talent: High-tier Magic Resistance
Your body has no magic inside it, and magic-resistant alchemical ingredients permeate your bones and brain, making you difficult to affect with magic. This Talent will turn a temporary quirk into a personal Talent. You will be able to resist and interfere with spells, and will have great difficulty casting magic of your own. Less effect on higher-tier spells. Magical items will have less effect on you, and weaker magical items degrade when in prolonged contact with you.

Again, Nathan didn't have to read the description to understand what it said. Wait, magic-resistant alchemical ingredients? Earth had no magic, which was probably why he didn't either, but magic-resistant alchemical ingredients didn't sound good. Maybe they were something common on Earth that wasn't common here?

And High-tier magic resistance? He read the description again with the eye of an RPG player. It sounded good, but it depended on how common magic was. The Talent would do better resisting minor spells than big ones, which was where you would need it most. *And* it prevented both beneficial spells and personal magic, which made it a big no-no for Nathan.

Maybe this was the basic Talent and he could make it better, to the point of not preventing his own magic? Being immune to his own magic would probably let him do all sorts of risky magical experiments. But the name suggested it was already a high-tier Talent. The lower-tier versions must be awful.

Nathan could feel the Talent waiting for his approval and almost declined it on the spot. He wanted to learn magic, and taking the Talent would make that impossible. But it didn't seem like there was time pressure, so he held off on making the decision. With another thought, all of the boxes vanished again. What now?

Well, I'm locked in a cell. It's not the worst cell, but it's still a windowless box with a door barred from the outside.

Nathan's anxiety ratcheted up as he realized how little control he had of his situation. He was being held in captivity by a man who didn't strike him as entirely trustworthy. But Nathan was not as anxious as he probably should be.

Either I'm just really excited about learning magic, or...

Nathan slapped himself in the forehead and started checking his memories, seeing if he could notice anything weird about his thoughts of the last hour.

You know, beyond the boxes. And magic. And being sucked through a portal to somewhere else.

Then he searched the rest of the room for other messages he might have left himself. There was nothing, just smooth stone that looked like it had melted and cooled in the shape of a room. The bed was somewhat crudely carved, and the mattress felt like it was stuffed with grass.

At least I don't have to worry about that fellowship application. Or my experiments. Though my experiment is totally shot unless this is all a really convincing dream. But that's okay! I can learn magic! Then if I go home, I'll demonstrate magic and become a celebrity. Maybe get shuffled off to a black site. But hey, then I get to confuse government agents, build up a rapport with the scientists studying me and save the world or something. It would be a welcome change from the daily grind.

None of that seemed likely, but it felt good to think about. Maybe that's why he wasn't feeling very anxious. His standard day-to-day worries of the last few months were gone. No more worrying about research, funding, lab politics or budgeting to cover the rent on an expensive studio apartment he'd originally planned on splitting with his ex.

And while there were definitely new things to worry about, they were *exciting* things to worry about. The sort of things that came with the territory of hopping between worlds and learning magic was real. And even if he didn't trust Taeol, he could learn it by himself!

Chapter 3

The First Discussion

Nathan didn't have too long to wait before Taeol dho Droxol, Grand Dimension Archmage of Giantsrest, came back. He heard the door being unbarred, heralding Taeol waddling in and sliding into the other chair. He wore a new robe, still in orange. It was embroidered with gold thread in patterns that could've been magical, but were certainly decorative. A man-sized stone statue in the same khaki marble as the walls followed the archmage in, bearing a wooden slab covered in food.

The golem set the food down in the middle of the table and withdrew to stand in front of the door. Taeol shook his robes back from his hands and dug in, slapping preserved meats onto soft cheeses and dipping them in fragrant sauces. He smacked his lips appreciatively and gestured for Nathan to follow suit.

As Nathan tentatively nibbled on the luxurious fare, Taeol began lecturing, continuing to eat as he spoke. "When I peered upon your world with my dimensional magics, I beheld marvels made common. Buildings taller than the clouds, metal traveling devices that flew faster than any bird. Ships the size of islands. A wonder of wonders, all without magic. I could not halt myself from imagining what could be done by clasping such knowledge in the same hand as one holding magic!"

Taeol took a bite from a log of cheese, pointing it at Nathan. "I tailored my spell to summon one with expertise in your 'science.' I built my spell to bring me one with the Insights necessary to build such wonders. So I *know* that you know of such things. First, and most importantly, what is your class?" He looked at Nathan expectantly, and gestured with what resembled a pickled chicken leg to answer his question.

There's a lot to digest there. I know a lot about science and technology, but I don't think I can build an airplane for Taeol. But let's not rock the boat.

"I'm sorry, but classes? I don't think those exist where I come from."

Taeol's jaw dropped, giving Nathan an unfortunate view of the masticated cheese log. He sprayed some of it across the platter as he spoke. "Hear me, but you *cannot* be serious." He gazed in wonder at Nathan. "But you are! No classes and still your world achieves such things."

He shook his head with amazement. "I expect a vein of gold and find it to be of oricalchum! No matter – surely you've received some kind of message from Davrar about classes, all people do as soon as they can understand. Just think about your abilities, and Davrar should grant you information in some way that makes sense to you. You have seen such a thing, haven't you?"

Nathan tentatively nodded, and Taeol grinned widely. "Excellent. We shall begin by making you my personal apprentice. I will start with initial training in basic [Mana Shaping] to unlock the Talent and your mana pool. Then we can speed along the basic leveling process with the enslavement mage progression.

Enslavement mage?

Taeol must have seen the confusion in Nathan's face, and the archmage looked self-satisfied as he explained further. "The enslavement mage path is the fastest path to mental magic if you have the resources. And I *do*. Hear me, but there are mental spells that allow directly imparting knowledge to another, and I would have you master them as soon as possible."

He nodded again, eyes gazing into the distance as he planned. "Then it will be possible to impart your knowledge to the necessary craftspeople and realize the wonders of your world here on Davrar. I had hoped you would have a teaching class already, so you could effectively explain things, but truly mages and magic are superior to all other classes in all things. Oh, is it not wonderful that I can design your advancement? Truly perfect." He squirmed in excitement.

Taeol had continued to shove food into his mouth as he spoke excitedly. The combination of chewing while speaking – and additional food sprayed from Taeol's mouth – turned Nathan off the platter, but not as much as the rising tide of dread sparked by Taeol's words.

I do not like where this is going at all. I want to explore magic for myself, thank you very much!

Nathan tried to get a word in edgewise to ask for clarification, but Taeol plowed right over him. "Of course, I must assuage my curiosity before we begin, and establish the conditions of our partnership. I will ask you questions as to how your world accomplishes these things, and you will answer. First, what is your full name? Then, how do those metal boxes move along the ground? There is no magic, but they move by themselves. What moves them? I must know."

He sure likes to talk. I can't just refuse to answer him, but I need more information.

He cast around for a good alternative subject to assuage Taeol, speaking as he thought frantically. "My name is Nathan Lark. And I apologize for answering a question with a question, but what is Davrar? Is it the name of your world? Is there a person named Davrar granting people power? How do these classes work?"

Taeol eyed Nathan and frowned for a second before responding. "It is understandable, I respect curiosity about such things. I would share frustration at being ignorant of something so basic."

He leaned back and spread his hands wide. "Our world is called Davrar, and it grants us the powers of Talents and classes and all the rest. Scholars of renown say that Davrar is the will of the world, ensuring that thinking beings survive against the horrors of monsters and Endings." Taeol smirked slightly. "One could wish it was a little more selective about what qualifies as civilized beings, and excluded some of the barbarians and intelligent monsters from its blessing, but we can fix that oversight on our own."

Fearing what he was about to hear, Nathan pushed more on that last point. "How will you fix that problem?"

Taeol turned expectant eyes from the remaining food to Nathan. "Of course, there is only one permanent solution. We must take control of their lands, and either civilize them appropriately or replace them with good stock. How else?"

So they're not just slavers, but genociders as well. I hate that I'm glad I look like them. But for now, I bet it makes him trust me more.

Taeol pointed a chicken bone at Nathan. "I see what you're doing boy, and I applaud you for it. You find yourself in an unfamiliar place and wish to learn as much as you can before you make any commitments. It reminds me of myself when I was your age, advancing up the ranks of the Ascendent Academy."

He tossed the chicken bone back onto the platter dismissively, locking eyes with Nathan. "But I must be clear as flawless gems, your only path here is giving me what I want. You have no other options. You shall do it willingly and

I will raise you up to stand Ascendent in magic, just under me. Else, I will dominate your mind and force you to tell me your truths. If you prove stubborn, I will transfer your soul to a golem core and extract your knowledge from a screaming husk."

Sweat broke out all over Nathan's body, and adrenaline shocked into his veins. Taeol seemed entirely serious, and he gazed at Nathan without hesitance or pity. Nathan did the only thing he could think of. He brought back the window for his pending Talent, and approved it.

This might make it harder for me to learn magic later, but I need all the protection I can get from this archmage who just threatened to rip out my soul. And I need it now.

Congratulations, you have accepted the 'High-tier Magic resistance' Talent. It will become a permanent part of your status and rank up as you use it. It starts at rank 1 and becomes more effective as it ranks up. Think about how you use your Talent's functions to aid in Talent Development at rank 10.

Aaaand... it says it's permanent. Well that's a problem for future Nathan. Current Nathan needs to deal with a genocidal archmage staring at me from across the table. Who just demanded to know how cars worked.

Nathan reached for a bite of food to give himself some more time to think, picking up a piece of cheese from the edge of the platter that looked to have avoided the worst of Taeol's messy eating habits.

I could just tell him. It's not like a basic explanation of internal combustion engines will start an industrial revolution. I certainly don't know enough to make one from scratch. There's a lot involved in a car.

But on the other hand – not only was this the start of a slippery slope, but maybe the very idea of how to convert expanding gas into rotational energy would interact with some magic Nathan didn't know about. Nathan couldn't be sure he wasn't handing some important secret to Taeol if he told him *anything*.

All of a sudden, Nathan found that somebody making direct personal threats against him to break his principles didn't make him anxious. It made him *enormously* pissed off. He was *not* going to teach this genocidal maniac about technology. He would rather die than enable Taeol's goals. That conclusion settled into Nathan's mind, and Davrar reacted.

Pending Talent: Moderate-tier Resolute Mind

> You have resolved to refuse to violate your principles in the face of overwhelming power. This Talent will make that decision into a personal Talent. You will be harder to persuade to change your mind, and be extra resistant to Talents and skills that can charm or influence you. You will also have minor resistance to mental magic geared at influencing you. Less effective on high-tier Talents and spells.

Nathan once more found he could understand the box's contents almost instantly. He rejected the Talent just as quickly.

Harder to persuade to change your mind? That sounds more like a curse than a blessing. It would make me useless at science... forever. For very little benefit. Only an arrogant idiot presumes they're always right. The only thing I'm sure about right now is that Taeol's an asshole.

Taeol tapped his fingers on the table impatiently. Nathan took a deep breath and tried to stop quivering with Rage. He was playing for time and information now, until he could figure out how to escape.

Time to put on an act. Maybe he has a truth spell or something. Try not to directly lie.

Nathan gave a faint nod to Taeol. "It does appear better for us both if I cooperate willingly. I apologize for my reaction, but you must have noticed that my world is generally peaceful. We have wars, but most people never experience violence. The talk of wiping out peoples is shocking to me." Taeol pursed his lips at Nathan, then shrugged, and with an offhand wave of his hand cast a spell.

[Charm]

Nathan's eyes saw double for a second. Had he really seen that gesture and heard that spell? Surely his good friend Taeol wouldn't do such a thing. He was a nice guy, and he was going to teach Nathan magic! Why was he refusing to talk about combustion engines – they were really neat! It was fun to explain the basics of science. Nathan had spent a lot of volunteer hours in college doing science demos and explaining basic science and technology to younger kids. He even had a cool explanation worked out for how combustion pressure was used to drive motion. Surely he could just explain this basic thing to Taeol. And then Taeol would teach him magic!

Taeol the Asshole who threatened me with the worst kind of mental magic. That [Charm] was pretty goddamn violating.

The moment faded, and Nathan felt the effect slide off him. The spell tingled as it disentangled itself from his head and puffed away, leaving Nathan clear-eyed and suffused with cold rage. While Nathan had been struggling with the spell, Taeol had been talking. Extolling the greatnesses of his culture, it sounded like.

"... And of course, the barbarians have none of that. What will they do when the next Ending comes, cower in their hovels and beg their ancestors to save them? No, Giantsrest brings enlightenment to those we conquer, and we raise them up for it. We are harsh at times, but it is an absolute necessity! Many peoples have strange and ridiculous superstitions and traditions that prevent them from properly fitting into our nation. But the Ascendent Academy is open to all peoples – if they can pass the entrance exam – and our civilizing influence will truly save the world. That is a truth of the fist." Taeol's eyes were positively beady as he surveyed Nathan again, gauging the effect of his spell and speech. He apparently decided it wasn't enough.

[Charm]

This time, Nathan felt the spell hit, and blinked his eyes closed for a moment against the tingling sensation. He stilled his mind in an instant to focus entirely on the feeling of the spell trying to dig hooks into his reasoning. The spell slid off once more, like a wave of pins and needles rippling over his skull.

High-tier Magic Resistance Rank 2 achieved!

Taeol had asked Nathan a question. "I'm sorry, can you repeat that?"

Taeol frowned slightly, then repeated his question. "Therefore, with such a glorious cause as ours, don't you think you can satisfy my curiosity? It's a simple question. How do those metal boxes move along the ground?"

It didn't seem like this was about Taeol's curiosity anymore. Nathan not answering the question had angered Taeol, and he wanted to establish his authority and get an answer.

Nathan didn't see any way to avoid the question. He hoped that Taeol wouldn't jump straight to mind control, but he couldn't think of an evasion. He thought about jumping Taeol, but there was a table in the way and the golem still stood by the door. He needed time to think and plan, to rank up his magic resistance before he challenged Taeol for real. He should go with a soft refusal.

"I'm so sorry Taeol, but I'm feeling overwhelmed and confused right now. You have some really good arguments, and I need to think them over. Can you give me some time to try to understand everything that's happened? I also want to hear more about how your culture governs subjects, and how the Academy works. It sounds like an amazing place to learn magic."

It was weak, and Nathan knew it was weak. But he'd been the target of two mind-affecting spells in as many minutes, so it was the best he could do.

Taeol seemed to agree. He sighed, and stood. "You're a soft, sentimental boy, but surprisingly resistant to charm spells. It would be so much better to have you cooperate willingly. We will try again. Next time, I won't threaten you, or mention the inferior peoples at all."

[Paralysis]

Nathan's body froze in his chair. He was breathing, but every voluntary muscle had frozen. He couldn't blink, couldn't move his eyes. It nearly caused him to panic until he focused on the adrenaline still coursing through him. He tried to throw off the [Paralysis] like he had the [Charm], but it wasn't working. The tingling of the spell stayed anchored firmly in his muscles, blocking or jamming all the messages sent to them. He focused on his right hand, trying to throw his entire will into twitching a finger. Nothing happened. He pushed harder and still nothing happened.

Taeol was slowly walking around the table, coaxing a faint glow along in his hand. He seemed to be muttering under his breath, but Nathan couldn't spare the attention to listen. He focused again on his right hand, this time imagining sucking the energy in his hands into his bones. He felt... something moving. Like there was another sense in his hand, detecting not pressure or heat – but something wispier. He drew that wispy feeling out of the muscles and into the bones of his hand and arm, naming the bones as the feeling drifted past.

Ulna, Radius, the big ones. All the phalanges in the hand, then the mess of small bones in the wrist. They're all sponges, soaking up the magic in the muscles around them.

His hand twitched and then came completely under his control once again. Satisfaction bloomed in Nathan's mind, competing with the terror. He focused on doing the same to the rest of his body. It wasn't easy, the paralysis pervaded him and wasn't letting go. But slowly, the spell started to unravel.

High-tier Magic Resistance Rank 3 achieved!

And he was out of time. Taeol's hand came down on his face.

[Memory Purge]

Chapter 4

Putting the Pieces Together

Nathan woke up in an unfamiliar bed, his back itchy against the lumpy mattress. He shifted, and the heavy blanket twisted with him. Much heavier than the blanket he usually slept with. What was going on? He opened his eyes and looked around the room, slowly waking up. He had a bit of a headache, and it felt like he'd had a particularly intense dream that he couldn't quite grasp. The last thing he remembered was dropping his backpack on his carpet in his apartment.

And what was up with this room? Seamless stone on all six surfaces, like it had been carved out of raw rock and then smoothed until the stone gleamed. All of the corners were slightly rounded. There was a light in the middle of the ceiling, and it looked like a... glowing rock. A table with two chairs sat in the center of the room, with a bowl of fruit set out on the table. On the other side of the room was a water trough underneath a... toilet seat? With an empty cup next to it?

That's not hygienic at all.

Nathan got up to inspect the strange room in more detail. Nothing was manufactured, all the furniture looked handmade. This seemed like way too much effort for a prank, and who would put in this much effort to prank him? Unless he was on a weird reality TV show. But those required waivers and things – unless they wanted to get sued out of existence. He recognized none of the fruit, not even from that weird asian fruit box his dad had sent him once.

Where was he? Something drifted up from his barely-remembered dream, a feeling of certainty.

A different world.

That must have been *some* dream he'd had. It still bounced around in his head, but nothing about it was clear beyond an overwhelming sense of fear and anger. But here he was, somewhere he couldn't explain.

Maybe I should give the dream more credit. I'm not one to get mystical at all, but this feels different from normal. Maybe I should have kept up with the lucid dreaming stuff.

Nathan realized he was parched, and looked in vain for another source of water. But there was nothing other than a handy cup near the toilet trough. Dammit.

He scooped up a cup of water and sat on the toilet seat to drink it, studying the wall from close-up. It was nice rock, well-polished, with a moderate grain to it. The sort of rock people paid a lot for in houses. The water was clean, and about as cold as you'd get from a tap.

Then Nathan blinked. Scratched into the rock in front of him was a familiar two-ring chemical structure. Caffeine? What the hell? And a single tick mark next to it. For some reason, that drawing filled him with anxiety, a yawning pit opening up in his gut. Nathan stared at the symbol of wakefulness and feared what it meant.

Wake up. That's what caffeine does to you.

Nathan staggered back to the bed, sitting on the soft surface as his breathing quickened. He pinched himself. He felt a crushing weight on his chest, like it was impossible to take a breath. He cradled his head in his hands, a foggy brain and tight chest threatening to make him pass out.

No. Sit up straight, deep breaths. This is why you learned to meditate. You don't have the app, but you can still clear your mind. Start by focusing on your breath. In through the nose, down the throat, into the lungs. Feel your lungs expand all the way out, the ribcage opening up. Then breathe out. Slowly. Again. Now focus on your body. It's a cloud of sensations and your consciousness fills all of it. You're not asleep because you can feel your body so clearly. Everything is contained within your consciousness, and you control all of it.

Minutes passed, and Nathan's mind emptied as his breath came deep and even. Once he felt calmer, Nathan broadened his thoughts past his physical sensations.

What now? I have clues. I'm somewhere weird, with all sorts of inexplicable things. A glowing rock, handmade furniture, weird fruit. And a weird toilet. I have a fragment of a dream in my head about being in a different world. And there's a chemical structure I know well carved into the rock in my cell. That is the sort of message I would leave myself. Did I forget something? Was I made *to forget something?*

Everything pointed back to the dream. He needed to remember what it was about before his sense of it faded entirely. Nathan shifted his entire focus to the hazy memory in the back of his head and he tried to call it up, to relive the dream. But it was slippery, passing through his fingers of concentration like a wispy cloud.

No. It's like there's a thin pane blocking my efforts. The dream's right there, but something's stopping me from remembering it.

Nathan captured the sensation in his mind's eye, examining it within this meditative state. It was like an angled piece of glass deflecting his attention to the side. Nathan pictured himself dispersing it, like he did unwanted thoughts. There was a distinctly physical sensation, like a skintight net around his head falling apart, and then he *remembered.*

Everything that had happened yesterday. Exposure to vacuum, Taeol's summoning room, the messages from Davrar, the subsequent conversation with Taeol, and the mind wipe.

Taeol is a rampaging asshole.

He opened his eyes and saw three blue boxes waiting for him.

High-tier Magic Resistance Rank 4 achieved!

Good. Ranking up that skill was almost certainly his path to survival and freedom.

Pending utility skill: Low-tier Focused Mind
You have used mental exercises to avoid panic and focus on what was necessary. This skill will help you attain a focused and undistracted state more easily when you need it. Requires you to be seated, unmoving and with eyes closed to use.

As far as Nathan could tell, that was only beneficial. And there didn't seem to be a limit on the number of utility skills he could have. Even if there *was*, being focused and calm was invaluable. He accepted the skill.

Congratulations, you have accepted the 'Low-tier Focused Mind' utility skill. It will become a part of your status and rank up as you use it. It starts at rank 1 and becomes more effective as it ranks up.

Think about how you use your skill to aid in skill Development at rank 10.

Then Nathan turned to the third box.

You have leveled up to level 3! Congratulations, you have defeated high-tier mental magic with very few resources! It will be harder to level up as you gain a higher level.

That was nice – it seemed like he didn't have to kill anything, just overcome difficult challenges to level up. Now what? It was time to plan, time to figure out his next steps. Nathan wished he had some scratch paper and a pencil to list what he knew and what options he had. It was the same way he planned experiments, and he wanted to use the familiar process to help organize his thoughts. But he hadn't seen anything like that in the room, and he didn't want to leave any evidence for Taeol to find next time he knocked Nathan out and erased his memories.

If there is a next time. He implied he'd take more drastic measures eventually. What was it? Oh yeah, "stick your soul in a golem core and extract knowledge from your screaming husk." Charming.

Nathan closed his eyes and took a few deep breaths to calm himself down. He'd never felt anger like this before. Luckily, [Focused Mind] helped him stay on track.

I need to think clearly. This isn't a situation anger will get me out of.

If Taeol *did* decide to go another round with the mindwipe, Nathan needed to put in more insurance. He looked around for an object to mark the wall with. The only metal object in the room – aside from some nails holding the furniture together – was the dish the fruit came in. It wasn't ideal, but it served to make another tick mark next to the caffeine molecule.

Nathan sighed, thinking about other ways to help him remember if Taeol wiped his memory again. He could just write, "You've been mindwiped," and so long as he saw it and Taeol didn't, he'd have a bit of insurance. Nathan was also pretty sure Taeol didn't understand English.

But if he can teach me a language with a spell, he might be able to translate it back. Anyway, let's plan on how to get out of here without *getting [Memory Purged] again. My new skill should help!*

Nathan closed his eyes and focused again, once more finding it easier than ever to banish extraneous thoughts and focus on how to deal with Taeol and escape. Should he try to catch Taeol by surprise and attack him as soon as possible?

That plan *would* let Nathan punch Taeol in the face, which was certainly appealing. And Taeol wouldn't expect an attack right after the mindwipe. The longer Nathan waited, the more chances Taeol would have to catch on. *That* would probably lead him to take drastic measures.

On the other hand, Nathan knew nothing about where he was, or anything about Taeol's magical defenses. He needed more information to develop a plan beyond "punch Taeol in the face and try to find an exit." What if he was in the middle of the academy that Taeol had mentioned?

I also can't help but think that [Magic Resistance] is my trump card. I want to wait as long as possible and rank it up as much as I can before it's revealed.

Okay, so if attacking Taeol was a bad idea, how about sneaking out? Nathan wouldn't have to confront the archmage, but he still faced all of the same problems, in addition to a bar on the door. It was worth keeping in mind, but there would have to be a good opening.

So, it seemed that Nathan would have to talk to Taeol again, and pretend to know nothing. Nathan knew he wasn't *great* at being deceptive, but it didn't look like he had a choice. At least all he had to do was play dumb. But how could Nathan get the information he needed?

Well, the first step to manipulation was to look at the other person's perspective. Taeol believed in his own superiority and the power of his magic. He'd wiped Nathan's memories of their previous conversation and was probably taking time to plan out the perfect series of lies to get Nathan on his side.

It would have been smarter for Taeol to not give Nathan any time to break the mind magic. But Taeol probably thought his magic was flawless and there was no way for Nathan to break it. Maybe he wanted Nathan to stew in an unfamiliar setting before swinging in to rescue him. Or maybe he simply had other things on his plate than a dimensional abductee with the secrets of industrial revolution.

Seems unlikely. He wants me to help him change the world.

Well, if he wasn't going to attack Taeol, Nathan should conform to the archmage's expectations as much as possible. He should act confused and be grateful to Taeol for any friendliness or explanation. But that had to have a limit – he had to have a justification for refusing to follow Taeol's plans. Should he get Taeol to teach him magic? It would be tricky to do without giving up anything, but the possibility was there.

On the other hand, Nathan reminded himself there were some really good reasons not to learn magic. His magic resistance skill would interfere with it, and that could clue Taeol in on what was happening. Also, there was a chance that if he picked up more skills or Talents right now, then his magic resistance skill would not rank up as quickly.

I just don't know enough about how this system works to want to rely on it for any part of this plan. The magic resistance I understand, at least partially. But how that interacts with other Talents, classes and skills is unknown territory.

Come to think of it, that would have been a good reason to hold off on accepting [Focused Mind]. But it was already proving its value, letting him plan without being interrupted by gibbering fear about deciding to oppose an apparently genocidal city/kingdom/empire single-handedly.

But I want to learn magic! Come on, it's right there! Just get Taeol to teach you.

Tough. Nathan wasn't going to jeopardize this plan to learn what Taeol called magic. Magic didn't have to be manipulating mana. Talents seemed like a close approximation and that would have to be enough, at least for now.

Should he try to pick up any other Talents or skills immediately? If he could find anything to help with the immediate situation, he should probably take it. But unless he could figure out a Talent to burrow through solid rock, the only thing that made sense was getting better at lying to Taeol and stringing him along.

Nathan opened his eyes to yet another blue box.

Low-tier Focused Mind Rank 2 achieved!

Nice. Now it was time to try lying to a wall for a while to see if he could pick up a deception skill.

Chapter 5

The Second Discussion

It turned out that Davrar did not reward lying to inanimate objects. That was fair.

Not long after he'd finished failing to convince the wall that it really was, in fact, made of small particles of silica and was not truly a contiguous solid, the door opened and a golem walked through, carrying a plate of roasted vegetables.

Nathan did his best to act like a confused world-traveler with no knowledge of how he had gotten there, asking random questions starting with, "Where am I?" moving on to "Who are you?" and ending with "What is this place?" The golem had ignored him, placing the food on the table and removing the now-empty bowl of fruit. When Nathan made a halfhearted move toward the door the golem had sped up, quickly moving to the door before closing and barring it.

Nathan inspected the meal, and was quite pleased to note that the roasted... zucchini(?) had come with a fork. A two-pronged fork where the prongs were nearly an inch-and-a-half apart. But still – a metal utensil. Huzzah! He sat down on "his" side of the table and quickly scratched three words in small text into the side that faced him.

"You've been neuralized" was pretty close to "You've been mindwiped," but the extra level of obfuscation through *misspelling* a pop reference seemed like a good idea. Added to his terrible handwriting and the unknown language, it seemed unlikely Taeol could read it even if he did find it. Unless there was a [Translate] spell that had a spellcheck *and* worked on cultural references.

Man, magic is bullshit. The kind of bullshit I want to use. But that's looking less and less likely. I pitted my ideals against my childhood dreams and the ideals won. It wasn't even much of a contest. That makes me pretty proud of myself, actually. Go Nathan! Just need to deal with the consequences now.

Nathan sat down to munch on the plate of grilled green veggies. They weren't bad – cold and a little soggy, but naturally a bit peppery in a way that combined nicely with the crisped edges. Nathan could only hope it didn't contain allergens that would cause his throat to close up. He was almost done with the plate when he heard the door being unbarred again.

Nathan did his best to look up in a hopeful and confused manner when Taeol entered the room, the golem striding behind the archmage. Taeol was in another orange robe, this one decorated with shiny stones around the hems and sleeves. As he was sliding into the chair, Nathan politely asked "Can you please tell me what is going on?"

Taeol looked gravely at Nathan. "My boy, I do apologize but I must be clear as flawless gems with you. First, allow me an introduction. I'm Taeol dho Droxol, a researcher at the Ascendent Academy. You find yourself in a new world. As much as it twists my thumb to admit it, my understanding of what occurred is limited."

Taeol sat heavily in the chair, rubbing his forehead as if at his wit's end. "I believe that some cosmic force moved you across dimensions to this world. I was conducting an experiment to probe dimensional quasi-resonance and my utter harmonic went out of control. Entirely beyond expectation, and much expensive equipment was destroyed. But right where the primary phase-resonator had broken – I found you, lying on the secondary tuning rod. Before we continue, may I ask your name?"

That sounded like techno-babble intended to confuse him. Magi-babble? Regardless, it seemed like Taeol was trying to sell Nathan a story where he'd appeared here by chance, and destroyed valuable equipment in the process. He had to pretend to believe it and play into the effect that Taeol was going for. He wished he could take back telling his name to Taeol earlier in case it gave him some magical advantage, but he'd done it while trying to stall, and couldn't take it back.

"Oh, that is a lot to take in." Nathan made a show of taking a deep breath before looking back at Taeol earnestly. "My name is Nathan Lark. Thank you for the explanation, but I'm still so confused. I'm sorry to hear that I destroyed some valuable equipment. This is all a big shock for me, I was panicking earlier trying to figure out what was going on. I have a lot of questions. You must have incredible technology to be working on something like dimensional science"

Taeol seemed satisfied with the answer, and smiled gently. He gestured with a hand, and Nathan saw the spell coming before the word left Taeol's mouth.

[Charm]

Nathan let his eyes go unfocused for a moment, the same way it had happened the first time. He blinked slowly, focusing his mind to banish the seductive, foreign thoughts as they flowed into him with a prickling sensation.

Low-tier Focused Mind Rank 3 achieved!

"No, my friend Nathan, we do not use 'technology.' On Davrar, we use magic to bend the world to our will. I take it from your response that your world does not have magic? Would you like to learn magic?"

Taeol conjured a floating ball of smooth orange light over one hand, and his smile changed into something predatory. He knew what Nathan wanted, and was leveraging it and his mental magic to strike right at Nathan's weaknesses.

Nathan knew what the right response was. Luckily, it wasn't hard to channel his excitement for magic. He didn't have to try hard to make his eyes bug out at one of the first overt displays of magic he'd ever seen.

"Magic! That's incredible! Can I learn it? How does it work? Where does the energy come from? Is that an easy spell to learn? How long will it take before I could cast it?" He pointed to the orb of light, doing his best to act like he'd forgotten his misgivings and was entirely excited about learning magic. Pretty much the same as the first time he'd learned about magic from Taeol.

Pending utility skill: Low-tier Earnestness
You have done a good job conveying seriousness and honesty to a suspicious observer. This skill will help you portray your intense conviction and honesty when you speak to people. Cannot compel actions beyond what natural speech could, and cannot fool truth spells or skills.

Not exactly what Nathan had in mind, but beggars couldn't be choosers, and it seemed like it would help here. He accepted the skill.

Congratulations, you have accepted the 'Low-tier Earnestness' utility skill. It will become a part of your status and rank up as you use it. It starts at rank 1 and becomes more effective as it ranks up. Think about how you use your skill to aid in skill Development at rank 10.

Those messages were getting repetitive. While he'd been considering the skill, Taeol had started talking.

"... Forgive that, and I would be sure as a good glove that you can learn magic. I'd like to get you started on a mage class soon. With my enormous guidance we could have you casting light spells such as this by week's end. But if you have no magic, I would love to hear how your people do things! This technology sounds fascinating, and I would love to hear about it. If your people have no classes, how do you accomplish *anything*?"

Nathan nodded, noticing Taeol's slip – he hadn't told Taeol he didn't have a class yet. "I'm sorry, but classes? Do you mean something like educational degrees?" Taeol flushed a bit in response, so it was probably a mistake, and not Taeol trying to probe Nathan's memory.

The archmage rushed to explain classes again, this time omitting the mention of "less civilized" thinking beings that had drawn Nathan's attention the first time. Then he closed by saying, "But Talents, classes and skills are essential to all we do. My civilization – no civilization – could long survive without them against the monsters and Endings of this world. Then, I ask you, even if your world has no monsters, no Endings, how do you accomplish anything?"

Endings? Not actually important right now.

For now, Nathan had an opening to convince Taeol of his usefulness as a thinking, free agent, and hopefully put off the whole golem core thing. He leaned into his *earnestness*, speaking about something he cared deeply about. "I have dedicated my life to furthering our technology, and had nearly attained the highest education my world offers before..." he gestured around the room.

"Knowledge is shared freely in my world. We have a saying among my people: 'If I see further it is by standing on the shoulders of giants.' It means that even though I may not be as wise or as smart as my predecessors, I can learn all they discovered and then surpass them in knowledge." Nathan spread his hands, as though laying his secrets upon the table.

Low-tier Earnestness Rank 2 achieved!

Taeol clasped his hands tightly together, listening to Nathan with the slightly teary eyes of a man who'd just heard a beautiful sermon. "Amazing.

When we lose a titan, their skills and Talents die with them. When you lose one, their skills and knowledge are taught to the next generation. What a grand world that must be."

He wiped at his eyes, looking rueful. "Ah, but can we make it real here? My people hoard Insights like dragons, only to be dispensed to their trusted heirs and loyal students, if at all. Only a fist of steel, one armed with advantage and Insight beyond all others, could break that culture. Will you give me the strength of your fist in this, Nathan? Together, we could raise the banner of knowledge, take what is best of your world and use it in this one." He raised his hands dramatically with that, gesturing with one hand in a now-familiar gesture.

[Charm]

It was a remarkably persuasive argument, Nathan had to admit. But as the spell washed around him and passed by, Nathan reminded himself of Taeol's past actions. He was not the beacon of knowledge and truth that he pretended to be. Taeol dho Droxol was a scheming man convinced his own superiority justified any means necessary to assert his dominance.

He'd thrown away any chance of Nathan ever willingly cooperating with him the first time he'd cast [Charm]. Looking up, Nathan saw Taeol watching carefully to see his reaction. Then he gestured again, his voice louder, more insistent, and the glow from his mouth stronger.

[Charm]

The spell was clearly cast with more strength, meant to overcome any resistance. Nathan allowed his eyes to go unfocused for a moment while he bent his will to overcome the spell. A tingling latched onto his brain, but Nathan siphoned it off into the bones of his skull with precise concentration. The spell faded without effect a moment later.

High-tier Magic Resistance Rank 5 achieved!

You have leveled up to level 5! Congratulations, you have resisted your opponent's attempts to persuade you! It will be harder to level up as you gain a higher level

Nathan smiled, and Taeol smiled with him. Then Nathan gave the only answer that Taeol would accept, mimicking Taeol's speech patterns as best he could. "Of course I will help you. This is a much grander path than I expected to walk in life. But you do me honor by allowing me to walk it with you."

He's given me his best shot and I've pretended to buy it. There's never going to be a better time to probe for information.

"But please, I have *so much* to learn about this world. It is unlike my own, and I cannot picture what we could even accomplish here. Can I ask where we are? I want to know about your government and society, to learn my place within it? I don't want to disgrace you if I should meet another prominent member of your academy." Nathan could feel his Earnestness skill activating, guiding his voice and face to express honest curiosity and sincerity as he tried to pump Taeol for information.

Low-tier Earnestness Rank 3 achieved!

Taeol seemed taken in by Nathan's acting, smiling in a self-satisfied fashion. "It is good you are thinking ahead, but you should not have to worry about that for some time. We are currently in my personal research tower, a ways to the west of Giantsrest, and there are no other living beings in this tower to worry about. Just me, my golems and my experiments."

He waved a hand around, encompassing the room and the building beyond. "It was given to me with the title of Researcher, for it is traditional to conduct experiments away from cities and towns. We will not be disturbed, as we are protected by golem, ward and trap. There will be plenty of time to tutor you in scholarly etiquette before I present you to the Ascendent Academy and the council of archmages. I am not due back for a month at least, and I look forward to what we can accomplish in that time. The town of Halsmet is a short way to the south, and I will take you there next time I visit the brothel, to give you an introduction to our culture."

Okay then. That's the bare minimum of what I needed to know. And it's better than I could have hoped for. We're in the wilderness and there's nobody else around. I need to watch out for the golems, but I hope my [Magic Resistance] can help me deal with the wards and traps.

Nathan still hoped to get more information from Taeol, but every exchange increased the risk that Taeol would figure him out. It was time to switch priorities toward escape. Nathan nodded to Taeol and looked over at the golem, thinking about how to get the golem out of the room and get a jump on Taeol.

I don't know if my antimagic will do squat against the golem, and I don't want to risk everything on getting lucky. I probably need to wait for Taeol to send it somewhere. Can I ask for something? And then since Taeol needs to speak to cast his spells, I can hopefully punch him in the throat and just run.

Taeol asked, "How would you like to start our teachings? I have many questions to ask you, but you also must have many questions for me? Of magic?"

Nathan nodded absentmindedly, trying to think of a plan to divert the golem out of the room. "Is there anything you need to have the golem fetch to teach me [Mana Shaping]? I'd love to get started on that." Maybe Taeol would send the golem away, or at the very least Nathan could potentially get more exposure to magic and rank up [Magic Resistance] some more.

Taeol froze, and his eyes narrowed. He stood up and took a few steps towards the door. "I never mentioned [Mana Shaping]. Not today." Nathan, broke out in a cold sweat on realizing his mistake.

Shit. I blew it. After all my plans, one slip of the tongue throws the game

He stood up, and started slowly walking around the table to approach Taeol "No – I meant, you mentioned mana earlier, and it makes sense that you'd need the [Mana Shaping] ability to be a mage."

Taeol wasn't buying it, taking a few more steps backwards. "You've been strangely resistant to my [Charms]. You must have somehow broken my memory spell. You didn't think I would notice? You tried to fool me?" Taeol snarled in what was probably supposed to be an intimidating manner, but came off more afraid than anything else. That fear showed weakness, and Nathan lunged across the last few feet toward Taeol. Maybe he could get in close and hammer the archmage before he could get off a decisive spell.

[Paralysis]

But Taeol could cast spells as quickly as he could speak. Nathan felt his muscles lock up, staggering and falling mid-step as his body fell asleep all at once. He frantically pulled at the feeling of paralysis in his muscles, but his focus was broken by his cheek slamming into the ground in front of Taeol's slippers.

Nathan's head swam as Taeol spoke gloatingly from above. "Magic is superior to all! You have given up a chance many would cut off their thumbs for. And now you will lose all you have, you *stupid* boy."

[Slumber]

A heavy fog descended upon Nathan's mind, pushing at his consciousness. His eyes prickled and magically slid closed. Nathan desperately sharpened his attention with [Focused Mind], hanging onto awareness by his fingernails. Taeol spoke again, and the words were spikes of meaning that Nathan grabbed ahold of to avoid falling into the beckoning pit of unconsciousness. "Take him to the golem creation room and put him on the table".

When the sound faded, Nathan focused on the cold, stone hands that manhandled him into an over-the-shoulder carry. The hard stone of the golem's body dug into his stomach and hips, providing a discomfort Nathan brought to the front of his mind. As he was carried out the door and down the hallway, the suffocating tiredness lessened.

Nathan was still paralyzed, but at least he wasn't about to pass out entirely. He could feel the wispy sensation of the [Slumber] more clearly now. It was filling his head like a nasty hangover, itchy and cloying. It wouldn't slide off like the [Charm] spell, or sink into his bones like [Paralysis] did.

The sleep spell was a sticky net adhering to his thoughts, weighing them down to the point of unconsciousness. So, Nathan tried to burst the net. He recalled as much as possible of the manic state he'd found after trying some internet-ordered stimulants. He imagined bright blue skies over the mountains he'd grown up in, dredged up memories of the martial arts he'd practiced in high school, and the beautiful design of optics in super-resolution microscopy.

The net tore, swamped by the number of memories pressing at the edges. The spell fell apart in fragments, subsumed by Nathan's mind. He tried to sigh in relief, but he was still paralyzed and draped over the back of a golem.

Right. Of course. How could I forget? One thing after another, ain't that just the way

The humor kept the fear at bay, a bit. He knew how to break the [Paralysis], and concentrated on doing just that. This time it was much easier, and the tingling sensation quickly faded away. Nathan didn't know if that was thanks to his [Focused Mind], the rank-ups in the [Magic Resistance], or just practice feeling the spell and breaking its patterns. Before he was quite finished, the golem smoothly followed Taeol into a room and gently lowered him face-up onto a large stone table at its center.

Low-tier Focused Mind Rank 4 achieved!

High-tier Magic Resistance Rank 6 achieved!

Before Nathan could do anything, Taeol cast another spell.

[Chains of Restraint]

Nathan hastily shut his eyes again as slick magical chains sprung from the base of the table and wrapped around his limbs and across his torso. He surreptitiously flexed his arms and legs to check his paralysis, and the chains tightened to restrict him further.

Oh, come on! This guy is so damn paranoid. At least he's using magic and not real chains. I can break these cuffs!

He was definitely feeling a bit punch-drunk, but Nathan wasn't sure if it was a response to the mind magic he'd resisted so far, or his impending fate as an animated rock. Breaking the thin but immobilizing chains seemed like an important next step. Nathan tried tugging against the chains but felt absolutely no give in them. His admittedly limited strength was not the answer here – he needed to use his Talent. Once again, he reached out to a new kind of magic, hoping he could resist it somehow.

And it's not like I have a plan B!

He focused on where the chains dug into his flesh. There was a feeling... beyond the merely physical. He visualized the chains, felt them engraved in his consciousness by more than just touch. The feeling wasn't wispy this time, but harder, more structured. Nathan didn't think he could do the same thing he'd done to the mental spells here – the magic didn't flow. But maybe it could break? He tried hitting the structure with his will, imagining using his consciousness as a hammer to shatter the chains. Nothing happened.

Taeol was busy against the back wall of the space, sounding like he was sorting through a full toolbox. He commanded the golem, "Go get an empty golem core from the second magical storage space. A grandmaster-quality, I think. I want the highest-quality imbuing right now, minimal loss of memory would be best." Nathan heard the door open and close.

The golem is gone! Now or never. This may be impossible, but you only win if you play as if it is possible. How might it work? Winning answers only, please.

He'd succeeded in resisting magic before by utilizing the inherent magic resistance of his body and whatever magical *sense* the Talent had given him. To resist charm magic, he'd noticed and denied the intrusive thoughts, and the spell had evaporated. The paralysis had needed to be drawn out of his muscles and into his bones. The sleep magic had been overwhelmed by frantic thoughts. In each case he'd found a key element of the spell and subverted it until the whole structure had fallen apart. What was the appropriate key element of these chains?

They had a detailed structure, as if each link in the chain was a tightly packed mass of geometric shapes. It reminded him of how DNA was packed into chromosomes – strands of looped coil, each coil composed of a yet smaller string. Except here the string was made of tightly wrapped but unknotted energy? Force? The analogy fell apart at that level. The strings themselves felt tough, like an extremely thin metal wire. Nathan picked a chain that was tight around his stomach, where he imagined a single loop of wire in a coil. He focused on grabbing a single wire and *pulling*, yanking with his mental fingers right into his gut.

The string responded quickly to Nathan's intention. It flowed into him and stung slightly, like a needle poking skin. But as the magic entered his body it became less substantial, sliding down an energy gradient from solid to insubstantial to nonexistent. The link Nathan had focused on fuzzed out, and the entire structure of the chains loosened slightly.

Oh thank the gods. Whichever ones might exist here!

Nathan wasn't paying attention to his surroundings, and he flinched as his head was lifted by fleshy hands. Taeol placed some kind of metal disc under his head, folding up flexible metal arms that rested on his temples. Nathan tried to ignore it and pulled on more threads. He could only manage three at a time, focusing on his arms first. It only took seconds per chain, but there were a lot of chains.

Then, all of a sudden Nathan could do four at a time. Probably a rank-up, but he didn't open his eyes to check. Now that he could do something about the chains he was feeling claustrophobic, and he wanted *out*. The chains across his chest were suddenly unacceptably tight, and Nathan tried to ignore the rising tide of panic as Taeol turned and gathered his tools with the *scrape* of metal on stone.

I don't know what he's doing, and I don't want to find out!

The last chain around his arms loosened. It was getting easier now, the entire structure of the spell falling apart. From directly above him, Nathan heard a confused gasp, and knew he had run out of time. His eyes snapped open.

Low-tier Focused Mind Rank 5 achieved!

High-tier Magic Resistance Rank 7 achieved!

The boxes vanished with a twitch of intention. They revealed Taeol's face, wide eyed and staring at the snapped chain links. He stood to Nathan's right, holding a spike capped with a green gem in one hand and a small hammer in the other, poised to drive the spike into Nathan's solar plexus. Nathan's left hand came up across his body, his hips and shoulders twisting as he drove a palm into Taeol's face with all the force his back and shoulders could generate.

It'll be hard for him to concentrate with a broken nose.

Nathan's palm skated off a barrier of slick force a few inches in front of Taeol's nose. The orange-robed man staggered back a few steps from surprise, though the force of the blow seemed to not affect him at all.

Okay, now I have some more options. But they all start with getting free.

Nathan sat up, pulling away from jeweled and engraved metal arms folded across his forehead. He tugged at the last few chains around his ankles as Taeol took further steps back, pointing at Nathan with the spike and breathing heavily. "You... how? What kind of toxic power do you have?"

Instead of replying, Nathan shut his eyes again, frantically pulling on the strings of the remaining chains. They fell away in moments, and he quickly levered himself off the table and towards Taeol.

The mage had backed up until he ran into the workbench against his wall, and his eyes flicked to the door. Nathan sprung at him in the moment of distraction, but Taeol cast just as quickly as last time.

[Paralysis]

Not this time.

Nathan had seen the gesture coming and balanced himself so he wouldn't immediately fall. Then, he drained the magic out of his muscles nearly as fast as it came in, staggering but not falling. Taeol's eyes bugged out further, and he reflexively held his hands out in front of his face. Nathan charged into him a moment later, relying on momentum to get through the defense spell, or at least knock Taeol over. The barrier flexed as Nathan hit it, but he bounced off as if he'd shoulder-checked a stone pillar. Taeol wasn't pushed back in the slightest.

Ow. Magic is bullshit. Conservation of momentum is a core physical law!

At least Taeol seemed to be panicking. He stared at Nathan like a man with a hundred hammers seeing a screw for the first time. Nathan loomed over Taeol and started searching for a gap in the barrier a few inches above Taeol's skin, wrapping his arms around the man as he failed to find one. The shield flexed under his arms, but didn't break.

Time to test some hypotheses. Something will let me crack this shell and get to the gooey center.

Nathan dug his fingers into the barrier on either side of Taeol's shoulders and *pulled* as hard as he could, trying to rip the barrier apart. It cracked and tore, a brief blast of force pushing Nathan a few steps back. Taeol's lips were moving, and Nathan could feel the mana of the spell he was weaving from several feet away. It was more powerful than anything Nathan had felt Taeol cast before. Nathan raised his hands protectively in front of him.

[D-d-d-**DISINTEGRATE**]

A thin beam of pale green light shot from Taeol's pointing finger and hit Nathan's left palm. Taeol's face pulled into a satisfied rictus as Nathan's left hand fell apart. Pain blasted through him as first his wrist, then his forearm turned to black dust. He screamed.

High-tier Magic Resistance Rank 8 achieved!

The wave of magic swept down Nathan's arm and he felt his Talent fight the spell as it consumed his inherently magic-resistant flesh. Nathan clutched his left arm with his right hand, unable to do anything but watch his arm slowly disintegrate. The advancing wave of mana felt like a hungry void, a consuming pit that would never be sated.

High-tier Magic Resistance Rank 9 achieved!

Nathan pushed back, fighting to arrest the advancing tide of entropy. Not with any clever ideas, just with frantic desperation. And maybe it made a difference. As the spell passed his elbow, it slowed to a crawl. Both Taeol and Nathan's eyes were glued to the advancing line of disintegrating flesh. Then, a few inches from his shoulder – and with one final notification – it stopped.

High-tier Magic Resistance Rank 10 achieved!

Congratulations, you have maxed out this Talent! It cannot be improved any further. You must achieve Insight into this Talent to Develop it to the next level. As it is high-tier, the kind of Insight will affect how it Develops.

Nathan fixed tear-filled eyes on Taeol, whose victorious expression paled into terror. Nathan stalked forward.

[Paralysis]

Nathan barely stumbled, overcoming the spell with sheer rage and a rather significant desire to beat Taeol's face in. Taeol quickly gathered magic for another powerful spell, but Nathan took a long step forward and pivoted his entire body, smashing his right elbow into Taeol's nose. Nathan felt cartilage pulping under the blow, and continued his turn, stomping on Taeol's knee with his right foot. The leg folded with an unpleasant popping sound and Taeol dropped to the ground with a whimper past bloody lips.

Nathan's absent left arm *hurt*, and he tried to cradle the missing limb as he turned to the door, whimpering. It was hard to think through the haze of pain and loss from his *missing arm*.

Goddamn, that hurts. It is time to leave. *I've never wanted to get outside more in my life. And that golem is coming back.*

Nathan stumbled to the door, pushed it open and was ten steps down the hall before he paused and turned around.

I hurt Taeol, but he won't die. I need to kill him. He's tried to do worse to me. He deserves to die. He's a powerful, vengeful mage and if I don't kill him now he'll come for me later.

He's also a man named Taeol dho Droxol, who seeks knowledge. If I kill him, I kill a story, and all of the deeds he could ever do. The potential he represents.

Nathan's face hardened, and he walked back to the door into the golem creation room.

A potential for great evil. Fucker took my arm. Kill him now, moralize about it later.

He turned the corner, and Taeol looked up at him from across the room, pulped lips stuttering.

[t-t-Teleport]

And with an orange flash, he was gone.

You have leveled up to level 9! Congratulations, you have forced an extremely powerful and deadly opponent to flee! Please choose a class from the following list to continue leveling, as you have unlocked a higher level than 9!

Potential classes:

Student: You have spent decades learning knowledge from books and teachers. This class will enhance your capability to learn knowledge, offering skills to improve memory, comprehension and intellect. It may Develop into classes focused on discovering new knowledge, or teaching, recording and using already existing knowledge.

Scientist: You have spent years engaged in pursuit of knowledge via careful scientific experimentation. This class will focus on discovery through experimentation, offering skills to improve your intellect, precision and luck. It may Develop into classes further focused on discovering new or lost knowledge, or classes focused on using or communicating your discoveries.

Rebel: You have struck a blow against the Giantsrest Dominion and escaped their custody. This class will make you capable of striking back, offering skills for disguise, sabotage and combat. It may Develop into classes focused on assassination, rabble-rousing or political subterfuge.

Martial Monk: You have trained in hand-to-hand combat techniques as well as meditation and focusing your mind. This class will focus on mental discipline and using it to enhance hand-to-hand combat prowess, offering skills to improve mental focus, combat capability and heightened awareness. It may Develop into classes further specialized in combat, guiding others or achieving enlightenment.

Explorer: You have explored forbidding lands far from home, journeying across continents to see natural wonders and foreign cultures. This class will focus on travel into new lands, offering skills for increasing travel speed, adapting to new societies and surviving in the wild. It may Develop into classes focused on unearthing lost ruins, information gathering or trade and diplomacy.

Disciple of Magic: You can sense and manipulate flows of mana untrained, even if you have not yet cast a spell. This class will make you better able to sense and direct mana, offering skills for understanding magic as well as sensing and manipulating mana. It may Develop into a more powerful spellcasting class, or a class which lets you subvert the magic of others more easily.

Conman: You have lied to a prominent member of the Dominion and gotten away with it. This class will enable you to continue deceiving people, offering skills on disguise, deception and manipulation. It may Develop into classes focused on information-gathering, assasination or thievery.

Antimagic Brawler: You have hand-to-hand combat training and neutralized a powerful mage and his magic with your bare fists. This class will make you tougher in combat, offering skills to improve combat, toughness and antimagic capability. It may Develop into classes further focused on hand-to-hand combat or suppressing magic

~

Status of Nathan Lark:
Permanent Talent 1: High-tier Magic Resistance 10
Talent 2: None
Talent 3: None

Class: None, level 9+

Utility skills:
Low-tier Focused Mind 5
Low-tier Earnestness 3

Chapter 6

Escape?

Nathan stood in the doorway, caught between horror, relief and a haze of pain. Taeol dho Droxol, the man who'd abducted him across dimensions, manipulated his mind and nearly ripped his soul out, had escaped.

That's probably bad. He doesn't strike me as the type to forgive his injuries or forget the knowledge he wants from me.

Nathan was still furious, and if the archmage reappeared, he would do his best to crush the man's skull. But Nathan was having a hard time feeling bad over failing to *kill* a human being.

Maybe if he ran far enough, fast enough, Taeol wouldn't catch up to him. But he needed to start now. As if to emphasize the point, he heard a scrape of stone on stone as the golem rounded the hall to Nathan's right. Nathan turned and ran down the hallway without a second look, awkwardly cradling the stump of his left arm.

And I only have one arm now. Seems hard to forget that when it hurts so much.

He heard the golem's heavy footsteps chasing him and rushed around a corner to find a wide flight of stairs winding around a huge square vertical shaft. A bright light shone down from the top, and the stairs and balustrade were made of the same seamless, pale stone as the rest of the tower. Nathan started running down the staircase, skipping four steps at a time in his haste. The golem turned the corner behind him, its stone feet slamming on the steps as it descended. It was fast, but not great at turning corners on the staircase.

Nathan continued down, looking over the edge for an exit. Nearly a hundred feet down was a grand hall, with statues on the walls and a shallow fountain in the center.

I'm not going to make it. Taeol mentioned more golems and traps, and this golem is going to catch up as soon as I get to a straightaway. I need something.

Nathan had one more untapped resource, and he quickly reviewed the list of classes he'd been offered earlier as he bounced himself off a wall to turn onto the next flight of stairs. It was a good thing that the knowledge was more or less inserted into his head since he couldn't exactly ask the golem for a timeout. The pain from his arm was a gnawing, biting thing, and these were terrible circumstances to make a decision. But this decision needed to be made *now*.

Going off first impressions, most of the classes called to different parts of Nathan – except Conman and maybe Explorer. Student and Scientist both aligned extraordinarily well with his adult life goals. However, Disciple of Magic appealed to a younger Nathan, the one wishing for magic over birthday candles.

The one who feels betrayed learning that apparently the primary use of magic is to be a supreme shitlord.

Unfortunately, Davrar seemed to be long on genocidal archmages and short on opportunities for graduate students in biology or magic. Or at least ones that didn't involve giving up the knowledge of the industrial revolution to said genocidal archmages. Those were off the table – and would clash with his [Magic Resistance] anyway. Rebel called surprisingly strongly to Nathan – if ever there was a place in need of a revolution, Giantsrest sounded like that place. But when the authorities had mental magic, staging a rebellion seemed like an exercise in futility.

Nathan bounced off another wall. He wasn't gaining much over the Golem. He needed something to enhance his speed, and something to strengthen his antimagic to get through the locks and traps Taeol had mentioned.

I need something that enhances me physically. And maybe does something about this pain.

Both [Martial Monk] and [Antimagic Brawler] appealed to Nathan, and seemed like ways to immediately improve his chances to escape. Both were equally disadvantaged by missing an arm. But that was a problem for *future* Nathan, who was not running from golems into magical traps and an unknown wilderness.

What made the decision easy in the end was that [Antimagic Brawler] mentioned his antimagic, and [Martial Monk] didn't. Furthermore – his meditation was a means to an end, not an end to itself. Being a monk was a calling, a purpose in the way being a brawler wasn't, and Nathan didn't like the mention of enlightenment. Ultimately, Nathan didn't want to let Davrar give him a purpose, just a tool. A tool to escape this *goddamned* tower.

So, wishing he could have considered the matter more fully and without the pressures of running down a staircase while missing an arm, Nathan chose to be an [Antimagic Brawler]. More boxes and knowledge unfolded before him.

> Congratulations, you are now an **[Antimagic Brawler]**, and have unlocked three class skills! These skills are tied to your parent class, and their power will increase with your level in that class. Davrar applauds your choice, and hopes you will continue to survive and prosper.
>
> **New Class skill Stamina:**
> You have unlocked the Stamina resource! Stamina will accumulate during periods of rest, and can be spent to improve the speed and strength of your movements, or used for other skills or Talents that utilize Stamina.
>
> **New Class skill Brawler's Indifference:**
> You will be less likely to flinch and more capable of ignoring pain and wounds to continue fighting.
>
> **New Class skill Antimagic Blows:**
> Your blows and strikes will enhance your inherent antimagic, allowing you to break magical barriers and constructs with barehanded strikes.
>
> **You have leveled up to level 15!**

The pain radiating from the stump of Nathan's arm abated. His running became smoother, his gait more even. The pain wasn't gone, but the intensity was muted and he didn't feel the visceral horror of missing his arm anymore. [Brawler's Indifference] allowed him to ignore it. The arm wasn't what mattered right now, and being distracted by his stump would get him killed.

That's so much better. I hadn't realized how debilitating it was.

Next, Nathan used Stamina to run faster, which felt as natural as breathing deeply. Instead of skipping four of the shallow steps at a time, he was skipping six, then seven. The Stamina inside of him decreased steadily. It wouldn't last forever, but he was already leaving the golem behind. Once he had a healthy lead on the golem and was approaching the bottom of the staircase, Nathan stopped using his Stamina, which now sat steady at about 150/250.

That felt like hitting the nitro button in a racing game. Amazing.

The stairs ended in a grand hall at the bottom of the shaft, the walls tiled with an intricate mosaic showing some dramatic scene that Nathan didn't stop to look at. There were a few doors in the hall, but a large set of double doors large enough to drive a semi through was the obvious winner in the "door to outside" contest. Nathan sprinted over and threw his body weight against them. He bounced off. There wasn't a handle, bar or obvious locking mechanism.

Nathan pivoted his body and slammed his palm into the center of the doors as hard as he could, spending Stamina throughout the motion. He felt a layer of magic crack at the blow, and his next shove sent one of the doors flying open. A plaza of stone lay in front of him, and beyond it a road wound through scraggly pine trees. He took off across the plaza, spending Stamina again to get away from the tower. Hearing something, Nathan glanced over his shoulder and stumbled.

Behind him, flanking the door, were two twenty-foot tall statues of warriors. Well, they *had* been flanking the door. Now they were charging after Nathan, metal greatswords held ready in stone hands. The swords were nearly fifteen feet long, and glowed with a red aura.

Shit shit shit run faster!

Nathan turned his back to them and took off, spending Stamina like water and doing his best to emulate Usain Bolt.

Pending utility skill: Low-tier Sprinting
You are running very fast. This skill will help you run quickly in the future. It will not allow you to run in circumstances where you couldn't otherwise.

Yes please!

Congratulations, you have accepted the 'Low-tier Sprinting' utility skill. It will become a part of your status and rank up as you use it. It starts at rank 1 and becomes more effective as it ranks up. Think about how you use your skill to aid in skill Development at rank 10.

Nathan's chest rose and his toes pushed into the ground. It wasn't an enormous difference, but combined with his Stamina, Nathan made it across the plaza and into the trees in seconds. Once he was past the second layer of trees, he didn't hear the golems chasing him anymore. He turned around to see one of them throw a fireball at him. It flew at him with the speed of a baseball pitch, coming straight for his chest.

Nathan didn't flinch. He didn't have the time or bracing to dodge, so he brought his hand up in a Stamina-assisted slap at the fireball, which exploded away from his palm. The fire blasted out, and Nathan was sent stumbling backwards. He wasn't badly burnt, though it felt like he'd held his hand in a campfire for a bit too long – before somebody pointed a very large hairdryer at his entire body.

His robe was on fire, so Nathan darted behind a small mound of earth and dropped to the ground, rolling around to extinguish the flames.

Low-tier Sprinting Rank 2 achieved!

He peeked a quick glance over the small lump of earth, looking toward the golems, ready to take off again at any moment. The tree in front of him was aflame, the blowback from the fireball turning it into an instant torch.

Damn. That spell should have made me into BBQ. [Magic Resistance] proves it's worth yet again. I think [Antimagic Blows] helped me out too. Who says you can't punch a fireball?

The giant golems had turned around and were returning to the tower, but Nathan thought getting farther away would be a good idea. He ran further into the forest, careful to avoid a clear line of sight to the golems. He got another fifty feet away and slumped to the ground, checking his injuries. His arm wasn't bleeding, and his palm wasn't badly hurt. The hand was definitely burnt, but not into deep tissue.

What is it with me and hand wounds?

"Hail! May I request a word?" Nathan's head snapped around and he jumped to his feet, shaking with adrenaline.

A woman had come out from behind a tree forty feet away and was looking straight at him. She was short and wide, with dark brown skin and voluminous tied-back dreadlocks. Her armor was scuffed leather, festooned with pockets and a warm-looking fur cloak. Her hands were out wide, palms clearly visible and empty. She approached slowly, voice low and calm. "Are you okay? What is your name?"

Can I just have five goddamn minutes? I'm not sure I'd be better at handling this, but at least I'd have a minute to assess my situation.

Nathan eyed her, ready to run again if the woman made a threatening move. She looked nothing like Taeol, but he remained on edge and his voice was tense. "Sorry, but I don't want to tell you. What do you know about *that*?" He pointed back toward Taeol's tower, hoping her answer would tell him her intentions. He checked his available Stamina in case he had to run.

Stamina: 36/250

That's not much.

She turned her head to look at the tower, a grimace across her broad face. She kept her voice even and calm. "It's a research tower of Giantsrest, just taken over a few weeks ago by a newly raised archmage. We're trying to figure out what his research is and kill him if we get the chance."

They're here to kill Taeol? Well, that's certainly promising.

Nathan relaxed a bit, but kept pushing. "We? Who is we? And what is your name? And please stop coming closer." If she was telling the truth, he'd stumbled onto enemies of Giantsrest. But he had a skill to enhance his Earnestness, so it was only prudent to assume people could have skills that made them better at lying. And Nathan didn't like the way she was edging closer to him.

The woman stopped about twenty feet away, arms still held wide. "My name is Vhala, and I lead an Adventuring team out of Gemore. Artha, Emerald, come out."

Another figure emerged from the brush to Nathan's right, decked in a darkened breastplate, heavy chainmail and a sturdy helmet that completely blocked their face, leaving only the mouth exposed. Their visible skin was porcelain white, and a fancifully decorated rapier on one hip was balanced by a heavy cleaver on the other. Vhala gestured to the figure. "This is Emerald."

How do they see?

Nathan's attention was grabbed by another figure coming up behind Vhala. It was a centaur, but instead of a horse, the bottom half had a different profile. Thinner legs and bushier fur clued Nathan in – the bottom half was an elk. The top half was a well-muscled man wearing thin clothing, with skin the texture and color of gray maple bark. He had long hair and a large beard in a deep silver. Two large multi-pronged antlers sprouted from his head. He spoke in a deep, smooth voice. "And I am Artha."

With that voice and body, Nathan would have found him hot if it wasn't for the whole... elk thing.

Fantasy world... fantasy world. These seem like good candidates for Taeol's "barbarians and intelligent monsters," though. I'm in the middle of unfamiliar territory with no supplies – and I know the nearby civilization is hostile to me. I need help, and a guide.

That thought made him rethink his interaction with these people. He turned back to Vhala. "Thank you, I apologize for my caution. My name is Nathan Lark. I've had a rough few days. I just escaped from that tower. If you could help me, I would really appreciate it."

She looked him over again, eyes lingering on the burnt robe and stump of an arm. "Hear me, that appears to be true. Seems sure you're not a giant's agent after that spell, though I'd like to hear how you ate a guardian golem's fireball and came out just a little singed. Stick to my heels. We'll go to our camp and meet Wiam, the last member of my team."

~

Status of Nathan Lark:
Permanent Talent 1: High-tier Magic Resistance 10
Talent 2: None
Talent 3: None

Class: Antimagic Brawler level 15
Stamina: 36/250
Brawler's Indifference
Antimagic Blows

Utility skills:
Low-tier Focused Mind 5
Low-tier Earnestness 3
Low-tier Sprinting 2

Chapter 7

The Giantraiders

Nathan followed Vhala through the brush, questions boiling in his mind. *Should I ask about the politics of Gemore first, to be sure I haven't traded one dystopia for another? Basic knowledge about Davrar? It would be really convenient if I could just tell them my situation and ask what advice they had. But it seems like a bad idea to trust them so far just yet. Let's hold off on that decision for now.*

What he really needed was treatment for his wounds. Nathan's body was sending some pretty strong signals of pain now that the "fight" was over and his [Brawler's Indifference] was weakened. What remained of his left arm had started slowly leaking blood through the cauterization of the disintegration spell, and his right palm was burned from the close encounter with a fireball.

Vhala interrupted Nathan from his introspection, looking back at him and swearing lightly as her eyes traced his injuries. "Hear me, but it seems like you could use a [Cure]. Can I touch you for that?" She was still treating him like a skittish animal, but Nathan *felt* like a skittish animal, so that was fair. He nodded to her, and the dark woman approached, laying gentle hands on his right arm. His only arm.

[Minor Curing]

Nothing happened. Nathan had thought that was likely, but said nothing. Vhala frowned at him, then changed the subject. "It'll be dark soon, we'll stay at the same camp for the night."

She turned back to the game trail, increasing their pace through the wilderness. Nathan was impressed she could find clear trails in this difficult terrain. He would've quickly been left scrambling through bushes and up slopes.

Nathan was also flummoxed by her comment about it getting dark soon. The sun was directly overhead, and showed no signs of falling out of the sky. He didn't want to reveal any ignorance, so he examined his companions.

Vhala was leading the group, and had reclaimed the weapons she'd dropped to first approach Nathan. An engraved, unstrung bow made of several composited layers was strapped on her back, and two one-handed axes rested on her hips, both also engraved in flowing patterns. Artha, the buff elk-centaur dude, was carrying a lot of gear on a harness across his elk parts. He also had a metal-capped staff strapped to his side that was nearly eight feet long and looked like it could be used as a battering ram in a pinch.

Emerald was behind Nathan, but he couldn't see much about them – their helmet covered all of their head but the mouth. In addition, the rest of their armor was pretty heavy for this terrain, and he hadn't even figured out their gender – or if they were human. But despite the heavy gear and visorless helmet, they moved smoothly and silently over the uneven terrain.

I need to internalize that everybody has access to Davrar, with skills, classes and Talents of their own. So I might see a lot of things that appear impractical but are made possible by Davrar. It also means it'll be easy to underestimate people. An unarmed old lady might be able to punch down a mountain.

It wasn't long before they passed over a rise, revealing an empty glade between the trees that was their destination. A faint haze hung over the center of the space, and Vhala led them straight towards it. They walked into the area, and a campsite appeared from nowhere.

Illusions and stuff. At least we can see out well enough. And being in a hidden camp makes me feel better about being in hostile territory.

As the mismatched party trooped in, a figure leapt from the top of a tree and glided to land in front of Vhala. It was a bird-person, with a pair of broad wings emerging from their shoulders above a set of humanoid arms ending with clawed fingers. They were covered head-to-foot with reddish brown feathers underneath dark robes and had a birdlike face, complete with a viciously hooked beak.

The beak was apparently capable of normal speech, as the bird-person addressed Vhala in a thick accent. "Yo boss. Whatsup with the tall Gianter? Prisoner?"

Vhala turned back to Nathan and spoke reassuringly, "Nathan, this is Wiam, he's a mage and an illusionist." She gestured the group into the campsite as she addressed Wiam. "This is Nathan. As far as I can tell, he's an escapee from the new archmage's experiments. I'm sure we'll hear the whole story soon. First, we'll stay here tonight and head out in the morning. Make sure the spells that hide the camp are in good shape, then get ready for some healing. Send a [Message] too, about our return."

Emerald and Artha set to readying the camp, starting a fire and fetching water from a nearby stream. Meanwhile, Vhala gestured Nathan to a log, handing him some jerky, a waterskin and a rough blanket before she stepped aside for a quiet conversation with Wiam.

I know they're talking about me, but that's to be expected. Vhala's been good about not pressuring me so far. And this jerky is amazingly flavorful.

As Nathan covered himself with the blanket and devoured the jerky, Vhala and Wiam came back, asking if Wiam could try healing him. Nathan acquiesced, but Wiam's [Moderate Curing] had no effect other than slightly slowing the bleeding from Nathan's stump.

Vhala looked frustrated. She dug into a pouch for some bandages which she carefully wrapped around the stump of Nathan's arm to stem the bleeding.

Then, she sat back on a log on the far side of the newly kindled fire. "Alrighty, I gotta ask you some questions. Y'all, get your stinky feet over here, I don't think he'll want to say this twice." After the four Adventurers had gathered, Vhala addressed Nathan again. "It's okay if you can't tell me everything, but we need to know how to help you. There's something weird going on with magic around you, and you escaped from an archmage's research tower. Anything you can tell us will help us help you."

Nathan looked down at the remnants of the jerky and chewed them down as he thought.

What do I tell them? Vhala certainly made a better first impression than Taeol, and they've fed me and tried to heal my injuries. I want somebody *to trust in this crazy new world, but I haven't learned enough about them yet. I need to know more. I suppose I can ask – if they react badly to questions that'll be an answer in and of itself. But I really shouldn't be too suspicious.*

Nathan swallowed the last of his jerky, washing it down with a swig of water before answering a question with a question. "Vhala, you've been nothing but kind to me. I appreciate it, but please, can you describe to me what's going on between Gemore and Giantsrest? And what is your part in it?"

She looked at him with surprise. "Really been stuffing your ears, ain't ya? We're at war. Have been since Gemore was founded. They're a big damn empire, but they've never been able to take little Old Gemore since we broke off. They raid us for slaves, send harassment armies, but it's been at least fifty years since they sent a conquering army. We kill the mages we can, free the slaves we can, but don't push too hard. They could take us, but don't seem to want to pay the cost.

"And us? This motley band of adventurers?" She looked fondly around the fire, at her companions. "We call ourselves the Giantraiders. All of us have lost something to Giantsrest, and so we take these jobs. The ones that involve camping in hostile wilderness for a few weeks to maybe get a shot at their newest and weakest archmage. We were waiting for him to leave his damned fortress of a tower to get a shot at him."

As she finished speaking, Nathan's attention was drawn upwards, to the sun. It was still directly overhead and partially hidden by clouds, having not budged at all during their trek to the camp. But it was dimming, eclipsed in front of his eyes as a line of darkness swept across the glowing orb. The mountains and camp were suddenly engulfed in darkness. Night had fallen, the only light a pale blue-green glow from beyond the clouds. Nathan looked down at the rest of the group. "Is that how the sun always sets?"

He got a round of amused grins and Wiam asked, "Y'ever been outside, or did ya get raised in that tower?"

Screw it. They seem like good people, and I've certainly got something in common with anybody who wants to kill Taeol. They have enough hints that anything else would be an obvious deflection, and I need *their help. Time to rip the band-aid off and take a risk.*

Nathan looked levelly around the campfire. "As might be obvious, I'm not from around here. I'm from a different world entirely. Taeol summoned me to Davrar with some crazy magical setup, and tried to get me to tell him about some things from my world. I didn't want to tell him, so he tried to [Charm] me and mess with my memory."

Shrugging, Nathan dropped another bombshell. "Magic and Talents don't exist where I come from, and I picked up a Talent that lets me resist magic. When I resisted his mind-fuckery, he tried to shove me into a golem core. So I broke his nose, he teleported out and I ran away." The faces around Nathan were expectant, waiting for a grand end to his tale. "And then the big-ass golems outside the door chased me and I met you."

There was a moment of silence, then Wiam, the bird-person, fell off his log, laughing. He picked himself up, still chuckling. "That's one zombie of a story, my dude, I wanna watch you tell it in the Guildhall. What'd the archmage want you to tell him?" Vhala glared at Wiam, then she glanced at Nathan. "Nevermind that. How'd you lose the arm? Near miss on an acid spray?"

Vhala isn't pushing me for the secrets that Taeol wanted. That's a good sign.

"He tagged me with a [Disintegrate] right before I broke his nose. It's what pushed my [Magic Resistance] Talent up to max rank." If the previous faces were surprised, these were astonished.

Emerald pivoted their armored head to Nathan, speaking for the first time. Their voice turned out to be high and raspy, with a strong stutter. "Y-you... you survived a direct hit from a D-d-disintegrate? And then broke an a-archmage's nose with one arm?" Everybody else nodded their agreement to the question.

Nathan didn't know what to say. "Yes? I wish I'd broken his neck before he teleported out. *Such* an asshole."

Low-tier Earnestness Rank 4 achieved!

Vhala spoke up. "We'll all throw our shoulders behind that wish. I'd reckon our mission here is done. If you'd like, we'll take you back to Gemore and submit a report on the research the new archmage was conducting, and its failure."

She smirked, indicating Nathan. "Or at least that the *research* is out of Giantsrest's vile fingers. That'll fulfill our contract nice 'n proper." She frowned at his arm. "There's a few high-level healers who can heal your arm, but it'll be expensive. Especially if magic doesn't work right on you. You can't turn your Talent off?"

Nathan shook his head, responding to her question. "I'll come back with you to Gemore, if there's a place for me there. Hopefully with less slavery."

Vhala gave him a nod. "Gemore's home to a lot of exiles and outcasts. We'll help you find something if you want."

Wiam made a high-pitched noise, waving his arms around in protest. "But the archmage is gone! We could break into the tower and steal everything – or ambush him when he comes back! This is a great opportunity to get rich and knock his head off."

Vhala was already shaking her head. "The guardian golems are still functioning perfectly, and we don't have the skills or tools to knock *them* off. And there's no way this Taeol is coming back without reinforcements. We leave."

That seemed to settle the issue, though Wiam grumbled in a high-pitched caw.

Artha leaned forward and spoke softly, his deep voice resonating distractingly across the campfire. His big, leaf-green eyes fixed on Nathan. "[Magic Resistance] must be a Talent of amazing potency. I've heard of the like, but those who attempt such a thing must give up all magic. Even then, none have found the Insight to raise it past mid-tier. And giving up magic is" – he held his arm up and conjured a small ball of light which gleamed off his beard – "difficult."

This seemed like a golden opportunity to learn more about Davrar, and it was a better thing to ask about than healing his arm. "Actually, can you explain Davrar to me? We have nothing like it in my world, so I'm a bit lost. What happens when a class Develops? What's the difference between Talents and utility skills? "

Artha's chuckle was low and rumbling. "I could see it being confusing. We have lived with Davrar all of our lives, but I will attempt to explain. First it is important to know that Insights are pieces of knowledge necessary to initially acquire a Talent, skill or class, and Develop them to more powerful versions. Then, Talents let you do something that is otherwise impossible. With the correct Talent, I could walk on water." The big elk-centaur rumbled a laugh. "Or on air, as one famous Adventurer can do, but none have yet replicated her Insight."

He continued. "A utility skill will not do this. Utility skills cannot break the rules of the world, though when you rank them up to unique tiers, this line is blurred. Classes are in the middle, granting skills which are lesser than Talents, but more focused than utility skills. Your class will have a focus, a purpose, and will often adapt to your Talents. For Adventurers like us, our classes will usually focus on combat. Mage class skills will improve mana manipulation and give access to different types of mana." He cocked a silvery eyebrow at Nathan. "Do you have a class?"

Nathan nodded once. "Yes, I took [Antimagic Brawler]. Seemed useful while escaping Taeol."

Artha's eyebrows raised in surprise. "I apologize for my phrasing. It is not common to tell others your exact class, and you should only do so with those you trust with your secrets. To balance these scales, I will tell you mine in return. I am a [Heavyhoof Charger]." The enormous man nodded solemnly, as if a wrong had been redressed.

Then he kept going. "You likely unlocked a resource with your class? As it is a brawler class, likely Stamina?" Nathan gave an affirmative gesture and Artha gestured around the campfire, pointing to Wiam, Emerald and himself in turn. "There are many resources, such as mana for mage classes, focus for precision classes, and Stamina for classes like yours and mine that rely on brute strength. Many variations on those as well – often class Developments will change a resource, making it more powerful or more specialized."

He held up the ball of light in his palm. "All people have innate pools of these resources, and with some training can learn to utilize them even when not unlocked by a class. Thus, I can cast spells." The ball of light in his hand flared, then went out. "But never as well as a mage class, and never beyond tier two or maybe tier three without dedicated training and a Talent. And my mana pool will always be minuscule before that of a true mage."

He sighed and closed his hand. "Davrar is straightforward, but with many hidden subtleties. Insight into the world and your own abilities will be rewarded. But above all Davrar rewards risk, and overcoming deadly challenges to kill deadly foes. At least for those whose classes focus on combat. A good plan for your Talents and classes helps too."

He shrugged in the firelight and looked to the rest of the group. "Nathan seems of like purpose to ours. We should advise him on the basics of Davrar, as we would a calf. Vhala, I would ask you to speak of the utility skills." He nodded at the dark-skinned woman, yielding the floor.

I'm not sure I like being called a calf, but this background on Davrar is exactly what I needed. I'm glad they're not taking advantage of my lack of knowledge to get me to swear a magical oath or something.

The heavy set dark woman appraised Nathan for a moment, pursing her lips and thinking over what she was about to say. "There's a limit to how many utility skills you can get. It's not set in adamant, but after you've got seven or eight they get harder to pick up, and most say ten is the most. But I know somebody who swears they've got thirteen, so... Davrar's ways are mysterious."

She shrugged. "You can get rid of most utility skills if you need to, but it's better to get the ones you want in the first place since it sucks to re-train, and all of your Insights count for nothing. They're mostly for utility. Pick up ones that make life easier – Emerald's got one for cooking and it's half the reason we bring them along." The last sentence was told with the air of an often-repeated joke before Vhala gestured at Emerald. "Emerald, Class Developments?"

Emerald shifted uneasily from where they were preparing a heavy pot, slicing apart a set of vegetables. "C-classes Develop at levels 27, 81, 243. What c-classes you get offered depends on your Path, and your Talents and utility skills. W-when you Develop a class you get three new class skills and your old ones can change too."

Wiam broke in, interrupting Emerald's hesitant speech. "But Talents are the real cake, the core of any build. Everythin' depends off 'em, and they're where you gotta start. Mages all start with some kind of mana shaping, and a lot of other people pick it up for basic spells."

The birdfolk mage gestured to Artha demonstratively. "Being able to cast basic spells like cleanin', curin' and mendin' is pretty feckin' useful. I'm a mage all the way, so I'm working on gettin' a Talent to refill my mana faster, but it's hard. If I really wanna fly, I'd need a Talent for it because these boys aren't up to more than a bit of a glide on their own." He flapped his wings demonstratively. "But that's what the [Fly] spell is for. When I get the castin' down. It's tier six anyway, so that's a bit off."

Vhala took over from Wiam, waving him to silence."Yes, Talents are important, and are usually chosen *before* a class is taken." Then she raised a finger to emphasize her next point. "But they can be a bit tricky to pick up. A lot of the known ones you can get if somebody tutors you, but the general practice is the same. Think hard about what you want to do, think about how it would happen and try to do it. That's the Insight. But don't expect to get something for nothing."

She spread her hands, as if laying out the reality of the situation. "Most of the good Talents spend or manipulate a class resource, though there are exceptions. But you gotta be careful with Talents – some of them you can drop if you change your mind, but others are permanent, especially the ones that change something about your body or class. Those tend to be pretty strong and hard to get, but not being able to take them back can be a problem. Does your magic resistance Talent say 'permanent'?"

Nathan took a moment to check his status, grimacing before he responded. "Yeah, it does." He sat for a moment, thinking and sulking about being essentially locked out from casting magic. He looked up from the fire. "I – have a lot to think about. How can you get multiple classes?"

Vhala sucked a breath between her teeth. "It's supposed to be possible, but nobody really knows how. If it's an Insight, it's the most valuable kind there is. Somebody I know with two classes, the same lady with thirteen utility skills, says that the second class is very personal. None of us have two classes unless you folks have been holding out on me."

There were a few chuckles, and after a bit of thought Nathan asked again. "What does Developing a skill or Talent do? What happens when you Develop a high-tier skill?"

Everybody looked around for a moment, and then Artha spoke up. "Going from low to mid to high tier has straightforward results, if not always a straightforward path. First, you need an appropriate Insight for use in the Development. Then the skill or Talent becomes more powerful, and often loses restrictions. Developing beyond high-tier is complicated, and tied to the Insight used to Develop it. Often you will gain a new application, or some significant restriction will be removed. There are many different Developed versions of the same high-tier Talents and skills. It is often harder to Develop Talents than skills."

Phew. Ok. A lot to digest there. I needed to know all of that.

Nathan bowed his head in appreciation. "Thanks for all the answers. I'm sure I'll have more questions later, but for now I need to think."

The group broke up to their respective tasks. Emerald continued cooking, Vhala did weapon and gear maintenance and Artha set up a large tent. They seemed surprisingly incurious about Nathan and his world. Or maybe they were just giving him space? After watching them for a moment, Nathan stood up and looked around the campsite. He noticed that Vhala was keeping an eye on him, which was fine. She wasn't trying to hide it, which Nathan appreciated. In general this group seemed to treat him as a *person* in a way that Taeol hadn't.

Nathan found a good spot on the edge of camp and sat down cross-legged on a bed of needles, his back against a tree. He had some thoughts and plans, but was feeling pretty frazzled and really needed some [Focused Mind] time.

He closed his eyes, felt his lungs move and spent a while drifting in physical sensation. A lot of it was spent feeling for the left arm that should be there, but wasn't. By the end of his meditation, Nathan felt calmer and more centered.

It's hard to get used to missing an arm if I know I can get it back. And I'm not going to be much of a brawler with only one arm. There is a way to restore the arm with healing magic, but I would need to earn or borrow money for it. And I would need to evolve the Talent so that I can choose to be affected by some magic. Maybe I can figure out how to do that? I have no idea how that works.

How to Develop his rank 10 [Magic Resistance] definitely deserved some thought. Just because there was an obvious solution – changing [Magic Resistance] to allow friendly magic to affect him – didn't mean it was the best solution. In large part, it depended on his goals here. Now that he was out of immediate danger, what were his priorities?

Nathan was cold, so he walked back over to the campfire and sat, staring into the flames. What did he want here in this world? On Earth he'd had it mostly figured out – contribute to scientific knowledge. Do things nobody had ever done before, and be a small shoulder for the next generation to stand on. Along the way, try to live a comfortable life with loved ones, friends and good books.

But in this world? From what he'd seen, they had medieval technology, magic and constant conflict. Nathan *could* try to introduce ideas from his world to improve people's lives. It would be a way to make a difference that he'd never been offered on Earth. But Nathan had taken a minor in history. Technology improved lives, but the road to get there was long and fraught with pitfalls.

Assuming he could even succeed, and Davrar didn't prevent technology in some way, he would be responsible for what he unleashed. Beyond the simple efficiency of slaughter that technological weapons allowed, technology inherently concentrated power in the hands of those with the power and money to build it. The average quality of life during the industrial revolution had been pretty awful.

You couldn't keep broad technological development secret, and inventions tended to expand beyond the control of their creators. Before Nathan introduced *anything*, he'd want to trust the people he worked with. And he needed to ensure some level of information control, since who would be able to build steam engines and guns? Giantsrest, the big empire proficient in magic, or Gemore, which sounded like a scrappy kingdom of adventurers and runaway slaves?

Nathan had made gunpowder in college for fun. It wasn't easy, even with the ability to order pure sulfur and potassium nitrate off the internet. And if Nathan *did* try to introduce technology to Gemore, that seemed like a great way to get assassinated. With Taeol's escape, it wasn't as if he could hide his involvement in any sudden appearances of new technology that looked remotely Earth-like.

Taeol has seen Earth through his spells, after all.

Maybe that was a reason to do it anyway? They knew what was in his head, and would probably try to recapture him regardless. There was just so much he didn't know about the situation. He trusted the Giantraiders, but were they representative of Gemore as a whole?

Struck by a sudden thought, Nathan looked up at Emerald, who was now stirring the pot over the fire. "Does Giantsrest have spies in Gemore?"

Emerald didn't turn their head but simply answered, "Y-yes. And i-if what you are saying is true, they will be looking for you. Archmages are d-downright draconic about what they think is theirs, and they hate to be reminded their magic has l-limits." Emerald's pale lips twisted into a sneer, and they reached a hand up to stroke the ever-present helmet, as if reminding themselves it was still there.

It all came back to Giantsrest and the Ascendent Academy. Taeol had damned them in Nathan's eyes with his words and actions. Nothing the Giantraiders had said did anything to contradict that opinion. They would come after Nathan again, and probably co-opt any technology he tried to introduce.

Nathan would need to fight them. It appealed to him on a primal level, an outlet for the simmering anger that Taeol's words and actions had provoked. Giantsrest had tried to mind-control Nathan, break his mind and put him in a golem. Taeol's actions had declared a complete lack of respect for Nathan's being, his personhood. For no other reason than that, Nathan wanted to see him and everything he stood for *destroyed*.

And I find the very thought of a slave-empire built on those principles viscerally disgusting. Something like that shouldn't exist.

If Giantsrest's might rested on its magic, then Nathan could build himself to counter that strength. He could fight to win instead of fighting to survive.

When in desperate ground, fight.

He would level up, cast down the Giantsrest Dominion and maybe *then* start the industrial revolution.

Low-tier Focused Mind Rank 6 achieved!

Chapter 8

A Time to Rest

Emerald's dinner was a stew. The broth hadn't had time to thicken substantially, but some green vegetables – the same as what Taeol had given him – lent the dish a nice spice. It was awkward balancing the bowl on his knees to eat with one hand, but Nathan devoured three bowls.

Luckily, there was plenty, and after the meal Emerald filled up a wide-mouthed canteen and handed it to Nathan. "F-for tomorrow."

Nathan thanked the enigmatic armored fighter for the food, then checked his status again.

Status of Nathan Lark:
Permanent Talent 1: High-tier Magic Resistance 10
Talent 2: None
Talent 3: None

Class: Antimagic Brawler level 15
Stamina: 250/250
Brawler's Indifference
Antimagic Blows

Utility skills:
Low-tier Focused Mind 6
Low-tier Earnestness 4

Low-tier Sprinting 2

Arms: 1/2.

A bit of food and rest had completely refilled his Stamina, which was good to know. The Giantraiders settled into the big tent, except for Wiam who took first watch. They left a large blanket for Nathan, but he was too excited for sleep. Nobody was holding him prisoner and he had some ideas about Talents, so he wrapped himself in the blanket and huddled close to the fire, closing his eyes to activate [Focused Mind].

First, he considered his High-tier Magic Resistance Talent. It felt locked up, constrained by chains that he couldn't figure out how to unlock. That unlocking was clearly the "Insight" that Davrar and the Giantraiders had spoken of. But they'd also said that *what* Insight he used would change how the Talent Developed. He had some ideas related to how he'd used the Talent to neutralize magic, and if Nathan could get Wiam to cast some beneficial and harmful spells on him, he might be able to remove the blockage of beneficial magic.

Alternatively, he could try to remove the restrictions on casting magic himself. Based on what he'd been told, doing so would prevent him from allowing beneficial magic. He didn't have any ideas about how to do that, but being immune to magic while being able to cast it sounded great.

But that option means I won't get my arm back anytime soon – and I already took my class, which is not a mage-class. It's sort of as far away as you can get. And even if I succeed at allowing beneficial magic to affect me, I'll still need to earn or borrow a lot of money for a high-level healer.

Maybe Nathan was thinking about this the wrong way. His ultimate goal was to be as good at resisting magic as possible to help him fight Giantsrest. If he used *this* Development to make his Talent more flexible, then he wasn't using it to make the Talent better at its intended purpose.

Besides, there's a good chance I know more about human physiology than almost anybody here. I took that class on anatomy when I was thinking about pre-med. And I know more about stem cells than almost everybody on Earth, much less here.

Nathan concentrated on his right arm, the whole one. What was the structure? Bones, filled with marrow. Then muscles interspersed with veins, arteries and nerves. He couldn't visualize all of the details. Nathan remembered Vhala's advice.

You don't get something for nothing. The best Talents use a class resource.

He felt for his Stamina, and pushed it at the stump of his arm. He visualized the arm, the details he could remember, and tried to *push* his Stamina into that shape. His stump jerked, and felt cold. Nathan opened his eyes, and saw no changes, no blue boxes. The stump was covered with bloody bandages.Nothing had happened.

Okay, hypothesis one down. Let's go for number two.

Nathan closed his eyes and focused on the stump again, searching for the potential he knew was there. Inside your bones was marrow, and marrow had one of the highest concentrations of stem cells in adult humans. They were mostly Hematopoietic stem cells, the type that divided into the various cell types in the blood. They weren't the right kind of stem cells to differentiate into tissue, but maybe Davrar would help him bridge that gap. All it took was four transcription factors – the Yamanaka factors – to reprogram basically any cell into a pluripotent stem cell. Nathan had done it, watched the change happen. On Earth, it took a few days, up to a week for that to happen. Here?

Nathan concentrated on his Stamina, pushing it inside the bone of the stump, where the marrow should be. He felt Stamina drain away, and a feeling of heat in his severed appendage. But when he opened his eyes, nothing had happened. His stump was uncomfortable, but there were no blue boxes, and no growth.

He pushed the image of the arm at the heat in the bone of the stump.

The cells know what to do. They all have the necessary developmental instructions in their DNA to grow an entire body. If they're prompted correctly, they can reprogram back to pluripotency, then differentiate into any cell in the body. Normally that requires such a specific environment it's impossible. But with Davrar and the bodily magic of Stamina, it might be possible. I just need Stamina to enhance my body in this one very specific way.

At that thought, the bandage fell off his stump. Nathan could feel flesh growing. It wasn't growing from the entire stump, but there was a soft tendril of new flesh growing from the end of the bone in his left arm. It lengthened and thickened, and Nathan redoubled his focus on the image of the arm.

This is the gross structure. The cells know the details.

It was an indescribable sensation, and not at all pleasant. Like... peeling off a scab and touching raw flesh below. But far more widespread. The new growth extended, but only about a third of the distance to his elbow. Nathan tried *not* to think about how he was creating mass from nothing but Stamina, or how impossible it was for cells to double that quickly. As he banished the wayward thought, the growth stopped. He tried to push it farther, and nothing happened. He opened his eyes, exhausted from the brief effort.

Low-tier Focused Mind Rank 7 achieved!

Stamina: 0/250

Yeah. That would do it.

Pending Talent: Mid-tier Regeneration
You have recovered from a permanent injury using Stamina to fuel regrowth of undamaged flesh. This Talent will turn a difficult and costly effort into a natural process, allowing you to recover from almost any injury. You can spend Stamina to rapidly heal wounds. Larger wounds and replacing greater amounts of missing flesh will take longer and cost more Stamina. Regeneration will not prevent you from dying of grievous wounds, and will not protect against poison.

That looked pretty good. Nathan leaned back, wiping sweat from his brow. That effort had been *tiring*, and spent all of his Stamina. He should probably think this whole idea over a little more before he just accepted the Talent.

I just want my arm back goddamn. And that sounds pretty useful in combat.

Congratulations, you have accepted the 'Mid-tier Regeneration' Talent. It will become a permanent part of your status and rank up as you use it. It starts at rank 1 and becomes more effective as it ranks up. Think about how you use your Talent's functions to aid in Talent Development at rank 10.

Oh, it was a permanent Talent. Well, that made sense. Maybe that wasn't a bad thing. Vhala had mentioned that permanent Talents tended to be stronger and harder to get. Being able to heal himself *while* being immune to magic sounded like a very useful way to survive this world. And Nathan could still use his Magic Resistance Development to get *better* at resisting magic!

Important if I want to take down Giantsrest.

But! That was something to think about later. Nathan was tired, and he was hungry again. He grabbed the canteen of soup that Emerald had handed him earlier and sat next to the fire for a while, drinking his soup. The soup wasn't as good when it was only lukewarm, but the fire made up for that. It was gratifying to feel his Stamina refill. Energy suffused Nathan's body, and channeling it made him feel like he could run a marathon or climb a mountain. He funneled it all to his arm.

With the Talent, his [Regeneration] didn't require much focus and was more efficient. Nathan sort of vaguely directed the Talent at his arm, and it regrew. If he stopped, then the healing would slow down significantly, but he wouldn't start bleeding. It didn't seem to be something he could completely turn off, but operated tenfold faster if he directed the Talent.

As the growth extended past his elbow, soft cartilage solidified into bone. It was a gross process, with skin lagging behind the growth of muscle. It didn't take long for Nathan to empty his soup, as Wiam finished a wide circuit of the camp and came up behind him.

Mid-tier Regeneration Rank 2 achieved!

"Ya'know that soup is supposed to be for tomorrow, yeah?" the bird-man said as he eyed Nathan tipping the canteen all the way back. Then Wiam came around Nathan's side, saw the regrowing arm and jumped in surprise, squawking. It was a pretty impressive, wing-assisted jump, and Wiam landed nearly a dozen feet away, muting his surprised outburst to not wake the sleeping Giantraiders. "How ya doin' that? You can't cast magic, 'n [Restore] is sixth tier!"

Nathan nodded. "I just picked up a Talent that lets me heal wounds with Stamina. But I don't have enough soup left to finish healing my arm. Can I have yours?" He gestured to another canteen, strapped to Wiam's pack.

Wiam's eyes were glued to Nathan's still-regenerating arm. "Just picked up? I gotta see this. Sure." He handed over his canteen, and spent the next twenty minutes watching Nathan's arm completely regrow as he drained a second and then a third canteen of the peppery soup. All told, it had cost almost a thousand Stamina to entirely regrow the arm.

Not bad. As the Talent ranks up it'll hopefully get faster and more efficient. I'm not a certain Canadian superhero yet, but. Goals.

Mid-tier Regeneration Rank 3 achieved!

Nathan leaned back, his worries suddenly feeling small in comparison to the relief that swept through him as he flexed his tender, but whole, left arm. There was still a lot to think about, but he had two arms again. And he was exhausted. He bid an amazed Wiam goodnight, and took his blanket to the tent, where he was out in an instant.

~

Nathan woke to sudden light in his eyes. The sun was directly overhead, in the same spot it had been all day yesterday. The Giantraiders were rapidly taking down the camp around Nathan, and Artha had just yanked the tent fabric to the side and was folding it up in quick movements.

Nathan looked around bleary-eyed, and rubbed his eyes with his hands. Both hands. He clenched his left fist and stared at it, profoundly satisfied at having regrown an entire arm from scratch.

If only I could show that to my dissertation affairs committee – I'd be done.

Vhala stomped up to him, gesturing for Nathan to get up, and handed him a set of thick clothes. "We don't have anything that'll fit you. But Artha was able to cobble something together last night during his watch out of some spares. Wiam told me you picked up a Talent to regrow your arm. Very impressive and all that, but we gotta get moving. We'll fill your head as we move."

Nathan stumbled up, realizing he felt pretty good. He'd slept well, even if the ground had been hard and he had used his arms as a pillow. He looked around for something to help with, but the Giantraiders were nearly finished taking down their camp. Nathan retreated behind an especially short pine and changed out of his burnt gray robe into the mostly-brown clothes that Vhala had given him. They were made of mismatched thick fabric, homespun and sturdy. He kept the Giantsrest underwear, though. They were much softer than any of the new clothes he'd been given.

When he came out, everybody was packed and ready. Most of the gear had been packed into a series of large cloth panniers that hung over Artha's elk half, though they didn't look big enough to hold everything. The others clearly had gear, but it looked more like supplies for the day. Not to mention weapons. It was surreal to Nathan to see four people armed to the teeth like that. Wiam had at least six daggers strapped in various places and an enormous crossbow slung across his back.

They'd been waiting for him, and Nathan rushed to join them. "Sorry for holding you up."

After Wiam cast a spell to erase the remnants of the camp, they started off into the woods, following Vhala. They moved at a fast walk and Nathan could barely keep up without spending Stamina. Wiam sidled up next to him. "Don'tcha worry 'bout when you opened your eyes – you got up with the sun, and we figured ya'could use a rest after all the arm-regrowing. That's incredible as it goes, how'd ya do that?"

Nathan noticed that everybody was listening attentively, and started to explain. He did his best to describe how he channeled his Stamina to cause his arm to regrow. When Nathan mentioned focusing on stem cells that could regrow into other types of cells, Wiam bounced on his claws like a kid who wanted to ask a question. Nathan looked at him inquisitively.

He tilted his head in a very bird-like fashion. "It's real odd hearing ya talk about things we've never heard of. But basically, ya'know things about your body, how it's put together, and that let'cha make a good Talent?"

Nathan shrugged. "I think so? I spent many years understanding how these specific cells work, and was taught how my body was put together a long time ago. But a lot of that knowledge wasn't directly applicable to what I did last night."

Artha butted in, stepping closer. "These are Insights you have. They are valuable, and you should not give them away freely. And they would not be of much use to us, for we all have our own Talents and classes." Artha glared at Wiam. "Our only use for such things would be to trade them away, and likely do a bad job at it, devaluing what Nathan has. Sharing a degraded Insight is no favor to any."

Oh! They use Insights to gain and Develop specific Talents as a sort of meta-currency. If I were to guess from what Artha said, it applies to how to get classes and utility skills too.

"What do you use as normal currency?" Nathan asked. "To buy food and such."

Wiam seemed apologetic over his probing about Nathan's Insights, so he explained Gemore's coinage system. They used a standard system of copper, silver and gold coins of increasing value. The coins were minted by the Gemore Crafting Guild, and came standard with a hole in the middle to be strung on a cord. The cord was either looped around the belt or the neck, depending on how much money one had and how worried one was about pickpockets. Wiam was describing how some standard magical items were sometimes used as larger units of currency when he froze, then turned and spoke to Vhala with urgency.

"[Message] fer us. Slaving raid three days ago, hit Pilriden and took all o' the villagers. Weren't headed our way so nobody thought to tell us, but they'd laid a false trail and are headed straight to Halsmet."

"And the Giantsrest garrison there." Vhala's face was tight, clearly thinking through options. She spoke quietly. "That puts us right near their path. How many?"

Wiam shook his head sadly. "Big raid. [Message] says three enslavement mages, about twenty slave soldiers and two slave masters. Too much for us."

Emerald hissed through their teeth and checked their weapons. "Y-you know my choice," they said quietly.

Wiam spoke up. "Three mages though! That's beyond our distance. I wanna kick Giantsrest's nuts as much as y'all, but we can't take that fight. I'm sorry Emerald, but I don't think we can make a difference beyond adding four to their lines." He glanced at Nathan. "Five."

Artha pursed his lips. "It is a risk, to be sure. But would you wish that people would try to save you? If you were in their bindings at this moment? And I think we have another asset. Nathan." He turned to address Nathan directly, looking into his eyes and speaking formally, almost ritualistically. "Would you help us free our people from the thrall of Giantsrest? It will involve fighting, and maybe dying. But I will ask you all the same, for there is no cause worthier. We wait for your word to go save a hundred from a life of torture and pain. If you wish to enter Gemore as a hero, this is how you do it."

A hunk like this asking me to ride into battle at his side? How could I say no?

Nathan looked into Artha's green eyes and nodded. "Yes. I'll help you fight."

Chapter 9

A Time to Fight

Vhala let out a long breath, and leaned back against a tree. "Then I vote yes. We're doing this. Wiam, send a [Message] back to the Guild letting them know we're taking on the rescue, Davrar guide us. Artha, Emerald, you know the drill."

She turned to Nathan. "Okay, we'll need to get you up to speed quickly. We've done this fight before, but never against so many. The key is the mages. They're the power, the backbone and leaders of Giantsrest's slave raids. We kill them, and we win. The slave masters can keep the slaves in line and get them moving in the right direction, but it's the enslavement mages and their magic who will win or lose this fight.

The slave soldiers aren't a big threat – they're immune to pain, but these ones won't be too independent or capable. They'll be ordered to try to pin us down so the mages can hit us with something like [Dominate], [Slumber] or just [Chains of Restraint] so they can capture us. And they *will* try to capture us. Giantsrest takes pride in capturing Gemore Adventurers, and they have bounties on all of us specifically." She quirked a grin. "Time to push them a bit higher."

While she talked, Artha and Emerald set their gear neatly on the forest floor, stripping themselves of anything not important for imminent combat. Then, Emerald helped Artha withdraw a complex belting system and strap heavy armor plates over his body. The bags had to be enchanted to hold that much metal; there was no way it would fit otherwise. They were done remarkably quickly, and Artha's muscled form was replaced by a nine-foot behemoth of roughly engraved steel.

They all rejoined Nathan and Vhala as she explained Nathan's role in the fight. "We know how they'll react, and we can keep them distracted and get you close. But mages are tricky to finish off. Usually enslavement mages don't know any spells beyond tier five mind magic – so no [Fly] or [Teleport] or [Disintegrate] – but they'll all be [Mage Armored] in hostile territory, and they'll be quick with [Wind Blasts] and other spells to keep anybody from getting in close. If you can close the distance in spite of all that to crack their [Mage Armor] and knock one off, we can hopefully take this fight. Better if you get more, of course."

I'm about to fight for my life. Not just mine, but a hundred people I've never met before

Nathan tried to speak, but found his throat suddenly parched. He swallowed, then asked. "How long do we have? Do I have time to try to Develop my Magic Resistance Talent? I've got a few ideas."

The Giantraiders stared at him like he'd grown another head. Vhala finally answered "We probably have a few hours, but we should use that time to set up the ambush. If you think you can Develop your Talent in a reasonable way after we're there, I'd tell you to go for it. But usually people take a few days to prepare and have their Insight very clearly thought out."

Then she nodded, politely dismissing the topic without making it particularly obvious that Nathan had just asked a stupid question. "Regardless, I think I know where they'll pass. Let's hurry to get there before they do. We will need to set up our ambush carefully."

The next hour was a frantic run through the forest. Nathan had to sprint in bursts to keep up with Giantraiders, spending Stamina to save himself from falling behind on multiple occasions. His compatriots were fast and knew the terrain. For a third of the trip they ran along a wide ruined road, studded with cracked and broken paving stones. Eventually they broke from their path before a long bridge in much better repair than the rest of the road. In the center of the bridge was a ruined gatehouse, worn but surprisingly intact with a hundred-foot drop to the river below it.

Nathan wanted to ask about the weird ruin, but he was running to keep up with the Giantraiders, who ignored the strangely intact bridge. Thanks to the road and Vhala's ability to find clear routes through the difficult terrain, they reached her chosen ambush site before their enemies.

Low-tier Sprinting Rank 3 achieved!

It was a shallow ford in a fast-running stream, where the water was no more than a foot or two deep across a forty-foot width. Both sides of the ford were lightly dusted with tall shrubs, and had moderately sloped banks down to the stream.

Vhala rapidly distributed them, telling Artha to hide some distance away on the opposite side of the stream and charge into the slaving party from behind when they were about to finish crossing the ford. Wiam would be positioned in a tree about seventy yards away, to sow confusion with his spells and take shots with his crossbow. Meanwhile, Vhala was hidden in the trees on the side of the ford that Giantsrest would be crossing towards. Emerald and Nathan were placed in the bushes to either side of the ford on the same side as Vhala, to spring out when the soldiers were drawn away and target the mages.

Before they dispersed to their positions, everybody got together in a quick huddle. Vhala spoke softly. “These scum owe us a debt. A debt of blood and life and death. Today we collect some of that debt. We stand against their evil, so there will be fewer like us. Death to the Giant.”

The others all echoed her softly. “Death to the Giant.” The group broke up.

Artha put his armored hand on Nathan’s shoulder, and Nathan felt his heart thudding in his ears. Artha’s voice was deeper and rougher than it had been before. “I will gift you Insight. In this battle, feel your burning Rage against your foes. Stoke it, and feed your Stamina into the flame as fuel. It will make you stronger and should unlock some new classes. Fight well, my friend.” He trotted off across the stream.

Wiam gestured Nathan into his chosen bush and cast [Hunting Blind] on it, warning him to move as little as possible to avoid disrupting the spell. He repeated the process for Emerald in a bush nearly twenty yards away, then scampered off to climb his tree.

It was time to wait. Nathan took another drink of soup to top off his Stamina, before closing his eyes to clear his mind. He tried to think about his magic resistance. He needed to Develop it for this fight. They were about to go up against mages who specialized in slavery. They’d be good at all of that mind-fuckery magic that terrified him so much. His magic resistance needed to be stronger so he didn’t die or end up a mind-slave. Suddenly, Nathan found himself breathing faster, a sudden twisting in his gut and terror in his heart.

What am I doing here? There are twenty five people who are going to try to kill me and only five of us. This is insane. Why am I here? Somebody hot asks me to fight and now I’m willing to dive into the middle of battle? The elk half is a dealbreaker anyway, and now he’s manipulating me into fighting for him! I can’t kill somebody I’ve just met.

No. He was committed. Nathan stilled his mind, dissolving the thoughts of killing and death. He breathed slowly, listening to the sounds of the stream. After a little while, he revisited the thought of killing. These people were *evil* in a way that Nathan had never thought he'd meet back on Earth. You heard about rapists, traffickers, and slavers, but you never thought you'd *meet* one and know them for what they were. But if you believed in free will, in autonomy, then you *had* to oppose those people when you knew them.

Time to put your money where your mouth is. Or rather, your fist where their mouth is.

Nathan heard the sound of many people stumbling through the forest beyond the stream, and his jaw set with determination. His entire body trembled with anger. These *scum* took people, denied all of their desires, their dreams and any hope of choosing their own life. The slavers wanted, so they took. In so taking, they'd declared their disregard for concepts like natural rights, and voided their own *personhood*. Nathan wasn't killing people, he was killing *slavers*.

Low-tier Focused Mind Rank 8 achieved!

The right phrase for this is retributive justice.

Nathan felt strength flow through his limbs as he started to feed Stamina to his anger. He wasn't moving yet, and he felt his Stamina tick down as he watched the slaving party begin fording the stream. The rage felt *good*. He felt strong, strong enough to rip a man in half. But he waited for the plan.

The slaving party was centered around six lines of slaves, each with about twenty people bound together with metal chains. Leading the slaves were ten or so armored soldiers, marching in perfect sync with large square shields and spears. At the very back were ten more soldiers walking in step, guarding five unique individuals. Three of them were obviously mages, wearing robes like what Taeol had worn, but in green instead of orange. The other two were the slave masters, wearing an assortment of brightly colored clothes. They yelled and brandished whips at the slowly-moving mass of captives.

As the leading soldiers started to climb the bank on Nathan's side of the stream, Artha appeared over the crest behind the slaving party with a bone-chilling roar. He charged down into the soldiers, ignoring their spears and scattering them while drawing every eye.

The mages turned to study the rampaging elk-man. They reacted with excitement, one of them saying, "More captives! What great fortune!"

Another looked around, frowning and beginning to weave her hands together to cast some sort of spell. She faltered as a heavy bolt from Wiam's crossbow shattered an invisible force in front of her chest. One of the slave masters took an arrow from Vhala's recurve through the back of the head and dropped into the edge of the stream. The mages all stared at him for a second before looking back, seeing Vhala standing atop the nearest bank. She fired another arrow, but a mage waved his hand.

[Force block]

The arrow deflected, and the slave soldiers turned and began ascending towards Vhala. The female mage looked around again, frowning. "There are always more. I'll flush them out."

Nathan didn't catch the spell, but a *ping* of energy spread from her, highlighting everybody it touched in soft white light. Emerald's bush glowed white, and the mages turned and faced it as Emerald charged out, leading with a red-glowing rapier.

[Paralysis]

[Binding Web]

[Slick stone]

Hidden patterns on Emerald's helmet lit up, and they ignored the first spell but had to frantically dodge and swipe with the rapier to avoid the sticky strands of web that lashed out. Then, the ground under Emerald turned slick for a moment, until a conjured rain of dirt from Wiam covered up the patch.

One of the mages cried out. "That's Archmage Dennar's escaped slave! He's promised private tutoring to the ones who capture him!"

Emerald's snarl was audible over the clashing of metal. It was time for Nathan to stop hiding.

He sprinted from his bush, aiming straight for the nearest mage. His rage burned through him like a cleansing fire, and Nathan roared his hate at the mages. One of the men turned toward him and smirked to see an unarmored, unarmed young man charging them.

[Paralysis]

Nathan didn't even pause as the familiar magic sank into him, subsumed in his wrath. The mage's brow furrowed, but he didn't seem worried. At least, until Nathan drove stiffened fingers into his [Mage Armor] and *cracked* it open. The mage stumbled back and opened his mouth to cast another spell, but Nathan was right behind him, pounding a fist with all of his weight behind it right underneath the man's sternum. The mage fell hard, gasping for air.

"HALT!"

A bellow from Nathan's left caused him to freeze, straining. The slave master had some kind of non-magical control skill, and his barbed whip wrapped around Nathan's neck. "You'll stay still boy, or else I'll tear out your throat."

One of the mages blew Emerald into the stream with a gust of wind, and the other made Vhala stagger with repeated [Slumber] spells.

Nathan was frozen in place for a second, terror blazing through his mind. The man merely had to yank on the whip and it would tear out Nathan's throat. There was a split second of indecision, then Nathan committed himself. He fed Stamina to Rage like dumping gasoline on a fire.

It WILL NOT end this way.

His fury redoubled, and the terrifying paralysis vaporized. Nathan dug his fingers under the whip, tearing skin with his fingernails. The slave master snarled and yanked the whip back, ripping the skin from Nathan's neck, mangling his fingers and opening his windpipe. Blood spurted, and Nathan hurriedly directed his [Regeneration] to his neck, setting it to seal the artery first of all. Even as life drained from him, Nathan's face set in a rictus grin. He had never felt more *alive.*

The slave master opened his mouth to command Nathan again, but his chest imploded as one of Wiam's broadhead bolts hit his sternum. The mage that had been targeting Vhala spared a glance at Wiam's tree and threw a lightning bolt, causing the top of the tree to shatter.

But Nathan was free. Bleeding, but free. He slammed into the mage that had thrown the lightning bolt, not so much with a direct attack as a hammering assault from every limb. Her force armor lasted for a second before splintering away, though it was long enough for the mage to flick a [Force Orb] at Nathan that knocked one leg out from under him. He grabbed the mage's robe and dragged her down to the ground with him, then rolled on top of her and started slamming his fists into her face. He twisted his shoulders and dropped his weight with each blow, feeling the *crunch* of bone from knuckles and the face beneath them.

After three or six punches, Nathan was knocked off by a ball of conjured earth. The third mage had turned to focus on him and was not playing around. He sent a [Force Needle Storm] at Nathan, hundreds of spikes that shallowly penetrated Nathan's skin.

When Nathan got close, the mage hit him with a [Wind blast], but Nathan leaned into it and pushed forward, snarling. His vision tinged red; Nathan was going to *end* this man. He leaped forward and speared his mangled fingers into the [Mage Armor], which shattered. But the mage retreated and conjured more [Earth Balls], firing them like cannonballs. Nathan managed to slap a few aside, but he was hit in the hip, the shoulder and then the arm. He felt bones breaking, and could not close the distance against the barrage.

Luckily, he didn't have to. Emerald's rapier suddenly protruded from the man's chest, and the mage gasped like a beached fish before a cleaver *chopped* into his neck, spraying blood. Nathan knew the fight wasn't done yet, so he stumbled over to the man he'd first punched in the solar plexus, leaving a trail of blood and feeling something grating in his hip. Nathan stood over the man wheezing on the ground and looked down into his eyes. They were terrified and pleading. And Nathan's Rage bled away. He didn't think he could kill a helpless man.

He didn't have to. Emerald was *there*, cleaver chopping. They quickly moved to the third mage. Nathan didn't know if she was alive with her face pulped like that, but she definitely wasn't after Emerald stuck their rapier through an eye socket and *stirred*. Nathan's victorious thrill turned to nausea, and he fell to his knees and threw up. Bloody bile came out, and Nathan's neck stung in a new way.

Right. Torn windpipe. How's my Stamina?

Stamina: 23/250

Nathan's cough had an edge of laughter. That had been close.

It still could be close.

He glanced at the soldiers. They were advancing slowly and methodically on a staggered Vhala, but Emerald was picking them apart from the rear. If they needed help... Nathan couldn't help them. He needed to not die first. He cataloged his injuries, thanking Davrar for [Brawler's Indifference] and absolute *torrents* of adrenaline.

His neck wasn't gushing blood, and he didn't seem to have immediately fatal internal bleeding from the [Earth Ball] hits. His upper left arm was definitely broken, possibly shattered. His hip was either cracked or bruised, same with his right shoulder and a few ribs, and he'd definitely cracked a few metacarpals in his hands. He was covered with superficial cuts and bruises from various spells. Nathan wanted to breathe normally, so he directed his remaining Stamina to his neck, sealing off the most obvious bleeding and closing his windpipe. Then he collapsed onto the ground, feeling woozy.

Oh, bad. Blood loss shock or one hell of a lot of violence and gore. Probably both.

Mid-tier Regeneration Rank 4 achieved!

He rolled onto his back, and saw Artha pound across the stream. The big centaur's armor was dented in places and one leg was bloodied, but he looked otherwise fine. Artha looked down at Nathan, assessing if he needed help. Nathan gave him a jaunty little wave from the ground. Artha charged off, probably to handle... stuff. Nathan just wanted to lie there. He wasn't dying. He was pretty sure he wasn't dying. But he felt more exhausted than he'd ever been in his life.

A few moments or minutes later Vhala appeared over him, said something and offered him a hand up. Grudgingly, Nathan took the hand, wincing at the dull pain. She hauled him to his feet and pointed up the bank to where Artha was. Vhala then turned to free and calm the slaves.

Ex-slaves. Nice.

Nathan looked up the bank of the stream, and started slowly trudging up it. Blue boxes appeared in front of him as he walked.

You have leveled up to level 23! Congratulations, you have defeated multiple deadly foes many levels above you!

Low-tier Sprinting Rank 4 achieved!

Huh. An hour of sprinting through difficult terrain had leveled that skill once. And thirty seconds of frantic running around in combat had leveled it once. Using a skill in a life or death situation probably caused it to level faster. Neat. And his Stamina seemed to go up by 10 per level, plus a base of 100. It was probably similar for other resources?

Nathan stumbled over the top of the bank, and saw Artha and Emerald forcing a vial into a blackened Wiam's beak a few dozen yards away. Nathan staggered closer to see if the irreverent bird-mage was still alive and if there was anything he could do to help. Emerald looked up and held up a hand for him to halt, then tossed him a bag of jerky and a waterskin. Nathan looked dumbly at the items where they'd landed next to his feet, then crumpled down and devoured the jerky. He hadn't been hungry at all, but as soon as he saw the food it felt like a bottomless pit opened up inside him.

Nathan spent a few more minutes resting on the ground, just staring up at the sky. He finished the bag of jerky and continued regenerating his wounds, focusing on the broken bones first. He sighed with relief when his arm bone reformed, and he was confident there wasn't any internal bleeding going on. The rest of the wounds were just superficial bleeding, so he used his remaining Stamina to fix his fingers. Hand wounds made Nathan shiver. He was still bleeding slightly, but the biggest problem was shock caused by blood loss.

Hold on a second, blood loss should be easy to fix with regeneration. Hematopoietic stem cells are some of the most common stem cells in the body at my age.

He sat up and looked over to Artha and Emerald, who were coaxing along a coughing Wiam. Good. He wasn't dead. Nathan liked the flighty bird-man.

Heh. Flighty.

Nathan croaked something, and they looked his way. He swallowed and repeated himself. "Can I have some more food and water? Out of Stamina."

Artha snorted, then pushed himself up from his knees, trotting over and dropping a canteen of soup into Nathan's hands. He promptly fumbled it to the ground. Then Artha turned around and went back to Wiam, casting another [Minor Curing] into him.

Nathan busied himself with his newly acquired calories, chugging down the soup between deep breaths. He fought down a few bouts of nausea, and used his rapidly replenishing Stamina to close the rest of the bleeding wounds. Then, he funneled his small but growing pool of Stamina into his bones again, aiming for the bone marrow. The stem cells there were *supposed* to replenish his blood cells, so they should replace his lost blood fairly easily. He closed his eyes and took a deep breath, feeding Stamina into the core of his bones and hoping like hell he wasn't giving himself a blood cancer.

Mid-tier Regeneration Rank 5 achieved!

Man, that Talent is ranking up quickly.

At least he wasn't suffering from blood loss anymore, since he wasn't nauseous and everything definitely seemed sharper. The Regeneration Talent had almost certainly saved his life, bringing him from near death to fully functional. All it took was a few minutes, a bag of jerky and a canteen of soup. In fact, the Talent seemed to be able to replace flesh without anything near the right amount of food. As he ranked his regeneration Talent up, it was getting noticeably faster and more efficient.

I'm glad I'm immune to just mana-based magic and not all the other cool stuff Davrar can offer. Stamina definitely seems able to break the rules of reality. It might not be magic *magic, but it seems a lot like magic to me!*

Nathan pushed himself to his feet and looked around again with new focus. Artha and Emerald appeared to have Wiam well in hand, so he turned and looked to Vhala. She was busy unchaining the lines of slaves and directing them up the stream bank, away from the bloodied stream. There was definitely something wrong with them. The ex-captives' eyes were stupefied, and they were dreamily wandering as if unsure where they were or where they should go. Nathan kept any from wandering off into the woods, directing them to sit down in a clearing on the edge of the stream. After a few minutes Artha started helping him, and soon enough they had nearly a hundred and twenty people seated in a disorganized mess.

Nathan checked on the slave soldiers, wondering if any of them could be freed as well. But they were all dead. Some of them appeared to not have any wounds, and had keeled over at the end of the fight without being touched. Nathan made a note to ask somebody about that later.

But, there were more important things to deal with right now. According to Vhala, the prisoners were under the effect of a [Mass Daze] spell that made them unfocused and easy to guide. The Giantraiders had rescued slaves from raids before, and Vhala showed Nathan how to snap people out of it with a mix of light slaps, strong-smelling spices and loud yells. In short order they'd freed the villagers and left them to organize themselves on the riverbank. After he helped Vhala break the captured villages free, he went to check in on Wiam.

The bird-man was mostly fine, though one of his wings had healed badly. Artha hadn't set it properly before giving him the healing that had probably saved Wiam's life. With his scorched feathers he looked less like a hawk to Nathan and more like a bedraggled crow. But Wiam seemed in high spirits regardless – in his own words, "After all this, the coin for a proper heal won't be a problem. Heck, I bet half the healers will give me a discount. Besides, ladies love a tercel with a few scars and a story to go with them!"

Nathan looked around, seeing if there was anything else he could help with. Emerald hadn't spent much time with the rescued. Instead, the faceless fighter had gone down to loot all of the bodies. They emptied the pockets and pouches of the slave masters and completely stripped the mages, bunching up their robes around whatever loot they gathered. After that, and with Artha's help, they stripped the armor from the slave soldiers and cast all of the bodies into the stream. Nathan wasn't sure why and added it to the list of things to ask about.

There's just so much I don't know about Davrar, and the practicalities of life here.

A bedraggled elderly couple stood out among the rescued, organizing the cluster of scared people before making the rounds to check in on everybody. They introduced themselves to Nathan as Sora and Dwoh, and were apparently the leaders of Pilriden, the hamlet which had been attacked. They effusively thanked Nathan for helping to rescue them, and subtly inquired if he could spare any healing or beneficial skills for people who were tired or hurt. They were still nice when they found that Nathan couldn't help, but moved on quickly to organize the rest of the farmers.

Eventually, they were ready to move out. Vhala told Nathan that there was a group coming with supplies and extra protection, but they'd be best served by heading back to meet them as soon as possible. Without much preamble, they started back towards Gemore.

Chapter 10

Davrar Revealed

The Giantraiders hadn't had much to say to Nathan with so many shellshocked captives to take care of. That was honestly fine with Nathan – he was feeling a little shell-shocked himself. The violence had been so explosive. And he'd been a part of it, rampaging through the mages like a bull in a china shop. They'd been experienced fighters, but Nathan had resisted their best shots and that had been enough.

Emerald approached Nathan as he ruminated.

The ex-slaves gave the slim armored fighter a wide berth, and Nathan understood why. They'd been a vicious presence on the battlefield, and shown no qualms about dealing with the dead afterwards. But Emerald had saved Nathan's life at least once, and from what he'd heard during the battle, they had good reason to hate slavers.

"T-thanks. Y-you did a lot better than I-I did. A-and sorry. I took your k-kills." Emerald's stutter seemed worse than usual, and Nathan could tell they weren't comfortable with the number of stares coming their way.

Nathan relaxed. "No, it's okay. You saved my ass from the last guy, and I... Well, I've never killed anybody before. And thanks to you, I still haven't. I don't view that as a problem. Even if they were slavers, I can't help but be grateful I didn't have to look into anybody's eyes before I killed them. Is stealing somebody's kills a problem?"

Emerald tilted their head. "A kill levels you m-more. A-and that last mage was over l-level 81. I leveled a l-lot from that. You could have leveled more if you had k-killed him."

Nathan paused for a moment. That sounded a lot more like a game mechanic than something he was comfortable with. Especially when it incentivized murder. But then he shrugged. It was another useful data point on Davrar, and something to keep in mind for the future. Nathan worried about what it meant for society on Davrar if you got extra levels for killing people.

He eventually responded to Emerald. "I leveled plenty, don't worry about it. I'm glad nobody was seriously hurt except Wiam, that seems miraculous given what we went up against. Also, I wanted to ask earlier, but why did the slave soldiers all die? Can they not be freed?"

"N-no. T-they die if they think they're about to be captured. It's p-possible to dispel, b-but hard to do in a fight. You learn to d-deal. They're already dead. A-and I'm glad you're ok. That Talent is good."

That made sense, and made Nathan curl his lip. Why did Giantsrest do that? Spite? Preventing any captured soldiers from turning on them, most likely. Looking at Emerald, Nathan realized they probably had a point. Then he realized something else that had been bugging him. "Why didn't they have any golems? They seemed like they would make excellent soldiers."

Emerald shook their head. "Not good in c-chaotic situations. A-also expensive and get lost easily in rough terrain. Too easy to t-trick. Better as g-guards with simple instructions. Or shock t-troops with a construct m-mage. Slave soldiers still think."

Nathan swallowed. The thought that the slave-soldiers were conscious disturbed him. There'd been more death than he'd ever experienced, and he wasn't done processing it yet. It still felt unreal.

Emerald seemed done talking, so Nathan thanked them and walked on, reflecting.

How do I feel about the Giantraiders? A bit shocked at the amount of violence they demonstrated. But I was an active participant. Do I want to do that again? If I want to take on Giantsrest, I'll need to get used to it. Now that I've had one near-death experience, I'm not sure I want to actively pursue more. Regardless, there's mountain of things I need to learn about this world before I make any final decisions.

The rest of the day was spent journeying back towards Gemore. Nathan didn't talk much with the rest of the Giantraiders, instead walking to the side of the large group of subdued ex-captives. He tried to distract himself from dwelling on the violence by making a list of utility skills he wanted. He had three so far, and they all seemed useful. [Focused Mind] had been immeasurably useful in helping Nathan deal with the unexpected, and it helped him more easily gain new skills and Talents. A multiplier on top of whatever blessing Davrar had given him for being disadvantaged sounded like a good thing.

Sprinting was also pretty useful. Being able to move fast was great for a lot of reasons. Sure, being able to fly would be better, but that likely wasn't on the table. Unless his last Talent slot could make that happen? Nathan shook his head. Wiam had mentioned that *he* could get a flying Talent because he had wings, but it probably wasn't that simple for Nathan. Unless he could make a shapeshifting Talent? Nathan shuddered a bit this time. He *hated* body horror.

Earnestness... was a little bit confusing. It seemed like a great skill for a lot of reasons. Useful for certain kinds of lying, useful for being serious. It didn't directly help him fight people, but it helped avoid fights and improve social situations. Maybe Nathan could scope out other socially-oriented skills and try to pick up something worthwhile.

So, what other utility skills would be useful? A few things jumped out to Nathan – something for memory, or something to give him local knowledge. He had no idea if either were possible, but he had some ideas for the memory skill. A utility skill to help him remember things from Earth seemed like a great idea, but it maybe wasn't the most pressing issue. A skill that helped him know more about the world might prevent him from accidentally offering somebody a deadly insult.

What else would be useful? Utility skills couldn't help him do things he couldn't do otherwise, so what did he wish he was better at?

That question made Nathan remember something – his plans to Develop Magic Resistance. He hadn't Developed it before the fight, and it seemed to require serious effort. He remembered his first fumbling resistance of magic, when Taeol had tried to [Charm] him. Nathan had needed to pull apart each spell, feel what it was doing and work to counter the effect. When the Talent had hit max rank up and he'd gotten [Antimagic Blows], it had required a lot less attention, at least when he was hitting things. But he didn't want to lose sight of how he'd interacted with the magic to counter it the first few times. It could be the key to Developing the Talent in a useful direction.

The sun was far from dimming when the group settled in a wide glade for the night. They were in the middle of the cold wilderness, and the villagers needed some time to eat and rest to stay healthy. The ex-slaves were ravenous since they'd been fed nothing but starvation rations after being captured. They would probably eat through most of the food, both the Giantraiders' stockpile and that acquired from the slavers. According to Vhala, the backup squad was going to travel through the night and should arrive sometime mid-morning.

Nathan staked out a spot near Wiam, who had propped himself up against a tree. They would be sleeping rough tonight, the tent and heavy blankets going to some of the elderly who had struggled with the overland march. But there was a fire nearby, so it wasn't too bad.

Wiam seemed to be doing better, but not great. He would need that session with a healer, and Nathan hoped he got it. But he had some questions for the hawk-man first. Questions about magic.

"Hey Wiam, hope you're feeling better." Wiam lifted one hand and made a fist, which he bounced side-to-side.

Nathan continued. "I've got some questions about magic if you've got time. I want to know how you cast spells. If somebody had mana shaping, and was trying to cast their first spell, what would you tell them?"

Wiam coughed out a bit of a laugh, then shrugged. "A bit of a funny question a'comin' from you. But I'll tell ya what I got told when I was a chick. When ya can shape the mana, you sorta tie it in knots of specific shapes. Basic spells like this [Light Orb]" – a ball of light manifested in his palm – "are real simple, just take some basic mana. Throw it around like this, and there ya go." He looked at Nathan a moment, then seemed to realize something. "But you can't sense the mana, so it's not gonna work great. Mana shaping would letcha sense the mana I'm throwin' around for this spell. Try it ya'self." Wiam withdrew his hand, leaving the ball of light floating in midair.

Nathan studied the orb of light, both with his eyes and with the elusive sense he'd felt while resisting Taeol's spells. *Nothing*. He reached out and touched the ball. Right before it flickered out, he felt it. Like an insubstantial, uneven ball, or a knot of fuzzy string. Nathan's brows furrowed. "I think I can sense the mana, but only when I touch it. I could feel the shape of that, a bit. Are there different kinds of mana other than 'basic' mana?"

Wiam clattered his beak a bit. "Weeeiiird. I heard of some other Talents that letcha sense mana, but they're mostly bad versions of mana shapin'. Funny that magic resistance would do it. But yeah, buncha kinds of mana for different spells. One o' the big parts to bein' a mage is learnin' to change the type of mana ya put in a spell. They're all different and a lotta mages get class skills for new types of mana, but you can learn to use other mana types e'en if you ain't got the skill. I do a lot with shadow mana and I got a skill for that one, but I also do some earth stuff and that's just an Insight and some practice, and easy to get to from shadow. But I'd need fire 'n force for a fireball, and I can't do neither."

That was... fascinating. Themed mana. "Can you sense what kind of mana is which? And how do you learn to swap the types?"

"Ayup, all the types have a different feel 'bout 'em. Basic is fuzzy 'n soft, while shadow is dark 'n brittle. Earth is heavy 'n moist, but none of those're great explanations, ya kinda gotta just feel the mana and figure out what's what. And for the swappin'... well thatsa Insight right there, and not mine to give. But it's one of the keys to magery. That and bein' shown what weaves make what spells. And practice to get skills 'n stuff to make the mana go into a spell faster. A new mage'll take a hot minute to put together a simple light spell, nevermind a [Paralysis] or whatever."

Nathan had an idea. His magic resistance seemed to give him the ability to sense mana when it was in contact with him. When he'd been ranking up his magic resistance Talent the first time, he'd needed to feel out Taeol's different spells and work to neutralize them differently. What if the same was true for all magic? Did he need to understand the spellwork, or at least understand how to pick it apart, in order to properly neutralize it? It *felt* like a good way to go about the Talent evolution to Nathan. So he asked Wiam for a favor.

"Hey Wiam, feel free to turn me down if you're not up to it, but do you think you could cast some spells on me? Nothing harmful, I just want to focus on what it feels like to resist magic. I think it'll be helpful for Developing my Talent."

Wiam's eyes bore into Nathan, and he cocked his head to the side. "Ya know what, sure. Usually this sorta thing'd come for a cost, but with all that's happened I owe ya a bit, even if you're the vote that got me blown out of a tree. But hey, if ya make it big, remember the little folks?"

Nathan was confused by that last bit, but Wiam immediately moved on to casting a variety of spells on Nathan. They started with various stealth spells and worked their way up to some basic attack and "inconvenience" spells. Using [Focused Mind], Nathan learned to pick out some of the shapes of the various spells, and how to pull them apart faster or slower. He also started getting a sense of what different kinds of mana felt like. Wiam's explanations had been spot on, with basic, unaspected mana being soft and fluffy, shadow mana being dark and brittle-feeling, while earth was dense and wet. It was almost as if the density was more a sensation of weight than of actual mass. It was hard to put into words.

After a plain but filling meal, Nathan settled in to meditate. He wasn't frantic or panicking, but it seemed like a good idea to keep up the habit. The absence of his smartphone and its app was annoying, but [Focused Mind] more than made up for it. It really was a useful skill for his own sanity, if nothing else.

Nathan drifted, focusing on his breathing. In and out. In and out. How did he feel? A bit scared. Guilty for killing people, even if he hadn't delivered any final blows. He heard the refugees moving in the camp around him and relaxed. The fight had been for a purpose, and that purpose had been worthwhile. In hindsight he'd been quick to agree, but knowing the outcome he didn't regret the decision.

The violence had come easier than he'd expected. Nathan remembered the sensation of the mage's face crunching under his fist, and then remembered what the mage had done. He called up a bit of the visceral hate that had sparked his fury, and Nathan found he didn't even regret the violence, just the risk of his own death. With that thought, he let his feelings of the fight go and cleared his mind for proper meditation.

Low-tier Focused Mind Rank 9 achieved!

After a time, a more centered Nathan opened his eyes to the darkness of night. Once again, he was shocked at the rapid transition from a bright day with a sun directly overhead to full night. But unlike last night, the sky wasn't cloudy, and he could see what the clouds had hidden. The entire sky glowed with white, blue and green. It took Nathan a moment to parse the swirls of far-away clouds, the blue of oceans and the yellow-green of continents.

It was like looking at the surface of Earth from the Moon, but covering the whole sky, and dimmer. The total light was only slightly more than that of a full moon, but Nathan could see a whole world laid out in the sky above him, glowing with reflected light. He was starstruck. Or *worldstruck*.

After a few minutes of just looking up, Nathan organized his thoughts. He didn't recognize any of the continents, and couldn't make things out in great detail. Assuming Earth-sized continents, the distance was probably about half the distance from the Moon to Earth. Big error bars on that. But there was definitely a lot more real estate up there than what existed on Earth, and Nathan gave up after counting over a dozen continents. There were also enormous scattered patches of black and white, looking like infections on the world above. Each patch was about half the size of a major continent, and either completely white or completely black.

Bizarre. Is there a giant mirror way up there or... is this world two disks, stuck face to face?

Nathan turned towards Wiam, who was watching him. Nathan had no experience reading bird-person expressions, but Wiam's eyes looked amused. "Didya sky look different, where ya came from?"

Nathan looked back up. "... Yeah. Yeah it did. What is it? Has anybody ever been there?"

Wiam poked at the fire as he responded. "It's all Davrar. We got some tales about people who make it to the other side, see home. It's a thing in some of our stories. If you *see home* like that, above your head, it usually means you ain't never goin' back. All sorts of ways to get over there in those stories. Sometimes mages fly it, but apparently it's harder than just 'go up and keep going,' but the stories don't tell why, and not many are strong enough or brave enough to try. Usually it's just poking somethin' you shouldn't, get teleported up there by some artifact. But it's all Davrar."

Nathan nodded, pondering. This world *did not work like Earth did.* There wasn't an obvious solar system, and the sun couldn't work on the same principles as Sol if it was in between this... *layer,* and the one visible up in the sky. Maybe there was a giant sphere of one-way mirrors around the planet, which reflected the world back down at them while allowing sunlight through?

It *could* be a construct like a dyson sphere or a ringworld, but neither of those explanations fit with his observations. Though Nathan had never been inside a dyson sphere before, he assumed the other side would be so far away he wouldn't be able to make out any continents.

Like Mars far away. I wouldn't be able to see any details at all.

Regardless, those possibilities ignored what might be possible with magic. *Something was going on* with how this world worked, and it was something he could investigate!

The thought was both exhilarating and terrifying. At various times he'd wondered what it would have felt like to be one of the early scientists during the Enlightenment, where so much was unknown but ripe for discovery.

And now, maybe he would find out.

Chapter 11

Adventurers and Adventurers

They didn't move on the next morning, instead staying in place and caring for the ex-captives who needed a break. Nathan was sent to collect deadwood for fires and help dig holes for makeshift latrines. He didn't mind, it was a way to help out that didn't demand much of him. And these people needed help. Nathan wasn't sure how he'd feel to be kidnapped from his home and barely escape being enslaved by mental magic.

Well. That's... exactly what happened to me. But these people are pretty helpless to prevent it happening again.

But there was another critical difference between Nathan and these refugees. His terror and horror had been tempered by wonder. Wonder at a world with magic, Talents and an entire world above your head. Nathan looked up from his digging, to the clear sky. If you looked past the blue sky, you could still see the surface opposite. It was hard to notice unless you looked closely, appearing like faint, wispy clouds until you saw the spiral of a storm the size of a small moon, or the faint deep blue glint of the ocean.

Nathan finished digging the new latrine. It wasn't all that bad to use – one of the refugees had a Talent or skill that could somehow process normal leaves into a passable imitation of toilet paper. It required careful hand placement, but Nathan had been on camping trips with worse accommodations.

Nathan went to find Wiam again. He wanted to practice sensing magic again. It was so *cool* to feel magic, to tug apart component strands of mana. Walking through the camp, he noted how the ex-captives treated the

Giantraiders with a sort of hands-off awe. It struck Nathan like a cross between hero worship and keeping your distance from a snarling dog. The only villagers he'd talked with this morning were Sora and Dwoh, who acted as liaisons with the adventurers.

He found Vhala first, sitting on a stump and stitching up a hole in her armor with a huge needle. Nathan asked her directly. "The people we rescued seem pretty wary of us. What's up with that?"

Vhala looked around. "Yeh, pretty normal with Adventurers. We live with violence and they hope it stays far away from them. Sure, we save them from stuff, but they pay for it and we're still associated with whatever the problem was. And for every story of adventurers saving a town, there's one where some idiots piss off a local monster or open up an old ruin and unleash some horror."

She paused for a moment and pointed at him with her needle. "That reminds me. Got a few rules. If you enroll as an Adventurer you'll learn these in more detail, but I should tell you now. One; run from fights you can't win. Two; don't touch things you don't understand. That means ruins, like the ones you'll find all over the countryside. There's scary shit in a lot of them that'll kill more than just you. Three; don't chase levels or loot. Your job is to stay alive and keep other people alive. That's it – just didn't want you wandering into any crypts of Quaz because you don't know any better."

Nathan swallowed. He wasn't sure how to take that advice. But Vhala didn't expect a response from him and turned back to her mending.

He turned and continued looking for Wiam, eventually finding him lying down and picking at his blackened feathers. Nathan waved a hand through his line of sight. "Hey Wiam, hope you're feeling good."

"Ya, I'll be good. Want more magic practice? Ha, closer to practice for me, ain't it. It's great, I can toss some real murder your way and it just..." He made a gesture like jazz hands, indicating something poofing away into nothing.

Nathan grinned. "Yup, I guess we both get something out of it. Go ahead, give me your best shot."

Wiam's best shot turned out pretty effective, turning the soft dirt under Nathan's feet into slimy, sucking mud that pulled him under. He was only able to break the spell by diving into the mud, leaving him covered in dry dirt once the spell fell apart. During the more relaxed session that followed, Nathan felt like he was getting the hang of feeling Wiam's different kinds of mana and how they wove together. He still needed physical contact with spells to break them apart, which was pretty limiting. They finished with a round of Nathan trying to guess what spell was cast on him with his eyes closed and ears covered.

Low-tier Focused Mind 10 achieved! Congratulations, you have maxed out this utility skill! It cannot be improved any further. You must achieve Insight into this skill to Develop it to mid-tier.

Pending utility skill: Low-tier Spellsense
You have used a rudimentary mana sense to identify mana types and how they go together to make spells. This skill will help you identify mana types and spell weaves more easily. Does not grant understanding of how a spell works or how to weave mana together for specific spells.

Oooh yeah. That was cool. Magic!

Congratulations, you have accepted the 'Low-tier Spellsense' Utility skill. It will become part of your status and rank up as you use it. It starts at rank 1 and becomes more effective as it ranks up. Think about how you use your skill to aid in skill Development at rank 10.

Opening his eyes, Nathan heard a commotion from across the camp. The rest of the Giantraiders were gathered to the side of the clearing, the refugees clustering around to watch. Emerald and Artha came from where they'd been butchering some sort of enormous six-legged creature that had tried to sneak up on the camp. Any other day, Nathan would have been fascinated by its weird biology, but he wasn't feeling the blood and gore today.

The relief group had arrived. Leading the way into the clearing was a large human man in plate armor, bald head gleaming and arms spread wide. Behind him was a large group of armed adventurers, nine heavily armed and armored fighters loaded with packs and boxes. The man walked forward to meet Vhala and clapped his gauntleted palm on her shoulder. Hard.

"Aha! The redoubtable Giantsraiders, claiming glory and acclaim with yet another daring exploit!" He withdrew his hand, and waggled his finger in front of Vhala's face. "But I hear it was a near thing for you. If only we of The Vanguard had been there, the fight would not have been close at all!"

He gestured to his fighters, beaming. "But! The Vanguard will save the day in another way, at least. We could not have these fine folk starve! And now they will not. Come come, let us distribute the rations we've carried so far and be on our way." The rest of the Vanguard filed past the man, happy to unload their packs of food and other supplies for the refugees. One of them eyed Nathan briefly, then shrugged and handed him a small knapsack before moving on.

Nathan peeked inside, finding a rough blanket and a collection of traveling food – bags of nuts, hard cheeses and tough biscuits. A side pocket contained a small steel knife in a sheath and a piece of flint; a waterskin was looped around the whole thing. Nathan blinked at the well-thought-out kit and looked over to Wiam as the birdman slowly got to his feet. "Where did all of this come from?"

Wiam looked down at the kit with a jerky shrug. "Adventurer's Guild keeps 'em as backup. This sorta thing happens often enough that it's worth the salt to keep 'em ready. Another thing though." Wiam gestured and cast a spell, muffling the sound from the camp.

"That there's Eldred. Eldred Vanguard, he calls himself." Wiam pointed his beak at the bald man who led the Vanguard and greeted Vhala. "He's good in a fight 'n all. Cares mountains 'bout his reputation. But he keeps his eyes on his own coinstring, ya get me?" Wiam waited until Nathan nodded, then continued. "Ya might wanna keep quiet about what's up with ya. He'd try to see what you're worth and maybe recruit ya without much of'a polite way to say no. And I betcha he'd at least think about earnin' some cash on the side from Giantsrest. Though the Guildmistress'd gut him if she found out."

Wiam cocked his head, and the noises of the camp rushed back in as he dismissed the sound-dampening spell.

Then Wiam marched off to go greet a friend from the Vanguard, loudly cackling about the Giantraiders killing *three* enslavement mages.

The Vanguard took over leading the group of refugees, relieving the worn-out Giantraiders. Nathan got the sense that Vhala could have challenged Eldred and remained in command of the group, but she was happy enough to turn over responsibility for the refugees to Eldred and the Vanguard.

After a break to eat their newly acquired rations and finish butchering Artha's kill, the group set out from the camp at a sedate pace. They followed steadily-improving trails through the rocky hills, and Nathan noticed more and more ruins. They ranged from remarkably well preserved, like a fortress carved into a mountain in the shape of a face, to simple piles of rubble. The group steered away from all of them, and Nathan noticed both the Vanguard and the Giantraiders relaxing as they left each ruin behind.

These ruins are just everywhere. I must have seen a few dozen by this point, and everybody's treating them like they're all dangerous. Given Vhala's warning, I'm guessing that's pretty true. But how are they dangerous?

Eldred's assumption of command freed Vhala from her duties, and in the afternoon she approached Nathan again.

After ushering him off the trail, she turned to him and spoke. "We've had time for a bit of a chat about what we owe you for the fight. The reward from the Guild will go five ways alright, but we owe you a chunk more than that. You swore no oaths to fight slavers, and Artha didn't have a right to ask you for it."

Vhala paused to look Nathan directly in the eyes. "So to pay that off, and since you're new, we've agreed to each give you an Insight we think would suit you. This offer's got more heft than you might think. Insights are usually only gifted to boon companions and children, or traded for other Insights." She raised her hands placatingly. "If you'd prefer, we'll give you the entire monetary reward for the rescue instead. But I think you should take the Insights."

On the face of it, this seemed like an easy question. The Giantraiders were experienced adventurers, and probably knew what skills Nathan needed better than he did. But, it sounded like he'd be turning down a pile of money for it. Money that would help Nathan stabilize, get his feet under him. Maybe leave town for somewhere less dangerous. If he wanted to do anything other than fight, taking the money was probably a better choice. But he wanted to *end* Giantsrest, and so did all of the people around him. What could Nathan do that people born to this world, this war, couldn't?

Well, there's an expert on that right here.

Nathan looked at Vhala. "Do you think I should be an adventurer? I want to fight Giantsrest, but can I make a difference?"

Vhala blew out a long breath, considering her words carefully. Then, her dark eyes looked into Nathan's again, and her voice was deadly serious. "You're underestimating what one person with the right Talents can make happen. Your Talents..." She trailed off, then shook her head.

"Gemore is kept safe not by many adventurers, but by a few. It's an open secret that a few high-level adventurers good at killing mages are what really keeps some archmage from dropping an [Earthquake] on us from a mile up. Our elites can't kill the whole Giantrest Senate, but they could kill a warmonger or ten in revenge. It's also the sort of thing that the Questors would join in on, and then things would get messy."

Vhala's eyes locked back onto Nathan's. "You have the potential to become one of the adventurers that Giantsrest fears. Your Talents are better for fighting mages than absolutely anybody I've ever seen." She scoffed. "A blanket magic resistance Talent? And you Developed that giants-damned healing Talent in one night! If you don't die in the next five years, you'll be a terror to mages. One we need. And if it's metal jangle you're after, there's more to be had exploring ruins than anything else. It's too dangerous for most people because there's so much ancient magic floating around. But." Vhala gestured to Nathan as if answering a question.

"So. With the Talents you already have, you'd be wasted as anything but an adventurer, and I will personally sponsor you to the Guild. Spend a few years doing basic shit, learn what's what and level up, then come back to me." Vhala's wide face turned up into a vicious grin. "And we'll kill some slavers."

Chapter 12

System Questions

Nathan considered Vhala's words. She'd just told him he could be the *best* and earn fame and fortune on a righteous cause. To his millennial self, it struck a bit of a nerve and triggered a sense of suspicion. It sounded like it was too good to be true, and therefore it probably was.

On the other hand, Vhala seemed entirely sincere. And she was right that the Talents Nathan had acquired were pretty absurd. It seemed like magic stood at the pinnacle of might in this world, and it wasn't hard to understand why. Nathan's *current* Talent made him mostly immune to it. After he Developed it, it would presumably get even better. And given some levels and a smart build to provide him with plenty of Stamina, Nathan could recover from almost any blow that didn't immediately kill him.

And that was the difference between Davrar and Earth. Nathan didn't have great power in either place, but he could acquire great power here. And there were great wrongs to right with that power, if he could resist the temptation of power for its own sake. Nathan closed his eyes, and released a deep breath. He wasn't committing himself here, but this was definitely a step toward becoming a person who could bring down Giantsrest.

A Killer. There's a lot I haven't considered about what it means to take on Giantsrest. But it definitely means I'm going to have to kill people. Not something I've seriously considered before.

Then he turned back to Vhala, who had been watching him patiently.

"Thank you for that. I needed to decide what I am doing here. But I think you're right. Adventuring sounds good. I will accept your Insights."

Vhala looked relieved. "That's gladdening. To give you expectations, Artha said he'd continue talking to you about Rage. His clan specializes in the path of Rage, and he's definitely got some class skills about it, so hear him out. Wiam is already working with you on something to do with magic. Not sure what you can get out of it, but he thinks it's worthwhile and if you agree, that's between you. I'm not sure about Emerald. They said they've got a few ideas, but you'll have to talk to them to figure it out. As for me, I want to give you a choice."

She looked around, at the forest and hills they were passing through. "The first option would be to teach you about ranging the wild. Finding paths, food, tracks. Hiding camps, hiding yourself. I can help you guide your next class Development in a more ranger-focused direction, and if you don't want that, we can get you a utility skill or two that'll help out. Are you interested in that?"

Nathan considered for a minute and shook his head. "It sounds useful, but I don't want to specialize in operating in the wilderness too much, especially with what you've said about where my potential lies."

Vhala nodded, dreadlocks bouncing on her back. "The other one is something I learned from my ma, and a bit of a personal secret. I'd ask you to swear to not sharing the Insight for this one around. It's a specific utility skill focused on perception. Called [Notice], though I've got it Developed past that. Means important things stand out to you more. Sounds like something you're interested in?"

Nathan nodded along, and as soon as she gave him the chance, voiced his agreement. "That sounds useful in almost all situations. Is there a catch?

Vhala's dark lips quirked. "Not everybody agrees. It isn't a craft, it doesn't make you stronger, help you run faster or hit harder. Lots of people would rather learn [Easy breathing] or the like. But no, it just helps you see and hear more than you would without it, and figure what's important from all that. Do you want it?"

Hell yeah. Perception is the best skill in D&D. It lets you avoid ambushes, find secret treasure, and notice important details. It might not win a fight, but it lets you choose fights you can win.

Nathan thought about it for a second more, but this skill sounded priceless. "Yes. And I swear on my honor not to tell anybody else the Insight without your permission."

Vhala paused, amused at Nathan's oath. "The basics of it are to accept that you don't *notice* everything that you see." She gestured around them, to the forested mountains. "There's a lot of detail here. Different rocks, slopes, trees. The wind, small movements. But you don't *notice* it, because not much stands out. If I were to ask you where the tallest mountain we passed was, could you answer?"

Nathan shook his head. He'd heard something like this before, about how unreliable eyewitness testimony was. "I also couldn't tell you what color clothes Dwoh and Sora were wearing."

Vhala nodded, enthused. "Right. And those details aren't a big deal. But if you train at it, Davrar can help you see more, and figure out what's important without thinking about it. It's a hard skill to pick up, but what you gotta do is realize how much of the world you're missing, and try to pick up more. Not just limited to sight either, and if you only work on sight you'll get a worse version of the skill. Make sure you think about smell, touch, sound – even temperature. There's some tricks to it I can share later, but everybody does it a bit different, and I don't want to send you off in the wrong direction."

They walked in silence for a bit, while Nathan appreciated the natural world around them. It was a severe but beautiful landscape, with slopes of evergreens punctuated by sheer walls of gray rock. The occasional ruin or enormous carving gave a sense of *weight* to the landscape, as if grand events had once happened in this valley. Nathan struggled to notice as many details as he could. The shape of the rocks on the trail they walked, the pattern of new growth from a wildfire on the opposite hill.

After a time, Vhala interrupted. "Seems you're on the right path. Keep trying, but keep thinking about how you notice details, and why specific things stand out to you. It's not just practice, it's an Insight that I'm building you up to. I'd be pretty surprised if you got the skill before we got to Gemore tomorrow, but the Giantraiders will be sticking around town for a bit, so we'll keep working until you get the skill."

Vhala turned and walked away, looking over her shoulder as she departed. "It's easier to get skills and Talents in dangerous situations, the more dangerous the better. If you can spare a moment during a fight, focus on an Insight you're working on. Just don't get killed. Anyway, I'll send Emerald over. They wanted to figure out what you were interested in. The refugees are taking a break, so you have some time."

A few minutes later, Emerald approached Nathan, raising a hand in greeting. They spoke quickly, if with a stronger stutter than usual. "T-there's a few things I could teach you. D-do you know what k-kind of thing you're interested in? You probably can't get my c-class, and the special Talent I h-have might not be useful to you..." They trailed off, uncertain.

Nathan had a reply ready. "You've seen me fight. I want to be better at it. I know it's not common for utility skills to help you fight better, but I saw how well you were able to dodge earlier. Are there any skills that you can teach me for that?"

Emerald was silent for a moment, then spoke. "Yes. But you'll n-need to take it seriously. What I have d-doesn't sound like a fighting skill. It's..." Their shoulders hunched, and they kicked a rock. "It's a d-d-dancing skill. Called [Dancer's Footwork]. If you'd r-rather, I have a Talent that makes my armor lighter."

Nathan answered. "No, the dodging skill sounds interesting. I bet it helps keep your feet steady and dodge around like I saw during the fight?"

Emerald's awkward hunch froze. "Y-yeah, it does. But it doesn't sound like a skill for f-fighters. I-if you learn it, don't tell anybody you have it. They will m-mock you and won't want to w-work with you."

Sounds like macho idiocy to me. There's a reason boxers learn to dance.

He considered the armor Talent – but it just didn't seem to stack up to his other Talents. Instead, Nathan asked Emerald to teach him [Dancer's Footwork], and they started running through footwork drills on a relatively smooth piece of bare rock as they watched the villagers rest below. The drills emphasized agility by keeping weight on the balls of the feet and practicing how to change direction quickly while maintaining balance.

"Emerald, can I use Stamina during the workout? Will it prevent me from getting anything out of it?"

Emerald shook their head. "No, you should use Stamina on this i-if you can. People with Stamina can exercise l-longer and harder than other people, so in addition to Stamina they tend to be s-stronger than other people. Just b-be careful, it won't save you from being sore, and we still have a ways to w-walk."

They kept up the drills for a bit longer and Nathan started to get the hang of it. The movements were smooth and he was expecting the skill to pop up any second. Unfortunately, Artha came to get them since the group had started moving again. They had to run to catch up.

With all these exercises and running, my legs should be killing me. But they're fine. Probably [Regeneration]. I'm a little worried that I won't gain muscle from exercise, but I set up [Regeneration] to focus on cell growth, so it probably just means I can make new muscle at superhuman rates. Cool.

That evening, they made early camp in the lee of an ancient roadbed. Nathan kept away from the center of attention, trying to stay away from Eldred and his vanguard after Wiam's warning. They'd broken out some sort of liquor and were toasting a successful mission. After helping with the camp setup, Nathan figured it was a good time to sit down and try something.

Specifically, he wanted to try to Develop his [Focused Mind] skill. It was capped, and he had the lessons of multiple traditions of meditation to draw on to figure out the appropriate Insight. Nathan settled down, cross-legged, and started to meditate. He dedicated his attention to the practice. First, calming the breath and quieting internal dialogue. Then, finding the spotlight of his attention and diffusing it to fill his entire mind. He wasn't observing his mind from some point within the mind. He *was* his mind, and his consciousness was spread throughout.

Nathan opened his eyes, but did not let go of his meditative state. The world swam into focus before his eyes, an image made of color and light. He gazed broadly at the scene in front of him. The sun was gone, the landscape softly illuminated by the world above. He kept his gaze wide, aware of the world beyond himself. His consciousness pushed out beyond his body, filling the world. Or rather, filling the *model* of the world that was contained inside his brain.

The world that Nathan saw around himself wasn't true physical reality. It was a model of the world constructed by the fallible sensors at the end of his nerves. It wasn't always accurate, and it was a representation of the real thing, *not* the real world itself. Even now, looking out at the world, Nathan was stuck in his own head. But that meant what he saw was inside his consciousness, and he could change how he perceived it.

Everything I experience exists within my conscious mind, and I can control how I think about it.

With the thought – and the feeling of certainty – a blue box blossomed.

Congratulations, you have Developed the [Low-tier Focused Mind] utility skill into [Mid-tier Focused Mind]. It will start at rank 1 and become more effective as it ranks up. Think about how you use your skill to aid in skill Development at rank 10.

Utility skill: [Mid-tier Focused Mind]
This skill will help you attain a focused and undistracted state under most conditions. Requires you to be unmoving to use.

Sweet. Good to know that.

But Nathan wasn't done yet. He'd reminded himself of what Vhala had said about [Notice], and he used his newly [Focused Mind] to study the world around him. He tried to refine his mental model, sharpening it with details of his surroundings. The hum of conversation – how many people were speaking?

The crackle and glow of the fire – how many logs were in it? The feeling of the breeze – was it getting colder or warmer?

He continued like this for a little while. Wiam approached, opening his beak to speak, then stopped. Nathan studied him. He saw the impatience in a subtle shift of his feet, the excitement at continuing their training in the fluttering of his good wing.

Pending utility skill: Low-tier Notice
You have been able to deeply notice the details of your surroundings. This skill will help you notice details in the future.

The text on that was vague, but promising. Nathan nodded, satisfied, and accepted the skill.

Congratulations, you have accepted the 'Low-tier Notice' utility skill. It will become a part of your status and rank up as you use it. It starts at rank 1 and becomes more effective as it ranks up. Think about how you use your skill to aid in skill Development at rank 10.

Nathan considered his gains as he stood to greet Wiam. [Focused Mind] had lost its requirement that he have his eyes closed, and gotten more general. And [Notice] also seemed like a great skill – generally useful and probably synergistic with his other skills.

As he practiced his [Spellsense] with Wiam, his prediction was borne out. [Notice] helped him sense details of difficult spells, and Wiam was reaching the end of his spell repertoire. He was getting comfortable using more dangerous spells, and Nathan's struggles against them showed in his rank-ups.

Low-tier Spellsense Rank 2 achieved!

Low-tier Notice Rank 2 achieved!

Low-tier Spellsense Rank 3 achieved!

After they finished, Wiam invited Nathan back to "volley some words" with the Giantraiders. The atmosphere was relaxed, and while Nathan wanted to learn more about the world, he didn't want to interrogate the others.

So, he watched as the Giantraiders played a rhyming game where different people jumped in to complete a story. Their topic was the fight at the river ford, and with all of the embellishments and poetic license, Nathan didn't recognize the fight at all. It was hilarious to hear Wiam's departure from the tree described as "a majestic flight, escaping lightning's smite." Towards the end, Nathan jumped in with a few of his own verses.

Later, he learned more of the adventuring team whose company he shared. He might have been unlucky with his company on first entry to Davrar, but he couldn't complain about meeting the Giantraiders. He was a bit upset at Artha for asking Nathan to help in the way he had.

It would have been hard for me to say no, and he knows it.

But it was harder to be mad after Nathan learned that the big centaur's last name was Footspeak! Artha Footspeak. That was hilarious. His clan was a big deal on the neighboring plains, and led large trading caravans across dangerous territory. Vhala's last name was Bho, and her family had a legacy in Gemore, respected for martial prowess. Wiam's last name was Ayrbool. He was a traveler from far away, and spoke of escaping a crowded home for adventure. Emerald didn't share many details, beyond that they'd chosen the last name "Free," having been born into slavery.

In return, Nathan spoke haltingly of his world, and what his life was like before he ended up here. It was... complicated, since the closest analogue to academia Gemore knew was the Ascendent Academy at Giantsrest. Overall, they were shocked at how *safe* Earth sounded. Many deaths on Davrar were violent ones, and everybody had as many dead friends and family as living. Monsters, magic and the remnants of the ancients made Davrar dangerous.

~

Skill text comparison:

Low-tier Focused Mind:
This skill will help you attain a focused and undistracted state when you need it more easily. Requires you to be seated, unmoving and with eyes closed to use.

Mid-tier Focused Mind:
This skill will help you attain a focused and undistracted state under most conditions. Requires you to be unmoving to use.

Chapter 13

A Grave Threat

Nathan didn't sleep well. Davrar was full of wonder, and ruins they'd passed filled him with a sense of adventure. On earth, history was *known*. If you found a ruin, you could find out who had built it, and why. The horizons were charted, and the only mysteries left were in science. On Davrar, ruins outnumbered cities by a hundred to one. And each one promised adventure and – more likely than not – death.

With that in mind, Nathan couldn't help but wait for something to jump out of the dark. Now was the time, right? He paced around the camp, seeing a pair of the Vanguard on a desultory watch. They beckoned him over, but he shook his head and went back to his blanket. Eventually, he slept.

The next morning, Nathan woke bleary-eyed to quick movement and the clash of metal. His eyes snapped open, and he jumped to his feet, frantically looking around to find the fight.

It wasn't a fight, but a fully-armored spar between Artha and Eldred. It didn't *look* like a friendly fight, but everybody stood around and watched as Eldred defended himself from Artha's furiously twisting staff. The heavily armored human spun and wove, catching blows with the haft of his two-handed mace. After a breath he went on the offensive himself, swinging the mace deceptively quickly. Artha backstepped and deflected with his staff. One of the swings connected with the ground and rock shattered, sending shards zinging around the clearing.

Artha snapped forward to take advantage of the grounded mace, but

Eldred slid under Artha's strike and shoulder-checked him. Amazingly, the enormous centaur went down, toppling with a tremendous clatter. Eldred raised his mace over Artha, and the crowd tensed.

Nathan started forward, but then Eldred relaxed as Artha spoke.

"I yield. You have the better of me." He was tense, looking up at the human clad in heavy plate.

Eldred just spread his arms wide, holding his enormous mace negligently in one hand. He beamed around at the crowd, savoring his victory. Vhala and Emerald emerged from the crowd and helped Artha up, Vhala shooting Eldred a dirty look as they did so. They helped Artha up and moved to the side, leaving Eldred to a round of back-slapping congratulations from the Vanguard.

Nathan came up to them as Artha gingerly flexed his legs. "So, what was that about?"

Vhala turned to him with a grimace. "A bit of adventurer politics. He was pushing, and Emerald insulted him to distract him. He issued a bout-challenge in response, and Artha answered."

Emerald spoke next, quietly. "T-thanks A-Artha. You d-didn't have to do that." They were helping Artha remove his heavy armor, storing it carefully in the bag of holding Nathan had seen earlier.

Artha snorted, still breathing heavily. "You fight to kill. That bout would have only ended with heavy wounds, especially as he doesn't hold you in the same respect he does me. This gave him more status, and it should end here."

Nathan was flabbergasted. "That sounds really dumb. That fight was over pecking order? Or do I not understand what status means?"

Vhala shook her head. "No, you've got the right of it. Status, honor, bravado. To some adventurers" – she nodded towards Eldred – "it is their lifeblood. And he was pushing for information on you. Beware. With this loss, we cannot challenge him anymore on this trip." She frowned. Then called out, loudly. "Eldred! Congratulations on your victory. Should we depart? These people need to get to Gemore!"

The bald man wiped his brow with a rag and looked up at Vhala's call. "Yes! We should go. Come, one and all! To Gemore, and freedom!" He raised his mace high, the picture of a heroic fighter. He looked disappointed at the raggedness of the responding cheer.

Nathan spoke under his breath to the Giantraiders. "I'm really not a fan of that guy." They all nodded in response, then left to finish packing the camp.

Nathan made himself scarce, checking in with Sora and Dwoh and carrying a couple of extra bags for the weaker refugees. He tried to talk to them but only got scattered responses. The villagers seemed wary of him and the adventurers in general. Nathan understood why, but it disheartened him that these people's protectors weren't held in higher esteem.

Soon after, Artha approached. Nathan opened his mouth to welcome him, but the elk-centaur held up a hand. "I must apologize for my request earlier. I am glad you chose to fight with us, but I should not have posed a demand phrased as a question to which there could be no refusal." He inclined his head, resolute and grave. The picture of a muscular silver fox.

He's pretty hot. At least the human half is, I'm really not sure how to deal with the elk half. This crush is weird, and not just because he's admitted to manipulating me into a lethal combat situation. I don't really blame him for that – it's hard to look around at ex-slaves and not feel proud of my role in that.

While Nathan was distracted, Artha continued. "I think my debt to you is larger than an Insight freely given in the moment before a fight. I will continue to teach you the use of anger in combat, but I would also guide you in the ways of Davrar and Gemore. If you will accept it, at least?" He arched an eyebrow.

Nathan swallowed. "Yeah, that sounds good. I don't know what to ask, but I'll take you up on that later. Thanks. Do you have anything else to tell me now, about anger or something else?"

Artha nodded deeply again. "If you decide to follow this path, you should know how it will influence your style. Using Rage while fighting is powerful, granting you strength, speed and the ability to ignore wounds and some magic. A full berserker will rampage above their level and will not stop before death. And many Rage classes contain valuable class skills to surpass defenses or overcome restrictions. But, there are drawbacks. The [Rage] and many of the class abilities that stem from it consume your class resource quickly, and when you run out, you will be vulnerable. It is also harder to think strategy while enraged, and baiting somebody with a class on the Path of Rage is common among those with experience.

"These weaknesses can be corrected, with preparation. A skill or Talent for calmness or strategic thinking, which can be used in combat, will aid with the tempering of Rage. The rapid draining of your class resource is a harder problem. You can learn to manage it well, or shape your training to encourage class skills which expand your pool. Another solution is to pick Talents that will replenish your class resource. These are... difficult to gain, and situational. You would not be able to use the one I know of, so I will not teach it to you." He paused. "These words are between us, now. Do you want to walk this path?"

Nathan considered. It felt like the decision had already been made – he'd decided to fight, and this style suited him. During the battle, the anger felt natural. Right. He'd managed his anger all of his life, learning restraint and calm. Cutting loose had felt... freeing. The surge of adrenaline had been more than every extreme sport he'd ever done. No whitewater rafting or skydiving could compare to a life-or-death fight. If that's what the Path of Rage was, then that's what Nathan wanted.

He spoke as much, formally to match Artha's speech. "Yes, I will learn of Rage. How will you teach me?"

Artha smiled. "It can be hard to learn, for the only true practice is mortal combat. But the first requirement is to always summon your fury against those you fight. Once you gain a Rage class skill you will be less restricted, but you *must* keep the anger stoked, for every true fight in which you use it will improve your class. There are no true exercises I can give you, for the nature of these classes is a decision to remove restraint."

He was about to continue when a clanking stomp heralded Eldred's approach, head shining under the sun. He swaggered up, armor brilliant. Up close, Nathan noticed that the plate was heavily decorated, engraved with delicate lines of red, silver and gold metals. There were also tiny gems inset around the joints, though Nathan had no idea why.

Probably magical shenanigans. Looks expensive as hell.

He addressed Artha. "I think Vhala was lookin' for ya." He turned to Nathan, clearly dismissing Artha. "Hullo! I hope you're holding up under the travel well." Artha snorted, then opened his mouth. Eldred raised a hand "C'mon, who smacked who around in that little spar earlier, eh? Go on." He gestured away, towards the main group of refugees. Artha grimaced, then turned and left.

Ok. That was weird. Eldred won a duel so he can order Artha around now?

Eldred turned back to Nathan and stepped closer to him, working his shoulders. Nathan thought that Eldred was trying to loom over him, but it didn't work very well. Eldred was probably about six feet tall, muscled and bulky in his armor. But Nathan wasn't an inch under six-five, and definitely broader in the shoulders than the bald man, if not as heavily muscled. He looked down at Eldred from a foot away and refused to step back.

The armored man looked up at him and furrowed his eyebrows. "So, what's the tale with you, eh? You're not a villager, and you haven't been a slave. Some of my boys asked the villagers, and they said you fought with the Giantraiders, but didn't have a wick of gear on ya. It's a bit of a puzzle, and I like to solve puzzles. What's your name, and where you from, boy?"

Nathan answered easily. "I'm Nathan. I'm from a land far away, you've probably never heard of it. I got waylaid by Giantsrest, escaped and the Giantraiders found me."

Eldred's eyes sharpened. "This land, it got a name?"

"It's a republic called the United States of America." Nathan answered. For all he knew, Eldred had a skill to detect lies.

Eldred frowned. "United States... sounds big. Must be far away if I haven't heard of it. Got a big army?"

"The biggest in our... region. It's pretty safe there."

"Are you a member of that army, Nathan?"

Nathan shook his head.

Eldred's hand rose to stroke his chin. "So what's your profession, and what're you doin' all the way out here?"

This was an interrogation, and any pauses would be taken as indications of lies or misdirection. So Nathan responded immediately. Earnestly. "I do fine work with my hands, very delicate. And the trip wasn't really my idea. I've got no idea what direction leads home."

"How'd you help in the fight, then?"

"One of my Talents lets me interact with magic. I messed with the magic of the Giantsrest mages, helped the Raiders put them down. Same way I escaped from Giantsrest in the first place."

Low-tier Earnestness Rank 5 achieved!

One of Eldred's eyebrows raised artfully. "What you thinkin' about doin' when you get to Gemore? Artisan? Adventurer?"

Nathan was opening his mouth to form a response when he heard a yell from the back of the caravan. He turned and looked to see Wiam freaking out, waving his arms and shouting. After a moment, he must have cast a spell, for his voice boomed out, loudly audible to everybody. "That's a surge o' necromancy behind us. E'rrybody, get movin' forward, we gotta get some distance! Adventurers, get 'ere!"

Eldred swore. "Harpy tits." He turned and booked it towards the back of the convoy, where the Giantraiders and Vanguard were assembling. Not having anything else to do, and wanting to know what the hell was going on, Nathan followed.

He arrived to hear Wiam frantically explaining. "Naw, ain't an idea what's up. There's Necromancy that-a-way." He pointed, roughly behind them. "If't was a hundred feet away it'd be enough to raise a body. If't was a few miles away it'd be enough to raise an Endings-damned army."

Everybody turned in the direction of Wiam's pointing claw, seeing nothing but a sparsely treed slope leading down to a shallow stream at the bottom of a valley. On the far side, a steeper scree slope ascended to a tall hill. Nothing looked out of the ordinary.

That's probably not a good *sign. If we can't see the necromancy, that means it's farther away. And bigger.*

Vhala spoke first. "Wiam, message Gemore headquarters. They probably noticed already, but they might have forgotten where we are. We're all on rear-guard until we're back at Gemore."

The members of the Vanguard looked to Eldred. Who waved. "Theo, you're leading the column. The rest of us, arms up!" He reached back and unlimbered his enormous mace, The rest of the Vanguard followed suit, readying their weapons. One figure, presumably Theo, exhibited an impressive burst of speed to reach the front of the group of refugees and exhort them to move faster.

The next few minutes were tense, Nathan jogging up the slope while occasionally glancing back at the bare landscape. He was starting to relax, wondering if it could be a false alarm, when an extended roar sounded. It was a sound like a landslide, combining shattering rock with a deep basso exhalation that resonated in Nathan's chest. He squinted back, and made out rocks flying through the air. The airborne rocks were beyond the hill across the valley, and arced slowly over the next mountain back. Nathan swallowed. Given the distance, those rocks were the size of six-story buildings.

He turned and kept hustling up the mountain, followed by the adventurers. The path had progressed to switchbacks, and the refugees filled it from side to side. Nathan kept running, occasionally checking over his shoulder at more enormous sounds, their source blocked by the hill on the other side of the valley. They'd made good progress up the mountain when a multitonal bestial roar sounded, and Nathan turned and stopped.

A mountain of gray flesh had summited the hill behind them, nearly doubling its height. It was a single mass, but wasn't made of a single creature. A multitude of enormous skeletal snake heads emerged from the right side, while the left side was covered in long tentacle-like protrusions. The main body was a giant pile of exposed flesh and bone. Some of the parts were enormous – rib cages and vertebrae visible from more than a mile away. Some were smaller, jumbled, and about the size of human bones.

A wave of dark miasma billowed out from it, fast approaching. It was clearly magic – strong enough that the effects were visible to the naked eye. Before anybody had a chance to do much more than brace themselves, it hit. To Nathan, it felt like a slimy, wet fog, weighing down his limbs and draining energy from him. It was one of the most simple spells he'd ever felt – but there was so much that it blotted out the sun for a moment.

The necromancy – or whatever – was clearly debilitating to everybody else, and they sagged, dropping weapons and struggling to stay upright. The two exceptions were Eldred, who planted his feet and set his jaw, and Artha, who started a low chant that limned his body in a faint, white glow. Wiam had vanished, and both Emerald and Vhala were staggered, barely staying on their feet better than the rest of the Vanguard.

Nathan spoke, awed and terrified. "What the *fuck* is that?"

Eldred answered him through gritted teeth. "That's a *fucking* Grave Tangle. It's goin' to Gemore and we're *in the way*. Of all the hells-stupid ways to go."

The Grave Tangle advanced, sliding down the opposite hill with all the grace of an avalanche. Its heads reared back and a cavern opened in the center of its bulk, emitting another resonating roar from multiple orifices. A second wave of smoky energy approached, and Eldred groaned and lowered his stance to brace himself for this attack.

It washed over them, and Nathan felt strength draining from his muscles. He checked his Stamina and found it was down to 302/330. Eldred toppled, and Artha's chant faltered before he joined Eldred on the ground. Nathan was the only one standing. He turned his back to the monster and took off, straight up the slope, ignoring the switchbacks. The mana he sensed didn't even seem like a spell – or at least not a complicated one. There was just *so much* of it, and it seemed to inherently drain energy from people.

Low-tier Spellsense 4 achieved!

Nathan spent Stamina like it was going out of style, leaping up the slope in bounds. His awareness focused on finding footholds, using his [Notice] skill for all it was worth. He pushed his muscles past their limits, feeding them Stamina and regeneration to push himself up the slope in incredible bounds.

Low-tier Sprinting Rank 5 achieved!

Goddamn stupid, just a random monster pops out of nowhere! Whatever the fuck that is, it shouldn't exist. And why here and now?

Nathan was pissed at the whole situation, and he fed Stamina to his anger once more, feeling as if the anger was pushing him onwards.

I should have picked somebody up before I ran. But then I'd be too slow. I'll still be too slow.

His fury coursed through him, but instead of the thrill of battle, he felt sick anxiety. He tried to push his strides longer, to get *somewhere* safe.

An angled foot slammed badly into a rock, and Nathan *heard* something in his ankle pop. He tumbled and cursed, grabbing at his foot and slamming Stamina through it to heal as fast as possible. Nathan's skin grew red, inflamed by the aura of the creature. After what felt like minutes – but couldn't have been more than seconds – Nathan's ankle felt stable and he resumed his run.

While holding his ankle, Nathan confirmed that the Grave Tangle had crossed the valley floor and started climbing the slope. It was as wide as multiple football fields and moved deceptively quickly, its enormous size disguising the rapid movement.

Low-tier Sprinting Rank 6 achieved!

As Nathan approached the peak of the hill, he felt his attention pulled to a set of bright white specks streaking across the sky towards him. They advanced quickly, growing into humanoid figures in moments.

One of them never slowed down, losing their glow but not the speed. Nathan caught a glimpse of a silver-armored figure carrying a golden-glowing greatsword as it flashed over his head. The other figures slowed to a halt, two alighting atop the hill in front of Nathan while the other two remained in the air.

The flyers were clearly mages. One was surrounded by a halo of fire and lightning, while the other carried a staff capped with a brightly glowing crystal. One of the grounded figures drew an enormous bow, and a projectile *cracked* over Nathan, sounding like a supersonic high-caliber bullet.

The other grabbed a rock from the ground and threw it. As soon as the rock left their hand it began to grow, a fist-sized rock enlarging to the size of a person, then a car – and finally – into a boulder the size of a small house. Nathan's jaw was slack, his head turning to follow the boulder as it sped into the Grave Tangle, rocking it backwards.

The silver armored warrior had pierced into the creature's bulk and was barely visible from the surface, furiously chopping. Then, the mages started casting and the battle became hard to follow. Blue fire and white lightning struck the creature as more rocks pummeled it in a steady stream. More cracks sounded, and with each sound, a snake head disintegrated. Nathan slipped into [Focused Mind], throwing his eyes wide to catch all the details of the battle. A barely visible blue barrier had appeared over the fallen adventurers and refugees, shielding them from the debris of the fight.

Low-tier Notice 3 achieved!

The Grave Tangle struck back, the remaining snake heads vomiting fizzing liquids to strike at the new arrivals. They defended themselves with planes of force that deflected the spray to the side. The tentacles engaged the fighter, who dodged by kicking off thin air and slicing tentacles apart as the glow on their sword expanded to increase its length to something out of a ridiculous anime.

Or just a weapon suited to fighting something the size of a hill.

The tentacles shattered stone upon impact, and several snapped out like mile-long whips to attack the other arrivals. Nathan couldn't track them, but the *cracks* of their movement could be felt from hundreds of feet away. The sound was deafening. Nathan sent a dribble of Stamina to his ears to keep them functional.

Mid-tier Focused Mind 2 achieved!

The ranged fighters seemed to have survived, the rock-thrower hiding behind a now-shattered boulder, while the mages flew in erratic patterns, slivers of force dancing around them. Nathan couldn't see the archer, but he could faintly hear their continued barrage.

A deep inhalation drew Nathan's attention back to the Grave Tangle, and he saw it rearing back, blackened mouths open in preparation for another roar. Nathan could vaguely feel magic whipping past him, towards the monster. This burst of miasma would be more powerful than those before.

Low-tier Notice 4 achieved!

Both mages stopped dodging. A triple layer of shielding blossomed between the Tangle and the fallen convoy as the crystal atop the staff of one of the mages started shining brightly. The other mage cupped their hands, a bright light shining from the enclosed space. The beast exhaled with a mighty sound, less a beast's roar and more the sound of a waterfall or a crashing wave. It was muffled behind the shielding, but the tide of darkness that swept out was abyss-black.

The silver-armored warrior floating in front of the beast thrust their sword to the sky with a shout that somehow pierced the thunderous roar. Golden light shone from the armored figure and their sword, pushing back against the wave of darkness. Wisps of darkness swept around the light, which flickered. The wisps impacted the barriers, and the first of the three bowed back, looking like it would break any second.

I feel like I'm in the middle of a Godzilla movie. A bad place to be.

Nathan looked around for cover, trying to stay calm in the face of the incredible power being thrown around. There was nothing he could do to influence this fight. His options were to run away, hide, or stay where he was. If he ran away from the fight, he'd go directly past the rock-thrower and underneath the mages, and that was begging to get collateralled. If he hid, he wouldn't get to watch the fight – or run if the Grave Tangle kept advancing. Nathan settled for crouching next to a small boulder, ready to duck behind it at any moment. He reactivated [Focused Mind], sharpening his attention on what his defenders were doing.

It looked like there was a brief pause in the fight. There was no trace of the first barrier and only shards of the second, but the third had held. The silver-armored fighter was backpedaling as the Grave Tangle drew itself up, more tentacles sliding out from all sides. More skeletal heads emerged from the central bulk, mostly amalgams of smaller bones instead of enormous snake skulls. Portions of the monster were blackened, and chunks were pulverized by house-sized rocks, but it remained the size of a geographical feature.

I don't think of monsters in similar dimensions you would use to describe skyscrapers, no.

Nathan noticed that the tentacles were of two types, some thicker and plated with bone, others thinner and enormously long. As it prepared to rejoin the battle, Nathan heard a high-pitched howl from behind him. The mage with cupped hands had never stopped charging their spell, and now they were obscured by a purple-tinted blinding light. Tentacles snapped out, but the entire group had shifted to defense, and the attacks were blocked by barriers or intercepted by sword, rock and arrow. That pattern held for a moment, and Nathan struggled to perceive the attacks. They came like raindrops, spattering against the united defense of four impossibly powerful people.

Low-tier Notice 5 achieved!

The light grew brighter still, and Nathan had to look away, blinking against a blind patch of his vision. The screaming howl grew in pitch and volume, and Nathan clapped his hands over his ears. He looked back towards the Grave Tangle, which was quickly advancing up the hill, purple light reflecting off its front. Nathan hoped these new arrivals would get on with it, since the Grave Tangle was approaching the fallen convoy that contained Nathan's only friends in this world.

A blue barrier sprung up above Nathan, protecting him from overhead.

Nathan didn't get distracted, keeping his eyes on the monster even as his ears started bleeding and the light of the charging spell outshone the sun, casting the whole valley in harsh shadows. He wasn't going to miss *this*. The Grave Tangle abandoned offense and shielded itself behind armored tentacles, layering them in between it and the charging spell.

A moment later, the entire world flashed. Nathan squinted, trying to make out details with his damaged vision. A beam of blinding light connected to the Grave Tangle, punching through the defending tentacles and stabbing deeply into the pile of flesh. Then the beam spiraled outward, moving quickly and smoothly as steam and viscera jetted out in its wake. The Grave Tangle shuddered and attempted to shield itself, but anything in the way of the beam was annihilated.

It's not reflecting, and it has significant momentum. That's not light, that's plasma. That spell probably compressed air and contained energy until it converted the air to plasma, maybe all the way to starting a tiny fusion reaction.

Pending utility skill: Low-tier Identify
You have used external knowledge to accurately identify exotic effects. This skill will help you understand complex cues to understand strange objects and effects. Will not reveal curses without obvious clues, and will not help you identify types of mana or spellcraft.

Pending Talent: Mid-tier Blinding Resistance
You have gazed into a blinding light and kept some of your vision. This Talent will turn this decision into a personal Talent. Your vision will no longer be affected by intense light, and you will be able to discern details of bright objects regardless of their brightness. Will provide some protection from magical dazzling and blinding effects. Will not restore your damaged vision.

Nathan pushed the notifications aside, careful to not accept or deny them as he channeled Stamina into his eyes. He still had a reserve at 135/330. He focused on the top layers of the retina at the back of his eye, where the intense light would have damaged fragile optical receptors.

Mid-tier Regeneration Rank 6 achieved!

Mid-tier Focused Mind 3 achieved!

The plasma beam petered out, and Nathan stared down at the blurry image of the charred, collapsing pile of flesh that had been the Grave Tangle. Then it started moving again, pulling itself together, visibly struggling despite being barely half of its original mass. Now it was *only* the size of a 10-story building.

It's not dead? How do you kill it?

Low-tier Notice 6 achieved!

The high-level party was not idle, and the Grave Tangle was bombarded with arrows and rocks as the fighter and the mages approached. The ranged fighters focused on any newly appearing tentacles or heads, blasting them away as soon as they appeared. The Tangle could only offer token resistance as it was torn apart piecemeal. Large chunks were cut away by the glowing greatsword and enormous blades of scissoring force, then jets of blue fire were fired into the holes, cooking it from the inside.

Quickly enough, the Grave Tangle was reduced to a pile of smoking flesh. Sweeping walls of force collected the offal into an enormous pyre, into which the mages directed a constant stream of flame until it was fully alight. The fire was *enormous* and sent curtains of dark smoke into the sky. One of them gestured, and a light breeze blew the smoke away from Nathan and the villagers.

Nathan watched the whole proceeding, moving down the slope and back towards the comrades he'd abandoned. The flames were intense, and the corrupted flesh steadily crumbled to ash.

You have leveled up to level 25! Congratulations, you have survived a fight between entities an extraordinary number of levels above you!

~

Status of Nathan Lark:
Permanent Talent 1: High-tier Magic Resistance 10
Permanent Talent 2: Mid-tier Regeneration 6
Talent 3: Pending

Class: Antimagic Brawler level 25
Stamina: 130/350
Brawler's Indifference
Antimagic Blows

Utility skills:
Mid-tier Focused Mind 3
Low-tier Earnestness 5
Low-tier Sprinting 6
Low-tier Spellsense 4
Low-tier Notice 6

Chapter 14

Paragons of Adventure

While Nathan walked down the slope, he considered his new levels. 27 was the breakpoint where he'd Develop his class and get more class skills, and Nathan was a little disappointed that he hadn't hit it despite the Disadvantaged buff. However, more levels meant more Stamina and more powerful class skills – so Nathan certainly wasn't complaining. He looked over the pending options from Davrar.

Pending utility skill: Low-tier Identify
You have used external knowledge to accurately identify exotic effects. This skill will help you interpret complex cues to understand strange objects and effects. Will not reveal curses without obvious clues, and will not help you identify types of mana or spellcraft.

Pending Talent: Mid-tier Blinding Resistance
You have gazed into a blinding light and kept some of your vision. This Talent will turn this decision into a personal Talent. Your vision will no longer be affected by intense light, and you will be able to discern details of bright objects regardless of their brightness. Will provide some protection from magical dazzling and blinding effects. Will not restore your damaged vision.

The blinding Talent seemed like shit, and there was a good chance it would be permanent as well. He declined it.

Watch, being immune to being blinded is going to end up being really important.

The [Identify] skill though – that seemed incredibly general. Nathan hadn't been going for a skill like that, but Vhala had told him that it was easier to acquire skills and Talents in a dangerous fight. Nathan hadn't been a true combatant – but apparently being in the blast radius counted. And it had directly followed him identifying the decisive spell as plasma-based, likely with a fusion component. Regardless, Nathan guessed [Identify] would synergize well with [Notice].

Congratulations, you have accepted the 'Low-tier Identify' utility skill.

Nathan was picking his way down to the switchbacks when a voice called out from behind him. "You there! Are you an adventurer?"

Nathan turned to see a tall, rangy man with light brown skin and shoulder-length shining black hair. He wore an elegantly cut green shirt and tight, black leggings. His cheekbones were sharp, with a delicate jaw. His clothes were peppered with rips and small bloodstains, though Nathan could see no existing wounds. He had wide pouches on both hips, and was just finishing pushing a strung bow – that absolutely *should not* have fit – into the one on his left. Obviously, he was the archer whose shots had shattered skeletal snake heads as large as cars.

Nathan turned to give the man a respectful nod. "Not an adventurer yet – but I'm headed that way."

The man smiled, seeming to dance over the rocks to approach Nathan. "I'm impressed you were able to stay on your feet during all that, and your nerves are adamant. Here, drink this and come help me check on the others."

He pulled a vial out of a bag and tossed it to Nathan. Nathan identified it as a healing potion – having seen bottles after they'd been used on Wiam. Nathan glanced down at himself, noting his slight limp and reddened skin – inflamed from exposure to the Grave Tangle's miasma.

Do I try to impress? Yeah, probably. They went out of their way to protect us while fighting. And people able to beat that *are good contacts to have.*

He sent Stamina to his ankle, repairing the skin and soft tissue. His skin color returned to normal in moments, and he leaped down to the path, using Stamina to easily make the landing. "I'm good, but I can use it on anybody who's in a bad way." He tucked the potion into his satchel, remembering the part of [Magic Resistance] that said "weaker magical items degrade when in prolonged contact with you."

The man's eyebrows rose as he examined Nathan again, giving him a closer look. "I'm Leska, Leska Bhola." He seemed to glide casually down the rough slope, landing in front of Nathan, arm extended.

Nathan shook it, feeling hard, ridged calluses and dexterous fingers. "I'm Nathan Lark. Nice to meet you. Let's go help my friends."

They set off down the road, quickly arriving at the head of the convoy, where some of the villagers were shakily getting to their feet. Everybody seemed weakened and agitated – with raw, inflamed skin. But only a few were truly in danger. Those were spiderwebbed with weeping cracks across their skin. Nathan followed Leska's lead, feeding small quantities of healing potion to those unable to stand on their own. He grabbed Sora and Dwoh and brought them with him, intending to introduce them to Leska.

They worked their way down the convoy, arriving to find Eldred and Vhala conversing with a new figure. The new person was very short, maybe just breaking four feet tall. Nathan immediately noticed the dusky orange skin, long, pointed ears and sharp nose. Gray hair was worked into a complex braid that reached to the nape of the neck. They – she? – was dressed in tight-fitting clothes made of a black, supple leather decorated sparsely with snowy lace and looping orange embroidery that matched her skin. The outfit was spotless, completely unmarked by the fight. And *very* tight, emphasizing certain features in ways that were usually reserved for superhero movies. The white lace set off the colors nicely, contrasting in tone with the armored plates and knife-sheaths strewn across the outfit.

As Nathan and Leska approached, the orange-skinned woman turned away from her conversation to smirk at Leska. "I see you couldn't manage to keep your outfit intact. I cannot guarantee my aunt will grant the same discount twice. Is everything in order?" For such a short frame, her voice was surprisingly gravelly. Her eyes flicked briefly to Nathan, as if to ask why he accompanied Leska. Without his [Notice], Nathan would never have seen and interpreted that interaction.

Leska grinned and gave a hand gesture like an "okay" sign, but with all of his fingers bunched together. Given the context, Nathan assumed it had a similar meaning. "Yup, all good. The refugees are mostly stable, but we should let Kia at them and then get to Gemore as soon as we can. In fact, we should probably head back as soon as these fine fellows are all moving. We don't want to be short if another team sets something off." He paused, looking back at Nathan. "Let me introduce you. Xarian, this is Nathan Lark, he's the one who shrugged off the Grave Tangle aura. Nathan, this is Xarian Doulna. She throws rocks and looks good. And her aunt makes the best clothes in Gemore." Leska fingered a rip in his tunic mournfully.

Xarian lifted her chin as if offended, but the slight upturn of her lips betrayed that she enjoyed the banter. "I will inscribe our meeting, Nathan Lark," she said formally, before turning to Sora and Dwoh. The couple were goggling at the shattered valley-*cum*-battlefield surrounding the enormous pyre. "Are the good villagers of Pilriden ready to move to shelter? We must abandon you to return to our duties – but you are close and escorted by fine company."

Dwoh spoke hesitantly. "W-we thank you, great Adventurers. We appreciate your defense of us and can move whenever you say." He bowed deeply.

Xarian frowned and looked back over the gaggle of villagers, many sprawled on the ground or holding each other. "Do you speak truth, or do you speak that which I wish to hear?"

Dwoh rose from his bow and looked back at the villagers. He stammered, noticing all of the adventurers with their eyes on him.

Sora cut in. "I think what my husband means to say is that we're not in the best shape, but folk will push to get to safety. Any healing you have would be helpful – there are wounds aplenty, and those of us who can cast [Minor Curing] are out of mana."

Leska cut in. "Kia's headed over, so get everybody on their feet and ready to move out. She'll fix you up quick."

Nathan turned to see the silver-armored warrior bounding toward them, jumping off thin air to ascend the rocky slope at an insane speed. Having just run the distance, Nathan estimated it as closer to "car speed" than "running speed."

The metal-clad figure landed surprisingly lightly beside the party. They were about six feet tall, and the bare golden greatsword on their back was nearly the same length. They reached up to take off the shining Dark Souls-style full helmet.

Underneath was a pale woman, long reddish-blonde hair braided and tied around her head like a multi-layered crown. She looked like she'd just emerged from a two-hour session with a make-up artist – instead of a battle against a monstrosity the size of a skyscraper. There were scars on her face, but they enhanced the strong-jawed profile instead of marring it. Her eyes were a bright blue and faintly glowing.

When she spoke the voice was low, clipped but not urgent. "Status?"

Leska replied quickly. "No deaths. No serious wounds, no hidden threats. One possible anomaly, outside our purview." He tilted his head faintly, almost imperceptibly towards Nathan. "Hit 'em with an area heal and they can make their own way back."

The woman – Kia – nodded, then looked around, taking an instant to focus on the faces of each person in the immediate group. She reached Nathan and paused, narrowing her eyes. "You, no-aura, can anybody vouch for you?"

Nathan looked to Leska, but it was Vhala who answered. "Yes, the Giantraiders vouch for him. Do you require a full accounting?"

Kia was already turning away and putting her helmet back on, slipping it over the braid with no issues. "No. If you think it's worthwhile, I'll hear it later over a drink. We've got work to do."

She leaped up, the greatsword springing into her hand. She floated twenty feet in the air, raising the greatsword to the sky. Nathan heard a quick but emphatic prayer, growing in volume from barely audible to a shout that cut through the sound of the roiling flames from the pyre.

"By the goodness of these people, let them be healed. By my power, banish their weakness! By the holy light, no taint shall survive!"

The sword's golden glint intensified, as if it reflected the sun directly into Nathan's eyes. He saw a similar light shine on everybody around him. Nothing happened to him – but everybody else perked up. The villagers collapsed on the ground rose again. Nathan saw previously inflamed skin return to a healthy pink before his eyes.

Nathan felt the light on his own skin, but it didn't heal any of his scrapes or bruises. According to Nathan's [Spellsense] it was... just another kind of mana. It was different than any Nathan had sensed before, like a prickling of warm needles. There was also a righteous anger in the mana as it washed over him, as if the mana was made of emotion. It was different from any of the spells he'd felt before, and was rather unsettling.

Damn. Okay. Gods are real? Do I need to find religion?

More importantly, they're making a point of healing everybody here. If that was really a fusion reaction, it would have sent off a bunch of ionizing radiation. Should I watch out for radiation sickness?

From what Nathan remembered, radiation was dangerous in both the short and long term. In the short term it could shred cells, causing organ failure. In the long term, mutations would increase cancer risk. Maybe regeneration could properly fix those? Well, there wasn't much else to do. Nathan swept a wave of regeneration through his entire body, focusing on his brain and organs. He lost a surprising amount of Stamina. Then he did it twice more, losing less Stamina each time. He made a note to do it again later.

You don't fuck around with radiation.

The two mages seemed to decide that the Grave Tangle was well-roasted and flew toward the group of Adventurers, leaving the enormous pile to smolder. Nathan's inner Smokey the Bear worried about forest fires – but it appeared the wind was too calm for the fire to spread. A *lot* of trees had been torched in the fight, but the scattered fires seemed to be dying out instead of growing.

As Nathan came to that conclusion, Leska and Xarian were surrounded by a nimbus of white light and floated into the sky, Leska giving a jaunty wave. They joined the mages floating maybe thirty feet up. From there, Nathan could examine the mages in more detail.

They wore robes of a similar cut to one another, looking more like jedi robes than anything too loose or draping. One – the one without a staff, who'd cast the plasma-lance spell – looked like a flame, with layered blue, white and red fabric. He was a tanned human man in late middle age, with thin white hair and a wispy beard. The other mage with the staff wasn't human, and had a snout and upturned ears – they were some sort of humanoid cat or fox person. Their clothes were an enveloping wrapping of blue and green, covering brown fur streaked with gray.

Nathan saw the flame-garbed man do a double take as he scanned the group, focusing on Nathan. He swallowed as he met the man's shining eyes. It was like looking at an arc welder. But then Leska said something and gestured up the hill, and the entire group flashed away, accelerating rapidly back over the hill and toward Gemore.

Everybody watched them go. Nathan looked around and then asked, "Who the hell was that?"

Vhala answered him, a thoughtful look in her eye. "Those were the Guardians of Gemore. I've always heard they were ridiculous, but I'd never seen them in action. It must be a Delve day. That explains the Grave Tangle, too."

Nathan was confused. "Delve Day?"

This time, Eldred answered, turning to start hiking up the slope. Everybody followed his lead. "Every month or three, or when a Questor shows up, the council declares a Delve day. The Guildmistress approves a few groups to go into dungeons or tombs or whatever. There's an application process. Well, except for the Questors." He harrumphed. "And it's a day of readiness for everybody else. They put some real powerhouses on standby. In case something like *that* happens." He waved in the direction of the charred Grave Tangle.

Nathan swallowed. "So somebody... woke that up? Over there?" He pointed towards the valley where the Grave Tangle had emerged.

Eldred looked back. "Must've. I think there is a monastery of Quaz over there. Well, there *was*, it looks like it got scattered all over the place." He narrowed his eyes and pursed his lips. "I bet they'll issue a scouting job so they can check it off the threat-map. Might try to get that one."

The rest of the Vanguard moaned, complaining about looking forward to a rest and a bath after days tromping through the forest. Eldred only laughed and mocked their lack of an adventurous spirit. Then he proceeded to question their love of coin.

Nathan was busy chewing on some jerky to replenish his Stamina, but he quickly swallowed it and opened his mouth to ask what a monastery of Quaz was. Vhala caught his eye and shook her head. It must have been common knowledge, or maybe she just didn't want Nathan's ignorance to stick in Eldred's head.

Nathan's frustration was short-lived. It wasn't long before they crested the hill and looked down upon Gemore.

It wasn't what Nathan expected. He'd been expecting a heavily-fortified town. What lay in front of him was a colossal city, stretching across a huge basin in the middle of a mountain range. It was like looking down upon Los Angeles or Tokyo from a landing airplane, a metropolis that could hold uncountable millions that faded into the distance. Taller buildings stood here and there – some blocky and imposing, others smooth and graceful.

But all of it was ruins. Six layers of enormous curtain walls lay tumbled and crushed, regularly spaced over many miles. The spaces between were packed with partially and fully-collapsed multi-story buildings. Patches of greenery sprouted from various places, especially surrounding a river in the distance that meandered through city blocks and pooled in old city squares.

Then Nathan saw the heart of the city, barely visible at this distance. The seventh and final layer of walls were unbroken, cradled around one side of a steep hill, almost a mountain. The walls were tall and imposing even from here, surrounded by a wide clear zone. A killing field.

Gemore itself was built up one side of the tall hill, many miles away. The city ascended up to a ridge of overhanging rock that arched forward, threatening to fall onto intact buildings. The other side of the hill was a steep cliff of bare rock, terminating in the river that pooled on the other side of the hill. It was like looking at a town nestled under a stone wave just about to crash.

Chapter 15

Gemore at Last

It was after midday, and Nathan had joined everybody else in eating travel rations as they walked. The group seemed unwilling to stop and take a break when safety was near, implying they just had to push a *little* further and they'd reach safety.

He'd been told that they'd arrive at Gemore later today – but that confused him. They would definitely arrive at the ruined city in the next half-hour or so. But the central hill with standing walls had to be at least twenty miles away. Unless they were willing to push far into the night, Nathan couldn't see this group making it today.

Also, it would have been faster to go straight down the shallow hill towards the enormous breaches in the outermost curtain wall. But instead, they descended the hill diagonally towards a massive and ruined gatehouse. Nobody had discussed it, they'd just set out, following Eldred and the Vanguard. There hadn't been much conversation in general – even the Adventurers seemed beaten down and on their last legs. So Nathan kept his mouth shut and observed.

Hard to ask a dumb question if you stay quiet.

His questions were answered as soon as they reached the road in front of the gatehouse. It was intact and in good condition – a broad stretch of wide paving stones. The group quickly strung out as they stepped onto the road, and as he followed suit, Nathan understood why. Each step on the road carried you *farther* than it should. It was *bizarre*.

Nathan did a few quick experiments, watching the ground nearby as he stepped forward. Each step covered a normal distance on the road, but the terrain beyond the road blurred by. He picked up a rock and tossed it off the road diagonally. It didn't speed up or slow down as it left the road – but the *angle* of the throw changed.

It seems like there's some sort of lensing effect on the edges for objects, but not for light. The space on the road is compressed? Yet things off the road look normal and the road isn't blindingly bright? That's either magical fiat or a truly impressive feat of magical engineering. I hope I don't break this thing by walking on it.

Low-tier Identify 2 achieved!

If I only rank that up when I'm correct, there are some metaphysical implications to the skill. Can I speculate on the deep truths of Davrar and learn the truth by what causes an [Identify] rank up? Something to keep in mind.

The road seemed unharmed by Nathan's passing, and he resisted the temptation to feel out the magic beneath his feet. The party sped through the dilapidated gatehouse and into the city beyond. The road remained clear – though Nathan saw places where ruins had fallen onto the road and been cleared away. The rubble hadn't gone far, piled on either side of the passage. At these tight spaces the Vanguard and Giantraiders tensed, and Nathan noticed they'd grouped themselves to either side of the villagers, as if to protect them from flanking attacks.

Upon noticing that, Nathan began paying careful attention to their surroundings. They'd already passed another curtain wall, and the state of the ruins varied greatly. Some areas were barely distinguishable from wilderness – mounds of broken stone overgrown with squat trees and vines – while others looked like they'd merely been abandoned for a few decades. The stonework was amazing, tight-fitting blocks carved with detailed patterns and reliefs that now served mostly as purchase for vines and dirt. Here and there, traces of paint clung to stone in contrast with the greenery.

Farther along, Nathan saw why the adventurers were on edge. A group of six-legged, scaled creatures lurked in the half-tumbled ruins of a building a few dozen yards off the road, watching them. They were the size of small ponies, with long, triangular snouts and forward-facing beady eyes. A third eye was embedded in the middle of their foreheads, glowing with a subdued brown light. The creatures faded in and out of the shadows enough that Nathan couldn't tell how many there were. He guessed between five and ten. Looking around, nobody else seemed to have noticed. The creatures weren't *obvious,* but they weren't exactly invisible.

He looked again, squinting at the creatures, and felt something tingling against his eyes. It was subtle, like the feeling of brushing through barely-felt cobwebs. Nathan's [Spellsense] told him that this was some kind of soft, quiet magic.

Nathan pointed and called out, "Hey! What are those things in that building?"

Low-tier Spellsense 5 achieved!

Low-tier Notice 7 achieved!

One of the Vanguard standing near Nathan followed his finger and then looked back at him quizzically. But Wiam was just a few steps further ahead. He paused and cast a spell – causing the shadows in the building to ripple and then shred in a flurry of motion.

The birdfolk cursed. "Harpy's tits! W'got earth stalkers!"

The earth stalkers prowled out of the building, six limbs moving with a smooth, low-slung grace. The Vanguard and the Giantraiders reacted just as quickly, drawing weapons and forming up to face the approaching creatures. Vhala stayed a pace back as she unlimbered her recurve bow, nocking an arrow. The earth stalkers paused, evaluating the gathered adventurers and the villagers behind them.

Vhala raised her bow, aiming at the lead stalker. It tracked the gesture, then bounded off behind another building, followed closely by the other seven members of the pack. Everybody stayed tense for a moment before carefully resuming their journey.

Eldred swore. "Waking Giants, that was a near thing. They shouldn't be back, but" – he turned to Nathan, eyeing him appreciatively – "keep an eye out. Good job." He clapped a hand on Nathan's shoulder – not gently.

They continued walking, and Vhala stepped close to Nathan, speaking quietly. "Stalkers use magic to hide. They're hard to spot, even for me. Did you pick up [Notice]?"

Nathan nodded. "Before the Grave Tangle fight. Ranked it up a bit."

Vhala let out an appreciative whistle, and shook her head. "And your magic resistance helped you see through the look-away magic." She paused, choosing her words. "If you ever bargain with *that* Insight, be sure to mention that. I've half a mind to drop one o'mine and bargain with you for it. Are you interested in another trade? My family would drop some valuable Insights for this one."

Nathan took a moment to consider. Was there any reason to keep the Insights behind his [Magic Resistance] secret? Yes, there definitely were. He was worse at dealing with conjured projectiles than other magical attacks, and if other people understood his Talent, they could know how to best attack him. On the other hand – it was a valuable chip and he could potentially gain a *lot* by bargaining with it.

On the other-other hand, can I even teach it? Duplicating the lack of magic in my body and the "magic-resistant alchemical ingredients" is probably beyond... most people. I'd love to understand how all that works though. Eventually.

Vhala watched Nathan think, and by her pursed lips and slow nod seemed to know his answer even as he opened his mouth to speak it.

"Sorry Vhala, I'm both unsure if I should share it, and if I *can*. There was some weird stuff going on around me acquiring the Talent, and I don't know how we'd even start duplicating it."

Vhala waved her hand at him to dismiss his apology. "Yeah, that's the way with some of the more powerful ones, to be sure. But you might be surprised what we can accomplish, for a powerful Talent. So keep thinking on it. I'm gonna introduce you to the Guildmaster when I sponsor you to the Guild, and tell her about the magic resistance stuff." Vhala shrugged, justifying herself. "She needs to know."

Nathan didn't have much of a response to that, and following Eldred's instruction, he kept an eye out. They soon passed another curtain wall without a reappearance of the earth stalkers. At this point, unless the earth stalkers traveled on the road, they wouldn't catch up. There was also less cover, and based on the notable lack of whole stone blocks, Nathan guessed that Gemore had been mining the ruined city near the road for cut stone.

Before too long, they reached the gates of Gemore proper. The city had been visible from many miles away, and Nathan hadn't quite appreciated the scale. The entire interior behind the sixth curtain wall had been cleared into a treacherous killing field, broken into a low rubble that threatened to foul footing and provided no cover.

The walls surrounding Gemore were tall, over a hundred feet. The bottom sixty feet were a single smooth surface engraved with enormous symbols. But the wall had been built even taller, and the top portion was built from mismatched blocks clearly taken from different buildings in the ruined city. They'd also had faintly glowing symbols carved onto them, tying the whole structure together. Despite its patchwork nature, the wall looked very solid.

Not like I'm an architect, but it certainly looks like it's not going to fall over. Unless something like that Grave Tangle tested it. In that light, it's not tall enough. *But you don't build walls to keep out godzilla. Unless you're in Pacific Rim? Never understood the wall in those movies, it never did* anything.

The magical road of space compression carried them quickly to an open area where the effect faded. Six other similar roads approached from other directions, all ending in front of the only gate into Gemore.

And that gate was a doozy. Big. Metal. Magical. It looked less like a gate than a pair of movable walls. Which were currently standing open, thankfully. There was a portcullis that looked like it could be quickly dropped, and a set of guards standing outside waiting for them.

The guards were dressed in matching breastplates and chainmail, armed with halberds, swords, crossbows and signal horns. They split up and guided the villagers into lines, proceeding to inspect each and ask a few questions before allowing them to proceed through the gate.

The adventurers stood at the back, and while they were clearly looking forward to safety and rest, Vhala and Eldred had each reminded their groups that relaxing too early led to tragedy. They were on guard, eyes peeled. Nathan followed suit. *Damn,* this world seemed scary, if you really needed to watch for an attack on your own doorstep.

Then it was their turn to go into the gate, and there he hit a snag. The guard's helmet had a monocle held over one eye, and as soon as the guard examined Nathan, she jumped back with a yell, hand going to her sword hilt. Vhala was standing close by and stepped forward, raising her hand in a placating gesture.

"It's okay, there's a full explanation for his absence of an aura. I, as leader of the Giantraiders, vouch that he's as human as he appears, and not a threat to Gemore."

The guards all took a moment to process that. The one in front of Nathan looked from him to Vhala, then spoke. "Alright Vhala. On your head be it if you let a soul eater into the city. We'll make sure this goes on the record."

With that, they were through. The gate was more of a tunnel since the wall was nearly a hundred feet across. Nathan noted the murder holes and more portcullises. At this point, any competent foe would just find a way to go around instead of trying to take the gate.

The city beyond was quite urban. Wide, well-planned streets and buildings four to eight stories tall, mostly made of stone, with the top few floors sometimes made of wood. Past a wide plaza fronted by warehouses and inns, all of the roads went *up*. The overreaching ridge of stone didn't reach this far out, but the curling crest of the hill was still visible from here. It loomed high above the city, which carpeted the steep slope beneath it. Gemore *was* a city, Nathan's earlier misconception caused by distance. People flocked the streets, all with places to be.

Some sort of city officials were ready to take the villagers in hand, and the adventurers had fully relaxed on their home turf. They ambled up a road, past a few obvious inns, taverns and shops, and turned onto another street that ran parallel to the slope.

On the uphill side of this street was a large complex of buildings that was obviously their destination. There was a wide, wooden arch with a sign on it leading into a small stone courtyard. Around the courtyard wrapped several tall buildings of pale stone, but Nathan's attention was arrested by the sign on the arch. More specifically, the writing on the sign. Most specifically, the fact that the symbols were completely foreign to him.

Shit.

He caught up to Artha. "Is the writing on that sign the same as the language we're speaking?"

Artha looked at him, realization dawning. "Yes. You can't read it?" He pursed his lips. "You will need to learn. It's something to mention to the master-at-arms. This is the Adventurer's Guild, and where we will be staying."

Yeah, no duh I need to learn to read. Hi, is this Taeol spellcasting customer support? I have a complaint to lodge about a glaring feature missing from your translation spell.

Nathan stayed next to Artha as they went straight across the courtyard, where Eldred threw open a wide pair of double doors. They opened onto a huge hall – forty feet tall, well-decorated with colorful murals on the walls and banners hanging overhead.

The space seemed to serve several purposes at once, with a long polished desk against the right wall manned by one clerk, with space for many more. The central space was mostly clear – though there was a ring sketched out on the floor in chalk and some benches around it. Various doors and staircases led deeper into the building. The left side of the space looked like a hangout spot, with scattered tables and couches served by a bar and kitchen on the far wall.

The other notable feature of the room was the people. Maybe forty adventurers stood or sat around the room, and they were all applauding, cheering and stamping their feet. Eldred raised a hand in acknowledgement, but it was obvious that most of the praise was directed towards the Giantraiders. Vhala and Artha stood with heads raised high, accepting the praise with poise, while Wiam hopped from one foot to another, cackling and waving his arms.

Emerald looked uncomfortable but stood a bit straighter, hands on their weapons.

Nathan was busy examining the adventurers. They were a riot of color, in many shapes and even more different styles of armor and armaments. Nathan counted at least six species. Humans were the most common at a bit more than a third of those present. There were half as many of the short orange-skinned folk like Xarian, with skin colors ranging from peach to rusty brown. The rest were split between small numbers of other species. Some were centaur-like peoples like Artha, though there was variety in the species of the hooved-half. Others were bipedal human-animal hybrids. All apex predators, Nathan noticed. Mostly wolf or large cat-adjacent, though there was one other bird of prey like Wiam. Finally, there was a scattering of unique individuals – a hulking man with khaki green skin, bulging eyes and teeth that protruded from beyond thin lips, almost an archetypal orc. A figure in a corner looked to be made entirely of dark ice, standing near another person of pale stone.

Eldred had already sauntered over to the desk, talking to the clerk while a few people from the crowd came up to congratulate the Giantraiders. A gaunt man with sparse white hair that looked like Vhala's father came up and gave her a hug, while a few other centaur-people congratulated Artha with small bows and serious words. Emerald exchanged quiet words with the orc, while Wiam was mobbed by a small crowd of young mages of every species.

Vhala beckoned Nathan over. "Uncle, this is Nathan Lark. We found him escaping from the new archmage's tower, and he helped us take the fight with the slavers. Nathan, this is my uncle Kadid. He's retired now, but he was the sneakiest ranger in Gemore in his day. Taught me half of what I know."

The man, whose skin was a shade darker than Vhala, reached out a bony hand to shake Nathan's. "I'll take the compliment, but we both know my sister taught ya most of it. Speak her memory." He looked Nathan in the eyes. "You have my thanks for helping Vhala out. I'd hear that story if one of ya would tell it."

Nathan got in a "Nice to meet you," before Vhala spoke again.

"I'm sponsoring Nathan to the Guild today, hope to get him in this cycle. Uncle, I want you to look out for him while we're ranging. He's important, and earlier in his path than he looks."

The old man didn't look surprised, but did look over Nathan again, not commenting on anything in particular. He nodded. "I will – if Nathan will have me. Do you need help getting him settled...?"

Vhala shook her head. "No, I'm going to try to get a meeting with the Guildmistress, explain things. Has it been a busy Delve Day?"

Kadid answered with a wry turn of his mouth. "Not after the Grave Tangle. Kia said they weren't up for another significant fight, so a halt was called." He shrugged. "At least for the people who could receive and obey the signal. The backup team is The Seven Fools – and they don't have the weight for a fight like that. Apparently Sudraiel doesn't want to take chances this close to the Solstice."

He gestured around to all of the adventurers gathered in the hall. "So far the only losses are presumed, but we're pretty sure the Gray Moon Order isn't coming back – they went into the monastery of Quaz, the Grave Tangle came out of it. And the Wrecking Crew hasn't come out of the Fortress of the Face they went into early this morning, so we're worried about them. But that's the adventurer's life. If they're gone, we'll remember until the Ending."

Vhala mirrored his statement, and it sounded formulaic. "Remember 'till Ending."

Kadid continued. "Anyway, there's a break now between the rush of the recall and the day's accounting. You might be able to get a meeting with Sudraiel if it's important." He gestured with his chin toward the desks. "And it looks like Eldred's done."

The man was stepping back from the counter holding a set of looped strings threaded with coins. He went back to the Vanguard, who cheered as he passed out the strings.

Vhala caught Nathan's eye and jerked her head towards the desk, so Nathan followed her. The clerk watched them both approach, looking unconcerned. He spoke. "Hello Vhala. I am ready to receive your report – but it appears there might be some complexities to it. Do you want to bump this upstairs?"

Vhala nodded at him. "Thanks Velek. Yeah, this is something that needs the Guildmistress' attention. I know it's Delve Day, and this can wait if it needs to."

Velek was already taking something from under the desk as Vhala spoke. It was a small yellow gemstone, glowing with a faint inner light. He brought it up to his mouth, and his face blurred while his voice was distorted into nonsense. A few moments passed before another voice sounded, also blurred but with a noticeably different intonation. Velek nodded and put the stone under the desk, withdrawing something else as he stood."Follow me."

He slid out from behind the desk and headed toward a small door in the corner of the room. Vhala walked after him, and Nathan hastened to follow. He cast a look over his shoulder, and though most of the room was drifting back toward the bar, there were several sets of thoughtful eyes on him.

Velek used the key he'd grabbed from under the desk to open the door, which led to a narrow stairwell. They passed several sturdy doors on their way up, but Velek led them to the very top of the building. Nathan counted out nine floors in total.

On Earth, Nathan would have been out of breath from climbing nine flights of stairs. Here, his Stamina barely dipped. At the top, Velek unlocked another door and led them into a tall chamber with several comfortable-looking couches and cushioned tables scattered around. One side of the room opened to a broad, gently sloped staircase that led down. The other wall held a sturdy door.

And this was a *door*. It was bound in dark metal and covered with burnt runes, while being large enough for Artha to comfortably walk through. The wooden surface was dented and scorched but unbroken – as if somebody had taken a burning battering ram to it and the ram had lost. And *exploded*. A small desk, neatly organized with reports and documents, sat next to the door, overshadowed by the door's bulk.

Sitting behind the desk – just visible behind the stacks of paperwork – was a 3-foot tall man whose skin was a shockingly bright orange. It matched the abstract patterns embroidered on his voluminous purple robe. His beard and hair were a bright, pure white, tied in an elaborate braid of plaits that dangled in a regular pattern from ear to ear. White-irised eyes studied Nathan intently as he approached, but the man made no comment.

The enormous door swung silently open and Velek stepped aside, waving them into the room before he turned to leave.

Chapter 16

Adventurer Administration

Nathan and Vhala entered the room beyond, walking past the short orange-skinned secretary. The space was broad and tall, with a ceiling that slanted down on either side to match the roof above. There were large windows on the three walls that didn't house a door, overlooking the entrance courtyard and various training yards.

The rest of the room was simple – decorated sparsely with objects that had the sense of being placed *just so*. On a wall to the left hung a pair of crossed, wavy swords which had to be nearly eight feet long. Facing the swords on the opposite wall was a multi-string compound bow made of bone. A huge rug in muted colors was spread across the floor, almost fractal in its complexity. Six chairs stood on the rug.

Those chairs faced a desk which commanded the room. It was made of a wood a shade darker than that which made up the building, and held several stacks of yellowed paper along with a crystal ball and a magnifying glass on a flexible arm. A glowing, three-dimensional illusory map occupied the center of the desk, though it dissolved before Nathan's eyes, giving way to delicately carved wood. The haft of a spear, made of carved and varnished wood, leaned against the left side of the desk. It was placed in such a way to be easily grabbed by the woman behind the desk.

The woman in question looked up, and the door swung shut behind them with a *thud* that Nathan felt through his feet.

She put down a piece of paper and studied them for a moment. Her pink skin looked unhealthily blotchy. She had a threadbare cap on her bony head, and no hair was visible underneath it. Her hands were so thin as to be nearly skeletal. However, the gray eyes were bright and focused, banishing any sense of fragility.

Something told Nathan that this was a woman who expected respect – and usually got it. A bony hand gestured to the chairs, and Nathan followed Vhala's lead in sitting down politely.

The voice that followed was rougher than Nathan had expected from such a thin woman. "So. I had some time and expected to hear a story of how pragmatic, experienced adventurers – who should have known better – embraced a stupid risk and somehow triumphed regardless. But it seems introductions are in order instead?"

Vhala was more nervous than Nathan had ever seen her, which was strange. She'd just won a victory for this woman, and was being chastised for it?

"Guildmistress Elvaris, this is Nathan Lark. Nathan, this is the Guildmistress of the Guild of Adventurers, Sudraiel Elvaris." She turned back to Sudraiel. "I'll let Nathan give the details of his journey here himself, it's something you need to hear. Nathan, tell Guildmistress Elvaris *everything*. Quickly though, we don't have much time."

Nathan had decided to trust Vhala, and wasn't about to back out now. And she seemed to trust this woman. He shrugged internally.

I want this person to be impressed with me – if she thinks I'm worth it, she'll give me support and training.

"It's nice to meet you, Guildmistress Elvaris. To start with, I'm not from Davrar. I come from a different world, one with no skills, no Talents and no magic. I was summoned to this world about five days ago by Taeol dho Droxol, a new archmage of Giantsrest. He cast a spell that taught me this language, then tried to recruit me to his cause so he could learn things from my world. I decided I'd rather not teach him."

The Guildmistress raised two fingers, interrupting him. "Why not?"

Nathan hesitated for a moment, reflecting on his first days in Davrar and the decisions he'd made shortly after arriving in such a strange world. "My world has had genocidal maniacs. I've studied them, to understand how they convinced so many to follow them. That's who Taeol reminded me of."

Nathan felt a sliver of the boiling indignation he'd felt when Taeol had tried to *overwrite his free will*. "He sees himself and his people as the only possible good, and everybody else will either be used by him or destroyed. At the first sign of resistance, he used [Charm], then wiped my memory. I will not be used, and I'll kill him for trying."

A faint smile appeared on the pale woman's lips. "That sounds like a story worth the telling. How did you escape from an archmage?"

Nathan shrugged. "My world doesn't have magic. Almost as soon as I arrived, I was offered the [High-tier Magic Resistance] Talent. I accepted it before he tried to [Charm] me, and proceeded to bait more magic out of him to rank it up. He purged my memory once, but I'd left hints behind and broke the spell. Eventually, he decided to put me in a golem core. I broke free and almost killed him, but he teleported out." Nathan smiled at the memory of Taeol's terrified face. "With a broken nose and knee. I picked up a class good at fighting against magic and used it to break out of his tower – to find the Giantraiders lurking outside."

Vhala coughed, interjecting smoothly. "You didn't mention that he hit you with a [Disintegrate] first. You were missing an arm when we found you. And then you *slapped* aside a fireball from a guardian golem."

Over the course of Nathan's story, the Guildmistress' eyebrows had climbed steadily. She sounded apprehensive when she spoke. "I want to hear of the slave raid in a moment, but first. A missing arm? From [Disintegrate]?"

Nathan replied. "Vhala explained to me how Insights work, and I used some knowledge from my home to create a self-healing Talent that let me grow it back." He shrugged, flexing his left hand. "It's pretty cool."

Hopefully she finds that impressive.

A bony hand came up to pinch Sudraiel's nose. "I wasn't asking how you grew it back, I was questioning why there was anything left of you after the [Disintegrate]. But it seems [High-tier Magic Resistance] is the answer." She turned to Vhala. "So when the message of the slave raid came, you conscripted Nathan into fighting with you?"

Vhala opened her mouth, but Nathan spoke first. "I agreed to it. They told me what was happening, and I agreed to fight. It was a bit close, but we won." Vhala shot him a grateful glance, looking abashed. It was a strange look on the broad and heavily muscled woman.

Sudraiel noticed the interplay, but her response was short. "Elaborate on the fight, please."

This time, Vhala took the lead. "Classic anti-mage tactics, focused attention outward with front and rear attacks, then went for the mages with suitable fighters. Emerald and Nathan got in close and took 'em out." She shrugged. "That was it. I didn't see much of it, but Emerald said that Nathan shrugged off every spell they had and broke [Mage Armor] with a single punch. I will note that Nathan has not had his first class Development yet. He's being tutored by Artha in the ways of his clan."

That last part seemed to surprise Sudraiel more than anything they'd said so far. "Well then. I see. This is... hm. There are few better teachers for a path of Rage than an Elk Treeborn. Nathan, has Artha explained what this path entails? It is not for everybody." She suddenly looked concerned.

He nodded back. "Yes, he has. I think it will suit me. He gave me an Insight before the fight and it... felt right. Vhala mentioned that I should join the Adventurer's Guild?"

Vhala smoothly took over the conversation. "I did. One more thing. You'll probably get a report from the Guardians – when they saved us from the Grave Tangle, Nathan was unaffected by its aura. Dalo's detection spell didn't work on him, and I had to clear him at the gate too. He also noticed an earth stalker ambush before it happened. I think his Magic Resistance Talent is just amazing. It also seems to work well with other skills. I've given him some Bho Insights for his aid with the slavers."

She paused, then launched into what sounded like a rehearsed proposal to the Guildmistress. "I'm sure the current Adventurer training group is underway, but Nathan should be added to them. He needs a bit of help to Develop his class, and then a few years as a basic Adventurer. He needs to be protected from agents of Giantsrest that'll come for him. I think he should join a promising team undergoing training and be allowed to Develop himself safely." She shot a look at Nathan. "Well, as safely as can be."

Guildmistress Sudraiel Elvaris propped her head atop steepled fingers, considering the proposition. After a moment, she nodded. "You have had an eventful few days, and I congratulate you on your achievements thus far. Now, to briefly explain the situation that Vhala is inserting you into; I have long championed the need for an extensive training course that ensures competence and adherence to a shared set of rules for our young adventurers. We cannot tolerate blundering thugs. To insert you into the current group halfway through the training cycle goes against this – but the next cycle will not start for more than half a year, and I believe there are some candidate teams for what Vhala proposes." She paused for a moment, staring off into the distance with a faint frown.

Then she continued. "It is unheard of for somebody to be such an effective antimage so early in their Development. Your Talents seem very powerful, but this means you hold things of great value. Beware of those who might covet them. I will speak to Jolba in the morning and see you brought into the current class. There are decisions to be made on which team you will join... But! Today is a Delve day, and much remains for me to accomplish. Nathan, you should stay with the Giantraiders until Jolba comes to find you tomorrow." She gestured to the door and the stairs beyond, so Nathan and Vhala turned to go.

On the way out the door, Nathan looked over his shoulder, and saw Sudraiel studying him intently. She seemed to have a thought, speaking briskly. "And Nathan, later I may ask you for more details of your world. If for no other reason than to satisfy an old woman's curiosity. Think on what you would tell me."

With that foreboding comment, they were finally dismissed, and returned downstairs by a much larger and less direct route. Nathan noticed that the shallow stairs and high ceilings were built to accommodate Artha's centaur-people. Before long, they returned to the great hall, where they were greeted with further cheering, hot food and drinks. Vhala spoke to Velek at the desk and handed out several cords of coin to each of them, then guided Nathan through the worth of local coin and helped him order food.

Nathan ended up with a rather nice lemonade-like drink, served warm. A beer sounded amazing, but there were a lot of reasons to avoid getting even slightly tipsy. At least not yet. Maybe once he had a better lay of the land.

The food was great though. Nathan was familiar with very little of it, but the meat was tender and rich, the vegetables oozed with flavor and there was plenty to go around. After so long eating trail food, it felt like a feast. Nathan dug in gladly.

He ended up going through several of the warm lemonades by a local custom that resembled a toast. Somebody would approach, then they'd touch mugs and both drink wordlessly. According to Vhala, it was an appreciation of the deeds of the person being approached, and the depth of drink was a measure of the appreciation. A sip from either party was considered an insult to the other, and Nathan was careful to match other people's drinking. Afterwards most inquired as to tales of Nathan, and especially the fight against the slavers. Luckily, Vhala stayed around and told versions where Nathan distracted and struck down unwary mages with speed and guile.

After a few hours, the party headed into rowdy territory, with drinking contests, arm-wrestling and people challenging each other to increasingly violent contests in the ring. More and more adventurers returned over the course of the evening – most were exhausted and victorious, and spent little time at the party before disappearing into the rooms in the back. However, those who did stay and join the festivities were the centers of attention.

Nathan was feeling the burden of the day. Days, really. So when Vhala caught his eye during a break in conversation and jerked her head, Nathan was only too happy to follow.

Emerald had spent most of the night in a corner, quietly conversing with the orc and a few others. On seeing Vhala striding away, they bid a hasty goodbye and joined up, still wearing their helmet and armor. Artha had spoken to many, not spending too long with any given group. He caught up and exchanged a few quiet words with Vhala before again plunging back into the party. Wiam was gesticulating wildly amidst a group of young mages of many species. They left him to it.

Nathan followed Vhala and Emerald deeper into the building, where she led them unerringly to a cozy suite of rooms. There was a small lounge with basic amenities, and enough rooms for them all to have one each. A shared bathroom confirmed that the "trough of running water" approach was just how toilets worked on Davrar. The rooms were barely larger than the cramped beds. However, those beds were surprisingly soft, and Nathan was happy to get out of his stinking clothes and get some privacy.

Nathan was *tired.* Not physically – his Stamina was full, and he felt like he could run miles if he needed to. But his brain flickered through thoughts ceaselessly. There'd just been so much new information in the last few days, and he couldn't process it all. Or even rank the importance of things. This was an *entirely new world,* and things did not work like Earth did, from the cosmology to the levels to the legal system. Nathan was worried about agents of Giantsrest coming for him, he was worried he was being manipulated into being a good little footsoldier of Gemore, and he was worried about the city-destroying catastrophes that were apparently just *pretty common.*

That Grave Tangle was... yeah. It was like seeing a skyscraper that wanted to kill me.

He was safe now, and needed rest, but it wasn't going to happen. Not like this. He was jumping from speculating about Talents and levels, to thinking about the coinage of Gemore and the types of monsters and intelligent species he'd encountered – and not making progress on any of them.

So, Nathan did what he'd learned to do in these situations. He sat down on the bed, leaned against the wall, and thought about nothing for a while. Nothing needed to happen *now.* He started with the breathing, then just focused his attention on itself, nipping errant thoughts in the bud. He was better served doing nothing at this very moment than trying to figure out everything. He breathed, he centered himself, and paid close attention to nothing at all. It was time to live in the moment, and at the moment he was full, warm and comfortable.

Mid-tier Focused Mind 4 achieved!

Then, he was able to sleep.

Chapter 17

On the Town

Nathan woke to the smell of baked pastries. He reminded himself to get multiple sets of clothes that actually belonged to him, then put back on the borrowed clothes he'd been wearing for days, and emerged from his room.

Artha sat on one of the cushioned chairs in the lounge. He was talking to a bleary Vhala who'd apparently just emerged from her room. There was no Emerald or Wiam visible, and their doors were closed. Nathan's attention was drawn to a tray of pastries and a pitcher of milk set on the central table.

He hastened to break his fast, finding that the pastries were incredible – sweet and stuffed with honeycomb or fruit syrup. The milk was rich and warm, sweetened with honey. Either adventurers were treated like nobility, or the logistics of food preparation were different from what he expected. Well, Nathan wasn't about to complain.

He tuned into the conversation between Vhala and Artha. They were planning a shopping trip, and hoping to be able to afford various pieces of equipment with the money from the rescue. Apparently, they'd been saving for a more serious set of ranged armaments for Vhala and Wiam. Their goal was to be able to crack lower-level [Mage Armor].

Nathan joined in the conversation. "Can I come along? I have some basic supplies to buy. Everything to my name was provided by the Adventurer's Guild. Speaking of, do I have to return this?" He held up the bag he'd been given by the Vanguard which contained basic survival tools.

Vhala waved dismissively with a pastry. "No, it's yours. The Guild figures anybody who needs one deserves the extra possessions. Come along with us, we've got some time before Jolba will likely come along. If you're not looking for anything too magical, you'll be able to afford a lot with your share."

Soon enough, Vhala, Artha and Nathan left the remaining pastries on the table for whenever Emerald and Wiam awoke and departed the Adventurer's Guild. There was a cluster of shops nearby that focused on selling mixed high-quality mundane and magical goods to adventurers. When they picked up a travel pack for Nathan, he looked sadly at the displayed dimensional bags. They weren't even as expensive as you might expect – a pretty standard one would wipe out a bit more than half of Nathan's cash.

But it's a bag of holding! Magic that messes with the rules of reality! So cool. I'd be able to carry a hundred feet of rope without compromises! And a grappling hook.

But there was that line in his [Magic Resistance] that read, "weaker magical items degrade when in prolonged contact with you," and he wasn't willing to test that out yet. Especially on something that might *explode* when it failed. Maybe once he was an actual Adventurer and had more money to burn, or further Developed the Talent.

At a shop run by another short, orange-skinned woman, they picked up a couple sets of tough clothes – thick woolens in basic patterns that wouldn't rip easily and would stay warm through cold and wet weather, while also being loose enough for warm conditions. A thick blanket for cold and rough conditions completed the purchases before they set out to another shop.

On the way, Nathan asked, "Artha, can you explain the different species of Gemore? I've seen a lot of the short orange-skinned people, and don't know anything about them."

Artha nodded sagely. "They're called the Knulds. An old race, though not as old as humans. Pretty widespread, and their culture emphasizes appearance and poise. Knuld apparel is never the cheapest, but it's always high-quality, and they set the styles. The other peoples here are the Treeborn – four legged like me – and the various kinds of folk. Wolffolk, catfolk, birdfolk... We all tend to live in our own rural communities, but there's a neighborhood with many who have decided to come to the city from outside."

He snorted, twisting his lips in mild contempt. "While Giantsrest is a much bigger city than Gemore, they don't take kindly to any peoples but yours. There are a smattering of others here, often from far away. The orcish empire of Agon lies across the plains, but they think us uncivilized. A few Elementals as well, but their peoples are new, and very insular."

Nathan tried to formulate a question to that, but they soon arrived at their final stop, a blacksmith's shop run by a cousin of Vhala's named Beatred. The burly smith clapped her cousin on the shoulder and showed them around some of the enchanted gear for sale. The quality of the metalwork really impressed Nathan – the weapons and armor on display looked smooth and flawless. Many of the enchanted pieces had elaborate engravings and cutouts that looked like the product of a machine stop instead of a blacksmith's forge.

Nathan peeked into the working space in the back and saw that it was a lot more than just a forge. There was some kind of fly press back there, as well as a grinder and what looked like a drill press, though Nathan had no idea how they were powered. Magic maybe? Or just good old-fashioned muscle?

Artha guided Nathan to purchase a pair of sturdy knives, one with a wide blade the length of his hand, the other just a couple inches long. They weren't enchanted, but had a heft and balance to them that Nathan had never felt with kitchen knives.

They returned to the Guild to find Emerald sitting awkwardly next to a grizzled man with reddish-brown hair and a scruffy beard. He was dressed in a sharply embroidered but badly stained coat, taking sips from a jeweled flask. He looked worn down and tired, haggard in a way that seemed bone-deep.

Vhala inclined her head to him. "Jolba. Apologies for keeping you waiting."

The man stood and limped slightly towards the door, slipping the flask into his jacket. "I just arrived. Keep up the good work, all of ya. I'm here for this one." He waved a hand in Nathan's direction. "You ready to go? Best say your goodbyes."

Nathan hesitated, looking at the Giantraiders. It wasn't like he wasn't going to see them again. But he wouldn't be part of their crew anymore, however transient it had been. They'd been something he could trust in a strange world, answering his questions, giving advice and helping Nathan feel safe after his experience with Taeol. "Thank you all so much. I hope to talk to you all again. Artha, I look forward to your lessons."

The big elk-centaur nodded. "Yes, there are times for personal instruction during the Adventurer training. I will see you then, and if we are not around then Kadid should be able to help you."

Nathan turned to Emerald. "Good luck. I'll keep working on what you showed me. It doesn't matter what it's called if it does what I need."

The armored fighter nodded back resolutely.

Finally, Nathan turned to Vhala. He stepped forward and gave the stout black woman a hug. "Thank you for everything. In a few years let's talk about that plan again."

She returned the hug, then slapped his back and stepped back, a sharp grin on her face. "I'll wait for it."

Jolba led Nathan down the corridor and outside. They walked toward another building farther back in the complex. On the way, he detoured through a small park with a stretch of grass, a few trees and some heavy stones engraved with words. It felt like a small monument to some past war or tragedy. Jolba gestured toward a stone bench before he sat heavily.

He waited until Nathan sat next to him, gazing out towards the outer wall of Gemore and the taller ruins peeking over in the distance. "I don't like you joining the course like this. Sudraiel and I, we're trying to change the Adventurers with this training course. Teach some basic competence, enforce some standards on the next generation. Get Insights flowing, and help shape the teams of the next generation. Make the course into tradition, instead of just sending idiots out to die and calling the ones who survive Adventurers."

He paused after those words, staring off into the distance with a cruel twist to his lips. Jolba raised the flask and took another slug. After a moment, he passed it to Nathan. Nathan sniffed the opening. It smelled like fruity alcohol, and Nathan took a cautious sip. It was strong and sweet, like a peach brandy. He handed the flask back.

Jolba took it and continued. "I'm behind all that, and every exception undercuts it. And you Nathan, are an exception. Guildmistress told me that you've got two amazing Talents but are under level 27. And that I shouldn't ask where you're from, just toss you into the most promising team we've got."

He shrugged. "But this year, that means more than most. We just had to take somebody out from the Heirs last week, so that's where you're going. But I gotta caution, you're not stepping into a simple situation. You're old, low-level and your hands are soft. You ain't used to rough living, and you've got the guile of a beached fish, so I'd not do this without Sudraiel's order. But I won't throw a kid to a muckgrabber, so you deserve to know what's what. The Heirs are exactly what their name says, the inheritors of some of the strongest of Gemore – and their Insights."

He slipped the flask back into his jacket. "But they're also a right mess. Kia's adopted kid is trying to be the leader like his ma, but he's too busy being righteous and intimidating to think wise. The Caxol kid is smart, but is also a spoiled brat up her own braid on her magic. The Crusens twins are serious, but it's just them trying to be their *legendary* da. They all need to loosen up and figure out who they are, instead of being wrapped up in their parents' legends."

Jolba sighed, then turned to Nathan and waited until he looked back before continuing. "I'm telling you all this because you're older, and you've stared the ghoul in the eyes in a way that few of my trainees have. The Heirs are a bunch of horny youngsters who expect to be the heroes of the age. And they stand a half-decent chance, if they don't run towards the first stupid threat that comes along and get themselves killed. So. I don't want you to break the sky. I want you to keep the Heirs grounded until *they* can. Do you hear me?"

Nathan grimaced. Not because this was a bad idea – he could see where the Guildmistress was coming from. If Nathan was targeted by Giantsrest, might as well put him with the other targets so they could all be more easily protected. He also guessed that she wanted to tie him to Gemore with powerful comrades.

This sounds like college drama all over again. I think I might prefer to go fight one of the guardian golems outside Taeol's tower.

Still, he returned Jolba's sigh, and spoke. "Yeah, I think I can. Do you have any recommendations to make a good impression?"

Jolba eyed him for a moment, then seemed satisfied. "It's not hard. They didn't think the last guy was good enough, so they pushed him hard enough that he snapped. They'll test you, but if they think you're worth knowing, then it'll all flow downhill."

The grizzled man slapped his knees, then got up. "Time also flows, so let's get to it. Schedule is pretty simple: three meals in the dormitory, classroom work in the morning, then group training after lunch. There's time for individualized training after that, before dinner and sometimes after. We do bigger exercises at night sometimes, but not usually. The Giantraiders said they'd cover your individual training for the near future; is there anything else you want to ask about for that?"

Nathan sighed. "I was granted this language by spell, and it didn't teach me how to read. Can we take care of that during the morning classes?"

Jolba waved his hand. "I'll have a clerk take it over. Glad you don't need convincing that reading is important. The number of times I've had to convince kids without two decades that their job is more than killing things..." He shook his head. "We'll see it done. Anything else you think I need to know?"

Nathan hesitated, then decided.

If he wasn't told, then he needs to know. This, at least.

"There'll probably be agents of Giantsrest coming after me. I made a personal enemy of an archmage."

Jolba sighed, hand reaching for his flask before he stopped and smoothed his stubbled chin. "Sudraiel mentioned that's part of why we're tossing you into the Heirs. They're *all* targets. But if you pissed off an archmage..." He shrugged helplessly. "Be careful. It's not like there's much more I can do for security. To get to the training grounds you need to go through the entire Guild, and everybody knows everybody 'round here. And there's no teleportin' on the hill."

Then he stood, straightening his stained coat. "Well, let's go introduce you to your team. They should've just started lunch."

Chapter 18

Introductions to Last

Jolba led Nathan toward a low building further back in the complex, against the walls that braced the slope. It was up a staircase set into the steep hillside and surrounded by various bare areas that looked like training grounds. One looked like a shooting range with glowing targets, while another was a set of arenas with different kinds of environments – and yet a third appeared to be an obstacle course from hell, complete with deep pits and spiked walls, and a section that definitely involved dodging spinning blades. *Lovely.*

Jolba blithely ignored Nathan looking around nervously and walked straight into the low building, entering via a pair of arched double doors. There was a label over the doors, but Nathan *couldn't read it.* Dammit. They immediately turned left and entered a small cafeteria, filled with picnic-style tables, about half of which were occupied by people chowing down on food from a buffet on the other side of the room.

There were between four and six people at each table, and six tables of the nine were occupied. The people were as varied as the adventurers Nathan had seen before, and though the species were somewhat mixed, there was certainly a tendency for each table to be a majority of one species. The other thing Nathan noted as they entered was that the average age was rather young. He couldn't judge the other species in the room, but all of the humans looked like the college freshman from the introductory biochemistry classes Nathan had taught. Except they were pretty fit, and many were dressed in armor and had weapons at their sides.

Why are they armed? Didn't they just get out of class?

The room wasn't exactly quiet. Cutting through the buzz of background conversation was a shouting match, and Nathan and Jolba were walking towards the source. Two figures were standing chest-to-chest, glaring at each other. One was a wide black-skinned human in dark multi-layered chainmail, while the other was a wolfman in gleaming platemail looming over him.

Nathan tuned in to hear the wolfman, who was yelling louder. "... You will sit down unless you want me to sit you down!"

The black guy took a step backward, bristling. He opened his mouth. "You can't...!"

The rest of his words were cut off as Jolba strode forward. Suddenly Jolba's presence *filled* the room, and it was impossible to not pay attention to the grizzled man. Even the people in the far corners of the room turned in unison, and all conversation cut out.

Jolba stepped up to the two young men, his voice slow and resonant. "You bicker as sparrows. Remember that one day you may stand shoulder to shoulder against the End. Be seated."

The wolfman in shining armor opened his mouth, but Jolba silenced him with a look. The man in chainmail retreated to a table on the side of the room, while the wolfman sat at the table in the center.

Then, Jolba's presence quieted, and he was again just a man in a stained jacket. He looked down at the wolfman in shining plate sitting at the table with three others. His voice was softer, but tinged with scorn. "Khachi, you know better." He glanced toward Nathan. "I am here with a new fifth for your team. This is Nathan. He's got two powerful Talents and can contribute more than you know. He's also from far away, and so does not know you. Please introduce yourselves."

The wolfman in gleaming plate armor twisted around to appraise Nathan more fully, a hint of canine teeth visible behind thin, colorless lips. His face was fairly humanoid, except with outward jutting jaws and enlarged nostrils. Hair of a rich brown color crept down to his eyebrows and around his cheeks, hiding sallow gray skin.

His voice wasn't as deep when he spoke normally and was rough around the edges. "Definitely not from close by, and you have the look of a Giantsrester. I'm Khachi Cordavia, worshiper of the god Deiman and son of Kia Cordavia of the Guardians of Gemore. I lead the Heirs."

A snort from across the table interrupted him, and the handsome man sitting there broke in. "He's declared himself leader, at least. Gotta see if he can wear it as well as he does that stack of steel he calls armor. I'm Aarl Crusens, son of Stanel Crusens. This is my sister Sarah." He elbowed the lanky teenager sitting next to him, who rolled her eyes and scooted down the bench away from her brother, not taking her narrowed eyes off Nathan.

They were certainly related and looked about the same age. Coppery skinned with large, dark eyes and pitch-black hair, the pair radiated a serious intensity. Combined with their lithe muscularity and metal-inlaid leather armor, their presence was almost magnetic and definitely attractive. They were also both definitely under twenty years old, so Nathan wasn't going to follow that line of thought any further.

"And then there's me, of course!" spoke the last person at the table. She was clearly a mage, wearing green robes embroidered with spiky light-blue thread that seemed to writhe against itself. Her hair was gathered in a reddish-brown braid that was pulled forward over one shoulder, and her skin was pale and dusted with freckles. "I'm the one you really need to watch out for, since I'll blow you up! I'm Stella Caxol, and my parents are on Khachi's mom's team." She gave him a sly wink.

You know, I'm glad I got to see the Guardians of Gemore in action against that Grave Tangle, otherwise I'd be confused why they were leaning on their parents' names so much. So Khachi's mom was the paladin in shining armor who went toe-to-toe with the Grave Tangle, and Stella's parents were also on the team. Both mages maybe?

They kept their eyes on Nathan as he gauged his next move. They weren't giving much away, good or bad. Well, Nathan had made friends in the past by being earnest and straightforward, and this time he had a skill to help out!

"It's very nice to meet you all. I haven't had lunch yet, so I'm going to grab some food. It's all new to me, so every meal is an adventure of one kind or another."

He bid goodbye to Jolba, who had watched the introductions warily. As the teacher walked away and Nathan turned to get his food, something slapped against his leg like a pool noodle. It felt like magic. And if it'd been strong enough for *him* to feel, it probably would have knocked most other people off their feet. He glanced back at the table, where all four members of the Heirs still watched him. Stella had a surprised look on her face, and Nathan just threw back his head and laughed as he walked away.

As he collected food from the plentiful buffet, Nathan considered his next move. The Heirs were clearly testing him, trying to decide if he was good enough to let into their little elite club. And the presumption was clearly *no*. It was so dumb, playing status games with people the age of those he'd *taught*. But it would happen one way or another, as long as he wanted to join the Heirs.

Which he did – the Guildmistress had gift-wrapped him powerful allies, if he could just deal with some stupid power dynamics. From what had been said, it seemed they lacked direction, and had potential without *purpose*. It so happened that Nathan had purpose to spare and was happy to share it around.

But if he was going to play their game, at least he could do it on his terms instead of theirs – lean on his strengths, and talk about the true life-and-death experiences he'd had in the days since coming here. Jolba had seemed to imply the Heirs were a bit pampered, and true life-or-death stories fighting Giantsrest would likely hold their interest. Other than that, if he played along as one of the "gang," they would be unlikely to really get serious in their harassment.

As he walked back, he workshopped his response. Getting closer to the table and depositing his plate of roasted meat and stewed vegetables, he put forward his best effort in a wry tone as he sat next to the young mage. "Good thing you didn't try that as I was coming back with food Stella – I might have dropped the entire plate on you."

It got a chuckle out of the sister of the two siblings across the table.

What was her name, Sarah? Yeah, Sarah.

She seemed to be enjoying Stella's uncertainty over her spell not provoking the expected response. Khachi also eyed him with uncertainty as Nathan sat next to him and began eating as if the entire situation was the most normal thing in the world.

Their plates were already half-eaten, and they finished them off as Nathan wolfed down his food. The pastries in the morning had been good, but this food was well-spiced and as filling as any Nathan had ever had, and very effective at refilling his Stamina.

As he dug in, Aarl asked a question. "Jolba said you were from far away. Where?"

Stella broke in, speaking scornfully. "I bet it's a little hamlet a few weeks away, a bundle of cottages behind a dinky palisade. With what, like a hundred people?"

Nathan took a moment to respond, savoring a bite of some nicely marbled meat. "It's a country called the United States of America. Doubt you've heard of it. I didn't leave it by choice, but here I am."

Aarl shot questioning looks to Stella and Khachi, and they both shook their heads. He looked back to Nathan with brows raised. "United States – sounds like there's history there. What is it like?"

Nathan considered his answer for a moment before replying, leaning on

[Earnestness] skill to pull off a dramatic touch. He had to appear unique to seem equal to his new teammates. "It's a country of hundreds of millions of people, most knowing only peace. For all of our petty evils, we enforced peace and funded knowledge with no law declaring one above another. I hope to go back one day, once I've explored Gemore and toppled the towers of Giantsrest for their *evil*." He delivered the last line with a snarl, savagely tearing at the next bite of meat.

Low-tier Earnestness 6 achieved!

The Heirs were various degrees of surprised by his display. Stella only furrowed her brow, while Khachi rocked back, clearly perturbed. He spoke, suddenly hesitant in the face of Nathan's clear anger. "You speak of Giantsrest with true hatred. They are our foes true enough, but what drives you to speak such words?"

The question seemed to be asked with honest curiosity, and Nathan felt he had an opening. "Only what a would-be-chattel would know. It's not something you can forget, to face somebody who wants to make you a *thing*." Nathan's face twisted in a sneer, finding that the memory of Taeol made his expression less performative than he'd intended.

Nathan's anger colored his next words, and he met the eyes of each member of the Heirs as he continued. "Giantsrest is despicable, deeming itself above all. An archmage tried to convert me, and then control me. I broke his bones because violence is the only counterargument against that violation. Giantsrest would have everybody here in chains if it could. I'll burn their city to the ground and salt the earth."

There was a moment of silence as they processed his words. Then Sarah quietly asked the question they'd all been thinking. "What was fighting an archmage like?"

Nathan answered quickly. "Terrifying. I caught him off-guard and he still almost killed me, despite my advantages against magic. I wasn't able to kill him, but I broke his nose and knee before he teleported away. His name is Taeol dho Droxol, and he'll probably send people after me. From what I hear, you're all already targets of Giantsrest because of who your parents are. I've got a blood-feud with an archmage, so I'm in the same boat. I'll watch out for you if you watch out for me."

Low-tier Earnestness 7 achieved!

They were clearly off-balance, not expecting his serious turn of phrase and offer of camaraderie. Stella caught onto something he'd said, near to her interests as it was. "What do you mean, your advantage against magic?"

Nathan obviously looked around. "Let's not talk about that here. I've got some pretty unique Talents, don't want to talk about them somewhere they'll spread. I'm sure I'll have an opportunity to show you later. Anyway, I'm new here, this is my first day in Gemore. What can I expect from the training?"

Khachi was the first to speak, though Aarl looked like he'd been about to answer. "Next we will train as a group. After that is individual training. Do you have anybody coming to tutor you?" He asked the question as a challenge, clearly expecting Nathan to lack a tutor.

Nathan nodded. "Yup, I do."

Khachi frowned, but continued. "For the group training, I am thinking of a round at the target range, where Stella and Sarah shoot and we dodge. Nathan, are you feeling like target practice? I can heal you if you get hurt." His mouth curved up in a predatory grin, which had a new meaning on somebody with a canine snout and teeth.

Given the expectations, Nathan didn't have a choice in his response. "Definitely! I've actually been working on a Talent Development that could only be aided by somebody hitting me with as much magic as possible." He grinned in Stella's direction. "Do you think you can manage that?"

She *harrumphed*, leaning back. "Be careful what you ask for, you just might get it."

Aarl wiped his brow theatrically. "If you're volunteering to be the one chewing down fireballs, I'm all for it. Those things can blow through a solid wall."

His sister jeered at him. "That's just because you're slow. Get faster with your footwork skills and it won't be a problem."

He eyed her darkly. "Arrogant, coming from somebody who doesn't have to dodge fireballs as training twice a week. We should practice melee more often."

Stella broke in, smiling sweetly and speaking in a sing-song voice. "But that's not how we work! Between me and Sarah, we have the ranged advantage! If you chunks of muscle can keep the enemies at bay, we can take 'em down. And steal all the levels!" Then her eyes tracked to Nathan, and she pouted theatrically. "But if we've got yet a third close-up fighter, then maybe we'll need to change the tactics. *Annoying*."

Khachi spoke, clearly trying to re-establish his leadership. "We'll have to see how Nathan fights. It sounds like he's had combat experience already, so I'm sure he can do something. At least it sounds like he'll be better than that last idiot."

Nathan had reservations about how fairly the last guy had been treated – but raising that point didn't serve a purpose. He didn't have enough context to understand what was going on with the social dynamics here, and he didn't want to poison his relationship with the Heirs over guesses. As he mused, Nathan noticed that the people around them had started to get up and deposit their plates on a table next to the mostly-bare buffet.

Sarah looked around. "Looks like it's time to head out. Welcome to the Heirs, Nathan, I hope you fit in."

You mean you hope I measure up to all of you. We'll just have to see how that goes.

He responded in an upbeat tone. "Together we'll journey onwards and upwards."

Aarl slapped the table as he stood. "I like that! Onwards and upwards indeed."

~

Status of Nathan Lark:
Permanent Talent 1: High-tier Magic Resistance 10
Permanent Talent 2: Mid-tier Regeneration 6
Talent 3: None

Class: Antimagic Brawler level 25
Stamina: 350/350
Brawler's Indifference
Antimagic Blows

Utility skills:
Mid-tier Focused Mind 4
Low-tier Earnestness 7
Low-tier Sprinting 6
Low-tier Spellsense 5
Low-tier Notice 7
Low-tier Identify 2

Chapter 19

Training Magic

As they stood and deposited their plates, Nathan took note of the Heirs' weaponry. Stella bore a tall and knotted staff, deeply carved with runes, and with each knot inlaid with a glowing gem. Khachi picked up a polished steel kite shield that must have weighed at least forty pounds and a hammer that looked fit for demolishing walls. Interestingly, Sarah and Aarl didn't have any weapons, just wide pouches they wore like forward-facing fanny packs. Nathan would have bet dollars to donuts that those were bags of holding.

As they trooped outside, other trainees headed towards various training areas, with Jolba and a few other older adventurers talking to groups or supervising various activities. The Heirs ignored them all and strode around the side of the building, towards the very back corner of the Guild complex.

Another team was also moving in that direction, but they saw the Heirs approaching and decided to go somewhere else, ceding the private range of sand to the Heirs without a word or overt glance. The area didn't have fancy magical targets, consisting simply of a walled rectangle floored in coarse sand. The targets set against a dirt berm against the far wall were a series of X-shapes rather than bullseyes, but served the same purpose.

Nathan followed Khachi and Aarl out onto the center of the course while Stella and Sarah closed the gate and stayed back. Nathan stepped to the left, took off his shirt and sat down on the sand. He didn't recognize the exact meaning of the hand gesture that Aarl threw his way, but it was pretty clearly something along the lines of, "what the hell, man?"

He gestured toward Stella. "I want to try eating a fireball, and it's easier like this. Go ahead, shoot."

With those words Nathan focused on Stella, opening his senses to get everything he could out of what would follow. Nathan used [Focused Mind] to shape his attention, mimicking the state of mind that had helped him gain [Notice]. With a moment of stilled breath, everything Nathan observed gained a level of definition.

Stella shrugged, looked at Khachi, and said, "I'll start off with half a blow since I don't want to knock your head off within an hour of meeting you. That's the sort of treatment you earn." Then, with a flicking gesture she sent a globe of fire sailing toward Nathan.

She didn't speak the name of the spell like the Giantsrest mages do. Huh.

It was faster, more concentrated than the fireball that the Guardian Golem had thrown at him, but also smaller and not nearly as bright. Nathan barely had a chance to blink before the burning, ping-pong ball sized orb impacted his chest, and flame washed over him. He tried to pick apart the knot of the spell as it detonated, but the spellwork blew apart as it touched him. Nathan was left with the feeling of fire and force mana raging against his bare skin, trying to burn him and blow him backward.

Nathan failed to separate the two before his back impacted the ground, a burning sensation lingering in his chest. Nathan felt mana at play there and picked it apart, feeling a hot, fizzling sensation. It reminded him of the popping of a fire, with its frequent and spontaneous bursts of heat. It was not very pleasant, but the sensation faded quickly and left him with a mild burn on his chest. He healed it with a quick application of Stamina, sitting back up to find the rest of the Heirs watching him closely.

Khachi had taken a step toward him, his hand beginning to gather faint yellow light. But then he saw Nathan's reddened skin fade before his eyes and he paused, suddenly confused. He opened his mouth to speak. "... You're not a spellcaster. But you healed yourself. And that fireball was... weird. Stella?"

She shook her head, frowning. "It didn't explode right."

Nathan shrugged. "Seems so." He looked down at his chest, where burnt, shiny skin was healing over, scattered hair growing back at incredible speed. He was confused about this, because that wasn't how burns worked. If there had been enough heat to burn him, that heat should have stayed around and continued to burn until he'd cooled the area down with water or something. But as soon as he got rid of the fire mana, the heat had also gone away.

Huh. The heat itself is magical, not just the mana that made it?

He looked back up at Stella. "I think I'll need a few more to figure this out properly. Can you try throwing it a little slower, and maybe make it detonate slower?"

Stella looked bemused. "That's not very easy, only a few mages in Gemore could modify a spell like that." She paused for effect. "Luckily, I'm one of them. But I'll only do it if you tell me what you're doing."

Nathan responded with a wide grin. "You'll see. Gimme another. I'll spell it out for you if you can't figure it out."

Aarl groaned. "Great. Now there's two of them. At least they can be smug at each other."

After a moment of pouting, Stella tossed another fireball at him. This one was a bit larger, a bit more diffuse, and flew a bit slower. It hit Nathan's chest and burned for a moment before detonating. But the detonation was weak, the fireball's structure starting to fall apart the moment it touched Nathan's skin.

He sat back up, thinking about the spell. He'd *felt* the weave of it this time, how the mana had been loosely woven together. When it hit him, the force had expanded out to create a shockwave. That had activated and scattered the pattern of fire mana, generating a blast of explosive heat and pressure across a wide area. It was like a fuel-air bomb, where an initial blast scattered fuel across a wide area, which then ignited to cause the real destruction.

Low-tier Identify 3 achieved!

Neat! Nathan wouldn't be able to reproduce the spell, and he also definitely couldn't grasp how to design a spell like that from the ground up. But he understood how it worked, and how to make it fail.

Ahead of him, Stella frowned, her mouth lopsided and surprisingly cute as she glared at where the fireball had detonated.

"And again!" She hucked another fireball at him, just as diffuse as the previous one.

Nathan sharpened his magical senses, waiting for the exact moment he could interact with the spell, preparing himself to pull apart the tendrils of force mana that provided the initial detonation. The fireball impacted his navel and guttered as he scattered the key threads of force mana. He was left with an uncomfortable ball of fire and force slowly dissipating against his belly. Nathan pulled on the mana the way he'd done with Taeol's [Chains of Restraint], and the hissing ball fizzed away to nothing.

At this point Stella's frown had turned into a sort of delighted puzzlement. "I have never seen anything like that before. Hold on, let me try something. You can heal yourself, right?"

Nathan nodded, all of a sudden apprehensive as the short mage stalked toward him, her smile growing into something maniacal.

"Give me your hand." She grabbed the tentatively offered limb in one hand and pointed with the other. A thin jet of flame shot from her pointer finger and she brought it toward Nathan's outstretched arm. "Break this spell, I want to see how it works!"

Nathan flinched, almost pulling his arm out of her grasp, but Stella held on and touched the edge of the fire against his arm, near his wrist. Nathan felt the mana as soon as it contacted him, a concentrated and surprisingly complex working of fire. Nathan focused intently on the spell, hoping he could keep Stella from lopping off his hand with her magical cutting torch. The spell seemed dedicated to keeping the flame as concentrated as possible, so that was the aspect of the spell that Nathan attacked.

As the torch contacted his skin, the flames barely felt warm, the major sensation being the popping energy of fire mana. The angle was shallow, and even without his magic resistance, the fire would have burnt him but not scorched deeply.

Oh, she's not actually *trying to hurt me. She's just not great at communicating when she's excited.*

More methodically, he pulled apart the weave that kept the flames concentrated. The jet became more diffuse before the threads snapped back into place. Nathan looked up, and saw Stella staring intently at the jet, obviously exerting her own magical control to stabilize the spell. His own eyes narrowed.

Oh, it's like that, is it? You might be the mage, but I'm the antimage. Any spell you make, I can break.

Nathan pushed back, destabilizing the working even as Stella tried to force it back into shape. His Talent's basic function protected him from harm and made his manipulations of the spell inherently disruptive. Even though it was Stella's mana and she had the advantage, they fought for control of the little jet of fire. After a minute of back and forth, Nathan fully understood the nature of the spell, and how it worked. Around Stella's finger was a portion of the spell that channeled air into the flame jet.

Fire mana needs an oxidizer to burn? Then I guess the fireball working like a fuel-air explosive makes even more sense. That's both reassuring and very weird. It's magic, why does it follow the *rules of chemical reactions? I guess it would also be weird if it didn't.*

Nathan abandoned his manipulation of the guiding magic and attacked the air inflow-control, causing the fire itself to flicker. When Stella tried to stabilize that portion of the spell, Nathan took advantage of her diverted attention, disrupting the part of the spell that provided fire mana.

Stella let go of the spell and stepped back, letting out a long breath and slumping her shoulders. Then, she looked up and threw her arms to the sky in a pose of triumph. "[Mana Intuition] went up! Dragon's breath, that's awesome." She turned to Nathan, cheeks flushed. "Okay, that was cool. Thanks for going along with it. Is there anything else you want to try?" She grinned and winked, throwing Nathan off a bit.

He took a second to respond, examining the slightly singed hair on his arm. "Do you have any other mana types? I'm trying to Develop my [Magic Resistance] Talent, and I think I need exposure to as many mana types as possible. If not, I'd like to play with a spell that's pure force."

Stella's energy and grin dialed back a few stages. "No, I don't have any other types of mana except Fire and Force. Yet. But hold some patience and I might be able to set something up. I've never heard of a Talent like yours. It's amazing!" She gave Nathan a hand, boosting him to his feet before continuing. "Oh, and I know you're from far-off, but don't tell anybody what types of mana I use or that skill name I mentioned. Supposed to be secret, though if you're on the team it won't be a problem."

She proceeded to cast another spell wordlessly. A sheet of translucent blue force appeared in front of Nathan, about the size of a large shield.

Nathan walked over to it, inspecting the floating magic. It looked more like the force constructs he'd seen from the Guardians of Gemore than anything from Giantsrest. Nathan had seen much the same spell cast by the Giantsrest mages at the battle of the ford, but it hadn't looked like this. Theirs had been smaller and completely transparent.

Differences in spellcasting style maybe? Stella doesn't speak the spell names aloud as she casts. I can see that providing a tactical advantage but maybe being harder to learn.

He poked it with his finger, which let him feel the broad, flat bands of mana that formed the shield. They bent under his finger, and the pane of force audibly *cracked.*

Nathan nodded to himself, considering the feeling of force mana. It was massless but immovable, as if its position were immutable. Pushing on it from any angle felt like pushing on the edge of a knife that never quite cut you. That contrasted with fire mana, which he'd had more than enough experience with during the mental wrestling match over Stella's torch. Fire was an ever-changing popping sensation combined with heat – like scorching hot pop-rocks. Not a very pleasant sensation, but it was nice to easily be able to identify it.

Low-tier Spellsense 6 achieved!

With another movement, Nathan traced one of the major weaves of mana in the force block, which crumbled. The entire pane of force shuddered and collapsed into nothing. The other members of the Heirs had been halfheartedly stretching, but mostly just watching Nathan and Stella do their thing. At Nathan's casual destruction of the [Force Block], Khachi looked as if he'd finally solved a riddle.

"So that's how you wounded an archmage through his [Mage Armor]. Break the magic, break the man. What'd he hit you with?"

Nathan hissed, rubbing his previously-absent left arm. "A [Disintegrate], which took off my left arm. He waved the appendage in question at Khachi, who looked aghast. "I grew it back though!"

The wolfman worked his jaw for a moment, exposing some impressive teeth as he reconsidered Nathan. "That's one zombie of a healing Talent. It's gotta be a Talent. Does it heal non-magical wounds too?"

Nathan nodded. "With the Insight I have, I don't think it matters where the injury comes from."

Khachi stroked his elongated chin, whistling appreciatively and looking thoughtful. After a moment, he grinned quite wolfishly. "In that case, want to spar?"

Chapter 20

Bumps and Bruises

Nathan sighed. He had been hoping that the anti-magic demonstration had allayed their worries, and they wouldn't test him anymore. Maybe this spar was Khachi trying to get a fully-rounded grasp of Nathan's capabilities. And not just beat his face in to demonstrate his superiority.

If only I had confidence in that.

As much as Nathan wasn't looking forward to getting smacked around by the enormous wolfman, it wasn't a big surprise.

He turned to fully face him. "Sure, but I have to warn you that the first time I seriously fought anybody was less than a week ago. I've had luck catching mages by surprise, but I'm not going to stand up well to somebody like you."

Khachi and Aarl looked happier at Nathan's earnest assessment. He noticed that they'd both been tense, apprehensive because of his anti-magic demonstration. This was probably a good time to clear that up. "I don't think I'm ever going to be as good a frontline fighter as you guys. I definitely need to work on it, but I've got skills for fast movement and dealing with magic. I'm a mage-hunter, but against non-mages, a lot of what I have is useless."

Sarah pursed her lips. "Not all adventuring parties fight people; many focus on dungeons and monsters. What *else* can you do, where anti-magic is not as useful?"

Nathan's response was easy. "I'm not familiar with many monsters in this area, but my guess is the scary ones use magic in some way. The Grave Tangle knocked everybody over with just its magical aura, which I ignored. I also saw through the magical stealth of a pack of earth stalkers yesterday." He shrugged. "But maybe those were outliers. How many magical traps or dangers are present in dungeons?"

Sarah shared a look with Aarl, who shrugged and wiggled his eyebrows at her. She nodded as if acknowledging a point and spoke again. "Fair enough. Now, are you two going to hit each other or what? Unless you want a weapon, Nathan?"

I have no idea how to use any weapons but my fists, and I'd prefer not to look like an absolute rookie.

Nathan shook his head and squared off against Khachi. He considered putting his shirt back on but decided against potentially damaging his new clothes. He took a deep breath as they both set their feet, sizing up his opponent. He didn't expect to take the big guy down, or even get in any significant shots. Khachi was dressed in immaculate plate and bore a large hammer – and an even bigger shield. His hope here was to be slippery, maybe get behind the big warrior or trip him up.

He's in full plate. That's gotta be heavy as hell. Maybe I can just push him over.

Nathan noticed Khachi crouch slightly as if to lunge, and Nathan took a cautious step backward. They were more than ten feet apart. There was no way somebody covered in that much metal could cover that distance. Nathan's next thought was interrupted by the steel wall of Khachi's shield impacting his chin with a *crunch*. Darkness fuzzed his vision and he was airborne briefly before slamming into the ground, wind partially knocked out of him.

It hurt like a bitch, but thanks to [Brawler's Indifference] he wasn't completely stunned. His jaw felt wobbly, and he rolled to his feet and spat out a mouthful of blood, before staggering to the side and falling over again as the world tilted.

Oh that's a nasty concussion.

"I think you got me. I'm gonna need a minute." Nathan was *not* a fan of how much his voice slurred, and speaking sent intense pain through his jaw, even through the recognizable numbness of broken bones. His hands came up, and Nathan tentatively poked at his face. Yeah, that was a badly broken jaw. *And* a concussion. Would [Regeneration] work on head wounds? Did he want to use it for head wounds? Well, it was probably better to try it now, under controlled circumstances.

Heh, controlled head wounds. No such thing.

Nathan pictured a textbook diagram of a brain, unbruised and surrounded by healthy meninges. Then, he shoved that image at his own head along with

Stamina. Stamina drained at an alarming rate, but over the course of a few heartbeats, a mental fog he hadn't even noticed cleared away. His jaw was *also* killing him, and he became aware that Khachi was leaning over him, hand glowing as he finished a prayer.

"... Grace be granted, healing be sure." Khachi pressed his hand onto Nathan's shoulder, and Nathan felt the magic try to take hold before sliding off, accomplishing nothing. It had the same feel as the magic he'd felt from Kia, a warm prickling feeling that Nathan was powerless to accept. In that moment, he almost reconsidered his decision to improve his Magic Resistance to be more potent. Maybe healing was more important. And [Regeneration] was taking a *while.*

Nathan started coughing up blood as Khachi grew more anxious and chagrined. "What do I do? Can you heal it?"

Nathan sat up, spitting to the side and feeling very pressured. Why was he having to reassure people when *he* was the one who'd been injured? "Yeah, give me a minute."

He felt delicately at his jaw. There was a sharp bone protruding into his mouth, and the feeling of his tongue caressing a shard of his own bone did not feel great.

Ahhh that feels very wrong.

But he could make the problem go away, so Nathan closed his eyes and crossed his legs, sharpening his mind. His jaw was *definitely* misaligned, and he didn't want it healing that way.

This is getting to me on a visceral level that's hard to ignore.

He tamped down on the rising sickness and focused on the correct jaw structure. He told the bones not just to heal but also to shift into the right position, and only to heal after they'd finished moving. It was unpleasant, Nathan's attention barraged by discomfort and the blood that continued to fill his mouth. But he was patient, breathing through his nose and dedicating his entire attention to re-aligning his jawbones before healing the skin and fusing the bones together. After a minute – that felt much longer – Nathan opened his eyes to more blue boxes.

Mid-tier Focused Mind Rank 5 achieved!

Mid-tier Regeneration Rank 7 achieved!

So getting possibly-crippling-wounds also helps with ranks. The smallest hurrah.

The rest of the Heirs were grouped around him, looking various degrees of aloof or concerned. Stella ventured a question first. "Are you alright?"

Nathan cracked his jaw. Thankfully, it was back to normal. "Yeah, I think so. Anybody got some water? My mouth is full of blood." Sarah handed him a waterskin, and Nathan washed himself and spat a few times, gargling and then drinking to get the sticky feeling out of his throat. Then he handed the water-skin back to Sarah with a nod of thanks, before standing and turning to Khachi.

This is going to need to be handled carefully.

"You sure got me with that one, I didn't know you could move that quick. Nice. But I got a question, does your healing re-align bones or just heal things as they are?"

Khachi scuffed the ground with his foot, looking away. "It depends on the prayer. Mom always taught me to check for misaligned bones before healing somebody."

His posture told Nathan that he hadn't used a prayer that realigned bones this time. But at least the big wolffolk's first response had been to panic and try to help, instead of just laughing at Nathan.

Nathan nodded. "It's a good thing I was immune to your healing, or I probably wouldn't be able to talk right now. We'd have to carefully re-break my jaw, set it and re-heal it. Not fun for anybody. Just be careful with that next time – just because somebody's hurt it doesn't mean healing them is always the right action, yeah?"

Khachi looked up at him and grimaced. "You are right. It was just... you were hurt, it was my fault and I could help, so I didn't think about it as I should have."

Nathan shrugged. "No harm, no foul."

As much as I got my face beat in, I think I won that round in the social arena.

Khachi nodded. "Shall we go again?" His eyes had narrowed, and looked a bit predatorily at Nathan. Maybe Nathan had rubbed his nose in it too much.

To Nathan's surprise, Stella came to his rescue. "No, definitely not. Nathan is going to sit down, and you slackers are going to do the training you were *supposed* to be doing. Sarah, make it a good one." She glared at Khachi.

Stella guided Nathan to a set of benches at the back of the range, where he sat and watched Sarah hurling weapons at Aarl and Khachi. Her hands flick-ered in and out of her pouch, each time a new weapon in hand. They all quickly went downrange at the two fighters. The variety of weapons was amaz-ing, as well as the speed and accuracy at which they flew. Nathan noticed that all of the weapons were blunted. Nonetheless, arrows, hatchets, knives and javelins all went clattering downrange.

If you can dodge a wrench...

Aarl acted similarly, pulling out weapons from his own pouch with each movement to counter his sister's attacks. He swatted a hatchet from the air with one of his own, then produced a small shield to catch an arrow before sidestepping a javelin. It would have been more efficient just keeping the shield, but the slim man was clearly practicing swapping weapons for each threat.

Meanwhile, Khachi's job looked easier. He was hunkering behind his shield, shifting it to catch and deflect ranged projectiles. It definitely wasn't trivial, as Nathan noticed that whenever he took his eyes off Sarah, she'd hurl something into the sky, so it would come down atop his head unless he adjusted his shield or sidestepped. She also sent the occasional projectile at his feet, forcing him to slam the shield down or skip backwards. It was almost comical, seeing the enormous warrior in plate armor shuffling in place as blurs of metal came from multiple angles.

Nathan's Stamina was at 95/350, so he asked Stella if she had any snacks. She smirked, reached into a pocket of her robes and handed him a set of pastries that looked identical to the ones Nathan had eaten that morning. They were pristine and still warm.

He looked at her robe with surprise. "Better keep me away from that. I think I'll break any magic items that I'm too close to."

Stella looked at him with alarm. She'd been edging a bit closer to him, but reversed course and scooted further down the bench. "Hear me, that Talent's powerful but I'm definitely not jealous anymore. Can't be healed, can't use magic items? Not even as a joke." She shuddered a bit.

They sat in silence for a little while, watching as Sarah finally emptied her pouch of practice weapons. Once she was finished, they gathered up the projectiles while Khachi healed a few bruises and scrapes. Nathan hopped up to help, grabbing a few daggers and hatchets. They were all badly scuffed and dented, more like discards from a forge than actual weapons. He watched Sarah dump the weapons into the pouch, shaking his head. The item must've sorted and cleaned them as well, since she wasn't being careful to avoid getting sand in there. Wild. He handed off his gathered items.

Sarah looked up at him. She'd been the most aloof thus far, but Nathan didn't get a sense of dislike. Merely that she hadn't taken the lead here. "Thanks. Do you want to go? I can go gentle."

Nathan considered. He *could* do it. Being willing to get clobbered again would probably improve his reputation with the Heirs. But he just didn't want to. His jaw didn't hurt anymore, but the memory of the pain was still there, and he just didn't want to take more risks. Not today. So he blew out a breath and responded. "Thanks for the offer, but not today. There's something I want to talk to Artha about before I try dodging things."

Sarah cocked her head at him. "Artha Footspeak? Stanel, our dad, says he's one to trust true. What's he teaching you?"

Nathan blinked. "Yeah, that's him. The Giantraiders saved me from Giantsrest and he's teaching me the Path of Rage."

The black-haired girl was clearly surprised. "That's rare." She turned to call to Aarl, who was gathering javelins that'd flown past him during the target practice. "Hey Aarl, don'cha know Nathan's getting taught the Path of Rage by Artha Footspeak?"

Aarl grunted, looking Nathan up and down again. "That's a surprise. They guard those Insights. He'll have to answer to the clan for that." He turned to Nathan. "What could have made him agree to that?"

Nathan scratched the back of his neck. "If it's so valuable, I don't know if that's something I should share." To his surprise, everybody seemed to accept that explanation. The culture here really did get behind hoarding Insights. And disapproved of even the *hint* of prying them out of people.

He and Stella sat and watched as the rest of the Heirs resumed their practice. After just a few minutes, Stella sat back up and started throwing magic at Aarl and Khachi, forcing them to dodge or shelter from various small bolts of fire or force. Nathan thought she was picking on Khachi, and he was being slowly driven down the range by a rain of firebolts and one small fireball impacting his shield.

After a bit, they called another break, sitting around and drinking water.

Stella broke the silence first. "Sorry for trying to trip you back in the dining hall. I thought... well."

Nathan shrugged again. Holding onto grudges against these people wouldn't get him anything. They'd been jerks, but the culture here seemed rooted in proving one's strength. And honestly, it made sense. If you were Adventurers going up against Giantsrest and monsters, you had a lot more excuse to be macho than high school football players did.

And before I can really join their team they have to see me as an equal, somebody just as strong and with as much potential as they have.

"You thought I wasn't the equal of you and the other Heirs. But I'm heir to a tradition as weighty as they come. In my land we stand on the shoulders of giants, on our predecessors who reached the stars. It lets us see farther yet, plumb the mysteries of the universe. It's something I dedicated my life to, and now I will apply that legacy here."

Low-tier Earnestness Rank 8 achieved!

There was a beat of silence before the moment was ruined by Aarl's quiet question. "What's a star?"

Nathan blew a raspberry, thinking about how to explain. "It's something beyond the sky. We can see them from my home."

Soon enough the group training was over, and it was time for individual mentoring.

Chapter 21

Dodging Disadvantage

The Heirs exited the private training ground to find the other adventurers milling around in an open area, waiting on their individual mentors. Nathan spotted Artha easily and started walking in his direction, but was stopped by Khachi holding out a hand to interrupt him.

"Today we're having food with our families. Maybe another day you will share our dinner, but for today, we will see you back in our rooms. I have inscribed our meeting, Nathan."

With that, the big wolfman turned and walked away with the rest of the Heirs. Aarl and Sarah approached a wiry older man who was clearly their father, with the same coppery skin, dark hair and sculpted face. Khachi and Stella walked together, joking as they strode towards the familiar figures that Nathan had last seen incinerating the Grave Tangle.

Three of the five members of the Guardians of Gemore stood together, a wide buffer of open space around them. Kia was in full plate armor, with the giant greatsword stuck diagonally on her back. Her helmet was off, but it was hanging off her belt and in easy reach. Nathan watched Khachi approach and respectfully greet her, and she responded by jerking her head for him to follow.

Meanwhile, Stella was greeted by hugs from both of the casters of the Guardians. Nathan remembered the spell he'd been pretty sure involved a *fusion reaction*, and eyed the soft-faced man who'd cast the spell. From here he seemed shy, even effacing, while the foxfolk at his side was more effusive, cupping Stella's cheeks and asking her a question.

Stella's response involved pointing at Nathan. All three turned to face him. Nathan stopped watching them and sped up to meet Artha. He needed to keep in mind that the parents of his new "friends" could beat the pants off a monster the size of a *mountain.* One whose attacks had broken the *sound barrier*.

No wonder they wanted to keep most people at arm's length. That kind of power was bound to make nearly any social situation difficult. How did you talk to somebody when their parents were WMDs? Forget the trope of a dad threatening people with a shotgun, this would be like dealing with the daughter of a superhero.

That's really not a terrible metaphor here. They're even named like a superhero team.

With that in mind, he went to meet Artha. Talking to Artha again was *easy*. He didn't have to judge the effect of every word, or worry so much about his image. He'd fought for Artha, and Artha had fought for him. Back on Earth, Nathan wouldn't have any idea what that *meant*. But here, now, it meant that he wasn't quite so worried about how mere words would cause the big elk-centaur to think of him. It was surprisingly restful, to have that feeling.

So, when Artha took him to a secluded park on the edge of the adventuring compound, he didn't restrain his speech. "Did you see the team I was on? They're so *young*, and exhausting."

Artha seemed to think that was funny, chuckling as they walked. "Indeed. It speaks highly of you to be placed in such a team. But it has often been said that those born to greatness forever struggle to achieve it. I hope your team flourishes at their task. But now, we have training to do. Is there anything in particular you wish to focus on?

Nathan had been thinking about this. "I want to get some help from Emerald on something. Otherwise, whatever you think is best."

They spent a few hours talking of the Path of Rage, and Artha ran him through a few exercises. Many of them had him focusing on what made him angry, and ways to control and channel that feeling. Artha had him feel for the anger, taught him to think of it as something that was always present and could be called on whenever necessary.

It was clear to Nathan that the Path of Rage was a balancing act disguised as a surrender to emotion. In order to truly embark on the Path, you had to let your anger overwhelm you. However, you could still shape the path that the anger took, like guiding a raging torrent down certain channels. Nathan was glad he had Artha to teach him. There was an art to this not unlike his guided meditation. It was purpose without thought.

After some time they went to find Emerald, and Nathan asked them to run him through the footwork drill again. After a few repetitions, he asked both Artha and Emerald to throw some things at him and he'd try to use the movements from the drill to dodge.

It didn't go great, at least at first. Artha had grabbed whatever was at hand, and so Nathan dodged a rain of random chunks of wood and tools. He protested, noting that they could be using pillows or clothes, but Artha pointed out that Davrar didn't tend to respect non-hazardous training.

So, Nathan resigned himself to some bruises and got to dodging. At first, he was tempted to duck and weave, keeping his body weight low and stance even. But that wasn't the point of what he was trying to do. He wanted to use the techniques that Emerald had taught him, to quickly shift position and allow for sudden changes of direction.

After a few false starts, and a couple of times where Emerald specifically pegged Nathan in the foot, he started to get into it. The trick wasn't just to be light on your feet, it was to be careful and considerate of your momentum, and to be ready to change it at any time.

Pending utility skill: Low-tier Dodging Footwork
You have trained in moving your feet quickly to aid with dodging. This skill will help you move your feet to more easily keep your balance and dodge attacks.

He stopped moving and got belted with a metal ladle for his trouble. Quickly, Artha and Emerald stopped, and Emerald approached him.

"Y-you got it? Good, I was hungry."

They sat down to eat what Artha had quickly fetched, and Nathan nodded. "It's called [Dodging Footwork]. Says it will help me keep my balance and dodge attacks."

Emerald hesitated before answering, heaping vegetables onto a plate from a communal tray. "Mine is more general b-but doesn't mention dodging. J-just says 'easier movement and faster c-changes of direction.'"

Nathan was a bit surprised, speaking around a buttered roll stuffed with meat and gravy. "That sounds even more general. Nice. It's a really good skill."

Emerald shrugged their shoulders in response to the compliment, while Artha came forward. "Well done. It seems that many of your utility skills are geared towards fighting. While this is not a bad thing, I would caution you of making all of your skills related to combat and adventuring. Not only will it leave you unable to perform well in other areas, but it may make you feel trapped in this life, unable to imagine yourself acquiring other skills, other crafts."

He paused, then spoke again. "I apologize for seeding your garden with weeds. To achieve a skill one has been reaching for is truly something to be proud of. This one is not to be dismissed, for it takes long training to achieve such a thing. Indeed, I wonder at the speed at which you have picked up your Talents and skills in this place."

Nathan considered if he should mention Davrar deeming him "disadvantaged." Well, it probably wasn't the most dangerous secret that these two already knew, and understanding it would probably help with his training. So he told them.

"About that. When I arrived on Davrar, I got a message that I was 'at a disadvantage' and so I would have an easier time getting skills and Talents and level up faster until I wasn't at a disadvantage. Do either of you know when that'll happen?"

Artha furrowed his brow, tilting his head and staring to the side as he mopped his plate with another roll. "I've never heard of such a thing, not among my clan or in Gemore. Emerald?"

Emerald's voice was quiet. "I've o-overheard t-the words. It's something from Giantsrest, for n-noble kids. B-but I don't know what it means."

Nathan shrugged. "It seems fairly simple from what I have seen. If you don't have any levels then you get some sort of boost to help you catch up. I think it's helped me learn better versions of Talents and skills too. I'm not surprised Giantsrest takes advantage of it. Keep a kid from leveling up for a while and then they'll get better stuff later. I just wish I knew when it expired."

Both Artha and Emerald were taken aback. Artha spoke first. "How cruel. Children level slowly if properly cared for, and it is considered the mark of a precocious child that they level quickly. To keep them unleveled entirely... I cannot imagine it to be kind."

The big elk-man looked morose for a moment, then took a deep breath and continued. "But I do not know when this will expire. The next milestone is level 27, and that level is required for any proper Adventurer. It is sometimes said that the time between level 9 and 27 is the most dangerous in anybody's life, for Davrar rewards risk above all, and it is many levels to cross without the benefit of six full class skills. It would not surprise me if that is where you will lose this 'disadvantaged' trait."

Nathan nodded, frowning. If level 27 was where he'd lose the buff, then he should push that off as long as he could. And try to pick up and Develop as many Talents and utility skills as possible. The skills were easy, but Talents were a problem. Vhala had said that you could dump Talents, but that the better ones, the ones that changed you, tended to be permanent. Both Nathan's [Magic Resistance] and his [Regeneration] were permanent. So he didn't want to pick up just any Talent, he wanted something that would fit into his developing build. The problem was, he didn't know what he needed or where to get it. Were there temporary Talents he could take for now?

Well, there were people he could ask right in front of him. "Do you have any advice for temporary Talents I could take for my third slot?"

Artha answered again, sounding as if going over a familiar topic. "Taking a Talent and intending to replace it later is a matter of some argument. Many say it is wise to become as strong as possible – as quickly as possible. However, I say that is trading greater strength later for smaller strength now. You will delay gaining a more powerful Talent because you have Developed a temporary Talent, and may end up keeping the short-term Talent because you cannot bear to replace it. To add to this, many Talents tend to become permanent when Developed beyond High-tier. Finally, you may only receive Talents when you have an empty slot, which means that if you unlock a Talent in combat, you will not only be unable to accept it, you will never know you have done so. It is common practice to leave a Talent slot open for such an eventuality, or for after the level 27 class Development to round out a build. For these reasons, I do not recommend taking a temporary Talent. Do you agree, Emerald?"

The thin figure bobbed their armored helmet, giving no other answer.

Nathan shrugged. Regardless, it was time to move forward with what he had. He pulled up the box for his new skill and accepted it.

> Congratulations, you have accepted the 'Low-tier Dodging Footwork' utility skill

There was one more question Nathan had for the two, though he primarily addressed Emerald. "Should I try to get armor? I took a heavy blow earlier during training and it seems like I should wear armor."

Emerald started nodding, their helmet reflecting the light. "Armor is g-good. I can i-introduce..."

Artha cut in, stroking his silvery beard as he spoke over Emerald. "I must interrupt. A weighty apology, Emerald, but this is a place where I must guide Nathan on the Path of Rage, and I would ask you to depart so we may speak of it in privacy."

Artha waited for Emerald to leave the room with the remains of their dinner before continuing. "There is an early branching in the Path of Rage, between those who fight armored and unarmored. If you fight and train to reach level 27 without wearing armor – while taking wounds – you will almost certainly gain a class skill that will enhance your toughness while unarmored, which holds obvious advantages for you. You have said you are unable to use enchanted items, and armor without enchantments holds limited use. You also seem to prize maneuverability and fast movement, which armor and especially unenchanted armor would hinder. Therefore, I recommend against armor for now, though you may give it more thought after class Development. I hope your [Regeneration] Talent can protect you for now, and when you gain the class skill I hope the benefits are worthy."

That sounds like a pretty good argument. Armor would be uncomfortable, heavy and annoying to clean anyways. And expensive! I'll probably need to buy more clothes though.

~

Status of Nathan Lark:
Permanent Talent 1: High-tier Magic Resistance 10
Permanent Talent 2: Mid-tier Regeneration 7
Talent 3: None

Class: Antimagic Brawler level 25
Stamina: 350/350
Brawler's Indifference
Antimagic Blows

Utility skills:
Mid-tier Focused Mind 5
Low-tier Earnestness 8
Low-tier Sprinting 6
Low-tier Spellsense 6
Low-tier Notice 7
Low-tier Identify 3
Low-tier Dodging Footwork 1

Chapter 22

Backgrounds and Warnings

Nathan caught up on what the rest of the Giantraiders were doing – they all had a bunch of obligations before they headed back into the wilds, beyond just commissioning better weapons with their new cash.

Vhala was apparently stuck in an endless gauntlet of family obligations. The Bhos seemed to be a clan who did a lot of adventuring and catering to Adventurers, and Artha joked that her list of dinner invitations was taller than she was. She was also expected to share a few Insights with some kids against future favors. It sounded complicated in the way that only family politics could be, and Nathan wished her luck.

Nobody had seen Wiam since he'd disappeared into a wizard's tower called the Tower of Trickery, where he'd been trained. It was a bit of a strange cross between an orphanage and a magical school – and was run by a birdfolk mage called Gale Shullet. There seemed to be a lot of jokes about Gale and the Tower of Trickery, since they disdained attack spells and primarily focused on stealth, illusion and area control like Wiam's mud spell.

Okay, interesting. I was wondering why Wiam seemed less focused on direct conflict than the enslavement mages from Giantsrest.

However, Gale was unquestionably recognized as one of the stronger Adventurers of Gemore, leading a team called The Seven Fools. Her students had begun to prove their worth to the Adventurer's Guild in recent years – in large part due to their ability to cast [Message].

After a friendly exchange of goodbyes, Nathan headed back to the training section of the Adventurer's Guild. The cafeteria building was lit, and dinner was being cleared by a pudgy man with a perpetual smile on his face. He saw Nathan peeking around the door and gave a cheery wave.

Nathan explored further into the building. In the back were classrooms, some of which were occupied by students discussing things. They all looked at Nathan when he poked his head in, staring silently until he left.

Okay then. I guess some of the Heirs' unapproachability has rubbed off on me.

In the next layer back were the dormitories, divided into suites much like the one Nathan had stayed in with the Giantraiders. Most of the doors were closed, but one was open and Aarl sat in a chair next to it. He was sharpening an enormous sword that was laid on a cloth across his knees. As Nathan turned the corner, Aarl was looking over his shoulder and back into the room, smiling as he did so.

He and his sister are just so pretty. Those eyebrows are amazingly *sculpted.*

And that sword was *ridiculous.* Aarl spotted him and stood, hefting the blade and slowly feeding it into his pouch. It was taller than Nathan was, much less Aarl. Damn, with that much blade no wonder it needed a lot of sharpening. As the wiry youth finished, he gestured for Nathan to follow him into the room. Sarah was sitting there, whittling what looked like arrow shafts.

Aarl spoke to Nathan. "We have returned early, and expect the others back soon. Did your afternoon serve you well?"

Nathan nodded. "It did. Artha is a good teacher, and Emerald taught me a skill." He pointed to Sarah. "I'll be ready for that dodging practice tomorrow."

She smiled. "Good, I'm looking forward to another person's movement to practice against. I know all the tendencies of this walking target." She affectionately swatted at her brother's shoulder as he came to sit next to her. "Now, I will tell you this because Khachi likely will not. Try to sleep early tonight, we will wake early, and both Khachi and Stella need less sleep than decent folk do. Don't let them keep you up." With that, she went back to her whittling, her rapid knife movements somehow sending the wood scraps into a neat pile on the table in front of her.

Aarl looked put out. "Ah, you warn him of what Khachi will do, while we had to suffer it firsthand! He should've stumbled through his first full day with half a night of sleep as we did. It would be good practice!"

Sarah pointed her knife at him. "Beware this mean streak of yours, brother. It will be your undoing." But she tilted her head and waggled her eyebrows as she said it, which seemed to lessen the blow. Aarl only laughed.

Nathan spectated their interplay, amused. The two definitely seemed close. He was an only child, but few of the siblings he'd seen had been so friendly.

They were making fun of each other, but there was no meanness to it. Then again, he hadn't known any twins, so who knew?

Nathan didn't feel comfortable going to bed yet, even if he was tired. He wasn't so much physically tired, just mentally exhausted. So many new things had happened. He needed to process and think, but there just hadn't been time.

Now's as good a time as any.

He said his goodnights to the twins and then explored the rooms of the Heirs. There were five bedrooms and one bathroom – again with the strange trough with running water. One of the bedrooms had no personal items, and Nathan claimed it as his own, laying out his stuff on the small table.

It was a pitiful pile for being everything he owned in this new world. The knapsack he'd gotten from the Vanguard, packed with clothes and blankets. Strings of coins, some knives, a few extra clothes. Back home he'd felt secure with his phone and wallet. It had been comforting to know that as long as he kept those two items, he'd manage decently well anywhere with civilization. Anywhere on Earth, that was. But all of that had been stripped away by Taeol's spell. Now this meager pile of possessions was all he owned. However, it gave him a similar sense of security. He was starting to develop his place in this world.

Especially the coins. Starting from nothing, pulling myself up by my bootstraps! I'm such a capitalist.

So much of it had been due to his friends here. He'd found allies and a purpose; the money and belongings were incidental. In general, life was less comfortable than it had been back on Earth, but Nathan wasn't sure he regretted the change. Life on Davrar was dangerous and often short, but Nathan remembered the intoxicating thrill of the fights he'd been a part of. Life here was exciting and adventurous. The night sky was a world, and Davrar was chock-full of secrets to be explored, new things to learn. The extreme sports Nathan had done felt like child's play, a facsimile of the rush that was a *real* fight.

There was no chair, so Nathan sat on the bed to meditate. He glossed over his experiences of the day. There was no rush, just examining each thought in turn until there was nothing left. Then Nathan focused on the breath until his mind felt clear. He began to examine the flow of his feelings. What did he feel like? After the last few days he should be flushed with stress hormones, sick to his stomach. But he wasn't. He felt *invigorated*. Strong. And underneath it all, like a hidden flame in the center of his being, was a banked ember of anger.

Nathan examined that anger, studying it thoroughly. In this meditative state, he could dedicate the time to investigate. *Why* was he angry? What was the source? Was it justified? He remembered his introduction to Giantsrest, the damning words from Taeol's own mouth that had led Nathan to oppose him. Then there was the mind-fuckery that he'd barely escaped. That had made it personal, and when Nathan had broken his restraints Taeol had cringed and fled.

Coward. Fleeing the moment consequences could threaten him.

Nathan breathed out, feeling like fire was escaping with each breath. There'd been the fight at the ford, where the *enslavement mages* had gloated at the idea of recapturing Emerald, the escaped slave. Nathan's fury peaked, and his arms trembled. He wanted to run to Giantsrest and tear down their walls, break things until not one stone stood atop another.

He breathed in, keeping his eyes closed. He breathed out, feeling the anger wash through him in waves. It felt purifying. It felt like it gave him strength. And on Earth, that would have been a lie. Here, it was not. Artha's lessons made it clear that anger was a power, and a power that he could use.

After a time, Nathan dropped back, clearing his mind and focusing only on his breathing. He breathed clean, cool air in through the nose, breathed out his Rage through the mouth. A few minutes later, he opened his eyes. The anger wasn't gone, just receded, like a coal smoldering inside of him. Nathan was sure with a moment's thought he could call it back to him. Before him floated another blue box in acknowledgement of that.

Pending utility skill: Anger Control
You have demonstrated excellent control over your anger. This skill will help you control your anger in the future, allowing you to control your Rage and direct it as you see fit.

Artha had warned him about this. It could be a useful skill to somebody on the Path of Rage, to be sure. Nathan would have been wary of taking it because it gave Davrar control over his emotions, but Artha had further cautioned him against it. His tribe had learned that those who took skills to control their Rage ended up weakened. Their anger became a shallower thing, a switch to be turned on and off, and their future classes were weaker. So, Nathan refused the skill.

He rested on the bed for a little longer, thinking about the day. He seemed to be doing alright with the Heirs, if only by not taking their bait. Being the serious adult seemed to be paying off. That situation seemed fine. And he'd known them for less than a day. They seemed… alright. Still a bit of that teenage idiocy, but they *wanted* to be serious.

Well, Nathan still had traces of adrenaline in him from his meditation on anger, but he should heed Sarah's advice and try to sleep.

At least there aren't computer screens keeping me awake anymore!

Nathan rested, feeling at peace with the day. He lamented only that he hadn't gotten more of a chance to explore Gemore, to see the novelties of Davrar. But, there were good arguments for learning to defend himself as rapidly as possible. And here was where that happened.

Chapter 23

Basic Education

True to Sarah's word, the next morning started early. There was a pounding on Nathan's door and Khachi's enthusiastic voice sounded loudly. "Get up lead-foot! We're headed out. Don't hold us up!" Nathan heard a chuckle, then the pounding resumed.

Nathan had been warned about this, so his clothes were laid out and ready. Less than a minute after waking up, Nathan unbolted the door and stepped out. Khachi hid his surprise well, but seemed a bit put out that Nathan was up and dressed so quickly. Nathan hurried through his morning ablutions and emerged into the common room to find everybody just finishing getting ready. Stella and Khachi were almost insultingly bright-eyed and bushy-tailed, with Aarl and Sarah visibly annoyed about it.

What followed was a series of exercises that reminded Nathan of descriptions of boot camp training. It had clearly taken on the form of a ritual to the Heirs as well. Calisthenics, running several loops around the training hall, before taking on some of the obstacle courses in the pre-dawn light. Nathan kept up, if only by leaning on [Sprinting] and spending Stamina freely. They hadn't eaten yet, so it wasn't replenishing much, even when they did stop to take a breather.

The group was clearly used to pushing each other, and while Stella lagged in the running, she didn't drag or fall behind. Nathan did notice that there was something wonky going on with her run – as if each step was propelled by extra force.

Khachi led the exercises, disgustingly cheerful as he vaulted over obstacles in full plate, calling out to everybody in a sing-song chant. Nathan wanted to resent him for it, but the wolffolk just seemed to be having so much *fun* with it. Nathan didn't want to snark at his good mood, even if he wasn't a morning person himself.

After their exercises, they trooped into the dining hall as it opened up. The same pudgy man was depositing trays of food on the buffet table. The food looked basic, but delicious. Meat, eggs, starchy tubers and piles of vegetables in a rich gravy. The chef winked at them, wiping his hands on a stained apron as he walked out the door to fetch another load.

The Heirs loaded up their plates and sat at the same central table as before. Nathan asked the Heirs to stash food in their various magical holding items for him to use later, and they acquiesced with humor. Khachi joked that he wished *he* could replenish his Faith resource by eating instead of praying. But then he smugly mentioned that Faith allowed for miracles, and he didn't see Stamina pulling off any of *those*. Nathan waved his left arm at Khachi dismissively.

I think regrowing an arm is pretty miraculous.

Other teams were filtering in, but it didn't seem like anybody else had the morning exercise routine of the Heirs. Nathan asked about it, and apparently Khachi had inherited it from his mother. The parents of the other Heirs had leaned on them to participate, and now it was a habit. Stella did an impression of her father extracting a promise from her, clasping her hands in front of her before softly and seriously saying, "For no matter the power of the mage, sometimes it is smart to run away very quickly. And you can't fly yet, so you can't use that as an excuse like we can."

Nathan noticed that he wasn't sore after the morning's exercises. Probably [Regeneration] healing his muscles. Nathan wanted to find out if that strengthened them or not – but it was something he'd need to keep an eye on over time. Maybe tomorrow he should bring a snack and try to test it out.

Next they were off to classes and bid each other farewell. Nathan headed to his lesson on reading and writing, and received some ribbing for needing to learn to read.

His response was sarcastic. "I know how to read and write perfectly well, thank you very much! Just... not in whatever the local language is. You don't even use the characters I'm used to. Very rude. You should just use the twenty-six characters I'm used to."

Nathan spent a few hours with Velek – the clerk who had taken him to the Guildmistress – learning the characters of the local system. It was a phonetic alphabet, with only twenty characters. But there were four modifiers that could be used to change some pronunciations enough that it was closer to thirty-five. At least the modifiers were standardized. In fact, the alphabet seemed less like something that'd evolved naturally, and more like something somebody had *designed* at some point. There weren't as many idiosyncrasies as there should have been in a naturally-evolving language, and the use of the four modifiers was too systematic.

So? I don't exactly have proof, and even if I did it doesn't mean a lot. The Korean alphabet was also designed by some king who decided to design it from the ground up to be easy to use. It worked, too.

Nathan was just glad it wouldn't be too difficult to properly learn the language Taeol's spell had taught him to speak.

After that, Nathan was reunited with the Heirs in a large room with all of the other trainees for their next class. Jolba stomped into the room, freezing side conversations with a stern look, and lectured them on the rules of Adventurers. It was a dry list of responsibilities, expectations and privileges, but Nathan found the new information fascinating.

As Adventurers, they were neither free agents nor entirely in service to Gemore. It was more like committing to some amount of public service, which was tracked, and receiving special privileges in return. They would be provided housing, basic necessities and the "Adventurer discount" while being active Adventurers, but were expected to take up jobs in a 'reasonable' timeframe, and work not for their own enrichment but for the good of Gemore.

Jolba emphasized this multiple times, his favorite example being an anonymous adventurer given the choice between finding a magic item and stopping a ravening monster – called a muckgrabber – from entering a town.

"You end the threat. Protect those depending on you. That's the job. If you don't like it, go somewhere else and be a treasure hunter. But that's not what it means to be an Adventurer of Gemore."

From context – and some nearby mutters – Nathan gathered that these weren't old traditions. This mindset was something that Jolba and the Guildmistress were trying to bake into the next generation. And while the Heirs seemed to be on board, it was clear that not everybody was.

Regardless, it's a sentiment I can get behind. This isn't my city, and I don't understand all the complexities here – but the general culture seems pretty obsessed with machismo, and I'm in favor of people trying to change that. Macho behavior doesn't usually translate to responsible conduct.

The rest of the day proceeded much like the previous one, with Nathan settling further into the group. He was still an object of attention, but the trials of the previous day had mostly settled the Heir's doubts. When Khachi tried to suggest another spar, Stella shut him down hard, and announced that Nathan would practice with Sarah. She proposed an alternate plan. "Yeah, you big strong warriors should hammer away at each other with your oversized hunks of metal, it's what you're good at."

Sparring with Sarah was a learning experience for Nathan. He'd sparred in martial arts, but it had been with pads and for points. And while the lessons applied, the availability of easy healing made this an altogether different experience. They fought to surrender or incapacitation, and it should have been a grueling, awful experience. Sarah wasn't being brutal, and she was pointing out his mistakes, but she also wasn't holding back. Nathan had his wrists broken, his ribs cracked and his nose crushed more than a few times.

But [Brawler's Indifference] and [Regeneration] made the experience rather tolerable. He could ignore the pain and shock of the injuries to continue the fight while quickly healing the damage. Before long he was digging into the stashes of food to replenish his Stamina. Nathan wasn't entirely sure why he could just *keep eating* and replenish Stamina. But, no argument here. There was plenty of food, and it was well-spiced enough that Nathan wasn't getting bored of it.

If I keep eating food this spicy, maybe I'll pick up a Talent for fire-breathing.

At first Nathan held back his more vicious blows, but over time he learned that Sarah was superhumanly fast and flexible. So he restrained himself less, taking openings for crippling blows as they were presented. Going all-out felt great, and Nathan was thrilled by the spar. It wasn't the same all-consuming rush as his earlier life-or-death fights – but it had a bit of the same taste. A taste he hadn't felt in spars at home. Those had been dominated by the need for safety. After adjusting, Nathan started landing hits on Sarah. His larger build and use of Stamina made his blows hit *hard,* and Sarah had to be careful to properly block or dodge nearly every one of his attacks.

Between rounds, Stella healed minor injuries like bruises and black eyes, though she was visibly uncomfortable doing it. She frowned at Sarah's face as one particularly nasty black eye diminished.

Nathan took the opportunity to ask. "Stella, what's going on? Is there anything wrong with the healing?"

She shook her head, continuing to watch the progress of the spell. "No, it's just that the [Curing] spells are Davrar's. You channel basic mana in a specific shape and then the person heals. It's really not *magic.* It's... like a cheat. A lot of mages don't notice, but there's no way this mana shape is doing the healing.

You can tweak the [Curing] a little bit with the right inputs, but the changes make no sense, aside from more mana making the healing faster. It's like you're tying a useless knot with mana, but then a wound heals." The mage glared at the spell as if it personally offended her.

"The magic doesn't make sense. My mom tells me that it'd be impossible to heal people without it, but I don't like having no idea how the spell actually works! Khachi's faith is better at this kind of nonsense anyway, but mom says I need to practice. It's just that there's no rhythm behind this spell, and I don't know why some things work better than others. I like to understand why my spells do what they do."

Nathan nodded. That frustration made sense to him. But so did Davrar's guidance of healing spells. Bodies were complicated, and healing a wound in seconds was very different from detonating out mana like a fireball. This was *exactly* the kind of interesting puzzle Nathan would love to tackle. If he used magic, which he did not.

So he smiled sympathetically and said, "Yeah, that sounds frustrating. Maybe it just takes time to become comfortable using the spell on injuries."

Stella shrugged at his words, clearly wanting to avoid the topic. She went back to healing the injury, carefully gazing into Sarah's eyes to be sure there wasn't any lasting damage. Then, they went back to training.

Low-tier Dodging Footwork 2 achieved!

Only Nathan's lowest-rank skill had gotten better, but he'd been warned about that. While this training was somewhat dangerous, it barely counted to Davrar. On the other hand, Nathan had definitely *learned* more about taking and dealing blows personally, even if Davrar hadn't rewarded him for it. This practice had been so much more visceral than sparring. Nathan felt like he was getting a handle on the sudden bursts of rapid movement involved when people fought to injure and maim. There wasn't that moment of hesitation involved where a strike was pulled, or a kick was checked.

He headed to training with Artha in high spirits, and the elk-man talked Nathan's ear off about the Path of Rage. Nathan was approaching his second class Development – it was even possible that he'd hit level 27 with a few months of dedicated training. But if a deadly fight happened, he was certain to hit that milestone. Therefore, Artha was trying to stuff years of accumulated knowledge and practice into Nathan before that happened, so he'd be most likely to get the best class he could get.

Nathan returned to bed that night feeling tired but fulfilled once again. He settled into his meditation without a goal. He was working towards purposes on multiple fronts, and felt satisfied with his progress. So he set aside his thoughts, quieted his inner dialogue and drifted, at ease in his mind. Eventually, he readied himself for bed, and slept better than he had on Earth in some years.

Chapter 24

Finally, a Time Skip

Over the next several days, Nathan's interactions became more cordial with the other members of the Heirs. He didn't complain at their strenuous exercise and practice, and joined in to push them forward as he adapted to the schedule. In fact, he started pushing harder than any of them.

Nathan started requesting that they squirrel away extra food in their dimensional bags so he could replenish his Stamina. They made fun of him for it, but it was more good-natured jokes about the stupid amounts of food Nathan was eating. Stella in particular had innumerable dimensional pockets in her robes, and Nathan had yet to deplete those bottomless depths of snacks.

He was still somewhat of an outsider in the group. The Heirs had known each other for years, and Nathan couldn't expect to overcome that in a mere week. But the barriers of awkwardness were breaking down in both directions. Nathan didn't feel the need to consider every joke, and felt freer in having fun with each member of the Heirs.

He felt the closest to Stella, who regarded Nathan and his [Magic Resistance] as something wondrous and special. It was hard to resist a pretty girl paying you special attention, even if she was a few years younger. She started practicing increasingly lethal spellwork with Nathan, and soon enough he was dodging storms of [Firebolts], being inundated in jets of fire and shattering layers of force shields. Stella especially prized the time they spent directly contesting her spellwork, saying it was fantastic training for making her spells more resilient and controlled.

Khachi was trying to be friendly, regarding it important to be on good terms with every member of "his" team. But he clearly had a chip on his shoulder and was bad at being diplomatic.

Sarah was kind, and to some extent the most relatable. Stella and Khachi were driven and intimidating in their devotion to practice. They each spent a lot of time on their own practicing their magic disciplines with single-minded determination. This also translated to spending more evenings with their parents, undergoing specialized training or just spending time with family. Therefore, Nathan spent several evenings hanging out with Sarah and Aarl, trading jokes with Sarah about their schooling and practice as Aarl dourly maintained his arsenal, or joined his sister in whittling new weapons.

Aarl could be a bit brooding, and tended to avoid conversation unless forced to engage. When he did butt in it was usually with a comment so wry that Nathan had to stop and appreciate the levels of sarcasm on display.

He still hadn't seen much of the world outside of the Adventurer's Guild and the training complex, but that wasn't for the worst. Nathan was learning how to survive Davrar, and it would be hard to find somewhere safer than the training grounds of the Adventurer's Guild – despite the bruises, sprains and broken bones he received while training.

After almost a fortnight, his skills and Talents were advancing, but seemingly very slowly.

Mid-tier Regeneration Rank 8 achieved!

Mid-tier Regeneration Rank 9 achieved!

Low-tier Sprinting 7 achieved!

Low-tier Spellsense 7 achieved!

Mid-tier Focused Mind Rank 6 achieved!

Low-tier Identify 4 achieved!

Low-tier Dodging Footwork 3 achieved!

Low-tier Dodging Footwork 4 achieved!

His fastest growing skill was [Regeneration], which was not surprising given all of the healing Nathan was doing. And it wasn't just the injuries sustained during practice. It also included the muscle soreness gained from the frankly ridiculous amount of exercise Nathan was doing, both in morning and afternoon sessions. Stamina let him push his muscles farther, and [Regeneration] let them recover nearly instantly.

He wasn't benchmarking his progress especially carefully, and they weren't doing a ton of resistance training, but Nathan's muscles were getting *quite* defined. He could leap straight to the top of the walls on the obstacle course and could easily block even powerful strikes from Khachi's hammer, provided he had a weapon of his own. He didn't want to *say* he was the strongest member of the Heirs, but with his Stamina – it was definitely true.

Nathan meditated most nights, using [Focused mind] and [Spellsense] to help him understand more of Stella's spells. As he understood a spell, he got faster and more efficient at breaking it. The more he practiced understanding magic, the more it felt like the right direction to Develop his [Magic Resistance].

He'd tried to Develop [Magic Resistance] to the next tier, but even with [Focused Mind] and Stella's assistance in hitting him with spells, he hadn't had a breakthrough. High-tier skills and Talents were hard to Develop, and Nathan figured it was his lack of experience with a broad array of magic that was causing a problem. He could probably Develop his Talent to be excellent at dealing with force and fire magic, and maybe the shadow and earth magic that he'd practiced with Wiam. But the more general a Talent, the more useful it was. He mentioned this problem to Stella, who said she'd try to convince her parents to help him out.

Nathan was looking forward to getting [Regeneration] to rank 10 so he could work on Developing it – he had some concrete ideas about how to do it. He wasn't sure how to try to focus the Development – maybe making his healing faster or cheaper? He could probably angle the regeneration that way by focusing on either *more cells* differentiating, or by guiding the process more with his understanding of what differentiation entailed. Alternatively, if his focus was on using [Regeneration] in a fight, then maybe it would be better to make it automatic, so he didn't have to focus attention to heal. He was also well aware that he was weak to poisons. However, that was enough divorced from the Insight of 'guided cell differentiation' that underlaid his [Regeneration] that his Talent would need to be past High-tier to handle it. Regardless, he had to wait for the Talent to rank-up, which was proceeding slowly.

His reading lessons with Velek had been going reasonably well – after a few days of study, he'd been offered the [Low-tier Reading] skill. Nathan had almost declined it without a second thought – he didn't need to spend a precious skill on reading! Reading was something he could manage on his own without any Davrar-granted assistance, thank you very much.

Then he'd given it another thought. If he Developed the skill, he could learn to read *incredibly quickly*. And maybe even Develop it to read other languages, or... or... there was a lot of potential, and Nathan wasn't sure of the limits. He hadn't learned any details about what was possible with a reading skill from Velek or Artha. In the end, he left it open. The biggest problem was that there didn't seem to be all that many books around. He also probably didn't have too many utility skill slots left, and wanted to be careful how he assigned them going forward. But if he had a free slot – then [Reading] was certainly something to consider.

A few days later, Nathan approached one of his mentors about it. "Artha, what are the rules for acquiring utility skills?"

The big elk-man looked down at Nathan with a thoughtful expression. "Davrar will offer a utility skill for a task you are already proficient in. This is especially true if you are using the skill to help with a dangerous situation. However, Davrar is unlikely to offer you skills similar to those you already possess." He thought for a moment longer, staring off into space.

"Such lessons are basic, and I often forget you were not taught in childhood. Skills usable in combat are more difficult to acquire, and skills become harder to gain the more of them you have. Trying to get a skill will make you more likely to get it – it is rather uncommon for any but a child to be offered a skill they were not working for. Or those who are 'disadvantaged,' apparently."

He gave Nathan a slight nod before begging off. "I must return to the hall, for I am to meet a young Treeborn new to the city. Farewell, Nathan."

Jolba's classes in the mornings were another great source of knowledge for Nathan. The grizzled Adventurer didn't always teach – they'd had some other Adventurers or clerks in for lessons on geography and the bestiary of different monsters around Gemore. They didn't teach much history. The closest thing was descriptions of the different kinds of dungeons they might face, along with some details about the cultures that had produced those ruins.

Apparently the Cults of Quaz had been a necromantic cult that had built chapels and tombs over sites of mass death, suppressing and controlling the naturally-occurring mana and undead that tended to issue from such places. They'd served to contain dangers and make the countryside safer – or at least they had. Now, many of their seals had broken or reached critical mass, and regularly unleashed dangerous undead. They were widely considered some of the most dangerous dungeons around.

In most cases, the deaths had happened so long ago that the site wouldn't be magical if it wasn't for the Quaz constructs perpetuating the death mana. It was possible to enter and safely dissipate the necromantic mana before destroying those dungeons. However, the job was dangerous, especially if the built-up mana went out of control over an ancient mass grave. Nathan had had a front-row seat when the Grey Moon Order had failed to prevent that in a Monastery of Quaz on Delve Day.

It wasn't exactly front-row. But even the nosebleed seats are too close to a mountain-sized monster. And what kind of death event leaves behind enough bodies for that? There's history there.

But the Cults of Quaz were just the first example. There were dozens of other types of dangerous ruins and dungeons. The Fortresses of the Face had been waystations and strongholds to a long-forgotten civilization and were built around powerful artifacts that siphoned mana from leylines to power defensive wards and spells – only now, they were usually lairs of powerful monsters or nests that had started feeding on that mana, gaining powers and aspects of their mana source.

The Edrani Empire was another ancient nation that had heavily enchanted all of their buildings. The enchantments served to reinforce stonework, pump water – or summon armies of elemental or ghostly guardians, control automatic traps, and more.

Dungeoneering was both an art and a science, where you used history and archaeology to understand the construction of ancient cities and fortresses built by paranoid architects with access to insane resources, who wanted to ensure that their city-fortress-research center *would not fall.*

And they all fell anyway. Now Davrar is covered with hundreds of miles of monster-infested wilderness strewn with dangerous ruins. That's not a good sign, is it?

Finally, there were Nathan's lessons with Artha. They continued to be interesting, with a mix of theoretical concepts, mental exercises and physical practice. Artha had described to Nathan some of what his clan knew – but there was a lot to cover. Typically somebody had years to prepare for class Developments. Artha described how the young members of his clan tended to gather around fires in the evening to hear elders teach them of the Path.

A lot of the knowledge was certainly useful – like avoiding armor to Develop an unarmored defense skill, or to not take an anger management skill. Some of it was also likely superstitious. One such example was the practice of holding a body part close to a fire until it was almost, but not quite burnt. According to Artha, the idea was to feel the resonance between fire and anger, and that it would help you improve the Rage skill. Then he admitted that it was more a game that young Treeborn played to demonstrate how *cool* they were. Nathan wasn't planning on bothering with that one.

The indicator of a class on the Path of Rage was a skill centered around consuming a class resource, usually Stamina, in order to fuel a Rage state. While active, the Rage enhanced strength, speed and toughness substantially. The trio of advantages was apparently a big deal. Many fighting-type classes gave skills that permanently or temporarily enhanced strength, speed or durability, but no other class enhanced all three at once with a single skill. Furthermore, it was quite uncommon for classes to enhance more than one of the three before level 81. The primary downsides were the altered mental state and that usage spent the class resource.

Artha and Nathan had discussed what class skills he should go for at some length – at level 27 he would pick up three new ones. They were aiming for Rage and unarmoured toughness with the first two. With those skills, Nathan should be very resistant to mundane weapons. They weren't sure if his [Magic Resistance] would deal with magical weapons, but he could hope!

The third of the new class skills was still up in the air – they talked about a few options, from some ways to passively increase Nathan's strength, recover Stamina, or discount the Stamina costs of Rage. That last option was one of Artha's favorites, and Nathan had to agree. Class skills to recover Stamina were also appealing, but most of the ones that Artha knew were difficult and required four legs, so Artha didn't get into them. As a result, Artha had Nathan doing exercises to practice keeping his anger present, raging in his mind while not being all-consuming. Nathan didn't like how it felt, but he kept up the exercises regardless since that was a way to get a skill that discounted Rage. Artha also mentioned that sometimes the best practice was to not try to plan out every detail, allowing circumstance and Davrar to fill in the last pieces of a build.

At the very least, Nathan would be confronted with a list of choices for how his class would Develop, similarly to when he had first Developed his class at level 9. But class Developments were *developments* of the previous class, so he wouldn't be able to make a hard pivot and become a scholarly class like he'd been offered before. Regardless, Nathan was satisfied with his efforts.

~

Status of Nathan Lark:

Permanent Talent 1: High-tier Magic Resistance 10

Permanent Talent 2: Mid-tier Regeneration 9
Talent 3: None

Class: Antimagic Brawler level 25
Stamina: 350/350
Brawler's Indifference
Antimagic Blows

Utility skills:
Mid-tier Focused Mind 6
Low-tier Earnestness 8
Low-tier Sprinting 7
Low-tier Spellsense 7
Low-tier Notice 7
Low-tier Identify 4
Low-tier Dodging Footwork 4

Chapter 25

A Mage's Mansion

The next evening, Nathan had returned to the suite and was idly chatting with Sarah about different kinds of weapons used by adventurers. He had learned in the last few days that Sarah and Aarl's father Stanel Crusens was a famous [Weaponmaster]. He'd retired from adventuring after the death of his wife to raise Sarah and Aarl and run the training for the Gemore Guard. He was famous for being a master of *literally* any weapon he laid his hands on.

"... So when you reach the higher levels, a lot of strange weapons become usable. There was this orc trader from Agmon who had some skills related to chains, so his main weapon was this hundred foot chain with heavy metal balls every couple of feet. He could wrap somebody up in a snap, knock down a building or sling a boulder half a mile. There are still tools better at each of those tasks, but it's a good example of a specialist who doesn't sacrifice too much. Better than an idiot with a sword larger than he is. The real trick is getting class skills that are useful at low levels and let you explore more esoteric things at higher levels." The last part was partially directed at her brother, who was frowning at a scroll while he worked through a math problem.

Nathan wasn't sure if he should help Aarl with the math. It looked like relatively simple arithmetic and multiplication, though there was definitely some geometry involved. Nathan still couldn't read standard text very well, much less mathematical notation. Something to revisit after he could *read*. There was an awful lot on that list. Velek was planning on testing his general knowledge once they'd addressed the reading problem, so that would be a good way to compare Gemore's education to Earth's.

To be fair, I was working on the highest form of qualification my world offers. That being said, the Heirs have probably had about the best education you can get around here. But they really don't need as extensive a math education as I do. Did? Huh. Well I don't regret learning multivariable calculus, it was a required class and worthwhile to understand Maxwell's equations.

Stella bounced into the room, returned from a longer tutoring session and dinner with her parents. Khachi followed closely behind, looking resigned. Nathan could tell by his drooping ears.

Stella seemed especially enthusiastic. "Hey Nathan, you know how you wanted to get more exposure to different kinds of magic? Well my parents have invited you to our house tomorrow! It should be interesting for everybody!"

Nathan blinked at her, taken aback by the enthusiasm. He opened his mouth to blandly accept, but was interrupted by Khachi.

"I'm pretty sure it's going to be two of the most powerful spellcasters in Gemore trying to take you apart for a few hours," the wolffolk explained in a dry tone. "I'd rather go a few rounds with a Rotting Hulk. *And* she left out that her parents are also having a dinner party afterwards, with all of us and our parents in attendance. You'll be the object of attention, that's as sure as the sun."

Nathan looked to Sarah and Aarl. "Is that bad? That sounds like it's bad."

Aarl looked up from his chalk slate with a sharp grin. "They do these dinner parties every month or so; I'd forgotten that it was happening tomorrow. There'll be great food and the best Adventurers around swapping stories. Don't worry too much about it. If you accidentally insult Stanel and he chops off a limb, you can always grow it back."

This was not particularly reassuring to Nathan. But the first part *did* sound like it might be a good time to learn a lot more about magic, and potentially even Develop his Magic Resistance Talent. As for the dinner, well...

Nathan took a deep breath. He had a choice. He could stress about it and try to badger the rest of his team with questions to prepare. Or he could just not worry about it and hope it wouldn't be a problem. Not only was there not much he could do, if he got himself worked up about it then he might *create* a problem where none needed to exist.

So, Nathan settled down and asked Khachi about his mother's intensive tutoring while Stella made her way over to help Aarl with his math. She was apparently *quite* good at math.

~

The next morning, things proceeded as normal – morning exercises, obstacle courses, breakfast, and lessons. Nathan met back up with the Heirs for lunch, which was primarily some sort of gamey loin stuffed with pepper-like vegetables and a dark, salty sauce. Practice proceeded as normal, with some sprinting drills and hand-to-hand combat. Nathan wasn't *really* able to stand up to Khachi or Aarl in a fight, but it certainly wasn't because he lacked strength.

They've been learning to fight since they could walk, and it shows. The gap of skill is immense.

At the end of the session, Khachi wished Nathan an emotional farewell. "Nathan, I wish you luck in your upcoming challenges. I hope to see you well, if you can survive."

Stella glared at him, struggling to keep a smile off her face. She eventually reached up and flicked the side of his helmet, some kind of force spell making it ring like a bell.

And with that, Nathan was off, following the much shorter Stella across the courtyard to where her parents stood apart from all of the other mentors who were there to collect trainees. At first glance, the old foxfolk and gentle-faced man with deep smile lines seemed unremarkable. Kullal's fur was heavily streaked with gray, and Dalo's hair and wispy beard were entirely white. Their robes were more richly colored and decorated than most, though not the resplendent colors Nathan had first seen as they'd flown overhead after reducing the Grave Tangle to a bad-smelling trash fire. Nathan took a second to remember what he knew of them.

Right. It's Kullal and Dalo Caxol, they're married and Stella has talked about them some. Kullal is the foxfolk and specializes in force magic, especially protective barriers. Dalo is the white-haired guy and specializes in big elemental spells. And fusion reactions! Though they're high-enough level that they're definitely proficient at more than one thing. Stella said her mom is good with light magic, and Dalo's got incredibly fine control of enormous elemental spells when he needs it.

They drew near, and Kullal embraced Stella in a hug. It looked very soft. Meanwhile Dalo stepped up to Nathan and offered him a handshake with a gentle smile. Nathan spoke first, using a form of respect he'd learned from the orange-skinned clerk, Velek, as he bowed his head lightly over Dalo's hand.

"Archmage Caxol, it is a good day for a first meeting. Your daughter has been a great help to my Development. I'm lucky to be on her team."

The man's smile grew wider. "And from what she's said, she's lucky you joined. My daughter has said a few things about the Talents you have, and I would be in error if I said I am not curious." Dalo combed his fingers through his trailing beard. "But here is not the place for such talks. If my wife has finished greeting our daughter..." Dalo stepped over to give Stella a hug of his own.

Kullal turned to Nathan, tilting her head back to look at him. Nathan held out his hand, but she brushed by it to give him a hug too. Nathan hesitated a moment before returning the gesture, gently wrapping his arms around the diminutive woman in front of him. It *was* very soft.

After a moment, she stepped back. "Well, now that we've been properly introduced, let's get moving. I know Stella has high hopes for this afternoon. Come along."

As they were leaving the Adventurer's Guild, Stella asked, "Who's going to be at the dinner tonight? And what's the food?"

Dalo gave her an indulgent smile. "You'll find out who is there when they get there. But we've hired Cantas for tonight and given her the freedom she wants. I'm sure it will be memorable, if you can avoid the decorative flower arrangements."

Stella laughed and turned back to Nathan. "Cantas is the best chef in Gemore, though she sometimes puts things that aren't *food* on the table. I think the last time she cooked, Kia ended up actually exhaling flames. Though I've never been sure if that was the dish or just Dad playing a prank." She elbowed Dalo, who held up his hands placatingly.

"Everybody must have their secrets, especially once they reach my level. Come now, let us hurry. It sounded like you had more ideas than we will have time to try, my daughter."

After exiting the Guild, they turned and started climbing the hill that Gemore was built on. The streets were steep, and in many cases had large stones laid flat to form steps. Most of the houses were cut into the hill or standing on platforms so they could remain flat. The occasional crossing road switch-backed up the hill, allowing wheeled carts and wagons to climb to the higher districts without having to go straight up the slope.

As they climbed, Nathan turned his head, his eyes drawn to a building just down the road. There was a man leaning against the doorway looking at Nathan, and their eyes met. The man was pale and wiry underneath light chainmail. He had an unstrung bow in a quiver on his back and a short-sword on each hip, while his face was rough with several days of stubble. The man held Nathan's gaze for a moment, and Nathan felt like he was being intensely studied for weaknesses. He opened his mouth to ask Dalo and

Kullal, but the moment he did, the man stepped into the building and was gone.

Could be a man curious about who I am because I'm walking around with this company. But I think I'm going to trust my gut on this one. He was looking for me. *But I highly doubt anybody's going to try anything when I'm with this family. I'll have to be cautious and not go out into the city on my own.*

Low-tier Notice Rank 8 achieved!

As they continued to ascend the hill of Gemore, Nathan looked around for more suspicious activity.

His attention was caught by Dalo pointing off to the side at a jewelry shop. "I would say that place is newly opened, but I realize I haven't walked this road properly in years. Dear wife, maybe we should spend more time on the streets of the city we've sworn to protect?"

"But flight is so convenient and easy!" Kullal responded. She paused, tilting her head one way, and then another. "I do see your angle – it's easy to be stuck in our ways when we fly from our house to our favorite bar and then to the Guild. Maybe we should find some time to explore. Just like the first time I came to the city, hmm? I remember you were so excited to show me the sights. Now there may be new sights for us both."

Dalo drew his wife into a hug and kissed her before responding. "It is an idea we should hold onto, but I think Kia is planning another ranging. I'm sure we'll hear about it tonight."

He chuckled and bent to kiss her again, but Stella interrupted. "Hey! Don't forget we're here! You haven't met Nathan for more than five minutes and now you're not only ignoring him, but also being too... *that!*" She waved her hand at her embracing parents.

Kullal snuggled further into Dalo. "Well, if Nathan's going to spend time with us he should know what to expect. Though we *have* been ignoring him, for which I tender a faint apology." She nodded in his direction, before spinning away from her husband and leading them up the street.

Nathan replied, throwing his arms wide to gesture to everything around them. "No worries! I'm glad to get out and see the city. I'd previously only been in the area around the Adventurer's Guild, but there's definitely more to Gemore. However, I'd be curious to ask what you have planned for this afternoon. Stella goes with you every day for magic tutoring, but I can't imagine that's what you have planned for me."

Dalo chuckled. "Indeed not. As much as many mages would cut off their hand for some tutoring from us, that's not what the plan is today. From what Stella has said, you have a very peculiar and shockingly general Talent to resist magic. That's not something we've heard of before in all of our years of adventuring, so we're quite curious. And if you need exposure to more spells and mana types to help Develop the Talent, so much the better!"

They made some more small talk, climbing further into Gemore until they turned down a side street. They stopped before a small mansion that was set a little back from the street, behind a low wall of dark stone. Regularly spaced pillars stood atop the wall, sparking like tesla coils. They didn't have the loud pops that Nathan usually associated with that kind of display, but it was certainly eye-catching. In front of the mansion was a verdant garden decorated by trees bearing glowing fruit and bushes covered in patterned flowers.

Kullal stepped forward and waved a hand, opening a scrollwork wrought iron gate and summoning thin planes of force on either side of it to protect them from the lightning.

Huh, she didn't say any spell names. Stella doesn't usually either. I have no idea if that's a skill or just a different way of casting magic.

Nathan walked through the garden, momentarily dazzled by the sudden feeling of being in a jungle. Then they entered the house, which was large but cozy. Warm, polished wood gleamed from most surfaces, and fires crackled in almost every room without consuming any wood. Nathan's head swiveled back and forth, taking in the indisputably lavish surroundings.

I suppose being the best Adventurers around pays pretty well. And requires a shockingly *good security system.*

The group proceeded through a short hallway and descended into a richly carpeted lounge area that was clearly a viewing area for the space beyond. A series of padded benches were separated by a low wall from a large, empty room with walls of sturdy stone. The empty space had a series of training dummies on one wall and a large ring marked on the bare stone floor.

Stella took the lead, walking down an aisle and pushing open a small gate into the stone-floored training space. She conjured a flame and started tossing it from hand to hand, clearly excited as she whispered something to her mother.

Nathan made to follow her but stopped when Dalo put a restraining hand on his shoulder.

"Pardon, but I wish to ask some questions before we begin. I'm afraid I'm not entirely comfortable with providing aid to somebody we know so little about. Nathan, is there anything you can tell me about yourself to lighten my mind? Where you are from or what your goals are, for example?"

Nathan looked back at the kindly man behind him. Dalo's face wore a neutral expression, but his eyes were focused unerringly on Nathan's. Nathan remembered the first time he'd met this man's eyes and the blinding glare they'd held then. He could see that spark in Dalo's eyes now, and it was a reminder that no matter his [Magic Resistance], his friend's father could probably obliterate him.

And whatever hill I'm currently standing on.

Nathan took a deep breath, activating [Focused Mind] to push away a fearful shudder and plan his next words carefully. Then, he spoke. "I swear to you on my word and my honor that I have no ill intentions for you, your daughter or Gemore as a whole. You have saved my life, and I do not wish to betray that gift. I was abducted from my home by a Giantsrest archmage, and narrowly escaped enslavement at his hands. I may seek to return home *eventually,* but for now my goal is to fight Giantsrest." He spread his hands wide.

"I will never forgive Taeol for what he tried to do to me. And beyond him – the entire culture of Giantsrest seems focused around disregarding the agency and personhood of others. My ultimate goal is to see their philosophy destroyed, the elite of Giantsrest dead or scattered. It seems the only way to prevent them from enslaving all around them is with force." Then Nathan waved around the room, encapsulating the city. "I also wish to find a home on Davrar, and Gemore seems like a pretty nice place."

Low-tier Earnestness Rank 9 achieved!

Dalo studied him for a moment longer, pursing his lips slightly. Then, he released Nathan's shoulder and stepped back, his expression changing to a sad smile. "I understand, many who escape Giantsrest wish them destroyed. They are an enemy of Gemore. See that your desire leaves space for caution, and I would warn you to not drag my daughter or the other Heirs into a doomed fight. They are to be our *heirs*, not fodder for your crusade. If they decide to help topple the city of Giants, let it be when they are older, wiser and more powerful. But our purpose here today aligns with both of our goals, so let us proceed."

Chapter 26

A Mage's Insight

"Dad! You're being really rude! I told you Nathan's all good. You're not just insulting him, you're insulting my judgment of character!"

Stella's yell interrupted the man-to-man moment, and Dalo shrugged apologetically. The gesture seemed to say, "I'm sorry, but I had to check." He gestured Nathan forward with a slight bow of his head.

Nathan entered the ring, feeling sheepish. Stella looked annoyed, and Kullal was giving her husband a knowing and not-entirely-pleased look. Then she turned to Nathan and said, "We know how to teach magic, but that's not what you need, is it? Stella says you want to experience more spells and mana types, but how? If you don't have a way to manipulate mana, how can we demonstrate spells?"

Nathan looked around the room, then shrugged and walked to its center, before sitting on the stone ground and removing his shirt. He looked up at Dalo and Kullal. "Yes, that's about right. The way I learn about spells is by absorbing them. It takes a while before I get good at it, so please go easy on me at the start. I've got the most experience with fire and force magic because of practicing with Stella, but I've got some experience with earth and shadow. And I guess mental magic from Giantsrest, and necromancy from the Grave Tangle?"

Kullal rubbed her hands together. "We call the kind of mana that was in the Grave Tangle death mana. And most mental spells just require basic mana, though they are complex spells. But it appears somebody is volunteering to be a target dummy. Dear, I think you're best suited to starting out."

Dalo shrugged, then zapped Nathan with a small lightning bolt.

It happened instantaneously. One moment he was fine, the next there was a *crack* and his muscles gave a brief spasm. Nathan looked up to see Dalo inspecting him curiously.

"Can you do that again? A few times please, with at least five seconds in between."

Dalo's face split into a wider grin. "Indeed I can." Then he zapped Nathan again. And again.

Now that Nathan was expecting it, he focused his mind on the *feeling* of the magic. It was clearly a type of mana he hadn't experienced before. The mana felt like the buildup and release of a static shock, and carried a faint vibration like the hum of a high-voltage power line.

Once he had a grasp of it, Nathan focused on the spell, picking it apart as the fourth bolt struck him. It was simply a packet of insulated charge sent across the air and into him. He didn't understand how it was isolated and directed, but the source of danger was obvious enough.

I swear he's just sending free high-energy electrons at me using some kind of containment. But they're magical somehow? Where do they come from? Honestly, it's like asking where the conjured earth behind those [Earth Balls] came from. Magic!

Dalo pointed to cast the next bolt, and Nathan focused on controlling and guiding the magical charge around the surface of his skin, where it quickly dissipated. He'd meant to ground it into the floor, but just guiding it around him had been sufficient for the charge to be... absorbed?

Nathan felt his [Magic Resistance] *flex*, the otherworldly sense the Talent gave him sending a faint tingle through him. It was an intuitive feeling, but Nathan suppressed it all the same.

I think the Talent wants to Develop. Not yet, I can still learn more, expose myself to more magic. I'll hold onto the thought that triggered it for later. Absorption. Absorption is the key.

Meanwhile, Dalo looked at him, utterly perplexed. "How did you do that?"

Stella responded, pointing directly at Nathan. "It's amazing, Dad! That's exactly what I wanted to show you! He's gotten really good at getting rid of fireballs. Here." She tossed a fireball at Nathan.

Nathan rolled his eyes. Stella had been trying to surprise him during practice recently, wanting to test how well he could resist her magic without warning. It had been useful practice, and at this point it required next to no attention to deconstruct the fireball and *absorb* it into him.

Dalo had been slightly alarmed at Stella's casual fireball, but controlled himself as Nathan took apart the spell. Then he raised his hand once more. "Very interesting. Nathan, are you good to continue? You appear unhurt, but I would be sure."

Nathan nodded up at him, a feeling of excitement building in his chest. He had this Insight on *lock*. "I'm just peachy! Please move onto other mana types as quickly as you can."

Dalo raised an eyebrow at Nathan's strange choice of words, but proceeded nonetheless. "Let us proceed through the basic elements then. I skipped ahead with lightning, and you have already experienced earth and fire, but we will move on to air, cold and water, now." He raised a hand and a jet of wind assailed Nathan.

The spell was narrow and controlled, more like being the target of an air hose than a gust of wind. It was continuous, and though the force threatened to push Nathan backwards, he resisted and picked apart the feeling of the mana. Despite the speed, the mana felt... slow. Like it was always in motion, but never in a hurry to go anywhere. The spell itself was more complicated than the last, with some sort of spiraling pattern and a construct at the end to deliver the force effectively. Nathan bent that force construct, causing the wind to jet to the sides and destabilize the spell. It sent out a puff of air in every direction as it broke.

Dalo frowned again, shaking his hand slightly. "Fascinating. Every spell reacts differently. Now, for cold." He gestured, and the temperature around Nathan dropped. The spell chilled the air around him and tried to dig into his flesh. It slid off with no concentration on Nathan's part. The mana was absolutely still, conveying the impression of complete stasis. Nathan shook himself and the spell shattered as he imparted motion onto the mana around him.

The elderly mage didn't bother speaking, just stared intently at Nathan as he gestured again.

An orb of water appeared around Nathan's head. He hadn't anticipated it, but he had been expecting *something* weird, so he didn't panic, merely holding his breath. The spell only affected his head and followed with his movements. The water was formed of mana, and its constant motion reminded Nathan of the air mana, but slower. It damped his movement, suppressing and absorbing any energy released into it. The spell itself was surprisingly complicated, locking the mana to his head. He poked it with a finger, and the water mana flowed around his hand, resisting the attempt to flick it away.

Instead of trying to push the mana away, Nathan pulled on it, absorbing the mana into his pores, then into the bloodstream. His Talent *flexed* again, and it was all Nathan could do to keep it steady. He opened his eyes and took a deep breath.

Low-tier Spellsense Rank 8 achieved!

Mid-tier Focused Mind rank 7 achieved!

Kullal spoke up next, raising a hand to interrupt her husband. "My turn, you nearly drowned him. And since Stella has shown him some force spells, let's go with... *this*."

She made no gestures, but Nathan was suddenly encompassed by absolute blackness. It reminded him of his trip through Taeol's portal. The sudden shift was disorienting, and Nathan felt his ears pop, but it wasn't the eye-sucking vacuum of before. Nathan closed his eyes and reached out with his Talent.

There was mana there, but it was more... abstract. It was defined by an absence, like everything that made up the world had stopped existing. Nathan identified it as a new type of mana, and felt the weave of the spell. The mana felt like an *absence*, like it was the opposite of material reality. The spell was pushing things *away* from Nathan, with multiple layers of different spell patterns. Nathan guessed they were each pushing away a different aspect of the world. Not perfectly, as demonstrated by the thin layer of air around him. But all Nathan had to do was break the weave, which had already started to dissolve on contact. He sped up the process, using his Talent to grab the nothingness and *pull* it into him. The spell vanished with a faint pop.

Stella applauded, and Dalo stroked his beard again, looking pleased as he spoke. "See? It's not just elemental resistance. Void broke just like the others."

Okay, so that was void mana. Makes sense?

Kullal looked mildly frustrated. The fox-woman gestured for the first time, and Nathan's weight lightened until he began to float.

Gravity. Seriously?

Low-tier Identify Rank 5 achieved!

Nathan turned his attention to the magic, trying to ignore an immediate flash of nausea. The spell was both simple and complicated, woven of bands that felt of *weight*. There was no other way to describe it. The connections of the spell were also uniquely *dense.* They resisted Nathan's effort to break them, staying firmly anchored to one another as he pitted his will against the spell.

His concentration was disturbed by his head bumping into the ceiling. Below him, Stella chuckled, and Dalo shushed her.

This isn't working. How to break gravity? You don't. How to escape a spell that uses it? That's a better question.

He was the target of the spell that was tracking him – and only him – since there wasn't a cyclical air current in the room. As he looked again, he noticed another element to the spell. Thin wires bound the dense structure to Nathan, which he found he could more easily manipulate. They resisted for a moment and then snapped, sending him falling to the ground.

Low-tier Spellsense Rank 9 achieved!

Nathan landed on his feet, bending his knees and rolling to absorb the rather long fall. Nathan brushed a speck of imaginary dirt from his shoulder and turned towards Kullal. "Gravity mana is weird. Got any more?"

In response, beams of white light shot from Kullal's eyes and hit Nathan in the shoulder, tracing down his arm. They left a light burn behind, and Nathan focused on the feeling.

If that's a laser, it shouldn't be visible unless it's strong enough to ionize the air. And in that case, it should sound like a lightning bolt. You know, the way that this magic seems to follow some natural laws and not others is really throwing me. But it's magic, the entire point is that it doesn't follow natural laws.

The light mana was like a scorching hot wire vibrating against his skin at high speed. For all that, the spell was fairly... simple. Just lots of high-energy light mana absorbing into his skin to cause painful burns.

And it would probably blind me if it was hitting me in the eyes.

Spurred on by his earlier Insight, Nathan thought about absorbing the light without it damaging him. He didn't recall how silicon solar panels worked, but he knew photosynthesis, and he'd read a paper about how fungi could use melanin to absorb ionizing radiation. The trick was absorbing the energy as something *other than heat.* What other energy was there for him? Stamina was the obvious answer, and that thought resonated.

His Talent flexed again, and this time Nathan didn't stop it. Distracted, he spoke to the mages around him. "Please cast a variety of spells at me, *right now.*"

He closed his eyes and centered his attention on absorbing the light mana, using it to fuel his Stamina. As more spells impacted him, Nathan broadened the absorption effect. He could manipulate and resist *all* of these mana types. If he could absorb light mana, he could absorb *all* of them.

A blue box shoved its way into his vision.

Congratulations, you have Developed the [High-tier Magic Resistance] Talent into [Magic Absorption]. It starts at rank 1 and becomes more effective as it ranks up. Think about how you use your Talent's functions to aid in Talent Development at rank 10. Beware, it is harder to rank and Develop non-tiered Talents.

Permanent Talent: [Magic Absorption]
You have Developed High-tier magic Resistance Talent into a permanent pillar of your being. You are heavily resistant to all forms of magic, and can directly absorb the mana of spells cast on you into Stamina. You are forever unable to cast spells or access magic. Magical items cannot affect you and will degrade at your touch.

Mid-tier Focused Mind rank 8 achieved!

A voice penetrated into his trance. "What is *happening?* Stop, stop casting." The volley of spells quickly ended.

Nathan opened his eyes to the two older mages staring at him in befuddlement. Stella just looked excited. As soon as she saw him open his eyes, she jumped forward, bouncing from one foot to another. "Did you Develop the Talent? The spells started doing even less and all the mana got sucked into you! What does it do?"

Nathan felt his face blossom into a manic grin. This new Talent was *incredible*. He'd never use magic or magic items, but he'd already reconciled himself to that. And now he could use spells to recharge his Stamina.

He raised both his arms in triumph. "Yes! Now I absorb the mana of spells cast on me to replenish my Stamina." Nathan threw back his head and laughed.

Stella was just as excited as him. "All that I hear is that when my ally is wounded and surrounded by enemies, it's *absolutely* correct to hit him with a fireball."

They were interrupted by Dalo walking past them, holding out his hands. "I need a drink."

Two tumblers full of pink liquid flew toward him, and he handed one to Kullal. "Cheers. I think we've just witnessed the birth of a new school of anti-mage combat. Not entirely sure I'm pleased with this Development."

Meanwhile, Stella went to hug Nathan, but he held his arms out to decline. Not only was he still shirtless, but he was worried for her heavily enchanted robe. She looked upset, so he explained. "My Talent says, 'Magical items cannot affect you and will degrade at your touch.'"

"Oh." She took a step back.

Kullal choked in suprise on her drink, before elbowing Dalo. "Immune to magic, but he can't use magical items – that Talent has some serious downsides. Brightfruit isn't his only meal."

Dalo's expression brightened, but he still seemed somewhat bitter about Nathan's skill. "I bet he can use that to break curses. Do we still have that cursed wand from the Kalis Conclave teleportarium?"

Kullal frowned at her husband, pointing a finger at his forehead. "No! That's a soul-curse, and we're not experimenting with it. It's unreasonable, and you know it! *Maybe* once he's higher level, and understands the Talent better. Not before then. Now, come, I believe we have some more time to practice."

Dalo grumbled, but accepted his wife's rejoinder with only a little additional glaring on her part.

They spent the next couple of hours practicing with Nathan's Talent, and he was glad to have powerful mages on hand who could help him figure it out. His Development had made Nathan even more magic-resistant than he'd been before, though powerful spells that Nathan wasn't good at converting could still injure him.

> **Low-tier Spellsense Rank 10 achieved!** Congratulations, you have maxed out this skill! It cannot be improved any further. You must achieve Insight into this skill to Develop it to the next level.

It took some time to determine what the variables on the conversion efficiency of the Talent were, and they finally cracked it once Nathan stopped the mages from randomly casting spells on him, making them test one hypothesis at a time.

If Nathan understood the structure of the spells and purposefully disrupted them like he had earlier in the day, that made absorption better. He was more efficient at gaining Stamina from single-target spells that directly affected him and nothing else. Mana type also made a difference. He was pretty good with light, fire, cold, electricity and water; only middling with gravity, earth and air; and pretty bad with void, force and, surprisingly enough, basic mana.

The Stamina he replenished was dependent on the amount of mana spent on the spell. Nathan couldn't generate tons of Stamina from a low-powered spell. But, it seemed he could hit the max efficiency if he fulfilled two out of three criteria: if he understood the spell, if it was single target, or if the mana types were in his favor.

Awesome. Artha said I needed a way to replenish Stamina, and it's hard for me to think of a better way than absorbing magic. Especially when my enemies specialize in magic and I've got a prodigy mage on my team.

~

Talent text comparison:

Permanent Talent: [High-tier Magic Resistance]
Your body has no magic inside it, and magic-resistant alchemical ingredients permeate your bones and brain, making you difficult to affect with magic. This Talent will turn a personal quirk into a personal Talent. You will be able to resist and interfere with spells, and will have great difficulty casting spells. Less effect on higher-tier spells. Magical items will have less effect on you, and weaker magical items degrade when in prolonged contact with you.

Permanent Talent: [Magic Absorption]
You have Developed High-tier magic Resistance Talent into a permanent pillar of your being. You are heavily resistant to all forms of magic, and can directly absorb the mana of spells cast on you into Stamina. You are forever unable to cast spells or access magic. Magical items cannot affect you and will degrade at your touch.

Chapter 27

A Mage's Feast

They emerged from the basement into an absolute cacophony of noise coming from the back of the house. Nathan looked questioningly at Stella, who shrugged.

"It's probably just Cantas cooking. She gets a little intense. You want to see? Come on."

Nathan followed Stella, curious as to how one person could be making that much noise. It sounded like a construction site, not someone cooking. They poked their heads around the corner into the kitchen, and Nathan was amazed. Cantas was a thickset woman with pale skin and a shaved head. She was missing an ear, her arms were heavily muscled and she was using clearly enchanted tools.

Behind her, a set of knives were busy chopping vegetables. A pot stirred itself over a magical fire, the spoon banging against the sides. Cantas herself was busy dissecting an animal larger than Nathan with an enormous cleaver. He couldn't tell what it was, given that it was already in six pieces. As he watched, she removed a rib roast from an oven, plopping it into an enormous bowl full of smoking, dark liquid.

It was starting to smell *good*. There was a spiced fragrance reminiscent of tikka masala and another like smoke and pepper. Judging from the piles of food being processed, this was not going to be a small gathering. Nathan looked to Stella and asked, "How many people are coming today?"

Stella shrugged. "It changes. It's usually Stanel and the Guardians of

Gemore. Usually Aarl, Sarah and Khachi come along. Sometimes some other adventurers get invited and occasionally various Guildmasters. My mom banned too many of the council from coming at once or else it becomes a work meeting."

She led him away from the kitchen and they rejoined her parents, who were cuddling on a couch in the foyer. It had a nice view overlooking the entrance.

He and Stella took up other seats, settling into overstuffed armchairs that were scattered around. Nathan was tempted to speak up and ask more questions, but Dalo and Kullal seemed content to sit in silence, and Stella had pulled out some sort of scroll and started reading.

So, Nathan just sat quietly, thinking about his afternoon in more detail. His new Talent changed... everything. [Magic Absorption] was better at protecting Nathan from magic than [Magic Resistance] had been, *and* it restored his Stamina at the same time. It filled the hole in his build that Artha had pointed out and would make him a peerless anti-mage. Even Dalo had acknowledged that, though he still seemed off put by the very idea of Nathan's Talent existing. He had all but asked Nathan to not teach it to anybody.

Nathan took a deep breath, trying not to run away with his excitement. Against normal soldiers and monsters that didn't use magic, the Talent would be useless. Well, not entirely. Stella had already caught onto the fact that she could recharge his Stamina by blowing him up. It would even hit any nearby enemies as well. Nathan was a bit worried about what that meant for his clothing costs. Maybe if he got the unarmored defensive skill he could go into battle with less clothing? Nathan snorted at the idea. He'd heard of the Celts running into battle ass-bare, but had never imagined that he'd consider it.

I'll go on a quest for indestructible boxers if I need to. I'm sure one of these random doom tombs has a pair lying around somewhere.

Returning to the thought of Stella replenishing his Stamina, he'd noticed that both she and her parents could cast seemingly without end. Mages were supposed to have mana as a class resource, scaling with their level and recharging slowly but constantly. It was likely they had some powerful Talent or skill that either dramatically enlarged their mana pools or gave them ridiculous regen.

"Hey Stella, just asking, but it seems like you have really high mana regen. I don't need to know how, but as long as you're around it doesn't seem like I need to worry too much about Stamina regeneration. Is that right?"

Dalo looked over with a frown. "Observant little meatroach, aren't you? We did go all the way up the mountain just now, so it's not a surprise. *Don't* mention it to anybody."

Kullal rolled her eyes and licked Dalo's ear, eliciting a squawk. "Don't be a wight, they're on a team together. They should know each other's strengths and weaknesses" She paused to nestle against him. "I know you want to stick your sword in, but don't be a nuisance. Our daughter seems to have given her trust."

Dalo harrumphed. "We'll see what Kia says. I just want to make sure they don't make any youthful mistakes. And the mysterious stranger from far away is *still* not a story I trust."

Stella looked chagrined at her parents' interplay, shooting Nathan an apologetic look and fingering her braid.

I appreciate Stella being apologetic about this. I'm getting annoyed at all the gatekeeping, and feeling like she's on my side makes me a lot less upset about it. Still frustrating for Dalo to act this way when I feel like I've proved myself multiple times.

Before his flash of anger could push him toward anything unwise, Nathan stilled his mind, counting out a few deep breaths.

He tried to look at the situation from Dalo's perspective. A strange man had joined his daughter's adventuring team. A man without any verifiable past and abilities that seemed tailor-made to pose a threat. Dalo knew that there were people who would attack Stella, and was paranoid from a life of adventuring.

In that light, it made a lot more sense. He'd convinced the Heirs he deserved to be among them with his powerful Talents and some amount of braggadocio. Now he needed to convince their parents he'd help keep their children safe and wasn't going to unnecessarily endanger them through betrayal or any suicidal plans to attack Giantsrest.

~

It soon became clear they were seated in the front room so Kullal could magically open the gate every time a guest arrived. The guests trickled into the foyer, sitting and chatting.

Nathan was drawn into conversation a few times, but he was keeping a close eye on the door to make sure he noticed everybody who arrived. The first was Leska Bhola, the stylish, dark-skinned archer of the Guardians. He was once again dressed in tight leather pants, but this time wore a sharply cut purple vest that left his well-muscled chest bare. He had brought his enormous bow, but left it and a small quiver propped on a stand next to the door. He hugged Kullal before giving Dalo an elaborate handshake.

Kia was next, with Khachi in tow. They were both dressed in shining armor, which brought out a certain family resemblance that wasn't otherwise shared between the muscular red-haired woman and the young wolfman. Kia wasn't dressed in full plate like Khachi – merely a breastplate, vambraces and greaves of shining metal. Seeing Kia next to Khachi, it was clear that she had a qualitative advantage in shininess.

Do they have a skill for that? Might be part of the whole paladin-thing.

They also left their weapons at the door, Kia's oversized greatsword resting on a rack clearly meant for it. She was still armed with a dagger and shortsword, while Khachi had a small mace strapped to his shin. Keeping weapons at hand was just an *obsession* with these people. Though that might just be Kia, she struck Nathan as a "constant vigilance" sort of person.

Aarl and Sarah came through the door next, accompanied by a man who had to be Stanel Crusens. He shared their copper-skinned good looks, with a sharply trimmed black beard and a similar pouch on his belt as his children, probably likewise containing a whole armory's worth of weapons. He was corded with muscles and covered in scars, most old enough to be faint lines.

Xarian Doulna arrived last, the diminutive orange-skinned woman dressed in a classic "little black dress" that clung to her curves just as her adventuring leathers had. And they were some *curves*. She wasn't carrying weapons besides a small purse, but Nathan remembered how she'd turned pebbles into fortifications and projectiles worthy of siege warfare.

The Guardians made smalltalk for a little longer before Xarian drew Nathan into the center of attention. "I recall your face, Nathan Lark. I'm a bit surprised to see you again, given that the last time you were part of a refugee convoy from a Giantsrest Raid. Village folk don't often join the Adventurers, and are even more rarely placed in such company as the Heirs."

Kia responded, twirling a goblet in her hands as her eyes tracked Nathan like a pair of battleship guns. "But he's not from the villages, is he? My greetings, Nathan Lark. Khachi says good things about you. When I spoke with Vhala, she said you'd escaped from an archmage research tower, and defeated three slaver mages in ambush. She did say that you had a fire in your core, and rare advantages that few may claim. May I ask you for your story?"

Nathan noticed that the other conversations had trailed off, and everybody was listening. About half of them had heard this story before, and Sarah gave Nathan a subtle encouraging gesture. Nathan took a moment to calmly meet Kia's eyes. She was one of the most intimidating people he'd ever met – tied with that one Nobel laureate whose lab Nathan had interviewed for. But he'd give her calm certainty, and earnestly stick to the story he'd decided on. It had to be the fourth time he'd explained this, but he supposed it made sense for people to keep asking.

"I was abducted from my home by Taeol dho Droxol, a Giantsrest archmage working on dimensional research. He yanked me through a portal from my home into his tower. It didn't take me long to learn that he's the kind of person who *will* have what he desires, regardless of what those around him want. So, I escaped. It wasn't a simple process, and I gained a powerful antimagic Talent along the way. I later Developed a self-healing Talent to heal the injuries sustained on the run."

Kia didn't seem surprised by any of that. She broke eye contact to look down at her goblet. "This was something Vhala said too. You won conflict with an archmage? With yourself being under level 27? I will not ask for your class, but it must be worthy of a lich." She seemed skeptical, but not disbelieving.

Cards on the table! I have the feeling that evasion would not serve me well with a paladin.

Nathan smiled at her skepticism. "I wouldn't say I won that conflict. He removed my arm with a [Disintegrate]; I broke his nose. I wasn't even level 9 at that point, and I picked my class while fleeing from his Golems after he teleported out. It was the most terrifying thing that's ever happened to me, and the only thing I cared about was escaping the clutches of the man who sought to own me."

Low-tier Earnestness Rank 10 achieved! Congratulations, you have maxed out this skill! It cannot be improved any further. You must achieve Insight into this skill to Develop it to the next level.

Kia's frown deepened and she shook her head. "I cannot tell if you speak the truth, and it concerns me. Somebody of your age, under level 9? For this story to run true, your home must indeed be a strange place, and your antimagic Talent must exceed any I've ever heard of." She looked to Dalo. "Dalo, have you tested it?."

Dalo ran a hand through his beard. "It is... potent. I can see how it would allow somebody to surprise an unprepared archmage, even without a class to back it up. They really *do* depend on magic for everything, and Nathan's Talent is powerful against all magic. Given its nature, I would expect it to be extraordinarily effective against mental magic in particular. I don't believe that the archmages of Giantsrest would encourage the Development of such an Insight. It would be far too easily turned against them."

Oh, was that *what they were concerned about? I guess it makes sense – I escaped from a Giantsrest research tower with a new Talent none of them had ever seen before.*

Kia gave a short "hmmm," then asked a simple question which seemed to carry a deeper meaning. "Does he have the spark?"

Dalo nodded, looking to his wife with a sigh. "Yes, I do think he does."

Nathan shot an inquisitive glance to Stella and Khachi. Khachi wasn't looking his way, but Stella shrugged in response. She didn't know what they were talking about, or couldn't explain.

Kullal clapped her hands together, and changed the subject. "Well, I do believe we've kept Cantas waiting long enough. Up and down my friends, let us enjoy our meals."

Most of the group collected their drinks and got up, though the dark-skinned archer – Leska – clapped Nathan on the shoulder. "I'm pleased to see you again, friend. It's rare enough we Adventurers get to save people, and rarer still to spend time with those we save. I'm hoping that you'll be with the Heirs 'till the End. Or at least until they earn a different name."

With that, they went to eat, drink, and talk. Cantas appeared to have left after depositing serving plates on the table, but the food was amazing. It was very different from anything Nathan had ever had before, but that just added to the thrill.

Is this thick, curry-like dish going to be sweet, savory or spicy?

Nathan didn't know until he tried it! Nobody breathed fire from the heat, though a few dishes pushed the edge of Nathan's tolerance. [Regeneration] didn't make him immune to lighting his taste buds on fire.

There was small talk around the table, but it either referenced the excellent food, or dealt with adventurer politics that Nathan didn't have the context for. There seemed to be some controversy over assignments on the last Delve day, certain teams claiming they hadn't even gotten through the doors of their targets before the day was called off due to the Grave Tangle. These "traditionalists" were calling for extra favors due to the inconvenience.

After the meal had been demolished, Kullal used a spell to stack the plates and sent them into a wash basin, where Dalo summoned a small whirlpool. Then, several fluted bottles of colored liquid flew out of a cabinet, accompanied by small glasses.

"Ah. This kind of convenience is why we do this *here*. No need to serve yourself when the magic can do it all for you!" Stanel stretched back in his chair, reaching for the glass floating toward him. It evaded his hand and bonked him on the forehead before landing on the table. He glared at Kullal, but she looked like butter wouldn't melt in her mouth.

Stanel broke off, clearly giving up that battle as unwinabble. He turned to address The Heirs, who were all seated at one end of the table. "Anyway, something else we wanted to tell you all. You're going on your Blooding Patrol in two days. We've arranged for it to be the first of your class. Won't be too bad, just out north, a little ways and back. Dice a few stalkers, maybe even pick up some levels."

There was a moment of silence, while the older Adventurers waited for a reaction.

Sarah provided it. "Isn't the north the most dangerous part of the near ruins? More people go missing there than in any other part of Old Gemore."

Kia answered, pouring a drink of a dark purple liquid. "Yes. But for you, nothing else is suitable. The Blooding Patrol is an old tradition about the first mission a new team takes. Observing that tradition properly, while integrating it with the new training course, will quiet some grumbling about Sudraiel's changes. So. The near north sector. Without support."

There was another moment of silence, which Xarian promptly broke. "Weapons up, friends. You're ready for this. Don't get in your own way and things will be fine. I remember our Blooding Patrol well. A couple of earth stalkers and a lost siegeboar, it wasn't anything to worry over even back then. Easy levels."

Khachi spoke up, argumentative. "But Nathan doesn't even have a weapon! He's good with his fists, but that won't do much against an earth stalker, much less a siegeboar!"

Stanel shrugged, drinking from his own cup of glowing amber liquid. "Easy enough to solve. What's your preference, Nathan? Any Talent or skill benefits or restrictions?"

Nathan was pouring himself a drink of the purple liquor. He didn't know what it was, but it was purple, and that was cool. He looked up at Stanel's question. "I really haven't trained with any weapons, and none of my skills or Talents have anything to do with weapons. Except my antimagic Talent says I'll degrade magical items with a touch."

Everybody around the table reacted with varying degrees of surprise. Kia merely raised one elegant eyebrow. Leska goggled a bit, his eyes going wide. Stanel merely looked thoughtful, then snapped his fingers.

"Here, I think this might serve nicely." His hand flickered, and all of a sudden a spear landed next to Nathan's seat with a *thud*. The butt of the spear had hit the floor and the shaft was leaning against his chair, vibrating slightly with the force of the toss.

Stanel continued as if he hadn't just thrown a weapon across the dinner table while holding a glass of alcohol. "A spear's easy to use. You'll have the reach on most things, just keep the pointy end facing them. Maybe poke a little. That spear *is* enchanted for extreme sharpness and durability, but only the spearhead is enchanted. The haft's just made from Everoak. Don't touch the spearhead and it'll do well enough."

Nathan tentatively touched the polished haft, looking up towards the spearhead. The shaft was made of a heavy wood, so dark red as to be nearly black. The spearhead was a broad triangle of polished, orange metal about the size of Nathan's hand, etched with tiny symbols.

Nathan looked back at Stanel. "Thank you very much. I appreciate this."

Stanel waved a hand. "I am glad to give to somebody who would stand with my children. Wield it well. Now, drink your Umna, I only assume you picked it because you didn't know what it is."

Kia, who also had a glass of the purple liquor, loudly slurped a mouthful. "Don't listen to him. He hasn't had taste since he caught a fireball with his face."

Nathan tried the purple drink – Umna? It was thick, almost syrupy. The taste was very fruity, but not overbearingly sweet and with a tang of acid. Nathan had always liked his drinks fruity, though it would probably be improved with ice. But ice in drinks didn't seem to be a thing here. He shrugged and drank his syrupy, purple drink as the conversation moved to other topics.

Some hours of good conversation later, Nathan walked with the other Heirs back to the Adventurer complex. Kia was with them, and both she and Khachi seemed to have healed themselves from the drunkenness. They wouldn't share, and Nathan couldn't do the same with [Regeneration]. He'd tried. And he wasn't drunk, just... tipsy. Rather tipsy. He was glad that Kia was with them, otherwise he'd feel paranoid about getting jumped as they staggered down the steep hill.

Some water later, they'd all gone to bed, resolved to train with new vigor in the morning to prepare for the Blooding Patrol. As Nathan sat and thought about the day before sleep, he was sure of one thing. The Blooding Patrol was a very ominous name.

Chapter 28

Preparations for a Patrol

The next two days passed even more quickly, the impending trial lending an air of determination to their exercises. Stella pushed harder during the morning run, and Nathan was once again rewarded for his intensive exercise.

Low-tier Sprinting Rank 8 achieved!

Nathan filled everybody in on the basics of [Magic Absorption]. It seemed necessary to explain why he *wanted* to get hit with fireballs now. They already knew he was resistant to magic, but he told them he now directly *benefited* from it.

He received a round of disbelieving reactions.

Sarah's response was wry and self-deprecating. "Nathan's becoming the real monster-eater, showing us how adventuring is really done. All we've got is our parents' treasure."

Aarl remained unfazed, a faint wry grin on his face. "He still needs us for some things. Like showing him how to hold a spear. *Not like that!*"

Aarl proceeded to drill Nathan in combat exercises with his new spear. It really was a very simple weapon, and a basic thrusting motion was usually the best choice. And very effective. So long as Nathan kept the spear pointing the right direction, nobody could get close enough to hit him without having to do something fancy to get past the point. A few times Nathan was tempted to twirl it like a staff, but Aarl chided him when he suggested it.

"If you had a short spear that might be more effective. But your spear is about eight feet long and not weighted for that. You've got a longer reach than anything we might face except a muckgrabber, and if something gets in close you're better off using your fists. I'd give you an ax instead, but your class seems focused on punching things." Aarl snorted, shaking his head at the idea of a fighting class that didn't use weapons.

The next day Jolba introduced the Blooding Patrol to all of the trainees. Most were already familiar with it, but Jolba went over the plan in detail. Every other day a different team would go out into the ruins, patrolling near the transit roads to keep the vital links between Gemore and the villages safe. Given the size of the ruins, it was one of the most common Adventurer jobs in Gemore, with a carefully managed schedule ensuring that every section of the roads was patrolled every month or so. They didn't patrol the eastern road very often, since it led to Giantsrest. The people who went that way most often were Adventurers, and they could handle themselves.

Jolba then went through appropriate responses to different situations. If the team found a small threat, they dealt with it. If they found a larger threat, they were expected to determine its scope and retreat to Gemore so a specialized team could be sent to deal with it. Most of the common monsters were considered "small threats" unless encountered in excessive quantities. The chatter around the classroom indicated it was considered shameful to retreat in the face of stalkers, lesser undead or similar monsters.

Jolba tried to dispel that notion, slapping down the loudest voice. His name was Simla, the same black-skinned human man who'd been in a shouting match with Khachi when Nathan was first introduced to the Heirs.

Jolba rode roughshod over his protests. "Your priority is to come back *alive and unmaimed*. It's called the Blooding Patrol because it's the first time you spill *monster* blood, not an attempt to spill your own blood. We need these roads safe to keep Gemore connected to the villages that feed us. That means we need to have teams to do that. Those teams need to prioritize staying alive, so they can keep doing their job! This isn't about glory seeking, it's about keeping you and your teammates alive, so you can keep *Gemore* alive."

Without [Notice], he wouldn't have caught Simla's muttered response. "Retreat just means you aren't good enough."

If Jolba heard it, he didn't respond, and the lesson continued. Jolba laid out the schedule for when each team would go, and approximately where they would patrol. Nobody besides the Heirs were scheduled to patrol the northern ruins. Most of the patrols were located to the south and east, and the target areas were close to the city. The Heirs' patrol stood out on the map like a sore thumb, located about a third of the way along the north transit road.

The patrol itself was relatively simple, with no set route. You went to a landmark and then searched the ruins nearby. Most teams had some way of detecting monsters, be it magic, tracking or perception skills, and they were expected to use them to investigate the area. The patrol was to take the entire day, leaving shortly after the sun started shining and returning before nightfall.

That afternoon, they had their final practice before the patrol. They went through some group formations and worked on some last minute techniques. Of particular interest was the new strategy of "Throw fireballs at Nathan." It was a lot more effective if the fireball landed *close* to Nathan instead of *hitting* him. If Stella squarely hit Nathan, he tended to absorb the entire spell. It led to some amusing *blip* sounds instead of the normal *kaboom.* But if Stella instead landed the fireball near to Nathan, he didn't get back quite as much Stamina – but he didn't absorb the entire spell either. Nathan suggested they name the practice "Danger Close," which he would yell when requesting a fireball, or Stella would yell if she was hucking one in his direction. It also helped Aarl and Khachi know when to back up.

Nathan practiced dodging to the perfect distance from the fireball, so he would absorb as much of the spell as possible without disrupting the portions of the blast aimed away from him.

Low-tier Dodging Footwork 5 achieved!

The night before their patrol was quiet, almost contemplative. They all returned from their tutoring before dinner, with Nathan still contemplating Artha's lessons on how to hold onto tactical thought while in the grips of Rage. It boiled down to being able to control the target of your Rage – being mad at the *right* thing instead of *everything*.

The meal was good as usual – chunks of roasted meat with dark grain, spiced with herbs that tasted a lot like rosemary. But the Heirs sat around the table quietly and ate their food without conversation. There was a faintly funerary air in the dining hall. Nathan didn't like it at all. But if he started speaking loudly about unrelated topics it would only highlight the dour mood.

So, better to be productive. "Hey, let's go over our formation and doctrine tomorrow. Jolba talked about good positioning and target prioritization, but we should figure it out for ourselves. Yeah?"

Khachi shot Nathan an odd look. They'd discussed this topic before, during their practice sessions in the private arena.

Nathan responded by flicking his eyes and rolling his head in a circle, to indicate all of the other trainees in the room.

We're supposed to be examples of what Gemore Adventurers should be. So, let's be examples.

Khachi adopted a pensive expression, then raised his head and looked around the table. "Yes, this is a good topic to speak on. My mother had some advice on this. We have two powerful ranged strikers, but they lack mobility. She suggested a diamond formation, with Nathan at the front, Sarah at the rear, and Stella in the center. Aarl and I take the sides, where we can react quickly towards threats coming from all sides. Sarah is responsible for keeping an eye on the rear, but to all accounts and purposes, Nathan has the best perception skills of any of us. Is this acceptable?"

The other members of the team nodded, looking thoughtful but not offering any insights. For the sake of conversation, Nathan asked, "Why not a simple line formation? Melee fighters at the front and rear, Sarah and Stella in the middle?"

Aarl answered, warming to the topic. "The diamond gives us room to maneuver. If somebody is attacked by surprise then they have room to retreat. Additionally, it allows us to most easily form a fighting line facing any direction, especially the front, without anybody running into anybody else. Clearer sight lines. We're also less likely to all be caught in a single trap or area effect. To reach Stella, an attacker would need to go through one of us, and it's least likely to be Sarah given our direction of movement. Lots of reasons to take that shape."

Nathan nodded, surprised by none of this. As he looked around the still-quiet dining hall, it was clear that most of the other trainees were listening in. "Sounds good. But we should plan on those contingencies. It sounds like our overall strategy is to rely on Sarah and Stella to attack from range, and the rest of us should defend them and deal with anything that gets too close. Or are us melee folks planning to be more offensive?"

Khachi shrugged. "It depends on the threat, and what approach is best suited to dealing with it. We're lucky we have a lot of ways to deal with enemies, between Stella's magic, my hammer and the Caxol twins' flexibility. Stanel's famous for always having the right weapon for the job, and with two miniature versions of him, we can approximate that."

Sarah punched Khachi in the shoulder as Stella stole his dessert – but the mood was broken. They sat and chatted about the various monsters they might face. The process of talking about it had renewed their confidence. They knew what was waiting for them tomorrow, and they knew how to deal with it.

The mood carried into their suite after dinner, where the team sat around the table in the common room, talking more specifically about their responses to various threats. Nathan was a little frustrated since his role mostly boiled down to, "use [Notice] to spot enemies, then hold the line with his spear." It didn't seem like his skillset was very helpful in most situations they expected to run into. Especially given how many of them were easily solved by Stella hitting the threat with a fireball. She was quite pleased with that.

I mean yeah. Judicious application of explosions solves a lot of problems.

As it was getting late, Nathan asked one more question. "What if Giantsrest tries to ambush us while we're out on patrol?"

That brought the mood down again.

Sarah answered slowly. "It's possible, but unlikely. Old Gemore is big, and nobody knew where or when our patrol was going until today, and even then it's only approximate. The ruins are our territory, not theirs, and Giantsrest doesn't know the dangers very well. If your archmage decides to come for us... Well, I wouldn't be surprised if our parents were on the lookout for that. I know there are ways to detect [Teleport] spells. They're not supposed to watch over us directly because Davrar won't award levels if you're never in any danger, but I expect there are preparations we don't know about. And *won't* know about, unless they're needed. And what else can they do? We're supposed to be *Adventurers*, not children who need babysitters."

There was nothing much more to say, so they went to bed quite early. Nathan felt like it was the night before a big test. Which it was, in a sense, just with higher stakes than any test he'd ever taken.

I dunno, some of those big standardized tests had pretty high stakes. I can't imagine how my life on Earth would have gone if I'd flunked the SAT.

So, Nathan did what he'd learned to do to calm down. He meditated. Not with any specific goals in mind, just focusing on how he felt. He was anxious, unsurprisingly.

Somewhere between five and fifteen minutes later, Nathan was relaxed instead of anxious. He opened his eyes and had a realization that brought back most of the anxiety.

Shit. I might lose my disadvantaged status from Davrar tomorrow. If we fight, and I level up past 27, there's a good chance. Okay. Did I have any ideas for specific skills and Talents I want to get? That I can *get in one night?*

Nathan thought about it for a minute. He didn't have any great ideas for Talents. He'd been meaning to spend more time considering it, but his days had been busy. He didn't want to gamble on a Talent that might end up permanent.

He had more ideas for skills, but he was starting to get close to the cap. And a lot of his skill ideas would be great for his *old* life. But Davrar really didn't have much in the way of pipettes or culture hoods. He needed skills that would be useful *here*. And utility skills were rarely directly useful for combat – so he almost certainly couldn't just practice old martial arts forms and hope it gave him a skill.

Put like that, there was one skill that Nathan had never doubted he'd try to pick up. However, he first brought up and rejected the [Reading] skill. His reasoning was fairly simple – he could do a fine job without it, and he didn't want to risk having a pending skill preventing further skills from being unlocked. He needed to be capable of reading, but he didn't need to excel at it. He *did* need a skill to improve his memory, to help him remember technical details from Earth. It was time to figure that out.

Luckily, Nathan had some knowledge and experience from Earth to help him with acquiring a memory skill. He'd read about memory techniques a few times, first when he tried to memorize the first hundred digits of pi in middle school, and then later when he was thinking about applying to medical school. After watching Sherlock in the first year of graduate school, he'd used a Mind Palace to help him retain facts for his qualifying exams. He hadn't used the technique a lot since then. He'd had all these grand plans to learn everything there was to know in his field and use his Mind Palace to remember it all. But then he'd gotten busy, and hadn't had the time or energy to make it happen.

But! He remembered the basic shape of the Palace he'd built. Nathan closed his eyes and focused, imagining the familiar structure. He always started at the back door of his childhood home. Inside the home he'd put biology knowledge. The yard outside held everything else. He'd always liked the irony to that. The living room with comfortable couches held the basics of biochemistry. The big loveseat represented the central dogma, and each pillow stood for a process in converting genetic code to protein. The world map on the wall was covered with the flashcards he'd used to learn the amino acids, laid over various landmasses. The bookcase was full, but only four books were important. Each one held the core chemical structures and common variations of the four primary classes of biomolecules. The TV cabinet was associated with central carbon metabolism, with each process of glycolysis as a separate VCR tape. On top was The Lion King, representing good old hexokinase, turning glucose into G6P. The citric acid cycle was represented by the DVDs stored on the next shelf down.

Nathan breathed through his nose, surprised at how well it all came back to him. This part of the house was easy – this was all bedrock knowledge he'd remember even if he didn't have the Mind Palace. He left the living room, walking past the kitchen where all of the chemistry relevant to biology was. Then there was his dad's office, where he'd put microbiology. His bedroom had eukaryotic cell biology, long a favorite topic, and the associated bathroom was bacterial cell biology. Fitting. But again, that wasn't pushing the limits.

He went upstairs to the computer room. This was where he'd put the eukaryotic transcriptional regulation knowledge. He'd gotten used to looking up the transcriptional regulatory networks instead of trying to remember them. But for his qualifying exam, he'd memorized as many as he could because one of his committee members had been infamous for grilling people over minutiae.

It was hard, and took effort and focus. Nathan first recalled the hours he'd spent playing *Starcraft* in this room when he was young. He remembered the shape, the way the tables were piled with boxes of hardware, disc cases and scattered books. The slightly musty smell of the old carpet. But he couldn't remember the details he'd assigned to all of them.

Start with the big things, the obvious things. The chair in front of the computer was mTor, that one was easy. The things on the tables around it interacted with it. That book on the Colorado Watershed was Atk, or protein kinase B, which he knew interacted with mTor because the book was right next to the table. It encouraged cell proliferation and tended to be involved in cancer. He knew that without the mental construct, but then he saw the bookmarks in the book. In real life, each of those had marked a river that Nathan's dad enjoyed kayaking. Here, they stood for important details about how Atk worked. The first one had something to do with fats. Lipids?

Nathan continued to fill in half-remembered details based on his memory of the room. He'd stuck details about epigenetics and chromatin packing into the pile of magazines in the corner, which he used to leaf through while waiting for matchmaking. Most of the details were things he was sure he couldn't recall without the memory construct.

Nathan proceeded like this for some time. It felt like hours passed as he explored every corner of the room, before mentally returning downstairs and heading outside. He remembered the yard in detail, but hadn't attached many memories to it. When he was experimenting with the Mind Palace, Nathan had associated the plots of some of his favorite books with the garden, but it hadn't gone very well. There was a bit of math knowledge in the treehouse, and he spent some time going over the linear algebra and multivariable calculus that he'd studied in undergrad, trying to associate it with the treehouse. He wanted his skill to help him recall *past* knowledge, not just remember things he already knew.

With a sigh, Nathan opened his eyes, hoping for a blue box. He was rewarded.

Pending utility skill: Mid-tier Enhanced Memory
You have created a detailed mental construct to aid with memory. This skill will help you store and recall memories quickly. Only provides fast recall for memories gained after gaining this skill, or memories stored in your mental construct. With time and effort, you can recall older memories and store them in the mental construct.

I could certainly hope for more, but it'll do. Mid-tier, too. Thanks Davrar!

Congratulations, you have accepted the 'Mid-tier Enhanced Memory' utility skill

With that, Nathan looked around his room. All was set and ready for bed, but now he was excited about the new skill! He *should* sleep, but first he wanted to try and see what he could recall. It was time for all that late-night, curiosity-driven Wikipedia browsing to pay off.

As a first experimental topic, Nathan decided to see what he could remember of gun design. Nathan had never mucked about with gunsmithing, but he'd taken classes on the Meiji restoration and the American Civil War and become interested in gun design off that. He'd also read about the history of the old west revolvers, and had scanned across a few design schematics and YouTube videos of how revolvers, lever-action and bolt-action rifles worked. It was fascinating to track the development of gun design over time, since it was almost an evolutionary process. Successful ideas would take over the industry, and then variations would be created until a new, optimal design was found.

Nathan didn't know if he wanted to make a gun, and he *certainly* didn't have the metalworking expertise to do it on his own. But it was hard to imagine how his *actual* expertise in human cell biology could be applied here beyond [Regeneration]. He could grow cells in a flask and do some pretty cool things with them, but he'd noticed a distinct lack of flasks, media and incubators around here. By contrast, Nathan had been surprised at the tools and quality of metalwork that Vhala's cousin Beatred had. It hadn't been a modern machine shop, but it was a lot closer to it than Nathan had expected to see in a world like this. And alchemy was an established field, though it seemed to focus on magical elixirs more than anything else.

Nathan decided it was time to make a new Mind Palace to store his recalled memories. He liked what he'd built in his childhood home, but it seemed like a relic of his life on Earth. He wouldn't be in a rush to forget it, but he also didn't want to fill all of the available space with technical knowledge for use on Davrar. That would require a new Mind Palace.

What would be a good setting? It didn't need to be a physical place, though it was definitely the easiest. A place that you knew well was ideal, with a lot of unique objects you could use as prompts for various pieces of knowledge. A map from a video game? Maybe the world map of one of the *Horizon* games? After a moment of thought, Nathan smiled. He knew *exactly* what he'd tie his new Mind Palace to.

He'd spent more time in the lab in the past four years than doing anything else, and could remember the location of hundreds of reagents, pipettes and consumables. Time to tie some facts to those!

Mid-tier Enhanced Memory 2 achieved!

Some time later, Nathan finally slept.

~

Status of Nathan Lark:
Permanent Talent 1: Magic Absorption 1
Permanent Talent 2: Mid-tier Regeneration 9
Talent 3: None

Class: Antimagic Brawler level 25
Stamina: 350/350
Brawler's Indifference
Antimagic Blows

Utility skills:
Mid-tier Focused Mind 8
Low-tier Earnestness 10
Low-tier Sprinting 8
Low-tier Spellsense 10
Low-tier Notice 8
Low-tier Identify 5
Low-tier Dodging Footwork 5
Mid-tier Enhanced Memory 2

Chapter 29

A Blooding Patrol

Nathan kicked himself the next morning for staying up late. He'd been sleeping well recently, but staying up late last night to recall firearms knowledge had made it harder than usual to wake up. Whoops. Well, he'd made some good progress, remembering details of the process for manufacturing black powder, as well as several compositions for primers and the basics of cartridge and gun design. If he actually wanted to follow through on this plan, then he'd be at the mercy of local craftspeople. However, knowing a few different methods would help him work through the problem with somebody else.

Anyway! It's time to get going.

He joined the rest of the Heirs in the main room, where they were eating a quick breakfast. Everybody else was nervous, Khachi fidgeting while Aarl obsessively checked his various weapons. Stella conjured little bursts of fire as if to remind herself she could still do it, while Sarah stared at her breakfast as if it was her mortal enemy. Her spoon was sticking straight up out of the porridge.

Nathan plopped down and gathered some of the breakfast pastries and porridge. He started ladling syrup into it, grinning all the while. It didn't take long for somebody to notice.

"Why the bright face Nathan? Did you get bitten by a cheerful snake last night?" Sarah asked him, affronted by his smiling face.

"Something like that! I picked up another utility skill. It won't help today, but I hope it'll be great in the long term. Gonna keep quiet about it for now, though."

The rest of the team didn't look particularly thrilled with his news, with Stella in particular giving him the stink-eye. It didn't take long for Khachi to slap his gauntleted hands together with a metallic *clang*. "It is time to go. We all know what is to be done."

With that, he stood and walked toward the door. Nathan carefully stacked his plates on the tray to be picked up later, then followed, grabbing his spear from the rack next to the door. He reflected on his general lack of equipment compared to the other Heirs. They all had gear and preparations galore.

Khachi was a brown-haired wolfman in full plate, with dimensional pouches affixed in various places containing different tools. He carried his hammer and shield, and looked like he could bulldoze through a herd of cows and smash a brick wall at the other end. His divine blessings were hinted at in the shininess of his armor. The metal always seemed to catch the light and glow dazzlingly.

Stella was such a fantasy mage cliché that Nathan would have made jokes about it if anyone would've understood them. She wore the same green robe as when Nathan had first met her, the one with pockets of holding and magical protections. Her hair was done in the same long braid, which was tucked down the back of the robe. She was carrying her staff, even if she was in the habit of shoving it into a pocket in her sleeve when she didn't need the extra firepower it provided.

Aarl was decked in a flexible leather armor with metal plates inlaid at various points. He had solid steel vambraces and greaves, and Nathan knew the pouch on his belt was a veritable armory of melee weaponry. He had a gymnast's build, and his short dark hair matched his eyes and sculpted eyebrows.

Sarah shared her brother's build and intensity, though she was a touch taller. Her armor was similar as well, though it was lighter and without the reinforced vambraces and greaves. Her pouch was identical to Aarl's but contained a wide variety of ranged weapons instead. Her hair was longer than her brother's and was gathered up into a high ponytail to keep it from catching on anything.

Nathan reflected on his relationship with the Heirs. They were new friends, but they were definitely friends. He'd trust them to have his back, all for different reasons. Khachi's stubborn pride wouldn't let him fail a teammate. Stella liked Nathan, and despite her pranks she was loyal to her friends. Aarl was not as boisterous as Khachi, but he wanted to be a great Adventurer and follow in his father's footsteps. To his mind, great Adventurers kept their team alive. Sarah was the quietest member of the team, but she'd struck Nathan as the most inherently decent of them. She'd risk her life to save anybody, teammate or not.

He didn't have too many regrets about joining the Heirs. Regardless of the protection he got from being around them, he enjoyed their company. Maybe he wouldn't be able to be part of their team forever, but... he could see himself in a few decades, sitting around a table with the Heirs and looking back on many successful adventures. The image conflicted with his previously stated goal of burning Giantsrest to the ground. But he'd gained some distance from the events that had sparked his hatred. Did it still burn as hot?

As Nathan followed the Heirs out of the building, he considered that. He remembered Taeol's adamant belief that he owned Nathan and all of his knowledge. He remembered the lines of slaves trudging along, and the people he'd met after they were freed. The flame of his fury flared once more, and Nathan clenched his fists. He was a member of the Heirs, and he would protect and help them. But his mission was the destruction of Giantsrest, and that hadn't changed. He'd spent some time learning about Davrar. Gaining a home base, a team, a plan to level up. But when his level was higher and the time was right, he would go with Vhala and dismantle Giantsrest.

As they left the Adventurer's Guild and headed toward the city gate, Nathan snorted and shook his head. None of his musings changed the current situation. The other Heirs looked back at Nathan, and he waved a hand. "It's easy to get stuck in your own head, heading out like this. Anybody know some jokes?"

Sarah straightened her shoulders. "What can't read, makes inappropriate noises and isn't dressed for the current affair?"

Nathan shrugged. "Sounds like me. I would like to say that I'm following Artha's advice to not wear armor."

"I was going to say a goat, but if you think that describes you, go for it."

Nathan frowned, but Khachi and Aarl chuckled.

Nathan retaliated. "I spy, with my little eye, something so shiny that everybody will see us from a mile away. Anybody want to guess what it is?"

Khachi looked down at his gleaming armor. "I am not given a choice about my level of shine."

Stella kicked him while he was down. "Well, you got to make the choice once. And you chose to be as shiny as possible! But we don't rely on stealth like those Illusionist's Tower people. And good thing too, or else I'd have to think twice before throwing a fireball. And that's not my favorite thing to do."

Aarl and Sarah traded a look, then chorused together. "We noticed."

They continued in that vein down to the gate, which was just opening as the sun blossomed overhead. The city was bathed in light, and Nathan turned to take one last look up the hill. Gemore was a pretty city, though by Earth standards it was barely a town. The gate guards waved them through respectfully, a few dipping their heads in faint bows.

And with that, they were out of the city. They took the northern road out of the great plaza. Nathan was tentative about stepping onto the magical transit road. But he didn't feel any mana when he stepped into the space-distortion effect, and his Stamina didn't tick up. There definitely weren't magical glyphs exposed on the surface. Maybe underneath it? Maybe it was a city-wide enchantment, buried deep underground? Regardless, his Talent didn't mess with the effect.

That suggests there's definitely still magic that can hurt me – it's just way beyond anything I've seen living people practicing.

He kept an eye peeled for stalkers or other people on the road, but there was nothing. Just Nathan and the Heirs striding at incredible speed through an *enormous* ruined city. The northern portion of the city contained fairly intact ruins, without many of the collapsed buildings or extensive swaths of greenery that were common throughout the rest of the city.

They didn't have to go too far to find the landmark for their patrol. It was a small city square offset to one side of the road. Part of it was composed of an overgrown park. The other side was dominated by a ruined, cathedral-like structure. One of the spires had fallen on the vaulted roof, crushing it. But the other stood like a spike of rusted metal thrust into the sky.

"Our first step is making sure the old community center and green space is cleared, then we fan out from there." Khachi wasn't saying anything they didn't already know, but the Heirs stepped off the road and fell into their diamond formation.

Nathan was in front because he could see through magical stealth, *and* had [Notice], [Focused Mind] and [Identify]. So he put them to work, scanning the buildings. He stopped a few times to activate [Focused Mind] in order to discern more details. But nothing moved, aside from a faint breeze stirring the foliage.

They made for the cathedral-like building first. It was the sort of space that various creatures liked to hide in, and with the proximity to the road that was unacceptable. After a careful check, they were pretty sure that nothing had lived there in some time. They also climbed halfway up the spire since airborne monsters had been known to nest in it. It gave a good view over the surrounding area, which appeared to mostly be a wilderness of six-to-seven story residential and commercial buildings. Most were ruined or scarred in some way.

Nathan looked over the view and shivered. The sun was shining, and the greenery rippled peacefully, but it looked a *lot* like post-apocalyptic cities he'd seen in Earth fiction. Nathan closed his eyes for a moment and breathed in, then out. He opened his eyes and scanned again.

This time, he saw something.

About five blocks away, something moved inside a building whose shadows seemed just a *little* too deep. Nathan added some kind of spyglass or binoculars to his wish list and shaded his eyes to look closer, searching for the feeling he'd noticed when piercing the earth stalker's stealth. He felt it, like tiny threads of magic interfering with his vision.

Nathan pointed at the building. "Stalkers. Earth, I think. That building, with the collapsed roof."

Sarah, who was also scanning the horizon, squinted at the building. "I can't see them." She shook her head. "But I wouldn't. Let's go check it out."

"I bet I could hit them from here," Stella put in, standing at the edge and coyly looking over her shoulder at the rest of the team. Her smirk belied the statement as a half-joke.

"And then any survivors would scatter and lay ambushes every chance they'd get," Khachi rumbled, his lips turned down in a frown. "It will be cleaner to take them on where we expect them, and not have them trying to pick us off all day."

Aarl clapped Khachi on the shoulder. "And *we'll* be more useful than nipples on a breastplate."

They descended the tower, making for the building where Nathan had spotted the stalkers. A block away they started moving more quietly and angled their formation towards their supposed targets.

Nathan was focused on the building, watching every doorway and broken window. It looked like the bottom floor had been a series of shops, with residential housing above. The upper floors were complete with large windows, none of which had more than a few stray shards of glass remaining.

They'd gotten relatively close when Nathan spotted the Earth stalkers taking positions in the windows above them, relying on their magic to hide themselves. The six-legged creatures moved smoothly, their brown scales blending into the stone of the building. Most of them stood at about four feet, and their third eye glowed above a snout bristling with fangs. Nathan spoke low but clearly. "We've been spotted. Earth stalkers waiting to leap."

Khachi replied in a tense whisper. "Stella, shield above us on Nathan's word. Prevent any from landing on us. Sarah, don't let any get behind us. Weapons ready but down, we want to draw them in."

The team continued walking forward, pivoting to stay pointed at the stalker-infested building. Nathan checked out the other buildings quickly but didn't see any trace of stalkers having snuck around them.

They reached the front of the building, and Nathan could see some stalkers trembling, resisting the urge to leap. There was a faint rumbling *hiss*, and all of the stalkers tensed as one.

He yelled, "Shield now!" and brought up his spear. Nathan was moments from a life-or-death fight, and the realization thrilled through him like a roller coaster drop.

Low-tier Notice Rank 9 achieved!

The stalkers leapt as a single unit, aiming to land among and around the party. A conical blue shield appeared overhead, sharpening to a point. The Earth stalker that had aimed to land on Stella in the middle of their formation was impaled, and the others that had aimed for each party member deflected off the shield. One caught a spinning ax to the face as it fell. Another landed in a tangle in front of Nathan, and he burned Stamina as he leaped forward to stab it in the underbelly with his spear. He'd taken a moment to judge where its ribs were and jabbed the spear between two of them high on its chest.

The stalker convulsed at the blow, and Nathan continued to spend Stamina to tear the spear up and twist it, enlarging the wound as much as he could before freeing the weapon. The orange spearhead had cut through the underbelly scales like butter and sliced a wide path through the creature's body on the way out.

However, Nathan didn't have time to evaluate the state of that stalker, as another swarmed past it to attack him. He flicked his spear towards it and the monster halted as suddenly as it had appeared. Nathan stepped forward to spear it, but another stalker leapt over the creature that Nathan had stabbed and flanked him. He skittered to the side to dodge a quick *snap* of jaws but had to retreat in the face of the two reptilian foes. They coordinated their attacks, and it was all he could do to ward them off with rapid jerks of his spear. He was using Stamina to be as fast as possible, but they were nearly as quick. A third came from the left, and Nathan had to dodge another biting jaw.

Low-tier Dodging Footwork Rank 6 achieved!

Nathan bared his own teeth as he faced down the three earth stalkers. He should feel terrified, confronted by a group of foes he *could not* take on his own. But instead, Nathan felt like he was bursting with energy. He stepped forward to charge them, mouth opening in a roar.

Then he heard the sweetest of sounds. "*Danger Close!*"

Nathan continued his sprinting advance, knowing what would follow. A fireball flew past him, impacting the middle stalker. The magic blew the creature in half and showered the area with fire and gore. The other two staggered from the explosion. Nathan planted his spear through the neck of the one on the right, cutting deep and feeling the blade hit the spine and break bone. The stalker went limp, but his spear was stuck.

Nathan spun to the left, looking for the other stalker. It was badly burnt, and very upset. It skittered at him with a limping gait, favoring the limbs not charred by the fireball.

My priority is not letting it get to my head or chest.

Nathan braced himself and put his hands up as if he meant to stop the charging beast. Even with his height and the added muscle of the last weeks, it outmassed him at least two to one. At the last moment, he juked to the side. The stalker whipped its head at him, and Nathan punched it in the snout, deflecting a bite and cracking the creature's head to the side.

At that moment, a three-foot spike of rock shot toward him, zipping out of the shadows of the building. Nathan tried to dodge, but he was committed to his juke and it hit him in the side. There was definitely magic involved, since the rock that should have speared through his kidney just tore his clothes and dug a gouge in his skin as it disintegrated to dust. Nathan felt the tang of Earth mana in the rock as the magic flowed into him, refilling his Stamina.

In response to the magical attack Khachi yelled out a warning to the rest of the Heirs, "We've got a Patriarch, watch for conjured Earth spikes and quicksand!" Then he grunted, the sound of his hammer hitting pavement betraying the wolfman's own battle.

Nathan directed his attention to his side, feeling very indifferent to the pain. The stalker that had charged him punished him for the distraction, lashing out with its talons and weakly clawing into his thigh. Nathan staggered back, narrowly avoiding going to one knee. A thrown javelin from Sarah sank into the stalker's middle eye, and it spasmed before slumping to the ground.

Nathan looked toward the entrance to the building, seeing a hulking creature lurking beyond. Its eye glowed a rich brown, much brighter than any of the other stalkers. Nathan started working his spear back and forth from the neck of the dead monster. Another spike of earth lanced towards his head, but he'd been expecting it and jerked himself sideways with the spear, which came loose a moment later.

Low-tier Dodging Footwork Rank 7 achieved!

The Patriarch let loose a rumbling hiss and turned to flee. Nathan glanced to the sides and saw Aarl and Khachi each dueling a stalker – they didn't seem to need help. So he sprinted after the fleeing Patriarch. As he did, he felt a joyful wrath surge within him.

You run from me, you cowardly lizard?

The thought was followed by a flash of self-reflection. Running into this building might be stupid, the sort of risk that could get him killed. But his [Regeneration] made it much harder for him to die, his allies were close and could assist him soon, and the Patriarch was fleeing. If it got away they'd have to hunt it anyway. Landing a wound or depleting its mana would make that hunt much more likely to succeed. And to walk the Path of Rage, Nathan needed to follow his anger. And his anger was telling him to *wring its neck*.

Low-tier Sprinting Rank 9 achieved!

The moment Nathan crossed into the large entryway beyond the door, the extra-large stalker spun to face him. The spear in his hands seemed small as the creature loomed over him, its third eye glowing brightly enough to light up the room.

The floor started to soften, stone blocks giving way to slick sand. Except around Nathan's feet, where the stonework persisted. He smirked and ran forward. His foot sunk into the sand with each new step, but not far. Nathan spared half of his attention to drawing in the earth mana directly underneath his foot, and the loose sand solidified under his feet. Nathan used a burst of Stamina to push hard off the resolidified surface as he yelled out the magic words. "Danger Close!"

He stabbed at the stalker's face, but it twisted to take the blow on the shoulder. His spearhead cut through skin but deflected from bone, leaving a deep but ultimately superficial cut. The creature turned back towards him, fangs bared. Nathan tried to push the snout away with his left hand, but its jaws slammed shut on his upper arm, cracking bone and leaving his left arm almost entirely inside the stalker's mouth.

Aw, not again.

Instead of tearing his arm the rest of the way off, the Patriarch was blown backwards by one of Stella's fireballs, releasing Nathan's mangled arm as it screamed. Nathan's Stamina once again climbed to full from the proximity of the blast, and he leapt forward to stab at the stalker's head with his spear. The creature shied away, feet scrabbling to dodge Nathan's one-handed thrusts. Only half of its legs seemed to be functional after the fireball.

It was enough. Nathan disengaged, stepping back from the stalker and retreating to the corner of the room. It couldn't escape anymore, and he didn't need to be the one to kill it. Nathan focused on healing his arm, dropping his spear to grab his left arm with his right. He manually lined up the bones. Then, he regenerated the punctures from the stalker's teeth, careful to start from the bottom of the wound to avoid trapping any debris under his skin. Lucky for him, stalkers – even Patriarchs – didn't have venom.

He kept an eye on the stalker and watched Khachi run into the room. The wolfman was standing on a horizontal plane of force inches above the quicksand. His armor *flashed*, blinding light shooting in every direction. Nathan merely blinked away faint spots in his vision, but the stalker Patriarch *screamed*, its head jerking away.

Khachi brought his hammer down on the monster's head, crushing it to the stone floor outside the radius of the quicksand. There was a second of silence, and it seemed the fight was done.

"We're done? Got them all?" Nathan's voice was harsher than he meant it to be, but Khachi didn't take it amiss.

He gestured them outside, and Nathan followed Khachi out the door into the bloodied street. Nathan was splashed with blood, some of it his own. His shirt was ripped and bloody, and his pants had a few tears. Khachi's hammer was covered in blood and he had spatters covering much of his armor. As Nathan watched, they started to dry up and flake away.

Aarl was carrying his favored greatsword, the upper half of which was crimson. He'd been sprayed with blood. His arm was especially bloody, and it looked like something had taken a finger-sized chunk from his upper arm. Khachi hustled over and muttered a prayer. Golden light emanated from his hands as he grasped Aarl's arm. It healed over in moments.

Stella and Sarah were a short distance away. They hadn't moved far from where they'd started the fight and both seemed uninjured.

After a moment where all the Heirs looked at each other and ensured everybody was in one piece, they all broke into grins. Nathan raised his arms to the sky. "Woohoo!"

You have leveled up to level 27! Congratulations, you have slaughtered a nest of deadly monsters and personally killed some! Please choose a Developed class from the following list to continue leveling, as you have unlocked a level higher than 27!

Nice.

Chapter 30

Discoveries

Still shaking from adrenaline after the fight, Nathan looked over his new class choices.

Oh man, this is exciting.

Potential classes:

Magic Suppressor: You are adept at suppressing magical effects and countering spells actively cast on you. This class will enhance your antimagic capabilities, granting skills and modifying existing skills to enhance antimagic range, speed and allowing you to actively drain mana. It may further Develop into classes focused on stealing control of magical spells, breaking permanent magical effects or denying magic in a wide area. This class will weaken your physical combat abilities.

Magebane Berserker: You have bent your anger to empower your offensive martial ability. This class will enhance your physical strength and mage-killing prowess on the battlefield, granting skills and modifying existing skills to enable Raging, where Stamina will be spent to become significantly tougher, stronger and faster. Additional skills will enhance your base strength, as well as lethality to mages while in Rage. This may further Develop into classes focused on extending and enhancing your Rage, adding extra effects to your Rage, or transforming into a different form while raging.

Antimagic Boxer: You have become adept at using your fists to fight magical opponents. This class will enhance your hand-to-hand fighting ability, granting skills and modifying existing skills to improve the power and accuracy of your hand-to-hand blows, while increasing your overall Stamina pool. It may further Develop into classes focused on disabling enemies with hand-to-hand strikes, or broadening your focus to other forms of unarmed combat.

Antimagic Fighter: You have learned to use weapons effectively to fight magical opponents. This class will enhance your ability to fight in melee, granting skills and modifying existing skills to aid in learning various weapons, as well as improving your striking power and armor-penetrating capabilities. It may further Develop into classes focused on specific weapons, or become a generalist class that can utilize many weapons. This class will weaken your antimagic abilities.

Spellbreaker Juggernaut: You have embraced your anger and thrill of battle and used them for unrelenting assaults. This class will make you an unstoppable force, granting skills and modifying existing skills to enable Raging, where Stamina will be spent to become significantly tougher, stronger and faster. Additional skills will enhance your durability, as well as your ability to disrupt spell effects, especially those aimed at hindering or slowing you. This class may further Develop into classes focused on breaching fortified defenses, extending or enhancing your Rage, or further enhancing your antimagic capabilities while raging.

Antimagic Scout: You are the member of your team responsible for detecting threats and warning others about them. This class will enhance your ability to scout out threats, granting skills and modifying existing skills to enhance movement, perception and stealth. It may Develop into classes focused on stealth, long-range observation or assassination.

> **Antimagic Monk:** You have embraced Meditation to help you Develop martial combat skills to fight hand-to-hand against magic. This class will enhance your hand-to-hand fighting ability, granting skills and modifying existing skills to change your Stamina into Qi, which can be spent to allow various effects. Additional skills will improve your physical precision and control, as well as allow you to meditate to regain Qi. This class may further Develop into classes focused on achieving enlightenment through combat, protecting a specific place or dedication towards an ideal.

Nathan stood in the street of a ruined city, next to his friends and teammates. Surrounding them were the scattered corpses of more than a dozen Earth stalkers. Their blood painted the street red in a wide arc. The bodies were lean and predatory, with six heavily muscled legs and smooth scales of a dull brown.

Nathan shivered as he looked over the landscape of the fight. He was coming down from the adrenaline high and thrill of battle, and he could retrace the flow of the flight from the bodies and their wounds.

There was a clear spot where the Heirs had first stood – it had been protected by Stella's shield. That oasis was surrounded by blood and gore. On Aarl's side lay five dead stalkers, most still curled around the weapons that had ended them. One had gotten a spear through the mouth, another a large ax to the neck. The next was missing two limbs and had a slash through the stomach that spilled viscera all over the street. A heavy throwing ax from Sarah had split the skull of another, and a final stalker had been blown into pieces by a fireball.

Two of the bodies on Khachi's side had suffered severe blunt force trauma to the head and chest, while another four had been killed with ranged weapons and magic. It also seemed that an additional two had tried to sneak around the back to get to Sarah, but one of them had a crossbow bolt sticking from its third eye and the other looked to have been partially bisected by a blade of force. Bisected *the long way*. And then there was the one that Stella had gored on her force shield, which had fallen next to Nathan's kills after the shield had dissipated.

Aarl and Sarah went forward to retrieve their weapons, cleaning them off before returning them to the dimensional bags at their hips.

Stella was clearly counting bodies in the same way Nathan was. "Looks like... six for me, two for Nathan, three for Aarl, two for Khachi and four for Sarah. I'd say that Khachi, Nathan and I all got the Patriarch. And that's why you keep the ranged people safe! We'll do all the heavy lifting." The short redhead flexed her bicep before twirling in place and giving an amused Sarah a high-five.

Their work wasn't done yet, and they spent a good portion of the next hour stacking the bodies on the edge of the street. The third eye of certain stalkers had some valuable magical properties, but they were hard to extract and preserve. The Heirs weren't equipped for it. With a few exceptions, monster parts were usually harvested only by teams that specialized in doing so. Aarl did grab the stalker canine teeth – which didn't have magically valuable properties but were a nice ivory and would serve as proof of the kills. The teeth from the patriarch would likely make a striking handle for a sword or weapon.

After they'd stacked the dead monsters, Stella proceeded to use a spell specifically tailored for incinerating bodies. It was slow and not very focused – but it was mana-efficient. Over the course of the next five minutes the stalker bodies were reduced to a charred pile of melted fat and burnt muscle. Their goal wasn't to completely get rid of the bodies, but to prevent any of them from rising as undead or becoming a host for various parasites or diseases that liked fresh corpses.

Nathan was glad they had a powerful mage on their team. Jolba had described other ways to deal with monster corpses after a fight, and they didn't sound pleasant. There were alchemical solutions that burned or dissolved flesh, but they were expensive. The more common approach was simply to hack apart the monster corpses, scattering the bits over a wide area. That seemed a bit...

He glanced at his bloody spear and torn shirt and grimaced.

"Stella, can I get a spare shirt from your bag of holding? Aarl, could I ask you to clean off my spearhead? Sorry for the trouble, it's just that I've got this whole thing with magic? You know."

Stella laughed and threw him a replacement shirt.

Aarl just sighed, and the sweaty copper-skinned man pulled out the set of cloths he'd just stowed away. "Carry on like this and you'll never learn how to maintain a weapon. But you owe me a favor. A few years of this and it might even be worth an Insight. You seem to have no end of valuable ones."

Nathan hummed, a little taken aback by how *good* Aarl looked in that moment. A little sweaty, a bit exasperated. "You know, maybe we should talk later about trading Insights. I've got a utility skill that I'm pretty sure makes it easier to figure out other Insights. It's a bit of a pain to rank up, though." He was thinking of [Focused Mind], and also wondering if it would be helpful for mages and their spellcasting.

Khachi interrupted the conversation. "A good conversation to have. *Later.* For now, we must resume our patrol. With a nest of stalkers this large, it is unlikely that there is anything else threatening, but we must fulfill our job, and much of the day remains."

The party spent a few more minutes resting. Nathan chewed down some of his stored rations, mostly spicy jerky. He'd never been particularly low on Stamina during the fight because of what he'd absorbed from Stella's spells, but it didn't hurt to top off. And he was hungry.

While he chewed, he considered his new class options again. They were a lot less varied than the options he'd gotten the first time – but that made sense since they were all Developments of [Antimagic Brawler]. Nathan was excited to talk to Artha about his choices and speculate on what kinds of new skills he might get. He was also thinking of getting advice from his fellow Heirs and maybe their parents.

All of that would happen in safety – once they'd returned to Gemore proper. His initial thoughts were that both [Magebane Berserker] and [Spellbreaker Juggernaut] were on the Path of Rage. Artha had been guiding him towards it, so he knew what he was getting into and had a mentor to help him figure out how to use them. Both were likely contenders. His gut pushed him towards [Spellbreaker Juggernaut], though Nathan wasn't sure if that was just because the name sounded cooler.

Meanwhile, [Magic Suppressor] went further into antimagic in a way that appealed to Nathan. Being able to drain mana from people sounded pretty strong. And [Antimagic Monk] could be *really strong,* if Nathan could replicate magical effects with Qi while keeping his hand-to-hand combat abilities. Was it a D&D-style Qi or Cultivation-style Qi? Nathan didn't know, and he didn't think there was anybody he could ask. He also had to keep in mind that he probably wouldn't have a mentor to help him figure out how to use it. Regardless, Nathan wasn't going to make the decision immediately.

Unless I gotta, of course...

Let's hope I didn't just jinx it. But if I do need to choose in a pinch again, *I like [Spellbreaker Juggernaut] best. It follows the Path of Rage and explicitly calls out the durability Artha was going for. Maybe something else is better, but this is sticking to the plan.*

They set off once again. There was a lot of ground to cover – and the mostly-intact buildings meant that they had to walk down nearly every street. There was little chance of getting lost since they all paid attention to the landmarks they passed. Khachi in particular seemed to have an excellent sense of direction. Nathan stayed on high alert, using [Notice] and [Focused Mind] as before.

Nothing stood out to him. The city was empty, and they were surrounded by buildings too ruined for anything but demolition. Nothing moved except the occasional bird or small prey animal. Chipmunks were the same no matter where you were.

By lunchtime they'd looped back to the square where the patrol began. The Heirs made sure the green space was clear and sat down to have lunch. Stella was proud and a bit embarrassed since her parents had given her enough food for everybody and made her promise to share. The food was still trail food – preserved and prepared to be eaten without cutlery. But the quality was high, with a rich, savory pemmican and honeyed biscuits washed down by sweetened juices.

Nathan made sure to be appreciative, and to make fun of Stella for being spoiled by her parents. It was all good natured – Khachi defended her, explaining his mother's idea of trail food. Apparently Kia thought unflavored jerky, ground oats and rainwater were perfectly suitable for days on end.

After the brief break, they crossed the main road and scoped out the ruins on the other side. It was boring work. Once or twice they saw markings that looked like tracks, and they found a pile of large bones that could have belonged to a siegeboar. But the bones were old, yellowed and jumbled together. The tusks were missing, which likely meant a party of adventurers had killed it or at least found the skeleton.

Hours passed uneventfully, but Khachi reminded them that there was still a good chance of danger. The Heirs tried not to relax their guard. They'd patrolled in a wide arc away from the road, and the ruins had become more irregular. More of the buildings were collapsed – leaving rubble blocking some of the roads.

After a little while, they found another large boulevard that they decided delineated the outer edge of their patrol responsibilities. It didn't mean they were done, but they would walk along it before sweeping back to cover another swath. Once they returned to the transit road, they'd be done.

The boulevard was wide and spacious, with scattered islands of greenery breaking through the flagstones in places. It didn't have the space-compression magic that increased travel speed, but had clearly been a major thoroughfare. Nathan was on the far right side of the street, looking at the buildings next to him as he led the way. They were all five or six stories tall, with some having partially collapsed.

"What do you think these buildings were? They don't look the same as the ones near the community center."

Aarl was directly behind Nathan, and he answered. "I don't know, but I don't think people lived in them. Maybe where people worked? But I don't see shops or anything at the bottom. It's strange."

Nathan turned around and saw the rest of the Heirs looking up to the right, studying the buildings next to them. His [Notice] twigged about something, and Nathan was confused. There was nothing to see – the road was boring, nothing moved in the buildings, and his party members were all present.

But why are we in a line? We've been in formation all day.

All of the Heirs had their backs facing the center of the street, intently studying the buildings that Nathan had pointed out. A chill ran down Nathan's neck, and he determinedly spun to face the center of the boulevard.

He called out. "Arms up! Spread out! Something's funky."

Nathan took a few steps forward, studying the street. The stone was smooth and even all the way across, the flagstones looking as if they'd just been laid. Nathan noticed that they weren't even dirty.

That's weird – none of these streets have been so pristine.

He raised his eyes, looking at the buildings opposite. They were completely normal, nothing unusual with them. Then, Nathan took a deep breath and activated [Focused Mind].

The buildings were normal – but even with [Notice], Nathan couldn't see a *single identifying detail* about them. Literally nothing stood out. He looked away, and realized he couldn't recall if the buildings had been tall or short, the shape of their windows – *literally nothing*. He searched his mind for invasive magic and felt an amazingly subtle vapor that burned away as he focused on it.

Mid-tier Focused Mind Rank 9 achieved!

Low-tier Notice Rank 10 achieved! Congratulations, you have maxed out this skill! It cannot be improved any further. You must achieve Insight into this skill to Develop it to the next level.

Nothing changed, except that Nathan found it easier to look towards the buildings opposite. There'd been a subtle but powerful look-away effect there, maybe combined with something that made you unable to recall what you'd seen. And now that he was able to pick out details, he saw the too-clean street wavering faintly, as if hidden by a heat-haze.

Bet that's an illusion.

Low-tier Identify Rank 6 achieved!

Shit.

"Illusions!" Nathan took a few steps forward, entering the area where the road was clean and feeling it out with his hands. If this was a Giantrest ambush, he needed to break their illusions as soon as possible so they could see their foe. His hands stopped, pushing against what felt like a brittle pane of glass. The scene flickered, and Nathan recalled the feeling of shadow mana he'd felt when practicing with Wiam. This was like that, but much more complicated. The spellwork was made of more than shadow, with at least two other types of mana layered together. Light and... something new. Something that felt like the softest touch of warm fabric.

Dream mana?

Nathan ripped with his hands, shredding the illusion and absorbing it into himself.

A few things changed. The building across the way was revealed to be a squat, blocky thing about thirty feet tall. The windows were high up and barred, the walls around them made of enormous blocks of well-fitted stone. There was a metal door fit for a nuclear shelter sealing the entrance. Short bunkers flanked the building on both sides. Each one had a turret on top, which were aimed at the Heirs. A half dozen floodlight-like constructs decorated the front of each bunker, also aimed in their direction.

Even worse, the previously empty road was no longer empty. Eight spindly metal constructs had been slowly advancing across the road – but when Nathan broke the barrier, they shifted into a run. The street they charged across was dotted with corpses.

Corpses in armor. The corpses of Adventurers.

Chapter 31

Repercussions

A lot of things happened very quickly. The turrets on top of the bunkers fired with a faint *wuff*, and a projectile blurred in Nathan's direction. He dodged to the side – but it had been aimed at his center mass and was moving *fast*. The spike of metal impacted the right side of his chest and went through his entire body, snapping ribs and coring a lung before hitting the street behind him.

Nathan spun and fell, struggling to breathe as blood bubbled from the wounds in his chest and back. Stella cried out in pain behind him. Nathan looked back for a second and saw her sprawled against a wall, another bolt sticking out of her chest. Khachi moved to cover her with his big shield, but Nathan was exposed, the constructs fast approaching.

The sound of metal on stone grew louder, and Nathan pushed himself up. He grit his teeth and focused on the lung wound, burning Stamina to heal his lungs before too much air escaped into his chest cavity.

My [Regeneration] needs to be faster. My lung will collapse at this rate, and I don't know if [Regeneration] can fix that.

He advanced towards the metal constructs as they skittered across the street. They were tall, with four thin, metal legs holding a central body about five feet in the air. A tube-like head was fused to the top of the body, and they were all pointed towards Nathan. More concerning were the two arms protruding up from the central body, tipped with long cutting blades. Overall, they looked like bugs from the movie *Starship Troopers* – but in steel and chrome.

That movie was good satire, but bad at engaging with Heinlein's original.

Nathan shook the distraction aside and snarled as he ran forward. He could feel his lung starting to operate again, his ribs re-knitting. What the *hell* was going on here? The classes in the Adventurer's Guild had never described whatever the fuck these foes were.

> **Low-tier Sprinting Rank 10 achieved!** Congratulations, you have maxed out this skill! It cannot be improved any further. You must achieve Insight into this skill to Develop it to the next level.

As they closed in on him, the bug-constructs' heads split open to reveal cannon-like barrels. Magic kindled and varied spells began flying from the constructs. Two of the barrels sparked with lightning that struck out at Nathan instantaneously. Two more volleyed small bolts of fire at him like machine guns. Another two shot out blades of force – one at chest level and another at thigh level. The final two fired sprays of acid.

Nathan didn't try to dodge any of it. His clothes were charred, sliced and dissolved in an instant. One of the blades of force cut his spear shaft clean through, and the remaining pieces of wood started to bubble and liquify under the acid. Nathan discarded the ruined weapon.

That's really not *how acid works. Magic!*

Nathan himself was relatively unharmed. He had light cuts from the blades of force, and the acid burned his eyes and made his skin itch. The lightning had barely registered, and the fire was doing nothing. It took a bare moment's attention to heal the cuts and soothe the inflammation.

> **Mid-tier Regeneration Rank 10 achieved!** Congratulations, you have maxed out this Talent! It cannot be improved any further. You must achieve Insight into this Talent to Develop it to the next level.

Nathan's Stamina was completely filled by all the magic flying past, and he started feeling jittery, like he'd had too much caffeine.

As he sprinted forward, he examined the spellwork coming his way. Everything cast on him had been a *simple* spell. But the simplicity wasn't the kind of basic working of mana that was easy to understand. It was the simplicity of something with no extraneous parts, a spell pruned for absolute efficiency. Each of the fire bolts that impacted Nathan were identical, elegant weaves. Nathan saw a truth of magic, in that moment. Truly efficient spells used single strands of mana to fulfill *multiple purposes at once*.

Congratulations, you have Developed the [Low-tier Spellsense] utility skill into [Mid-tier Spellsense].

Utility skill: [Mid-tier Spellsense]
This skill will help you identify mana types and spell weaves more easily. Helps you understand what individual elements of spells are accomplishing. Does not grant understanding of how to weave mana together for specific spells.

Nathan broke through a cloud of acid to find that the bug-constructs had reversed their direction. They maintained their distance from him, continuing to pepper him with spells from afar.

Then, the spotlight-like constructs arrayed on the front of the bunkers lit up. There were twelve of them in total, and three cast their beams on Nathan. The others focused beyond him, on the Heirs. Nathan felt a pressure on his mind – not dissimilar to the [Sleep] spell that Taeol had cast on him. He brushed it off easily, furious at the attempted invasion of his mind.

The bug constructs transitioned between different types of spells, trying to find a weakness in his defenses. Nathan was barraged by rays of freezing cold, spikes of ice, scorching beams of light, bolts of death mana, a variety of force workings, and conjured balls of stone. All they accomplished was to knock Nathan around a little bit and keep his Stamina topped off. He spun around to see how the Heirs were doing.

Magic Absorption Rank 2 achieved!

They didn't seem to be doing well. Stella was still collapsed against the wall in a pool of blood. Nathan couldn't tell if Khachi had healed her, since the wolfman was hunkered in front of her with his shield. Several bolts were stuck *through* the shield, and Nathan saw red dripping to the cobbles from Khachi's kneeling form.

Aarl and Sarah were dazed, gazing dreamily at the spotlights illuminating them. As he watched, Sarah shook herself and leapt high into the air while loosing a glowing arrow at the beam emitters. The arrow sped through the air before exploding against a previously invisible magical shield that protected the bunker. The beams refocused on Sarah in midair and she froze. She'd been aiming for a window on the second story of the building. Instead of a smooth landing, she cracked her legs against the windowsill and fell to the street with a crunch.

Fuck. Those beams need to go down now. *And I think I'm the only one for the job.*

Nathan spun again, facing the squat building with its deadly bunkers and construct guardians. The metal bugs had stopped firing spells at him. Nathan raged at the way the ambush had played out so far – the Heirs were completely disabled, and he'd failed to deal with the bug-constructs. He leaned forward to sprint towards the bunkers, lips curling back. The bug constructs hurried to interpose themselves, and Nathan regarded their cutting arms cautiously. He slowed as he approached the first two, trying to juke around them.

One of them lunged forward as if fired from a cannon, and Nathan dodged to the side but failed to get far enough away to avoid the blow. He threw his right arm up to block, and the cutting arm went right through his wrist and sliced across his chest. Blood spurted out, and Nathan had to dodge low and skip backwards as another swept a blade for his neck.

Low-tier Dodging footwork Rank 7 achieved!

Nathan backpedaled and considered fleeing. These constructs were beyond him. This entire *fight* was beyond them. That blow aimed at his neck would have killed him instantly. But he could make it if he just... ran away. It would mean leaving the Heirs behind, but Nathan valued his life more than theirs. A few weeks of growing friendship hadn't changed that.

The bug constructs formed up into a half-circle facing Nathan. They advanced slowly to push him back, no longer firing spells.

Nathan looked to the side. If he just took off down the street, he would be able to get away.

Stuck in indecision, Nathan turned his frustration inwards. Specifically, to his injuries. His [Regeneration] was too slow, and it required too much attention. He shouldn't have to direct his Stamina. His every cell had his body's blueprint in their DNA through encoded hormone gradients. They could all divide and differentiate appropriately to heal without requiring his attention.

Congratulations, you have Developed the [Mid-tier Regeneration] Talent into [High-tier Regeneration].

Talent: [High-tier Regeneration]

This Talent will automatically spend Stamina to very rapidly heal wounds. Larger wounds and replacing greater amounts of missing flesh will take longer and cost more Stamina. Regeneration will not prevent you from dying to grievous wounds, and will not protect against poison.

What made him reconsider fleeing wasn't the Talent Development – or the thought of possible vengeance inflicted by Kia, Dalo or Stanel. It was imagining Kullal's reaction to being told her daughter was dead. He could easily imagine her face crumple and her frame shake. He heard Jolba's resigned sigh as yet more of his students went to an early grave.

Nathan had a *chance* here. He could make powerful allies, gain a home base that was safe from Giantsrest. If the Heirs died here, he probably wouldn't be welcome in Gemore anymore.

And it so happened that Nathan had another card to play.

Congratulations, you are now a **[Spellbreaker Juggernaut]**. Two of your existing class skills have Developed, and you have unlocked three new class skills! These skills are tied to your parent class, and their power will increase with your level in that class. Davrar applauds your choice, and hopes you will continue to survive and prosper.

Class skill Stamina remains unchanged:
Stamina will accumulate during periods of rest, and can be spent to improve the speed and strength of your movements, or used for other skills or talents that utilize Stamina.

Class skill Brawler's Indifference has become Juggernaut's Wrath:
You will be unflinching in the face of pain and injury, and serious wounds will enhance the intensity of your Rage. This skill will trigger your Rage without your consent if you are badly injured.

Class skill Antimagic Blows has become Antimagic Momentum:
Motion enhances your inherent antimagic, allowing you to break magical effects with your movements and blows. The greater the momentum behind the motion, the greater the enhancement. Effect is further enhanced while Raging.

New Class skill Raging Thrill:
You can voluntarily enter and exit a Rage state, where you will be immersed in the thrill of combat. This will rapidly consume Stamina, but will increase your strength, speed and resilience to damage.

New Class skill Juggernaut's Inertia:
Your motions carry greater momentum, and it will be harder to stop or slow you, especially with magical effects.

New Class skill Unarmored Resilience:
When not wearing armor your body becomes more resilient to damage from all sources.

Now that you have Developed your class, you will level up to the correct level! **You have leveled up to level 32!**

Chapter 32

Money Where Your Mouth Is

Nathan took a few steps backwards from the encroaching constructs as he considered his new class skills. He didn't have time to fully figure them out – much less their interactions. But they seemed to fit the ticket for what needed to happen, because the one thing that the Heirs didn't have was *time.*

One of these days I'll be able to sit down and actually consider my class choice. Only 49 more levels to go until my next chance!

Between one step and the next, Nathan reversed direction. He sprinted at the four-legged bugs as they skittered toward him. They showed no sign of surprise, raising their cutting arms once more.

Right before Nathan entered the constructs' attack range, he triggered his new skill. His *Rage* skill. The world seemed to pulse, then slow down. Nathan's vision narrowed and he looked across at the eight metal constructs. His foes. The one closest to Nathan executed the same aggressive lunge as before, but Nathan crouched and leaped forward, going low as the cutting blade whistled down.

Behind him. Nathan had moved more quickly than ever before and was underneath the bug construct. He was tempted to rip the metal limbs off the bug and beat it to death with them. But it wasn't the constructs he was most pissed at. It was the bunker. Just *sitting* there, with magical beams that could stun people from a hundred feet away!

The bug reacted quickly, striking out with its back legs as Nathan ran out from underneath it. Each of the constructs' limbs were serrated on the inside surface, and one of those vicious cutting edges struck Nathan across the back of his left leg. But a blow that moments ago would have torn his leg off only left a deep cut. And instead of being knocked down, Nathan just staggered for a few steps and kept running.

Another bug lunged at him from behind, the tip of its cutting blade slicing across Nathan's back. It caught on bone and jerked him sideways but failed to cut through his spinal cord.

Hah! I've got two different resilience buffs right now. Eat my dust, bugs.

Nathan jumped over an adventurer corpse and kept running. His thrill and fury had only intensified with each injury, and he felt like he was in a tunnel, with only the bunkers present at the other end. The pounding of metal on stone came from behind him as the constructs gave chase.

Nathan focused on the bunkers and the street he needed to cross to get there. His chest came up, arms driving down. He flexed his feet with each step, propelling him forward with Stamina and all of the enhanced strength his Rage provided. For the second time, he was in a race against constructs trying to kill him, and he was *winning*.

Congratulations, you have Developed the [Low-tier Sprinting] utility skill into [Mid-tier Sprinting].

Utility skill: [Mid-tier Sprinting]
This skill will help you run very quickly in the future. Will not allow you to run in circumstances where you couldn't otherwise.

His gait had started uneven due to the leg-wound, but it smoothed out as the cut healed. His hand was mostly regenerated too. But the combined costs of his rapid healing, Rage and use of Stamina to empower his movements took its toll. His Stamina flickered down.

Stamina: 105/420

High-tier Regeneration Rank 2 achieved!

There wasn't much he could do about it, except eat the invisible barrier that'd blocked Sarah's arrow. Nathan noticed the turrets aligning themselves in his direction. He started dodging and weaving, not expecting much warning before...

A metal bolt shot past Nathan as he juked. The one from the other turret hit him in the right shoulder. It pierced skin and sunk into bone, the tip barely emerging from his back. Nathan's vision tinged red for a moment, but he kept running. He grabbed the two-foot projectile in his left hand and yanked it free with a grunt. His Stamina briefly stopped plummeting, as the glowing swirls engraved into the bolt flickered and dimmed.

Low-tier Dodging footwork Rank 8 achieved!

Everything here is magic. Speaking of...

Nathan impacted the barrier of force in front of the building. It was thick, with multiple strands of force mana layered on top of each other. But Nathan had practiced against Stella's force mana a lot. He moved at a speed enhanced by everything Stamina, [Raging Thrill] and [Mid-tier Sprinting] could provide. And all that speed was fueling [Juggernaut's Inertia] and [Antimagic Momentum].

Mid-tier Sprinting Rank 2 achieved!

The barrier shattered into pieces, and Nathan greedily sucked in all the force mana he could. Then he hit a second barrier, which suffered the same fate. The third slowed him down such that he didn't slam into the bunker.

Instead, he plunged his fists into the spotlight-like magical constructs powering the stupefaction beams that were suppressing the Heirs. There were crystals of some kind inside, and Nathan yanked them out. The beam emitters were arranged in three rows of two, about five feet between each horizontal row. He leapt and clambered up the device framework to reach the rest of the magical constructs, ripping their innards out as he went.

A quiet whine pulled Nathan's attention to the right, where the turret atop the other bunker was tracking him. He jumped up, pulling with his hands as he pushed with his feet. The bolt that had been aimed at his head passed just in front of his knees, skittering off the bunker's metallic surface.

Wow. I can really jump with this [Raging Thrill]. Let's crush some uppity magical constructs.

Nathan felt exhilarated as he landed directly in front of the other turret. It also began to whine as it charged to fire. Luckily, Nathan could move faster than it could track, and he zipped around behind it and grabbed the base of the turret. It was solidly constructed, with a hard outer shell and a tough ring attaching it to the bunker. After a few seconds Nathan wasn't making any progress, even tugging with all the strength of his Rage. He hissed, wrestling with the stubborn metal as he tried to rip the turret out of its housing.

He was keeping the metallic bulk between him and the other turret, which seemed disinclined to fire.

Darn. That would have been easy.

The constructs had reached the bunker and were attempting to climb it. Luckily, they kept slipping off the near-vertical surface. Nathan's Stamina was running low, having depleted the boost from the magic barriers. He was about to reach inside the barrel of the turret when he noticed a new sound.

It was a harsh crackling, like a tesla coil. Nathan looked up and saw a crystal above the door that the bunkers were positioned to either side of. It served as the centerpiece of some kind of crest above the building's entrance. It was also clearly powering up, glowing with magical energy and sparking with loud *cracks*. Nathan hunkered down, holding tightly to the turret as it strained to rotate towards him.

For what we are about to receive, may we be thankful—

His vision whited out as the crystal unleashed its magic. It was certainly lightning mana, but Nathan could tell nothing about what the spell looked like. Even with [Magic Absorption], his body seized and his heart skipped a beat as the lightning *continued* for a few seconds. Nathan could smell skin scorching as the metal underneath his palms went red-hot. He released the turret. It sat there glowing and smoking, no longer turning to face him. He shook himself and felt the residual shock work out of his system.

Stamina: 395/420

Magic Absorption Rank 3 achieved!

Nathan ducked down as the other turret fired at his head. Now that he was up close to them, the turrets' charging whine made dodging them a lot easier. He stood up and looked at the turret; it was time for some revenge. He took a few steps backwards for a run-up – then leapt from one bunker to the other, laughing maniacally as he flew across the twenty-foot gap.

He didn't quite make it but caught the edge of the bunker with his fingers and hauled himself up. Once again, he skipped around the turret before it could reload and draw a bead on him. He looked up at the lightning-crystal – but it wasn't charging up again.

No such luck!

So, Nathan did the only thing that occurred to his Rage-addled brain. He stuck his hand into the barrel of the turret and felt around. He scratched his hand on the tip of the loaded bolt, then found a small metal tab on the side of the barrel. He grabbed and yanked, tearing out a thin, enchanted piece of metal. The turret jerked erratically and spun upwards to face the sky. It loosed a wild bolt high into the air, aimed at nothing.

Satisfied it was out of commission, Nathan looked down from the top of the second bunker. The emitters for the remaining stupefaction beams were below him, still focused on the Heirs. Surrounding him on every other side were the eight bug-like constructs that had harried him in the street. Nathan rubbed his hands together, calculating how best to jump down and take them out.

Wait a second. That's not the objective here. That's my Rage talking.

He took a few steps back from the edge, standing still to activate [Focused Mind] and examine the battlefield. It was a struggle to focus past the Rage. Khachi had gotten Stella out of the line of fire, but Aarl was still gazing blankly and Sarah was sprawled out in the street in the same place she'd fallen.

The image hit Nathan like a splash of cold water. He almost let go of his Rage, before clenching his fists and springing to action. He jumped off the bunker and landed on top of the two stupefaction beam emitters below him, striking with his heels as he landed.

The metal frames warped and deformed under his feet. Nathan's plan had been to repeat the motion, crushing all six of the magical devices as he descended the bunker. Unfortunately, the buckling metal robbed him of his balance, and he tumbled, scrabbling for a handhold.

He found one, grabbing onto the base of one of the beam emitters farther down with his left hand. It bent down towards him as his weight overwhelmed whatever mechanism it used to aim. Nathan pulled on the handhold to swing himself up and punched his right hand into the adjacent magical spotlight. As he did so, one of the bug constructs leapt and slashed, grazing Nathan's butt.

I think it'll take all of my Stamina and a little while to regrow a single limb, so let's try not to get dismembered. But I need *to get rid of these beams!*

Nathan yanked at the housing of the device he was hanging from with both hands, feeling the strength induced by his Rage coursing through his muscles. He didn't rip it off the bunker, but definitely broke the aiming mechanism. He'd also lifted himself up a few feet, dodging the next slash from the bug-constructs below.

Nathan looked down. Two more magical spotlights were aimed out at the Heirs. Below them, eight chrome-and-steel constructs waited with readied blades. Nathan's lips peeled back in a rictus grin.

This. This [Raging Thrill] is better than anything I've ever felt before. I've trashed whatever this place was. And here I am, about to leap into the jaws of shiny death for my friends. Who wouldn't dream of such a thing? What a rush.

Then, Nathan jumped. He slammed his feet into the beam emitters, hearing a satisfying *crunch* as his full weight bore down on them. He didn't try for a clean jump this time, instead toppling forward towards the nearest of the bug constructs. It swung both bladed arms up. Nathan caught them on the outside of his forearms, roaring in challenge.

The blades didn't cut his arms off, but they sliced to the bone. Nathan landed atop the central body of the bug. It staggered under his weight, almost collapsing to the ground. Nathan dodged preemptively, not needing to look for incoming attacks to know they were coming.

He rolled to the side, falling toward the ground. All of his attention was focused on landing on his feet. Going down here meant death. Another cutting blade hit him in the ribs, carving a deep gouge and slapping him into the side of the construct he'd just rolled off. One of his feet landed on a metallic leg of that construct, which buckled under him. It upset his landing – Nathan landed awkwardly on one leg, already falling to the side. He tucked and rolled under another construct. There was a rush of wind as more blades whizzed over him.

Hah! Invincibility frames. Can't hit me when I'm rolling!

Pending utility skill: Low-tier Tumbling

You have used acrobatic tricks to dodge blows from dangerous opponents. This skill will help you use unorthodox movements involving rolls and handsprings to avoid blows in the future.

Nathan was on his feet again, standing just behind a construct. It reared up to strike with its back legs, but he didn't care. It was *behind* him and couldn't stop him now. There was one more construct blocking his path, and Nathan took three steps and slammed his fist into the spot where the legs connected to the body. He put his full body into the motion, pushing with his legs and bringing his hips up into the blow.

The constructs were quite sturdy. The legs spasmed at Nathan's blow – but nothing obvious broke except some of his knuckles. All four of the construct's legs left the ground as the metallic bug lurched into the air.

Nathan ran forward, meaning to take advantage of the opening. Then, a blade hit him in the side of the head from behind. He staggered, almost going down from the blow. Only his single minded goal kept him moving past the burst of pain and confusion. And nausea, couldn't forget the nausea.

Gotta escape. Not dying here. Giantsrest will *hear from me again.*

Nathan wavered and wobbled, picking up speed as he ran. Blood coursed down from his head wound. All of his attention was focused on the building the Heirs had retreated into. It slid back and forth across his vision, and Nathan's balance was shot. He almost fell crossing the wide street twice, only catching himself by running faster.

Then he tripped over a corpse and ran headfirst into a stone wall. He fell, and the cool stone of the street pressed against his cheek.

Skill text comparison:

[Low-tier Sprinting]
This skill will help you run quickly in the future. Will not allow you to run in circumstances where you couldn't otherwise

[Mid-tier Sprinting]
This skill will help you run very quickly in the future. Will not allow you to run in circumstances where you couldn't otherwise.

Chapter 33

The Payoff of Risk

Nathan lost a moment, stunned from yet another blow to the head. He became aware of movement, of hands grabbing him.

Don't lose the plot now.

He settled into [Focused Mind] and tried to direct his [Regeneration] to his head. He pictured the proper layout of the brain and meninges – but Nathan couldn't fully hold the image. He squeezed his eyes closed, concentrating on staying conscious. Moment by moment his mind felt clearer and more focused. Then, the process stopped.

Stamina: 0/420

Mid-tier Focused Mind Rank 10 achieved! Congratulations, you have maxed out this skill! It cannot be improved any further. You must achieve Insight into this skill to Develop it to the next level.

Nathan's eyes cracked open. Aarl was carrying him though a ruined building. The wiry man staggered under Nathan's weight, but they passed through a door before Aarl roughly set Nathan down against a wall. Nathan was still woozy, but his eyes could mostly focus now. Khachi leaned over Stella in the corner, and Sarah slumped against the wall, sipping from a healing potion and holding her side.

Nathan reached up to touch his head wound. His hand came away sticky with blood, but there wasn't a great rent in his head that exposed his brain or anything. Unfortunately, he was still bleeding pretty badly. Blood streamed from the gouge along his ribs, and the cuts on each forearm welled with bright red blood.

Good thing I don't get woozy when I see blood. Oh, there's the shock.

He gestured weakly towards Stella. "Magic. Out of Stamina. Need some magic." They had extra healing potions, but when he'd tested them during training, they'd just tasted bad. Apparently alchemy was magical enough that Nathan was immune. It wasn't all negative – that result meant he would likely be immune to magical poisons.

Stella laughed weakly, coughing. "S-still need me I g-guess? Come over here." She waved Nathan over with a feeble motion.

Nathan got up, nearly overbalancing. Aarl grabbed him under the shoulder and helped Nathan across the room. His footsteps left blotches of blood on the floor.

Stella wasn't doing much better. It looked like she'd taken a bolt from one of the turrets to the chest. Her enchanted robes seemed to have slowed the bolt enough that it hadn't gone through her like the one that had speared Nathan. Khachi had removed the bolt and was continuing to heal her, chanting quiet prayers over her supine body. Khachi's legs were wet with his own blood, but he paid his own wounds no mind as he chanted over his friend.

"By the valor of Deiman, let these wounds be healed. Taken in righteous battle, this injury will not fell a valiant warrior. I ask you, Deiman, stem the flow of blood and mend this wound, that Stella Caxol may fight virtuously another day."

Nathan collapsed to the ground next to Stella. Her hand flopped to the ground next to him, palm lit with fire. Nathan took her clean hand with his bloody ones, cupping the fire like it was his only source of warmth in a blizzard. Stella laughed at that, her cough a little stronger this time. Then the fire increased in size, growing larger and larger until it would have touched the ceiling without Nathan absorbing the mana. It wasn't a complicated spell, just a larger but less-disciplined derivative of the blowtorch spell that they'd fought over on the first day.

This time, Nathan wasn't trying to disrupt the spell. He was trying to suck *as much Stamina* as he could from it, and then feed it to his injuries in order of priority.

It was a surprisingly intimate moment, with Nathan and Stella softly chuckling at the ridiculousness of the situation. She was healing him from life-threatening wounds... by setting him on fire. While she was also being treated for a deadly injury.

Sarah called over after a minute, her voice tinged with pain. "If you are enjoying yourselves so much, can I get Khachi over here? I need a bit of divine love on my ribs."

Khachi ignored her, finishing his prayer. "... Continue to be your faithful servant in righteous battle. Praise to Deiman, may his Grace be granted." He released Stella, who was looking much healthier. Then he rose and walked over to Sarah.

Nathan looked around for Khachi's shield and hammer. They'd been discarded in the corner of the room. The shield had two bolts sticking all the way through the heavy metal. The tips were red with the wolf-man's blood.

Aarl came back into the room. "The sentry constructs are keeping their distance for now. They don't seem to want to go too far from that building they're guarding. They seem... uncertain now that their support fire is offline." He threw an acknowledging hand gesture towards Nathan.

Nathan hadn't noticed Aarl leave, but he was glad that somebody was maintaining their situational awareness.

Sarah spoke through gritted teeth as Khachi poked at her ribcage. "Then they will be easy targets from here. Stella and I can take them apart from inside the building. Those constructs are too large to fit into these hallways."

Nathan was uneasy. In his mind, the correct thing to do was *run the hell away*.

Stella spoke next. "I want to take my pride from their carcasses. Nathan, you good? You're having a little problem with. Uh. Clothes."

Nathan *was* much better. He wasn't exactly full of Stamina, but all his wounds were healed. He looked down at himself. He was also mostly naked, with his underwear hanging off one leg. However, that was somewhat less remarkable than the fact that he was almost entirely covered with blood, all of it his own.

High-tier Regeneration Rank 3 achieved!

Nonetheless, he answered. "Uh, yeah. I'm better. Can I get some pants? And food? I think we should get back to Gemore *right now* and report this."

Khachi rose, pulling Sarah up. "I am running a bit low on Faith and still need to finish healing myself, but it seems that we are able to fight. This is a threat we encountered on our patrol, and we would be remiss to leave it behind. I agree with Sarah and Stella. We will not run back to Gemore when we have the ability to end this threat now." He started chanting again, this time with his hands crossed across his chest.

Stella had dug into her dimensional bag and handed Nathan a pair of short pants, a rag and some pastries. He stuffed a slightly bloody pastry into his mouth before turning around. Then he used the rag to start wiping away the worst of the blood before delicately putting on his pants. It would be a *terrible idea* to keep attacking whatever-the-fuck this building was. He tried to voice his thoughts.

"We almost died already. I don't think it's in our weight class. We should back off, get some experts. Remember the lessons on dungeoneering? You *don't* do a dungeon you don't know anything about."

Sarah responded curtly. "We didn't die, and I will not let a near fight scare me. We know what we're facing, and the threat is much less now that you have disabled many of the defenses. We aren't in the dungeon. We can knock down those constructs, clear a threat from the streets of Old Gemore. Then we can gather information on what this is, maybe peek inside and submit what we learn to the Guild. We might even get to come back for it. It's common for the team that discovers a dungeon to be offered the chance to clear it."

Aarl and Khachi nodded in agreement. But Nathan was growing even *more* convinced this was a bad idea.

The outermost defenses almost handed our ass to us. I don't want to assume it's out of tricks. And there's something else bothering me.

Nathan asked about what was concerning him. "Uh, guys. Why haven't we leveled? Is the fight still happening? Aarl, didn't you say the constructs were backing off?"

Khachi frowned. "That is somewhat odd. Davrar must believe the fight is not over. Aarl, you counted eight outside? Are we sure that none are sneaking up on us?"

Aarl nodded, and they all took a second to listen for anything off.

Sarah continued. "We should take a look out front. No need to commit yet. Nathan, nobody will accuse you of cowardice after what you did, but we must have our chance to prove ourselves here. Our parents have told us stories about fights like this for years."

And that's the problem! You all have heard stories of your parents, powerful Adventurers all, triumphing over terrible enemies. Survivorship bias, as well as unrealistic expectations. None of us are on that level of power yet! I don't know if we can even take on those "sentries." They threw a hell of a lot of magic my way at the drop of a hat.

Nathan hesitated, uncertain how to convince them without being demeaning. Stella was already walking towards the door, and Khachi picked up his hammer and shield and followed her. Nathan was forced to go after them just to continue the conversation. It wasn't a far walk to the front of the ruined building. There was an empty door frame and pair of wrecked windows that looked out onto the street. Nathan noticed another metal bolt sticking through the wall next to the door. He shivered.

Whoever built this place did not *skimp on defenses. There are definitely more layers, more contingencies than what I saw.*

With that thought in mind, he studied the front of the building. The look-away magic and illusions were starting to reassert themselves, but now that Nathan *knew* what was there, it was easy to penetrate.

All eight of the bug-constructs were acting just as Aarl had said, guarding the front door from approach now that the defenses were offline. Nathan studied the building carefully for a moment, breathing out and activating [Focused Mind]. He leaned into [Notice], looking for important details.

The building was nondescript but sturdy. The windows were heavily barred and set high in the walls. It looked something like a prison, but the bunkers out front made it seem like a military headquarters. There weren't a lot of obvious details, besides the windows and some carvings on the walls. The carvings were abstract, some crests and flowing lines of decorative stonework that embellished an otherwise barren facade.

Nathan didn't see anything unusual, but something bothered him about the building. He let himself relax, trying not to look for anything but rather see what came to him. After a brief moment, a pattern jumped out at him. Some of the bars on the windows subtly aligned with the carvings in the stone.

What really made him pay attention was that it reminded him of the mana flows he'd felt from spellwork. Not the engravings that made enchantments – it looked like a *spell* was engraved onto the wall, with the windows as the focal points. Recalling the spells he'd interacted with, the flows looked like a *light* spell, reminding Nathan of the beams of intense light that Kullal had sent his way when he'd Developed [Magic Absorption]. He never would have seen it without relaxing and letting his [Spellsense] work with his [Notice].

Congratulations, you have Developed the [Low-tier Notice] utility skill into [Mid-tier Notice].

Utility skill: [Mid-tier Notice]
This skill will help you notice details in the future. Especially useful for detecting concealed magical effects and triggers.

He elbowed Stella, who had been discussing target prioritization with Sarah in a quiet voice. "Do those four windows, and the carvings on the walls behind them, make a single symbol? One that reminds you of light mana?"

Stella frowned at him, then followed his pointing finger. "It's not an enchantment, but... I think I can see what you mean." She paused, narrowing her eyes and fingering her braid as she concentrated. "There's some mana flowing through it. But what can it do? It's not an enchantment on the building."

Nathan thought for a second. "Could it be a one-shot spell? You flow mana through a pathway in something solid and it makes the spell?"

Low-tier Identify 7 achieved!

I think that means I'm right.

Stella was backing up as she shook her head. "I... no. We can't do that, the material interferes... but if you could..." She looked up at the spell carved into the building and her eyes went wide. "It's *huge*. We should run."

Aarl had been silently listening, and he turned immediately, sprinting down the corridor. Stella followed him. Sarah and Khachi were slower on the uptake, but they quickly followed. Nathan took up the rear, figuring that if they were about to get hit with some sort of giant death-laser, he should probably be in back. He was tempted to stay and moon the building but followed the rest of the Heirs closely.

They ran through the ruins. There wasn't a back exit, but Stella solved that problem by slicing through the back wall with blades of force. The building creaked alarmingly, but they didn't stay for long. They all ran into the next crumbling edifice, clambering over some piles of rubble and working their way around a collapsed hallway. Eventually, the Heirs emerged onto the next street over.

Nathan was sweating, waiting for Davrar to decide the fight was over. That would *probably* happen when they were out of range of the presumable-death-laser. And now they were a whole block away, on the other side of two fairly large buildings, and it still wasn't happening.

Even I might not survive that at close range. Glad I didn't moon it after all.

Khachi barked at them to get into formation and directed the group a few streets away and back towards the transit road. They kept up a quick jog, not wanting to run into any terrible dangers. They'd almost gotten back to the transit road before Davrar finally decided the fight was over.

You have leveled up to level 43! Congratulations, you have escaped an extraordinarily dangerous trap that has felled many Adventurers higher-level than you, without losing a single teammate!

Phew.

Congratulations, Nathan Lark! Now that you have Developed your class and exited the fight, you are no longer at a **Disadvantage.** Davrar congratulates you on overcoming your difficult beginning, and welcomes you to the Davrar Experience.

Nuts.

~

Skill text comparison:

[Low-tier Notice]
This skill will help you notice details in the future.

[Mid-tier Notice]
This skill will help you notice details in the future. Especially useful for detecting concealed magical effects and triggers.

Status of Nathan Lark:
Permanent Talent 1: Magic Absorption 3
Permanent Talent 2: High-tier Regeneration 3
Talent 3: None

Class: Spellbreaker Juggernaut level 43
Stamina: 77/530
Juggernaut's Wrath
Antimagic Momentum
Raging Thrill
Juggernaut's Inertia
Unarmored Resilience

Utility skills:
Mid-tier Focused Mind 10

Low-tier Earnestness 10
Mid-tier Sprinting 2
Mid-tier Spellsense 1
Mid-tier Notice 1
Low-tier Identify 7
Low-tier Dodging Footwork 8
Mid-tier Enhanced Memory 2
Pending: Low-tier Tumbling

Chapter 34

Return to Safety

They moved quickly back to Gemore, traveling along the space-distorting transit road. At a jog it took only minutes, and Nathan marveled for what must have been the third time at the incredible enchanted road. He once again hoped his still somewhat bloody feet weren't causing problems for its magic. His Stamina wasn't ticking up from [Magic Absorption], so that meant something.

The guards at the gate raised weapons as the Heirs approached. Their rapid advance, combined with the blood and torn clothes, was probably pretty alarming. Or lack of clothes, in Nathan's case. Nathan saw their eyes lingering on the bolts still stuck through Khachi's shield. One of them called out, her voice booming across the square. "Threat incoming?"

Khachi slowed for a moment to respond. "No threats. We think we found a new dungeon out along the north road."

The statement was met with a mixed response. Some of the guards swore but relaxed from their ready stances. Others laughed nervously. Everybody started paying close attention.

The guard who was speaking moderated her volume as they got closer. "Then you'd be headed for the Adventurer's Guild. Gotta do some quick checks first, no amount of swimmin' in blood'll get you through without it." She eyed Nathan. "Right. You. Well, check all'a them first." She gestured to the rest of the Heirs.

They were checked over quickly but thoroughly. The guards were interested in what had happened but didn't want to hold the Heirs up for a full accounting. After a quick aura scan and cross-check that everybody could answer basic questions and account for each other, they asked every member of the Heirs to vouch that Nathan hadn't been replaced by anything that could duplicate his total lack of a magical aura.

They admitted that they'd lost sight of him for some time during the fight, and that caused the woman commanding the guards to sigh. She asked some more questions about the fight, her eyebrows climbing as Aarl recounted a very short version of what he'd seen. She shot a look at Nathan.

"He's got good protection from mind magic?" Every single one of the Heirs nodded enthusiastically. "If it was in the middle of a fight 'gainst constructs, there's probably not much chance of a soul eater. But we'll keep a note that there's a risk here. Sorry, we'll have to keep an eye on ya, and somebody'll check in with you in a few days. Protocol." She shrugged.

Nathan wasn't sure why she was so apologetic. He'd heard of some of the insidious parasites or magics that could infect people here. Some "merely" took a little while to trigger a psychopathic break, sending the infected into a killing frenzy. The worst, like the soul eater, could *spread* themselves to others if given time, *Invasion of the Body Snatchers* style. Nathan would put up with a *lot* of inconvenience if it meant they had better protection against something like that! He wasn't sure how magical that process was, or if he was immune or not. And he never wanted to find out.

Just watch, now I'm gonna find out. I think Davrar's making me fatalistic.

After being waved through the city gates, they made a beeline to the Adventurer's Guild. People stepped out of their way on the streets, and a hush descended in the main hall as they entered. Nathan saw people inside counting them, checking to see if all of the Heirs had returned. He supposed that seeing somebody covered in blood tended to do that, though none of them were pristine. Khachi went straight to the counter, where an unfamiliar clerk turned to greet him.

A heavy tread approached, and a hand clapped Nathan on the shoulder. Given how hard it hit him, Nathan knew who it was before he turned around.

"What's happen' with you, my friend Nathan Lark? You look like you got chewed up by a Castlebear and came out the other end! Here's hopin' you didn't find a few stalkers ta be too much."

Nathan looked down at Eldred Vanguard, assessing the man's shiny bald head and enchanted armor. He was very slightly tempted to see if his new Rage class could best Eldred in the ring. But he was almost certain it *wouldn't*. Eldred was high-level and had beaten Artha. Furthermore, it would serve no point and might make him an enemy.

Instead, he answered politely. "Had no problems with some stalkers, actually. But I think we found a new dungeon. Hidden under a nasty illusion that covered a bunch of Adventurer corpses. Wonder if that's why the north road has been so dangerous."

Eldred withdrew his hand, squinting at Nathan. "Huh. That so? A new dungeon *inside* Old Gemore? Big deal if that's what it is." He eyed Nathan slyly. "Buy you a drink if ya got any more details to share."

Aarl stepped up besides Nathan. "We think it prudent to let the Guildmistress decide what to do here. Debrief comes first."

Eldred sighed, then walked away, waving a hand scornfully. "You're bein' the Guidmistress' pets now, hidin' things from those who have need to know. But I'll not argue."

Khachi returned and eyed Nathan. "I think we're going up to see the Guildmistress in a minute. Shame that we can't hit you with a cleaning spell Nathan. Do we have any more spare rags?

Nathan spent the next couple of minutes wiping away excess blood. His hair was a sticky mess that was going to require a bath, and his pair of pants would require some *advanced* cleaning magic to get all the bloodstains out. At least now he wasn't going to leave smears on any surfaces.

They were interrupted by the front doors slamming open. Nathan caught a brown-furred blur before Kullal had wrapped Stella in a smothering hug.

Damn. I'm pretty sure that's the fastest I've seen anybody move since the Guardians of Gemore swooped in to take out the Grave Tangle.

"Oh, thank the Divine that you're alive. We heard you'd been wounded and I just couldn't stop myself. What was this about a new dungeon? On the north road? We should never have let you go out that way. But you're okay now, yes?" She patted Stella all over, fingering the tear in her robe and the replacement shirt that Stella had thrown on underneath it. "You got hurt! How? What could have gone through this enchantment?"

Dalo walked through the doors a moment later, looking worried. His clothes were notably mussed. "I couldn't stop her from flying here the moment she heard. Dear, leave them alone. I think they're about to go up and talk to Sudraiel. We can ask them what happened later. After all, they're *Adventurers* now. They need to follow the rules. We'll just wait here. It will be good to remember all the time we sat in this room. It's been years. Let's plan a close-call party after this?"

He collected Kullal, who only released Stella with reluctance.

She looked at Nathan and gasped. "Nathan! What happened to you? Is that all yours? I haven't seen anybody that bloody and still standing since Stanel... well. We'll hear your story later. It seems the Heirs have teeth after all!"

She flashed a smile with nearly as many teeth as Khachi, then spun and joined her husband. Nathan noticed that most of the adventurers shot Dalo and Kullal wary looks, giving them a wide berth.

Then it was time for them to follow the clerk upstairs to report to the Guildmistress.

Sarah spoke up in the stairway. "That was cute. Your parents are cute, and you shouldn't be ashamed, Stella. Stanel doesn't show himself to us that way. Sometimes we think he's just training us because it's what Mom would want."

Aarl shot her a complicated glance. She raised one eyebrow slightly and set her mouth in a slanting line. He just shrugged in response.

Twins, right. Not surprising they can communicate well.

Stella seemed more embarrassed now that Sarah had called it out, flushing pink. "My mom is great, but she is too loving sometimes. I know she cares *so much,* but it seems impossible to take risks sometimes without getting scolded for it." Stella waved her hand back down the stairs, recalling her mother's unstoppable tirade. "And I want to be an Adventurer, I want to make things explode! Use magic to blow up things I don't like!"

Khachi chuckled. "Well, we certainly took a risk today. Remember that your mother let you take this risk, and wasn't hovering high in the sky to watch over us. Good thing too – we wouldn't have gotten any levels at all. I was a bit worried about that, but now I've got the levels to prove that they weren't protecting us."

Nathan was feeling around for new scars as they climbed. He'd been cut a *lot* today. There were lines in his skin where he'd suffered the deepest wounds. They looked like faint, decade-old scars, but they were there.

I wonder if I'll be covered in those in a few years. I could probably figure out how to control it with [Regeneration] at the next Development. Something to think over later.

Nathan shook his head, looking up to join the conversation. "I don't think I would have minded having a little bit of support for that dungeon. We were fine with the stalkers, but that fight was *nasty*. I had to take my level 27 Development in the middle of the fight."

The Heirs all grew quiet, glancing around at each other. They seemed to elect Aarl. He had a thoughtful look on his face as he spoke. "I... noticed you had some new capabilities. They seemed powerful. I hope you took a class that suits you, and not something that cripples you or goes against your nature. We would be filled with sadness if you jeopardized your future to save us."

Nathan thought about that for a moment. The clerk was definitely listening in, and they were almost at the top of the stairs. "No. I don't think it did. I wish I'd gotten the chance to discuss with Artha, but... I think I made the best choice. Definitely don't want to continue making those decisions in the middle of fights. Twice is enough for me."

Stella looked down at him, her face concerned before it morphed to contentment. "I finally hit level 27 after that fight too. Today was my first time fighting without my parents around. Guess Davrar decided it was enough to finally push me over the edge, huh?"

What. Stella hadn't hit her class Development? Jesus Christ. I'd assumed with her firepower she was over level 27. What now, she starts shooting lightning bolts from her eyes?

Then they were at the top of the stairs, the door into the Guildmistress' office already open. Standing next to it and waving them in was the same Knuld with purple robes who had been here the first time Nathan had visited. They all trooped into the office and sat in the chairs before the broad desk.

Sudraiel raised her head from some kind of written report, looking past the Heirs. "Siltul, sit. If they've discovered a dungeon, then you'll need all the details as well."

The Knuld secretary stepped forward, grabbing the spare chair and setting it against the wall before sitting. He gazed unsettlingly at each of the Heirs with his glowing, white-irised eyes as he brought out a fine slate to take notes.

Chapter 35

A Violent Debrief

Sudraiel waited a moment, then waved a wrinkled hand and prompted them kindly. “Well then, Hisla told me what you told her downstairs. Can you give a more detailed report? Khachi, start from the beginning.”

Khachi was clearly intimidated by the Guildmistress, but after wetting his lips, he spoke. “Y-yes. Apologies. We departed on our Blooding Patrol early this morning, then reached our patrol area quickly. We surveyed the area and spotted signs of a stalker nest.” Khachi nodded his head towards Nathan. “Then we proceeded towards it, ready for their ambush. There were seventeen stalkers and a Patriarch in that nest, but we triumphed with no great risk and no expenditure of permanent resources.” He paused for a moment to see if there were any questions.

The Knuld – whose name was apparently Siltul – spoke for the first time. His voice was high-pitched, dry and clipped. “Three questions. Where was the nest? Were the bodies disposed of? Did you harvest anything?”

Khachi continued the report. “It was located about five city blocks west-southwest from the old community hall. Ruined residential building, nothing notable about it. Stella Caxol incinerated the bodies to an acceptable level after the fighting. We harvested a few teeth, especially from the Patriarch.”

Aarl brought out the two large canines. Nathan shivered at the sight of the foot-long pieces of sharpened ivory. They disturbed him more now as trophies than when they were in the mouth of the thing trying to eat him. Go figure.

Siltul made some notes on his slate, speaking as he did so. "Commendable for a first patrol, both in execution and cleanup. Please continue."

After a deep breath, Khachi continued. "After that, we proceeded to finish the patrol. We surveyed both sides of the transit road over the course of several hours. We encountered the new dungeon at maximum patrol distance to the east of the north transit road, on a secondary boulevard. I would be able to mark it on a map. As for the dungeon itself, it was hidden by magic. *Very well hidden*. There were illusions and mental magic involved, and I'll let Nathan Lark describe what happened. He got the best look past all of that. Most of us were... disabled."

Everybody's eyes tracked to Nathan. The Heirs watched him just as intently as Siltul and the Guildmistress. Nathan supposed that he wasn't sure how much of the fight they'd seen through the broken illusion, look-away magic and stupefaction beams. The Heirs hadn't taken a break to talk since then, and they probably wanted to know Nathan's perspective on the whole encounter. He considered for a moment before launching into his tale.

"We were walking along the street when I noticed we weren't in formation. I looked around and sensed a magical effect of some kind, both a look-away compulsion and an illusion. I thought it might be a Giantsrest ambush, so I broke the illusion. It was covering a fortified building, not a group of Giantsrest mages. There were two bunkers on either side of a single entrance, and eight of these weird four-legged metal constructs. They had two slashing arms and could fire a bunch of different types of magic."

Sarah broke in. "Sentry constructs of Old Gemore. Stanel described them to us once." She swallowed, as if just recalling something. "And told us to hope we never ran into any."

There was a moment of silence. Siltul's chalk made a few brief, hesitant marks. He looked uncertainly at Sudraiel.

The Guildmistress looked thunderously upset. "Describe their magic and attacks. In detail."

Nathan thought back, making use of his [Enhanced Memory] to replay the frantic seconds where the constructs had attacked him with magic. "They started by hitting me with... small bolts of fire, blades of force, lightning and acid. When that didn't work, they shifted to other attacks. I remember spikes of ice, a spell of pure cold, some bolts of death mana. Also light mana beams, sharpened bolts of force and balls of stone. They tried pretty comprehensively to find a weakness."

Sudraiel's face had grown darker as he spoke, and she hissed as he finished. "That matches their full spell repertoire. Siltul, mark that as confirmation of eight fully functional Old Gemore sentry constructs with *open engagement parameters*." She spoke the last words as you would a curse, then gestured for Nathan to continue.

"The bunkers had two armaments. Each one had a turret on top that fired enchanted metal bolts. Accurate and armor-piercing. One went straight through me, and others pierced Khachi's shield. Stella was hit in the first salvo."

Khachi lifted his shield, which served as a wonderful way to display the two-foot metal bolts and their penetrating power. Stella again fingered the tear in her enchanted robes.

Nathan continued. "But that wasn't the worst part. The bunkers also had these... beam things on the front. Six on each, twelve total. They cast a ray of barely visible light that could stun people. I don't know what it felt like, but those pinned down the rest of my team pretty well." He looked back at Aarl. "What was it like?"

Aarl replied, shaking his head. "Like somebody was casting [Daze] on you multiple times a second. We've all got our ways to deal with mind magic, but that was just too much. Especially when there were multiple of those things focused on each of us. Hear me, but it was a good thing Nathan was immune."

Nathan shuddered. That sounded *awful*, just being continually dazed while you knew death approached. Then he cleared his throat. "Right. This won't make much sense if I don't tell you I took my level 27 class Development right then and had some new abilities. Not going to go into details, but it let me get past the sentries and reach the bunkers. They were protected by a triple-layer force barrier. Each one was... tougher than what Stella can cast." He shot an apologetic look at the auburn-haired mage.

She waved it away, clearly not upset at being outclassed by an ancient dungeon's defenses.

Nathan turned towards Sudraiel again. "Right. So I got through the barriers, broke all of the [Daze] beams on one of the bunkers while climbing to the top to get away from the sentry constructs. I was trying to break the turret that was shooting bolts when this... crystal thing above the door hit me with a bolt of lightning."

Nathan did some quick math based on his mana conversion efficiencies and how much Stamina the lightning bolt had restored. "I think it was at least a... 700 mana spell?"

Enhanced Memory coming to the rescue once again!

There was a quiet exhalation from the other Heirs. Stella's shocked voice sounded from the side. "Dragon's breath. *More than 700?*"

Siltul broke in, his voice dry and a little sarcastic. "That number appears plucked from the grave. Do you have a way to quantify the power of spells cast against you? I find it hard to believe you survived such a spell."

Stella jumped in. "He survived a [Disintegrate]. And can estimate spell strength pretty accurately, at least with me and my parents in practice. Still, *700?* Nathan, are you sure?" Stella was looking at him like she'd never seen him before.

Nathan shrugged. He supposed that was probably about three times Stella's entire mana pool, so it made sense she was shocked. "The lightning nearly melted the turret I was trying to break. It was a strong spell. Anyway, I jumped to the other bunker and was able to break that turret *without* a bolt of lightning. Then I broke the other [Daze] beams and dodged past the sentries to return to the Heirs, who had escaped after I broke the [Daze] beams."

He equivocated a bit, waving his arms around. "It was a bit more complicated than that, but not in any important way. After that we thought about trying to take down the sentries, but there was some sort of light *spell* – not an enchantment – carved into the building that was powering up. So we left. And came straight back here."

Nathan paused, about to indicate his tale was done. Then he remembered another detail. One he probably should have mentioned earlier. "One more thing. There were bodies in the street in front of the building, covered by the illusion. They were wearing armor and some of them were pretty old. I didn't count them, but... maybe two dozen?"

Sudraiel put her palms over her eyes for a moment, then shot a look at Siltul before turning back to the Heirs. "To summarize and ensure understanding. A building of Old Gemore, hidden by mental and illusion magic. Behind that magic were eight sentry constructs, two turrets firing enchanted armor-piercing bolts, twelve [Daze] beams, and a short-range defensive crystal capable of extraordinarily powerful lightning magic. All protected by a triple-force shield. Then further unknown defenses you did not see activate, including a single-shot spellform glyph. The turrets and [Daze] beams are now disabled, assuming there's no [Repair] functionality. Yes?"

They all nodded at Sudraiel's summary. But there was another detail that was niggling at Nathan. "The sentries were creeping up to ambush us before the illusion dropped. If we were taken by surprise and not even paying attention due to the look-away? It would have been a very scary ambush."

Sudraiel just sat there for a moment. She was old, but every time Nathan had seen her she'd acted so intently that it was easy to forget her apparent age. Her gray eyes had been focused, her questions direct. Now she gazed off into the distance, looking positively ancient. Her mouth opened unconsciously, and Nathan thought she was going to moan, or start crying.

Then she stood up, and with a casual motion, hurled her chair out the window.

It wasn't a small chair, and Nathan goggled as the nearly skeletal woman casually hucked a large armchair with one hand. The window shattered and sprayed glass into the courtyard below. In two quick motions, her spear was in her hand and she *hurled* it out of the window, high into the night. There was a shriek as the chair smashed across the stones forty feet down.

"Harpy's tits, Sudraiel!" somebody shouted from below. "What in all of the secrets of Kalis was that for?"

The Guildmistress stood silhouetted by the shattered window, gazing out into the night. Her thin robe blew in the breeze, and her entire posture seemed ready to leap out of the opening and go to battle. She held out her hand, and the spear zipped back towards her and slapped into her palm.

Her gaze turned down into the courtyard and she swore at whoever had yelled. "Tvora, Go fuck a muckgrabber."

The Heirs sat stunned in their chairs, watching the furious Guildmistress stare out into the night. Backlit and with spear in hand, she looked more like a valkyrie than an octogenarian.

After a minute she turned around, jaw clenched. She stood behind the desk and stared at them. Her voice was calm, but with an undertone of cold fury "So, this is what's been killing teams along the north road. It has hidden so well our search teams did not find it. And it almost killed you as well. I am glad it didn't, and glad we know what lurks there so we can finally deal with it."

The fury leaked through, her voice increasing in volume. "*Why* did Old Gemore have to be so blasphemously paranoid! A bunch of stupid fools trying to save themselves is what they were, and now it's killed yet more good people! It's *yet another* secret police headquarters or military arsenal or research facility, with stupidly powerful and powerfully stupid security."

Siltul made a few more emphatic marks on his slate as the Guildmistress fumed. His voice was dry, even as his beard blew in the breeze swirling around the office. "I assume this dungeon will be prioritized for next Delve Day. Do we want to send a team to scout and disable the exterior defenses?"

Sudraiel looked around for her chair, then turned to look out the window. She sighed. "Yes, of course. We'll need a detailed written report from the Heirs by tomorrow afternoon. Start reaching out to the Delve Scholars. I'll ask Jolba for a debrief with the rest of the trainees tomorrow. This'll be a valuable learning experience. Oh, and all of you?" She looked over all the Heirs.

"I'm proud of you for this. This new dungeon has killed many before you, but you showed the best trait of adventures. You *survived*. Some teams would have gone back to kill the sentries, but you did not. This sort of behavior is exactly what I wish to encourage with the training course, and I want you to know that I appreciate your taking those lessons to heart. I will be proud to have you graduate on the Solstice."

The rest of the Heirs darted guilty looks to Nathan.

Sudraiel caught the looks and smirked. "Thank you for the debrief. I apologize for my outburst, and Siltul will see that you get a finder's fee for the Last Dungeon of Old Gemore. He will also walk you through the report and have you mark the dungeon's location on a map."

They recognized it for the dismissal it was, and were all getting to their feet when Sudraiel called out once more. "Nathan, can you stay behind for a moment?"

Chapter 36

Private Conversations

Stella looked surprised and on the verge of protesting, but Sarah grabbed her by the arm and towed her out of the room. Khachi gave Nathan's shoulder a firm squeeze before Siltul led him out and closed the door.

Sudraiel put her spear in the holder next to the desk. She came around the edge of the desk, pausing to open a drawer in the side and extract a bottle and two glass cups. She set them down and spun two of the chairs in front to face each other. She sat in one and offered the other to Nathan.

Nathan tentatively sat, taking the offered glass. Sitting across from the Guildmistress like this was odd – she looked positively ancient, but her every motion was imbued with strength; a certainty that suggested somebody strong and confident in their actions.

I wonder what level she is?

Sudraiel had taken a moment to collect her thoughts, then raised her glass in the familiar gesture for a respectful toast. Nathan clinked her glass gently, and they both drank deeply.

Nathan's nose was overwhelmed by the assault of strong, cinnamon-flavored whisky that had an extra shot of sourness. It was remarkably smooth for its level of spice, and he managed not to cough. The drink reminded him of Fireball, but a bit weaker and significantly more sour.

The Guildmistress watched him with an expectant look. "Many apologies for keeping you from the Heirs. I'm sure you have some celebrating to do, especially for reaching the level 27 class Development. I have my own work and will not keep you long. But. I believe this is a good time to seek a better understanding of you."

She paused, cocking her head and considering the weapons mounted on the walls of the office. "You saved the lives of the Heirs today. That dungeon should have killed you all. Single-handedly and without preparation, you managed to triumph over a threat I would have sent two accomplished teams against with every bit of foreknowledge I could provide. This is known to me and known to the Heirs' parents. That is a bond that does not weigh lightly. You are *somebody* now, Nathan Lark. Eyes will rest on you, including mine. I find myself wanting to know more about you. What is your background? What do you want?"

Great. Now she's going to ask after Earth.

Some hint of Nathan's thoughts must have showed on his face, because Sudraiel waved her hand dismissively. "I don't want to know the details of your world. Whatever Giantsrest wanted is not of interest to me. Waking Giants know we don't need more disruption now. I want to know what Nathan Lark's plan is, and *why*."

Her elderly frame was full of poise and strength as she gazed at him over her glass, clearly inviting him to answer.

Nathan took a deep breath to focus his mind and consider how to answer. He took another drink of the whisky-esque drink to stall. She'd stated her goals simply and left it up to him how to respond. In a way, this was about the most efficient and polite interrogation Nathan could imagine. He couldn't help himself respecting that and feeling like he should be straight with her in return. Which was probably exactly the intention here.

Well, I certainly appreciate it more than Taeol's approach. And Sudraiel genuinely has only helped me.

He opened his mouth and spoke. Slowly, haltingly. "Earth... is very different from here. There are many more people. No danger. No monsters or dungeons. Very little conflict. There are nearly eight billion people living there. I was born in one city of millions and was expecting to live my life in one such city or another, driven by where I could find interesting work."

That statement clearly shocked Sudraiel, but she didn't interrupt as Nathan continued.

"I had spent my entire life training for a job that is impossible to do here, and was close to reaching the most advanced qualification my world offers. It takes *twenty years* of education to get there. And I was almost there."

Nathan thought of his graduate school research project. The threads of evidence he had been pursuing that would push the edge of human knowledge a little further forward. It would have allowed for more precise stem cell manipulation, holding potential for therapeutics and understanding mammalian development. A small step towards growing stem cell therapies, artificial organs and better basic science. From here, his day-to-day experimental worries seemed less important. Even if his big experiment had failed, he would have learned *something*, and set it up differently next time.

"I was ready to be happy with that life. It would have been slow, philosophical. A lifetime spent building knowledge to give to the next generation, just as generations before me have provided a foundation on which to build. I was ready to be another step in the pyramid that delivered us from suffering and death."

Nathan realized his eyes were wet. He reached up to touch them, his fingers coming away wet with tears. He took another drink, looking at the ceiling for a moment as he tried to master his emotions. He looked back to Sudraiel, who watched him kindly. She didn't seem in a rush to interrupt, so Nathan took another minute to collect his thoughts, to think upon what had changed, and what his purpose was now. All of this had been swirling through his mind for weeks, but he hadn't *verbalized* it. Hadn't expressed it – even to himself.

"But then Taeol brought me here. I have *so many* reasons to hate him, but just one of them is that he took that life from me. An existence that I *wanted*. That I *worked for*." Nathan put down his glass and scrubbed at his eyes again. "Even if I could go back now, I would not."

The ember of Rage inside Nathan burned a little brighter, and he clenched his fists around his tears. "I've discovered a love of battle, and the Path of Rage calls to me. I had dedicated myself to a peaceful life searching for knowledge. But I did it because that was the way I was best able to help people. I love knowledge, but the reason behind it was always to simply *do good*. And I find I love fighting, the thrill of breaking my foes, just as much as I ever did learning new things."

Nathan's expression was firm, even as tears continued to trickle from his eyes. "Taeol showed me a great evil, up close and personal. What magic can do is *amazing*, and I wanted power like that for the longest time. I wanted to use it to fix things, make things better for all. But when I find people who have such power? They use it to control others, to subjugate their minds and make them slaves."

Nathan found himself crying harder. He'd wanted so badly to have magic, for so long, even if he'd managed to mostly forget that dream. And then he'd met those with that power and they were using it for the worst ends imaginable. Nathan's imagination spun out parallels between Earth's history of oppression and the horrors Giantsrest could accomplish with even *more* power and control. He didn't need to see Giantsrest's squalid slave barracks for himself to know what happened there.

It felt like a betrayal. Like Nathan's dream of wonder and power had turned to darkness and horror. He'd been confronted with a tool of great beauty bent to great evil, and Nathan found that his choices made him well-suited to ending the magic that made the horror possible. He couldn't use it, but he could break it.

Nathan took a deep, shuddering breath and continued. "I can do something about Giantsrest. If I truly have the values I think I do, then I must fight them. Maybe I won't topple Giantsrest, frustrate their genocidal ambitions and free all of their slaves on my own. But with my Talents, I stand a good chance of leaving a dent. A better one if I plan – and get help. Even if I don't succeed, then another will have an easier time because of me. Less people will be enslaved. Maybe one of them will overthrow that empire of slavers.

"That thought, that I will benefit those that come after, that's what drove me forward in science. It's the same thing driving me now. I *can't* be a scientist, here and now. I don't have the resources, I don't have the class. But I can fight for what I believe in."

Nathan rubbed his eyes again, before looking around Sudraiel's office. He delved deeply into his feeling of confusion. "But then I came here and saw this city. Gemore stands against Giantsrest, but your greatest threats are the dungeons and monsters of Davrar. And I think – can I take up this cause too? If a dungeon is built on magic, I can deal with it in a way few others can. I can help this city. Do I have that responsibility too?"

Nathan floundered for a second, looking for the next thought. But he felt wrung out. That was everything. He had done his best to honestly lay his dilemma before the Guildmistress in the hope she could help him.

Congratulations, you have Developed the [Low-tier Earnestness] utility skill into [Mid-tier Earnestness].

Utility skill: [Mid-tier Earnestness]
This skill will help you portray your intense conviction and honesty when you speak to people. This skill will encourage people to be honest in return. Cannot fool truth spells or skills.

He blinked the blue box away, waiting for the frail woman's response. She was giving his words due consideration, looking thoughtfully around the room.

After a moment, she gestured to the weapons on the walls. "Those belonged to my family. They're a reminder of what I have lost, and of my responsibilities." She pointed to the bow. "Silca died to a [Disintegrate] from Archmage Dennar of Giantsrest." Then she pointed at the swords. "Calah died to a trap in an Edrani Empire gatehouse dungeon we were clearing to make a shorter path to the village of Tarren."

She pointed at her own spear, still propped in the holder next to the desk. "I can make Gemore's Adventurers capable of clearing dungeons without casualties. Capable of *winning* fights against Giantsrest. Both are necessary. But I won't dedicate this city to Giantsrest's destruction. The majority of Gemore would not survive that fight, no matter how it went."

She pointed to Nathan last of all. "You have an aspiration to destroy Giantsrest, and I sympathize. By the Endings, do I sympathize. But, you also want to help Gemore against the dangers that assail us. Help us with our ongoing survival, and when you decide the time is right, I will help you with your goal."

She paused, tapping a finger to her glass as she considered something. "I will swear you an Oath, upon my title as Guildmistress and member of the Council of Gemore. May Davrar revoke my class if I forswear. Stay in Gemore for now, maybe until your next class Development. Help us, and work with the Heirs to ensure their safety and the safety of Gemore. Do this, and I will give you aid in your fight against Giantsrest. I will introduce you to somebody who shares your goal. Somebody powerful, with multiple classes, who wishes the destruction of Giantsrest over all else. The Heirs are unlikely to follow you to Giantsrest. This is their home, and those who make war on Giantsrest court a fate worse than death. You need allies when you decide to move against them, and I will bring you to their attention."

Nathan picked up the glass, then offered another toast to Sudraiel. She clinked his glass, and they downed the rest of the liquor.

His voice still had an edge of raggedness to it as he replied. "It's a deal."

There was a long minute of silence, as they sat there and considered what had passed. Then there was a faint knock on the door.

Sudraiel sighed and stood, collecting both glasses. "It seems the work must always continue. Do you have any final questions?"

Nathan was about to shake his head when he remembered one more thing. "I meant to try to build a weapon. From home, the sort of thing that Taeol wanted. Nothing catastrophic – just a personal weapon. I intended to ask Kadid and Beatred Bho about it. It involves new Insights, I think. Is that ok?"

Sudraiel's eyebrows knitted together for a moment. "I will trust your judgment on the knowledge you share. If you speak to any, the Bhos are a good choice. They hold their Insights tightly and are trustworthy. And Gemore knows better than to seek their Insights by guile or force, for those who insult the Bhos tend to regret it. And you can be assured they will *never* treat with Giantsrest."

A moment passed, and then Sudraiel waved towards the door. It opened as Nathan stood to leave. Siltul entered the room with some pieces of yellowed paper. Behind him stood Stanel Crusens, who was watching Nathan. He looked *gorgeous*, with corded muscles and sculpted features. Nathan was suddenly very aware he was shirtless, and that he had dried blood crusted into his belly button.

As Nathan walked out of the office, Stanel clapped him on the shoulder. "Nathan, we should talk." He turned, and they descended the stairs together. Stanel led the way, and he moved slowly. "I hear you ranked up to 27 and set your feet on the Path of Anger." Stanel looked back up at Nathan, his gaze unyielding.

"Does your Rage skill say 'uncontrollable'? Or that 'you will be controlled by your Anger?'"

Nathan paused for a moment, stopping to review the wording on [Raging Thrill] before he answered.

Class skill Raging Thrill:
You can voluntarily enter and exit a Rage state, where you will be immersed in the thrill of combat. This will rapidly consume Stamina, but will increase your strength, speed and resilience to damage.

"No. It says 'immersed in.'"

Stanel's face relaxed, his relief palpable. "That's good then. I've had some bad experiences with those who couldn't control themselves in their Rage. Sounds like yours is better. See that you remain *you* when you Rage." He shrugged and turned to keep descending the stairs, continuing to talk. "Heard you saved my kids' lives today. And the rest of the Heirs."

Nathan didn't say anything to that, just nodded a bit.

"You seem to be from far-off, and without much in the way of resources. Let me know if you need anything. Maybe a new spear?"

Nathan looked up, and Stanel was grinning at him while he extended the butt of a new spear to Nathan. It looked identical to the old one, from the golden spearhead to the red-black wood haft.

"I've got a bunch of those, I use them for throwing when I need a *lot* of penetration. I'll lodge a request that the head of the one I gave you gets retrieved, those are the pricy part."

Nathan took the spear. "Thanks. It was very useful against the earth stalkers. Less so against the sentry constructs."

Stanel shrugged. "That's the way of things. Different tools for different jobs." He grew serious once more. "Do let me know if you need anything else. Especially for adventuring. It doesn't seem like you'll destroy the bank on magical items, but I'll give you a thousand spears if you'll keep my kids alive with them."

Nathan stopped, mouth open. Well, this could certainly solve *one* problem for him. "Yeah, I have something in mind, actually. It might be a bit expensive, but it'll let me give Sarah a weapon neither of you have seen before."

Stanel turned and looked back up the staircase at Nathan. "Is that so?" He raised an eyebrow and his hand *flickered* to his pouch. A string of coins flew at Nathan.

They bounced off Nathan's chest, and he caught them. It was a full string of the highest denomination currency Gemore had before you started bartering magic items. Pretty much like somebody throwing you a hefty roll of $100 bills. On initial estimate, about ten times as much as Nathan had gotten from rescuing a town's worth of people.

"You've awakened my curiosity." Then Stanel turned and opened the door into the main hall of the Adventurer's Guild.

~

Skill text comparison:

Low-tier Earnestness
This skill will help you portray your intense conviction and honesty when you speak to people. Cannot compel actions beyond what natural speech could, and cannot fool truth spells or skills.

Mid-tier Earnestness
This skill will help you portray your intense conviction and honesty when you speak to people. This skill will encourage people to be honest in return. Cannot fool truth spells or skills.

Chapter 37

Back to Normalcy

The main hall was less rowdy than usual, with groups of Adventurers talking to each other in hushed voices. Nathan listened closely and caught snatches of whispers.

"... New dungeon on the north road, dangerous as a dragon's nest..."

"... Guildmistress furious there's still a dungeon in Old Gemore..."

It was clear that he and Stanel were objects of interest from the way people watched them.

A gaunt black man raised a hand in acknowledgement, and Nathan returned it, recognising him as Vhala's uncle. Kadid seemed like a fixture in the Adventurer's Guild, and Nathan had been meaning to talk to him more. Especially if he wanted to take advantage of the Bho network to implement anything from Earth.

Nathan looked around, but he didn't see any of the Giantraiders around – maybe they were on errands, or had even accepted a job out of the city.

Stanel led Nathan through the main hall and out into the night. Instead of leaving the Guild and climbing the hill, they headed to a set of buildings that Nathan had never been into before. After navigating through a short series of halls, they emerged into a cozy room with a subdued party already underway.

The Heirs and their parents were scattered among a number of tables. There were snacks and drinks aplenty. It was a lot like the party at Stella's house the night Nathan Developed [Magic Absorption], except that the mood was more subdued, and the Heirs were doing the lion's share of the talking.

As Nathan and Stanel entered, the attention turned towards them. Kia elbowed Khachi, and he stood. "A cheer for Nathan Lark! The hero of the Last Dungeon of Old Gemore! Now, can somebody please get him a shirt?"

The rest of the room raised their glasses with a laugh and a cheer, and Stella chucked Nathan a spare shirt for the second time that day.

He pulled it on, accepting a glass of the same purple liquor – was it called Umna? – that he'd drunk at Stella's house. Kia simply wore a thin, padded gambeson, revealing her incredible figure. Her hair was loose and fell in a red-gold waterfall down her stacked and muscular frame.

Man, all of my friend's parents are really hot. Also really badass. Those are definitely synergistic effects.

They settled back into the party. After they'd gotten comfortable, Stanel prompted the Heirs. "You have survived your first *true* challenge, where death was a true possibility. We are proud and relieved that you have returned whole – and at a higher level than this morning! But hear me, events like that are difficult. You should speak of your thoughts of the day. This place is safe – we will not judge you for what you say, and we can share our hard-earned wisdom. Aarl, can you begin? It can be simple as what you learned of your weapons."

Aarl nodded. "I truly enjoy the greatsword. The feeling of *momentum*, that no defense can block the next strike. The shorter weapons might be faster – but I prefer to end my foes with every strike, not harry them with smaller wounds."

Sarah spoke next. "I lack good armor-piercing weapons. I have javelins and heavy throwing axes – but they are heavy and bulky. Not well-suited to most fights. I need some way to penetrate armor that is more convenient." She shot her father a meaningful glance. "Any chance I can have an enchanted weapon like that?"

He snorted. "Not yet. I will not have you dependent on a specific weapon for now. Though..." he tilted his head and raised his eyebrows questioningly at Nathan.

Nathan shrugged and didn't say anything.

I don't want to promise anything yet. I'm not sure I can – or should – try to build Sarah a gun. I can always return the money later. Or not. He didn't attach a lot of strings.

Stella broke into the silence, excitedly talking. "I threw fireballs at live targets today, and killed a bunch of them. It was amazing! And throwing fire-balls close to Nathan and know that I'm helping him out was great. I worry about hurting my teammates with my magic, but his immunity makes me worry less. If he's swarmed by enemies I can just blow him up!" Then she grinned wide. "And I'll have even more options with my next class Development."

Dalo shook his head. "Stella. This isn't the time to speak of your class Development choices."

Sarah raised her glass, breaking the awkward moment. "A cheer for Stella Caxol! A mage unparalleled for her age and level. May we all be useless as she blows up our foes from half a mile away!"

Stella flushed, embarrassed as her mother wrapped her in yet another hug and squeezed tight.

Khachi rescued her by changing the subject. "I relied on the strength of my arm and the thickness of my shield. The Last Dungeon of Old Gemore showed me that some foes will always have an arm stronger than my own. I must rely on the strength of my faith as the hammer that will lay my enemies low, and the shield that will protect my friends. My Faith is more than just healing, for I worship the god of Righteous Battle." By the end of his statement he'd picked up a faint golden glow.

He looked to Kia for approval, and she gave him a slight smile and an even fainter nod.

Nathan almost didn't follow up but decided to contribute. "I have stepped on to the Path of Rage, and found my fury is mixed with the thrill of battle. It calls to me, draws me in with the excitement of the fight. I must learn to balance the temptation of direct combat and the power my Rage gives me against the advantage of being *smart*. I am best suited to attacks against mages or weak points. I can't let my Rage dictate my battle tactics."

Everybody nodded, though nobody made a comment. Dalo shot Stanel a sharp look, to which Stanel replied with a placating hand gesture.

I bet Dalo was also worried about the Rage. I hope Stanel can talk him down and I don't have to reassure Dalo and Kullal that I'm not going to snap and accidentally kill Stella in a fit of Rage.

Later on, the party more resembled a group therapy session. The Heirs talked about the terror of being helpless under the [Daze] beams, and the swiftness of the stalker ambush. A common theme was the worry of being unable to use your skills and training when you were disabled or ambushed by foes that you could normally defeat in a head-on fight.

Stella in particular seemed upset. "If we hadn't *known* where the stalkers were hiding, and that they were about to jump, they would have landed on every side of all of us. I don't think I could have done anything about that. I can kill a stalker with a fireball. But I can't fireball in every direction at once."

Dalo smirked. "Yet."

Nathan shared his own worries. "Against things that don't use magic, I am by far the weakest member of the team. I didn't fight the sentries, just ran past them. Two stalkers were nearly too much for me, even when I had a weapon that was effective against them."

"You aren't bad," Aarl reassured him. "We'll practice together and find out how you can improve, especially now that you've Developed your class. We'd cart around a lead brick if it could throw stunts like what you did at the dungeon."

Stanel *harrumphed*. "And those sentries are tough ghoul uncles, that's sure and certain. Bypassing them was the right choice."

They continued talking about the ways to deal with being ambushed, and how to avoid debilitating mind spells. It boiled down to being cautious, careful, and ranking up skills and Talents that helped you avoid dangerous situations or break mental spells.

Damn, the combination of [Notice], [Magic Absorption] and [Identify] is potent for all of that. And [Focused mind], too. Good job, Nathan. I mean, I picked up [Notice] and [Identify] because perception is the best skill in D&D, closely followed by things that prevent you from getting disabled, and abilities let you figure out important details. If you can understand the bad guy's ritual you stand a much better chance of sabotaging it.

In a slight break from tradition, Aarl mentioned that his [Warning] utility skill had ranked up a lot today. It was still too low-tier to be useful for anything but last-second dodges against known threats, but he hoped it would eventually provide a few seconds of warning against a trap or ambush.

Sarah vowed to find a way to Develop her mind-protection skill until she was immune from magical effects like that [Daze], and Khachi reiterated his desire to Develop his Faith beyond healing.

Later in the night, once everyone was more than a bit drunk, Nathan admitted something he thought he'd keep secret. The night was cozy, and it didn't feel like an atmosphere where anything was off the table.

"I thought about running away when one of the sentries cut my hand off. I could have just taken off down the street, and I think they would have let me go."

Mid-tier Earnestness 2 achieved!

Khachi and Sarah looked confused at the admission, while Aarl and Stella looked upset and judgemental.

Why did I share that. They're not going to trust me now.

The Guardians all looked serious after Nathan's admission, and traded glances to decide who should answer him.

Kia was the one to speak up. Her general mien was one of unwavering commitment to her cause, and Nathan expected her to judge him and call him a coward. "The righteous path is difficult to walk, and one does not achieve it by embracing ignorance. You walked the righteous path today, Nathan Lark, and that you considered other paths does not make you cowardly, it makes you wise."

She looked to Khachi, who was listening intently. Her next words were clearly meant for more than just Nathan.

"Sometimes the righteous path is shrouded, and you must consider every option in order to find it." The copper-haired woman sighed, looking at the floor. "I have never abandoned a comrade, and I dread the day when it will be the correct choice. If you could not have succeeded, and your only chance of returning to warn Gemore was to flee in that instant, it would have been righteous to do so. Even if I am not sure I could have forgiven you."

Well, that's a bit of a downer to think about. Maybe I was wrong about Gemore being closed to me if I abandoned the Heirs. Glad things turned out this way, anyway.

That moment of drama wasn't the end of the party – though the Guaridans seemed to have decided to lighten the mood. Kullal and Dalo started demonstrating some new spells they'd been working on.

Unlike most of the magic Nathan had seen, they weren't designed for combat, but rather beauty. Stella's parents worked to interweave different opposing elements, pushing them as close together as possible without letting the mana touch. The pair spent fifteen minutes building a sphere of fire and ice over the central table. The interlocking sheets and filaments of the two elements were gorgeous, with the clear ice diffracting and diffusing the flickering red and blue light of the flames. Kullal dimmed the magical crystal that lit the room, and the sphere cast an ever-shifting pattern of light around the partygoers.

I need to remember that magic is a tool. The kind that lets you fly, or blow stuff up, is pretty cool. It's just a big sword. The kind that lets you control *people is what needs to be exterminated. Stella has a joy for exploring Davrar's magic, and I love her passion for it. I want to see her discover more magic and help her along if I can. I can't explore magic myself, but I can help somebody else along that path.*

Nathan sat there, tipsy and sleepy, and looked around the room. The dappled light illuminated Stella, Khachi, Sarah and Aarl. He felt accepted now – it hadn't been a smooth road to get here, but they'd managed to establish a mutual respect and work through the initial bumps. Then there'd been the trials of the Blooding Patrol, and now this celebration had cemented the gains.

It was different from Nathan's previous friendships. They were still younger than him. Immature at times, but it didn't matter. It wasn't the bond of a family. Just... squaddies. Teammates, whatever you wanted to call it. They'd face whatever came their way together. And a few dumb comments hadn't mattered when they'd stood shoulder to shoulder against the monsters of Davrar.

It was a bittersweet feeling, since Nathan fully expected to leave the Heirs eventually, to return to Giantsrest and his crusade. But until then, as he leveled up, he could enjoy their company and help keep Gemore safe.

Not long after that, they went to bed. The party had defused the confusion and terror of the day and Nathan felt calm and centered. Nathan took a detour for a bath where he scrubbed himself clean. He'd gotten most of it earlier with rags, but the water cleaned out his fingernails, hair and belly button. The water available in the bathing room wasn't particularly warm, but it was fresh and constantly flowing.

Man, the Guardians have sure been around the block a time or two. That little party was masterfully done. We've worked through the tension and fear from the fight and bonded more as teammates. That I was invited at all suggests they approve of me.

After that, Nathan meditated briefly before going to bed.

The next morning started the same as most other mornings in the Adventurer training course. They moved a little slower in their morning exercise than usual, but nobody was around to see. While they ran, they discussed the report they had to write for the Guild, and that they'd spend a chunk of their group training time in the afternoon writing it up. Apparently Aarl had the best handwriting.

In the dining hall they got a *lot* of stares. People had clearly heard rumors of what had happened but didn't know the specifics. Nonetheless, the tension in the room eased as the Heirs sat down, joking and laughing with each other. If anything, Nathan thought the other teams were jealous of their laid-back attitude. He supposed it made sense – they'd passed through to the other side of the trail. Bloodied but unbroken. All of the other teams here had yet to undertake their own Blooding Patrol.

I just hope everybody's patrols are easier than ours.

In class that morning, Jolba did a debrief of the Heirs in front of the entire group. It was clear that this was more designed to show the other teams what their debriefs would be like than to pick on the Heirs. He had them show their patrol area on a map, confirm the location of the stalker ambush and recount what they'd done with the corpses afterwards. Aarl fanned out all of the stalker teeth on the desk and made a show of counting them and holding up the Patriarch tooth.

Even Simla looked impressed. The well-dressed dark-skinned Adventurer was normally hostile to the Heirs and Jolba's agenda, so Nathan would count that as a win.

Then, they got to the dungeon. Jolba made sure they didn't show where it was on the map. He sighed, looking out over the class.

"Yeah, the Heirs found a dungeon yesterday. It wasn't something anybody expected, and that's *exactly* what kills a team. When you find something like that, you *run*. You *leave*, and report back so we can make a threat assessment. We're not going to go into details, but that's basically what they did. With one exception. Nathan, join me."

Nathan walked up to the front of the room. Jolba put a gentle hand on Nathan's shoulder and looked into his eyes. He fanned them outwards, putting the conversation on display for the rest of the class.

"You ran towards the dungeon. Why?"

Nathan paused for a moment, uncertain. It seemed like everybody had approved of his actions? Was he going to get taken to task for it now in front of all the trainees? "There were magical devices that were suppressing the Heirs with magic. I had to take them down so we could run away."

Jolba frowned at him. "Yeah. And there were other defenses you were able to draw off as well by charging. I respect that. But, could you have run back and helped your teammates flee? Gotten them into the buildings, then returned to Gemore without risking everything?"

Nathan shook his head. "It wouldn't have worked. The sentries were charging at us, and I needed to distract them. And the other defenses. Me charging let the Heirs flee on their own."

Jolba nodded. He released Nathan and looked back to the class. "And that's the important part – I wasn't there, so I can't judge what would have been possible. *If* Nathan could have assisted his team in fleeing, then that would have been better. But since that wouldn't have worked, he did the right thing by disabling the thing that kept them from running away, and then *running the fuck away*."

"When you're the person standing in front of the fire, you make the decision with the information you have. It's important that you make the smartest decision you can, but you need to commit to it. Don't let me, or anyone else, second-guess you afterwards. I wasn't there. Just don't make decisions for glory. Endings, the Heirs ran the fuck away, and now they're getting praised and paid for it. That's the lesson I want you to learn."

Chapter 38

Connections of Crafting

After a more normal lunch, the Heirs went back to their rooms to write the report. This mostly consisted of Aarl writing down every detail each person could remember about their encounter with The Last Dungeon of Old Gemore. That name was becoming more and more official, and it's how they titled the report.

They made a small diagram of the street, with the buildings and bunkers marked out. Nathan noted the approximate extent of the illusion and described the behavior of the sentries.

He used his new Mind Palace to recall more details, including the exact shape of the front of the building. It wasn't what the mental construct was *for*, but combined with [Enhanced Memory], it let him draw out an approximation of the facade. Stella helped him with the details of the mysterious, light-based spell-glyph.

Mid-tier Enhanced Memory 3 achieved!

While Sarah and Aarl went off to deliver the report to Siltul, the rest of the Heirs talked about magic. Following off of their goals from last night, both Khachi and Stella wanted to Develop their magic.

Stella was waiting to go home in the evening for her class Development, but expected to get access to at least one more mana type. Regardless, with her new class skills and enlarged mana pool, she should be able to execute more complicated and powerful spells.

She confessed that she *really* wanted to get lightning or light mana. "My dad's an expert with lightning mana, and my mom can do art with light mana. And they're so cool!" Then she heaved a deep sigh. "But you mostly have to get light and lightning mana from class Developments – nobody understands them well enough to get the mana types from Insights. Well, except some Giantsrest archmages, but they keep that knowledge close."

Wait, I bet I can help with that! I know the physical basis for light and electricity. And I want to live vicariously through Stella discovering the truth behind them.

Nathan interrupted Stella's complaining about how stupid Giantsrest was with that thought. "Hey, I might be able to help with those Insights. Not promising anything, but it's worth a try? I know a little something about how lightning and light *work*."

Her gaze snapped to him, both suspicious and hopeful. "We'll talk after I Develop my class. I hope you're right. For your sake. Might be irrelevant, I think one of my classes will give me access to at least one."

Khachi watched the exchange, then apprehensively asked his own question. "Nathan, I hope you will help me Develop offensive uses of Faith. Even if you don't have any Insights to share," he added, teasingly. "I would still appreciate you being a *target* of my attempts. Your ability to feel mana and yet be immune to it is invaluable for practice. Kia has her advice, but much of it is 'go kill something.' It's of limited use."

Nathan smirked. He could definitely see Kia saying that. "Sure, though I have to say the divine mana is... weird. It's very emotional. Are you sure Deiman won't be upset by you using mana like that in practice? Frivolously, I mean."

Khachi looked confused by Nathan's question. "The Gods... do not intervene with mortal events. Their power exists and can be accessed with the proper phrases, conviction and Faith. But Deiman does not speak to me, and I do not ever expect him to."

Huh. Power without communication? Most D&D settings have Gods speaking to their worshipers to send them on quests or something. Or at least have it generally be known that it can *happen. Strange.*

Nathan shrugged. The cosmology here was weird, and it was on his list of things to investigate. But Nathan had already decided it wasn't a priority. He had his goals lined up in front of him, and number one was making himself and the other Heirs as powerful as possible.

Shortly afterwards, Sarah and Aarl returned with the coin for discovering the dungeon. Nathan's share was less than he'd earned for rescuing a village of people, but not by much.

Rescuing one (1) village. A good unit of measure if ever there was one. But I'm glad that they prioritize rescuing people.

The rest of the Heirs were excited to talk to their parents about their recent rank-ups and Developments. They'd have a *lot* to practice in upcoming days, it seemed.

Nathan was *also* excited – if for different reasons than the others. He did want to talk to Artha about his own class Development, but he was more intent on asking him about Davrar. The sort of questions that would immediately out Nathan as *not from Davrar*. Like what in the everliving *hell* an "Ending" was.

He'd needed to ask those questions when he'd first arrived in Davrar, and gotten lucky that the Giantraiders were good people. He'd considered bringing the Heirs in on the secret, but decided there wasn't much point. It didn't change much except increase the number of people who knew his secret, and among people who were still somewhat immature and could potentially spread it further.

He also wanted to talk to Beatred about the possibility of firearm manufacture. The more Nathan thought about it, the more he thought that he *did* want to try building a gun. At this point, he liked the Heirs. He wanted to leave them with some of his strength, if he could. And it might get him more credit with Stanel for future Insight bargaining if he provided the [Weaponmaster] and his daughter with guns.

But only if he could do it without unleashing the secret upon the world. There had been a period of artisans building exquisite, custom firearms on Earth before they'd become mass-produced. He could take several measures to avoid the possibility of ranks of slave-soldiers with muskets, keeping firearm manufacture localized to a few experts.

First, treat the details like an Insight, and tell only the Bhos and those they trusted how to make guns and gunpowder. If it worked out as well as Nathan thought, then they'd be plenty motivated to keep the secrets to themselves. He would almost prefer to do everything himself, but there was *no way* he would be capable.

Second, do *not* introduce the idea of a production line, at least until Giantsrest was already on the ropes. All of the guns Nathan wanted to make were going to be made by individual craftspeople doing every step of the manufacturing. That would help with secrecy and keep the volume down.

Third, make sure his *damndest* that the guns weren't sold on the open market. The worst case scenario would be for a Giantsrest agent to waltz into a store and buy one so that it could be studied and duplicated.

Fourth, because the guns wouldn't need to be otherwise enchanted very heavily, they could build in some sort of self-destruct mechanism once the owner died, or something like that.

And fifth, try to make the guns as *advanced as possible.* If he made something more complex and capable, it would be harder to understand, harder to duplicate. If you were making breech-loading, metal-cartridge rifles, then somebody else was much less likely to think it was worth building a smoothbore muzzleloader, even if they somehow caught wind of the critical Insights. People would need more information and skill to duplicate the design and would be more likely to fail.

But if they do succeed, then it is worse. Eh, you gotta take a risk every once in a while.

With that decided, Nathan followed the Heirs out of their rooms.

They all split off to their respective mentors. Nathan looked around, but he couldn't find Artha. After a moment he saw Kadid, Vhala's uncle. The dark-skinned man with white hair was waving vigorously at him, so Nathan walked over.

Kadid offered a handshake and a wide grin. "Glad ta' catch your attention. Vhala and the Giantraiders left in'a hurry yesterday on a job. Headed towards Giantsrest, as you'd'a expected." He shrugged. "Artha said 'sorry' and hoped your Blooding Patrol went well."

The man's face split into a huge grin again, as if sharing a private joke. "We know how *that* went. They're in for a bit o' surprise when they get back. Anyway, you'll have to make do with me fer now. I can't help ya too much with what Artha was teachin', but we could probably do some perception drills. Vhala told me what she gave ya. I don't utterly approve, but she's got the favors to make it not'a problem. So, whaddya want?"

Nathan was briefly disappointed that Artha and the rest of the Giantraiders had left. He'd have to delay his questions. But on a second thought – this would certainly work fine for his purposes.

"I want to try to make something. Or commission it. Something new. I need to talk to a metalworker, like Beatred, and an alchemist. I don't know if any of those are in the family, but I'd love to talk to them."

Kadid frowned at him. "No Bho alchemists, but I can take ya to Beatred and introduce ya to the guy we trust for important stuff. His name's Poppy, funnily 'nuff."

"Can he keep an Insight to himself? The things I want to make... they're the sort of things I don't want sold around to just anybody. And can we get both of them together? What I want to make requires both an alchemist and a weaponsmith." Nathan was hesitant – he wasn't sure if this was a common practice.

The old man stroked some white stubble on his chin, working his jaw. "Poppy's good folk. Is that how'it'll be, eh? It'll be expensive for that, dependin' on the Insight and their interest. But you've earned a bit of interest, and if you've got the coin, it's worth a conversation. Let's go get Beatred and drop by Poppy. I think she'll be able ta leave the store. My great-nephew's 'sposed to be there today."

Nathan shrugged and followed the man.

They stopped briefly by Beatred's place. Kadid mentioned that Nathan had something special to commission, and that she should follow them.

Beatred looked more like Vhala's sister than a cousin. She was a good deal taller but shared the same dark brown skin and burly build. Her dreadlocks were shorter and bound back tightly. She frowned at Nathan, clearly deciding whether this was worth her time.

Nathan held up his hands. "It's a new kind of weapon. It's dangerous. I want to give one to Sarah Crusens. If it works I won't be surprised if Stanel will want one. But we need to keep it secret, like an Insight."

Her eyebrows shot to her hairline. "Getting a weapon of mine in that Weaponmaster's hands? And you're on his kids' team, yeah? Alright, this is worth hearing." She called out to the preteen who was scurrying around the shop, cleaning the displays. "Hey Erlan, manage the shop. Don't let anybody haggle you on any of the enchanted gear – *at all*." She turned back to Kadid. "Where are we going?"

Kadid waved them out of the building. "Poppy's. Nathan's new weapon needs'a weaponsmith *and* an Alchemist. I'ma bit curious, but if it's an Insight, I probably don't need ta know. You can handle the family interests."

Kadid and Beatred walked Nathan to a part of the city he hadn't been in before. It was farther from the gates than the Adventurer's Guild and was dominated by moderate-sized shops selling finely crafted goods. Furniture, tools, artwork and basic enchanted objects were most common. A few stores had books, but if Nathan was parsing the signage right, they were pretty expensive.

They came to a shop labeled "Poppy's Potions." The exterior wood was stained an even, bright green, very much setting the shop apart from all the stone buildings on the street. It was also only two stories tall, compared to the four stories of most of the constructions. They pushed through the curtain blocking the door and entered a dim room lit entirely by glowing potions racked in glass-fronted cabinets.

"Welcome to Poppy's Potions. What wondrous mixture can I supply you... ah, Beatred? What brings you up here at this time of day?" The man speaking stood behind a desk, partially obscured by a haze of smoke coming from the pipe he was puffing on.

Beatred stepped to the side and tapped on a crystal above a shelf. It lit with a white glow, illuminating the inside of the shop in its entirety. The room was long and narrow, and at the back was a wide desk. Behind it stood Poppy, who was an orc. The second orc Nathan had seen on Davrar. The first orc had been a huge, muscular warrior with emerald-green skin back in the Adventurer's Guild.

Poppy had the same color of skin as that orc, but he was short, thin and balding. He put a pair of spectacles he'd been polishing back on his nose, squinting at the group. He straightened to his full height – which wasn't much taller. If Poppy was over five and a half feet tall, Nathan would be surprised. The orc didn't even seem especially old.

Kadid raised his hand. "See ya'll round. I'll be in the Adventurer's Guild." He slid through the curtain and out into the street.

Beatred gestured at Nathan, indicating it was his show.

With both of the crafters looking at him, Nathan took a deep breath. He knew what he wanted, but he wanted to be upfront about his conditions. He leaned on his [Earnestness] as he spoke. "I want to make a new kind of weapon that needs both alchemy and steelwork. I don't know if we'll be able to do it, but I'll pay to try.

And if it works – well, it's dangerous, so I want to be upfront that I want to treat the weapon and its manufacture like an Insight. Only to be sold to trusted people that I approve of. *But*. Part of the weapon needs to be replaced after it's used, so even after I make one, we'll have to keep paying you for parts to keep using it."

Both Beatred and Poppy were frowning at Nathan as he talked. Poppy *hmmphed* and spoke first. "If you gotta pay to use it, why'd anybody want it? Beatred, who's this Adventurer, and why are we listening to him?"

Beatred shrugged. "Vhala brought him in from the wilds a few weeks ago. He's on a team with the Heirs, ya'know, with Stanel's kids and all the kids of the Guardians. There was some hubbub about them discovering a new dungeon, so he's got some coin." She shifted her attention to Nathan. "What you've described sounds pretty shit unless it'll kill a wyvern. People've made poison capsule weapons before, you know. That ain't new."

Nathan shook his head. "That's not it. One of these *could* kill a Wyvern. From far away, without it ever seeing you. Look, let's sit down to discuss. I need to draw some schematics. And there are some *other* Insights I can share to sweeten the deal if needed."

Poppy shrugged and scrubbed his mostly-bald head with a green hand. "Alright, come on back into my workshop."

They followed him through another curtain into a back room the same size as the shop. There was a bench along the far wall that had multiple concoctions boiling away above magical heat sources. Some of them were connected to a complex distilling apparatus. A central table held more glassware, scales and several cutting boards. About a third of the room was dedicated to storage, with meticulously labeled but somewhat disorganized shelves and boxes. Nathan recognized the active labspace and immediately felt at home.

Funny that being in a lab makes me feel comfortable. Ah yes, nostalgia for dangerous chemicals!

There was a large slate propped against one wall, and Poppy scrubbed it clean before handing Nathan a piece of chalk. Then he grabbed a pair of stools, offering one to Beatred and taking the other for himself.

He yawned as he sat down. "Go ahead. We won't tell people about this, but no oaths or anything just yet."

Great. Now Nathan just had to properly explain how to make a gun.

Chapter 39

Explanations of Explosive

Nathan started by drawing a tube on the board. "You start with a metal tube. One end is capped, the other end is open. Then you put a piece of metal inside." Nathan drew a bullet-shaped piece of metal near the closed end of the tube. "Then, you put a *little bit* of something explosive here at the closed end of the tube." Nathan drew a star shape behind the bullet. "When you set off the explosive it sends hot gas everywhere. But the metal tube is strong, so the explosion can only go one direction. Out the tube, pushing the metal – we call it a *bullet* – along with it." Nathan added an arrow showing the bullet's motion.

He could see both Poppy and Beatred considering the diagram. They'd been nodding along with the explanation but didn't seem excited about it.

He continued. "The thing is, that if the bullet fits tightly in the tube – called a *barrel* – then it leaves going incredibly fast. It'll go really far and can go through a person. Or a Wyvern, if you use a bigger explosive and a longer tube." Nathan added a bunch more arrows to represent the bullet's speed.

That made Beatred consider. She shrugged, looking at the diagram. "A bow or crossbow'll do about the same in the right hands. Maybe not as fast, but Stanel can still kill a Wyvern that way. It'd be cheaper than this, and you would just need a pile of arrows, not a packed tube for every shot.

Nathan nodded. He'd thought about the bow comparison. "Yeah, but a *gun*, which is what this weapon is called, has three really big advantages. First, it can be a lot smaller than a bow or crossbow. All of the energy is in the explosive, not in the arms of the bow or crossbow. So a gun about this big," Nathan held his hands about a foot apart, "can still propel a bullet fast enough to kill."

"Second – because the bullet is lighter than an arrow or bolt and flies so much faster, it won't drop very much over time. If you cut grooves on the inside of the barrel, then the bullet will spin, which will make it fly straight. A well-built gun with a long barrel can hit a man-sized target from a mile away, even before classes and skills get involved." Nathan drew a spiral pattern down the length of his barrel to represent rifling.

"Third. You can make a system that opens the tube and replaces the bullet and explosive propellant – quickly. There's a few ways to do it. All of them put the bullet and propellant together into something called a *cartridge*." Nathan drew a casing around the bullet and explosive. "If you do it right you can fire another new bullet quickly. Like this." Nathan started snapping his fingers rapidly.

Poppy finally had enough and stood up, yelling, "Except that explosives are *fucking expensive*. You need magical ingredients and the most accessible one is an eye from a fire stalker. I can make about *this much* fireblast powder from a fire stalker eye." He held his fingers close together, almost touching. "This *gun* would cost as much as a bag of holding to fire *once*."

Nathan smiled. He'd wondered what their chemistry versus alchemy knowledge was, and why somebody hadn't invented guns before if they had fine metalwork. It seemed he had part of his answer. "I know how to make a *non-magical* explosive using things you probably have the ingredients for. Doing it properly requires some care, but looking around this lab, I think you could do it. And the ingredients are probably cheap."

Poppy stood open-mouthed for a moment, then sat back down very politely. "Carry on."

Beatred broke in. "We already have some enchanted weapons kinda like this. Bolters. They'll fire a bolt real hard just with the enchantments. Expensive as adamant, and they drain mana like nothin' else. But it ain't that different." She eyed the bullet. "Not much room for enchantments on one of those. And if it goes as fast as you say, then I doubt you can use the same one multiple times."

Nathan shrugged. Those were fair criticisms. He'd certainly give up *multiple* limbs to get the weapon that came to mind when he heard the term "bolter."

"I don't know how a 'bolter' would stack up to a gun. But we could probably make this without any enchantments at all. They'll be handy to light the propellant and keep the barrel from getting dirty from the explosions, but I know ways to do all of this," Nathan gestured at the board, "*without* magic. It's complicated, and there's a dozen problems that require solutions. But I think we can solve them and make this into a real weapon."

Mid-tier Enhanced Memory 4 achieved!

Mid-tier Earnestness 3 achieved!

They both sat with that for a second, thinking about it.

Beatred nodded first. "Not needing enchantments changes some things. It'd be a tricky piece of metal, especially to swap out bullets and close the tube again. And get rid of the leftover case from the last bullet. Interesting. Got a couple ideas. But if we get it to work, and somebody gets some skills around this weapon? It could have some real power. Depends on if we can work out a way to shoot faster or farther than a good bow."

Poppy pointed at the diagram again. "If it's in a metal case like that, how do you light the propellant? Especially without magic?" The skinny orc wasn't being challenging. His eyebrows were furrowed, and it was clear he was dedicating his full attention to Nathan's proposal.

"Simple enough. You leave a small gap in the back of the casing and fill it with a different kind of explosive that will go off with impact. It's called the *primer*. But if you recess it into the case a little bit, then nothing will hit it very easily by accident. The only way it goes off is if you have a metal rod that sticks out of the back of your cylinder like *this*, and strikes the back of your cartridge when you want your bullet to fire." Nathan drew more things on the diagram, finishing up by sketching a brief rifle grip profile around the barrel.

"And you know how to make this 'primer'?" Poppy was looking at him with surprise. His fingers were twiddling in his lap, as if they wanted to grab tools and start working. He was clearly enthused about what Nathan was describing.

Pending utility skill: Low-tier Lecturing
You have explained a complex and novel concept and taught two masters something new in their field. This skill will help you explain plans and details clearly in the future, smoothing over gaps and aiding in explanation and understanding. Will not help you convey details you do not know, and will not help you suppress people's doubts about what you are teaching.

Okay, that's something to consider. Let's find out if I'll be explaining anything more today.

Nathan nodded, lowering his arm from the slate. "Yeah. But before we get into any more technical Insights, I want to paint a picture for you. Imagine we figure out how to make guns, and they work well. We make a weapon that fires a bullet faster than the eye can see and can kill from far away. We figure out how to make it easily and make a lot of them for a lot of Adventurers. But then Giantsrest gets some and figures out how they work.

"They have legions of slave-artisans to make things, right? They put them to work making guns. And they issue them to slave-soldiers, who stand in ranks. A rank of slave-soldiers with guns, shooting *hundreds* of enchanted bullets. I think that would change the dynamic of warfare, and not in a good way. That could happen. I *do not* want that to happen.

So, before I tell you any more, we're going to swear to each other not to reveal this. We're going to treat all of the details on how to make guns as an Insight. Any guns we make are going to be one-of-a-kind, sold to people we trust. And I'd prefer them to have some kind of self-destruct enchantment on them." Nathan stopped and looked around, gauging their reactions. They were hesitating, looking at each other and thinking it over.

"I can give you other Insights too, from the same place these came from." He gestured towards Beatred. "Some tips on alloying and metallurgy." He pointed at Poppy. "And some tips on chemistry. We'll need to talk about what to share and what not to share."

Beatred put out one hand, palm up, and spoke. "I swear by my family and our history as escaped slaves not to share the Insights related to the manufacture of guns and cartridges without agreement of all here now. I will *not* see Giantsrest aided from any invention I make. I further swear that if any others share these Insights without my permission, I will bend all of my resources to hunting them down. May Davrar revoke my class if I break this Oath."

Poppy was visibly surprised, leaning backwards. He swore. "Harpy's tits. I don't have much of a choice, do I? But yeah, yeah, I'm in. I need to know how to make this non-magical explosive." His eyes were hungry, and he lifted his hand. "I swear by my own desire for knowledge, which led me to abandon tradition and home, that I will not share the Insights related to the manufacture of guns, explosives or cartridges without permission from both Beatred and Nathan. I will hunt down any who share this Insight without permission. I speak this Oath honest and true, and may Davrar strike my class from me if I break it."

He lowered his hand, shaking his head. "I'd have to be an idiot to trust

Giantsrest anyway. I've heard they don't take kindly to orcs. Idiots. They wouldn't stand up for five minutes to the true Imperial Army."

Then it was Nathan's turn. He considered his words for a moment, then spoke. "These Insights are mine, so I will not swear to keep them secret from all others. But, I swear by my desire to see Giantsrest destroyed that I will do all in my power to keep this knowledge from Giantsrest, and will discuss with you both if at all possible before I tell any others. I will hunt down any who break this Oath, with every ounce of strength left in my body. May Davrar revoke my class if I break this Oath."

No blue boxes appeared, but Nathan had a sense of foreboding. He wasn't sure about it, but the atmosphere in the room made it feel like there would be *consequences* for breaking an Oath made that invoked Davrar as punishment. And they probably wouldn't swear that oath unless it did *something*.

With a thought, Nathan accepted a pending skill. He could always ditch this one later. He strongly doubted it would be permanent. But it would be useful now and might be useful for teaching Stella.

Congratulations, you have accepted the 'Low-tier Lecturing' utility skill.

They all took a deep breath, and then Poppy grabbed another stool for Nathan. "Okay, now we've initiated the gun cabal. Let's get some Insights into the open, so it's a true cabal. I want to know how to make this explosive. Can you walk me through it?"

Nathan nodded, reviewing his recollections of black powder. "Yeah. It's got three components. I know them as charcoal, saltpeter and sulfur. Do you have them accessible?"

Poppy frowned, getting up and scanning his shelves of materials. "Of course I know what charcoal is. I use some ground charcoal to make inert water." He grabbed a small drawer from one of the cabinets and set it on the central table. It held a couple of small cloth bags that leaked black dust.

"I've also got some sulfur. Use a bit of it in a bunch of different stuff. Not particularly cheap." He pulled out another drawer which was sealed with a metal plate. "As for saltpeter... I don't know the term. What's it used for?

Nathan shrugged. "It's a pretty standard oxidizer. Hold on, I'm going to use a skill to see if I can get any more information." He sat down on the stool and closed his eyes, searching back in his memory for details about *potassium nitrate*. Saltpeter. It'd been mined and produced from manure in a variety of ways. What had it been *used for*, besides gunpowder? Well, fertilizer obviously.

It was purified nitrogen from manure, but it was usually easier to just use the straight manure unless you were doing chemistry. What else had people purified saltpeter for? Right, food preservation.

It's great for curing meat. Huh.

Nathan pulled out a packet of jerky that he kept on hand for Stamina replenishment. "Is this cured with straight salt?"

They both looked at him with some level of confusion. Poppy shrugged. "I don't know. There's a place that makes it not too far away. Let's go find out."

Poppy moved a shelf to free the door, then locked up the shop. He led them down the street.

As they walked, Beatred looked over at Nathan. "How do you know this stuff, anyway? I'm still not sure I believe it all, but if you can make the necessary *boom* – then that'll change. We'll need to go over specific designs for me to start working on. I think those casings might be tricky. Are they crimped around the bullet? Can't be steel if so."

Nathan grinned. "How I know it is a whole other Insight, worth more than this one. And yeah, the casings are usually made from brass. They can be reused if they're made right."

Poppy walked quickly, clearly impatient to get where they were going. The building really wasn't set all that far away and resembled a low warehouse with an abundance of chimneys.

They walked straight into the front room, which doubled as a store and an office. Racks of jerky and other cured meats were laid out, and farther back were large bags waiting for pickup. There was a skinny woman manning the desk in the corner. She looked up when they entered.

Poppy took the lead. "Kher, good to see you. A thousand apologies for the hurry, but we've got a quick question about the curing process, and we might want to buy something you use for it. Nathan?"

Nathan stepped forward. "It's a white powder, which you use to cure meat. Creates a red color in the meat when you rub it in. It isn't salt, but probably tastes a bit like it. Do you know what I mean?"

The woman looked up at them, a bit taken aback by the sudden onslaught. "Yeah, I think we got that. You want some? It ain't cheap." She named a price for a bag that made Poppy blanch. It was a fair chunk of change, and clearly a good portion of the jerky's cost.

Nathan stepped forward. "It's okay, I got this." He *certainly* had money to burn, especially with the money that Stanel had given him. He showed her the coins. "Can we see it, to be sure it's right?"

Kher shrugged and waved them farther back into the working space of the building. She led them to a storage room and pointed to a stack of large bags. The top one was open, and she scooped out a handful of small white crystals. It *looked* right. Nathan took a crystal and stuck it into his mouth. Salty, but not table salt. It tasted a bit *cool*, which was weird. If it was used to cure meat, it was probably potassium nitrate.

Could be sodium nitrate, which would still work but would be harder to keep dry. This stuff doesn't seem hydrated. Might be a mix of the two!

Nathan handed Kher the coins, then hefted one of the bags. They were the size of Nathan's torso, awkward and *heavy*. Nathan wouldn't be surprised if the bag was nearly a hundred pounds. He walked it back out of the building, then into the street. He focused on keeping a hold on the bag as they headed back to Poppy's shop.

Poppy was bouncing around like a puppy. The frail orc clearly couldn't wait to see what would happen. He unlocked the door again and ushered in Nathan and Beatred, then hustled to clear a space for the bag.

Nathan dropped the bag and stretched, looking around the room.

Poppy was already sawing away at the bag with a small knife. "What's the mixture ratio?"

The answer was on the tip of Nathan's tongue. "Fifteen parts saltpeter, three parts charcoal, two parts sulfur. All ground and finely mixed. It won't explode very well unless you do another step, but it'll burn real strong."

The orc was hurrying around, getting out a scale and measuring charcoal dust into a stone mortar. "I hope to the divine you mean those numbers are weight fractions."

"Yes. What do you take me for, a barbarian?" Nathan nodded in the affirmative, then stood back with Beatred as the alchemist spent a few minutes measuring the ingredients before carefully grinding them together. He stirred the mixture with a wooden stick for a moment, then looked at Nathan.

"Do I just light it on fire?"

Nathan looked at how much Poppy had made. It was a decent amount, maybe a pile the size of a fist. "Probably better to just do a little first, yeah? I don't know exactly how strong this will be. Let's put *most* of it somewhere safe and then light just a little with a long stick?"

Poppy rolled his eyes. "Do you look at me and see a fool? But fire will set it off? It won't go off if I drop it, like fire stalker extract?" He was already busily scooping most of the powder into a wide-mouthed glass bottle, which he stoppered and put behind some shelves. On a metal sheet in the middle of the table he left a small pile of dark powder, an inch or two tall.

Nathan stepped back, shaking his head. "It'll only go off with fire."

Beatred stepped further back as Poppy grabbed a heavy leather apron and donned a pair of thick glasses. He pulled out a magical rod and the end started smoldering red-hot. Without further ado, he poked the rod into the pile.

It *wooshed* to life immediately, sending a small plume of smoke into the rafters and leaving behind black residue.

Low-tier Lecturing 2 achieved!

Yeehaw!

Chapter 40

A Spot of Mechanics

Poppy frowned at the spot where, until moments ago, a small pile of prototype black powder had rested. The green orc reached up and scratched his thinning hair. "Huh. I expected more *boom*."

Nathan stepped up next to the alchemist. "Yeah, it's not *quite* done yet. If you mix it even finer that'll help. The other thing that needs to happen is to grain it, so you have tiny little pellets instead of a fine powder. The way you do that is to mix in a little bit of water. The goal is more of a putty than a slurry. Then you rub it through a mesh screen or squish it into cakes and crumble them. You might need to heat it to dry it out." He gestured at the metal sheet. "Carefully, of course. You want little grains of a consistent size that have all three components integrated nicely. I think the correct size for the biggest explosion is small, but not so small you're all the way back to powder."

Poppy pursed his lips. "Why does making it in grains help it explode? Seems like you would fit less material in the same space if it's not a powder."

"The saltpeter dissolves slightly in water, so I think it helps mix all the components more finely and keep them from separating. But having them in grains means there's a little bit of space between them, like you said. Because the grains have some space between them, the heat and explosion can propagate faster."

Poppy was still giving him a dubious look, so Nathan elaborated further.

"Say this is one grain of powder." Nathan marked a circle on the board. "And there are a few others piled around it." Nathan drew another three circles to the right of the first shape, making a diamond of circles where they each touched two others. He tapped the chalk on the leftmost circle. "When this one burns, the hot air and heat can pass through the gaps between the grains, lighting other grains *farther away* than if it was all just a mess of solid powder." He drew a line directly from the left circle to the right circle, across the gap in the middle of the diamond. "So, when a fire starts at one side of a pile of powder, it gets to the other side faster, and you get a *boom* instead of a *woosh*."

Poppy nodded in understanding. "You're good at explaining these things. Have you done some teaching?"

Nathan snorted. "Yeah, a little bit. Not on how to make explosives though, that would have been much more fun. Now, about that primer mix..."

Beatred had been lurking against the back wall, but now she spoke up. "So we can make the explosives, and I expect Poppy will need to experiment with them. What about *me*? I can tell you that I'm not going to make one of these right the first time off." She gestured to the large slate, where Nathan's crude diagram of bullet mechanics still rested.

Nathan nodded, turning back. "Right. Yeah, we can talk about the primer later. Though if we can't solve it, I bet we can just use a simple heat enchantment." He pointed at the enchanted metal rod that Poppy had used to light the gunpowder. "Before we can really get going on making the guns, we need to test stuff out. To do experiments will require some prototypes.

"We probably want to start with just a simple barrel that can be loaded by hand with loose powder and a small ball of lead to act as a bullet. Light the powder through a small hole, and then we can get a sense for how much powder is right, and how tightly the bullet needs to fit the barrel. That sort of thing. Get the exact ratios of bullet and powder weight to barrel size nailed down first.

"I think you guys will need to work together a fair amount to make sure you're not going down the wrong path. You need to figure out the details of the casing and bullet before you can really start going on gun design."

Nathan laid out a few more suggestions for a *scientific* approach to figuring out the right numbers.

Then he turned back to the slate, picking up the chalk again. "I think we should aim for two different designs for the gun and cartridge. The first uses a cylindrical cartridge, where the cartridge is the same diameter as the bullet all the way back. This will go in a short-barreled handgun, meant to be used to shoot a lot at close range. Smaller barrel, less powder, lower power. There's a few ways to design it, but the one that we're most likely to use is a simple *revolver*." Nathan sketched out a classic old-west style revolver as he talked, including the trigger guard, handle and hammer.

"The trick here is that there's a central cylinder which can hold multiple bullets. Between six and nine, usually. There's just one barrel, but when you fire it automatically rotates so that the next cartridge is in line with the barrel. The internal mechanism is kind of tricky, since what actually shoots the bullet is this hammer coming down on the back of the bullet. Either it's got a pin that hits the primer, or we just seal it with thin paper and the pin is enchanted. But you want it to fire when you pull this *trigger* here, which requires a sort of catch and lever thing *here*, with a spring somewhere in the handle that pulls it back into place after the shot..."

Nathan looked back from his increasingly detailed drawing to see Beatred watching intently, fascinated. Poppy was looking a little boggled.

Beatred stepped forward, taking the chalk from Nathan. "It looks like you'd have gaps in your barrel *here* and *here*, where the cylinder lines up with the barrel and where the hammer goes into the barrel. Wouldn't that explode your hand? And how does the cylinder rotate automatically?"

Nathan shrugged, pointing at the bullet. "That's why it's a lower power bullet. The seal doesn't need to be perfect, just *close*. And the hammer needs to be heavy and the pin small so it doesn't get blown back. I think you put a gear on the back of the cylinder, then you stick a piece on the lever attached to the trigger, so that pulling the trigger automatically rotates the next cartridge into place."

Beatred nodded. "Looks tricky. The sort of fine work that you don't get to do very often on weapons. But *critical* to this thing working. I love it. Okay, you mentioned two designs. This one looks fascinating, what's the other one?" She handed him back the chalk.

Nathan had to stoop low to access the last clear space on the board. "It's called a *rifle*. Meant for long-range, accurate shooting. Long barrel, lots of powder, strong explosion. You make a tapered cartridge where the bullet is smaller than the body of the cartridge, so you can fit more powder and make your bullet go faster. It also means that there's less air resistance on the bullet so it'll fly farther." Nathan sketched out the cartridge, showing where the casing widened out to hold more powder. It looked like Poppy wanted to ask a question when Nathan mentioned "air resistance," but he held himself back to let Nathan keep explaining.

"Because you have more powder, you need a stronger chamber. The design we'll almost certainly use is called a *bolt action*, where you put a cartridge into an opening, then push this lever forward. The bolt, *here*, moves the bullet into the *chamber*. Then the lever rotates down a quarter turn and the bolt screws into the back of the chamber, forming a tight seal. The firing mechanism pops the pin through the bolt and into the back of the bullet, though the mechanism also needs to move with the bolt, which can be tricky. You can either feed cartridges in by hand, or you can make *magazines* that go in the bottom. They've got a spring in them that pushes cartridges up into the gun. So, to reload you just turn the bolt a quarter turn, pull it back, replace the cartridge, then push it forward and screw it back in. You can also make a magazine setup where a spring pushes a new cartridge in from underneath."

Beatred looked enlightened. "It screws into the back of the chamber to form a seal, that's elegant! How do you clear the casing after the cartridge goes off? It needs to be gone, yes?"

"I'm not sure about this one, but I think you put a little lever *here* that engages when you pull the bolt back. It just flicks the casing out sideways. I can get you a better answer later."

Beatred didn't mind, looking over the diagram with a hungry gleam in her eyes. "Why does the back look like this? I notice you don't have a handle on it."

"Oh, because the cartridge is bigger and shoots the bullet harder there's a lot of *recoil*, or pushback from the gun firing. You brace this part against your shoulder." Nathan looked around the room and grabbed a broom. He aimed it at Poppy, who was watching with an amused look on his face. "See, so when the gun fires and jerks in your hand, it's braced against your shoulder." Nathan jerked the broom to simulate recoil.

Then he paused and took a breath, halting his frantic torrent of words. He looked over the diagrams, trying to think of important details he'd forgotten. There were a *hundred* important details he hadn't gotten to yet, but this would be enough to get started.

Oh yeah. The bullet!

"One more thing for now. The bullet itself is made of lead. It's softer than the steel of the barrel, so it'll engage with the grooves to spin properly without messing them up. It's also easier to make a bunch of lead bullets for reloading empty cartridges."

Beatred nodded along, pursing her lips as she thought about Nathan's point.

Low-tier Lecturing 3 achieved!

It was Poppy's turn to interrupt. "It's getting a bit late. Come on up to my place, I'll make dinner."

They followed the orc through another door and up a flight of stairs. Poppy lived above his shop, and he busied himself in the small kitchen while they continued talking.

It seemed like it wouldn't be easy to make mercury fulminate, which was the simplest primer that Nathan knew of. The problem wasn't the mercury – it was the nitric acid. Really, Nathan should have asked about nitric acid first, since guncotton might have been a better propellant than gunpowder. The basic problem was that they didn't have *sulfuric* acid in any quantity, and the acids they did have seemed to mostly be magical. Sulfuric acid was the starting point for most industrial chemistry processes, including the best ways to make nitric acid. Nathan would have to spend some time in his Mind Palace to remember more.

But that was a different rabbit-hole. Maybe he could shepherd Gemores' alchemists into better living through chemistry *later*. For now, they needed to use materials already on hand to make power multipliers for Nathan's friends without starting a chemical industry.

That would for sure have unintended consequences.

Beatred and Poppy were discussing their first priority, which was the development of a standard casing and bullet size. Beatred needed to make some casings before Poppy would have an appropriate way to test if his powder was good enough, and the size of the cartridges would have to be decided before she could get started on proper gunsmithing.

They asked Nathan a dozen more questions about the mechanics of various designs, or alternate ways to do things. Nathan had to face up to the fact that while he remembered a lot of useful information from Earth's history, he did not have much hands-on experience with what he was describing.

But that's why he'd asked Kadid for the introduction. He didn't have the tools, time or experience to make his knowledge a reality. These two did. There were risks, but Nathan thought he'd done pretty well at mitigating them. Actually...

"Is it possible for you both to install some more security on your stores?" Nathan asked. "I'll help pay for it." He dug for his money again.

Poppy was dishing up the food, a leftover stew pulled from an enchanted preservation box and heated in a pot. He raised his eyebrows as Nathan put some more coins on the table. "I won't turn that down for sure and certain. Appreciate the thought of security, though the best security will be preventing people from learning what we're doing. Don't go telling people, and we should be careful about it in the streets."

Beatred took her bowl and a spoon. "I should ask old man Buscar if he's interested in sellin' his shop. It's right next to mine, got a nice workspace. You interested in movin' down? Safer near the Adventurer's Guild. Not a lot of thieves want to run into a Gemore Adventurer. More Guard closer to the gates too."

Poppy hesitated, clearly thinking about it. He handed Nathan his bowl and got his own before speaking. "Maybe. I'm not really focused on Adventurer supplies, but it's lucrative for sure and certain. If these 'guns' go well, then sure. If they're as effective as Nathan says they are... we should definitely think about building in some kind of self-destruction enchantment. Keep the Insights safe. Who are you thinking of bringing in to do enchanting?"

Beatred pulled a face. Nathan wasn't sure if it was from the stew or the idea of needing an enchanter. It wasn't a great stew, if he was honest.

"I can handle a simple enchantment like the firing pins. For something delicate like a self-destruct, we'd need a *real* enchanter. I'd say we go for Aunt Herdin, but we've got to convince her it's worth comin' out of retirement. We can trust her farther than we can trust *me*, and she's forgotten more about real enchanting than I've ever learned. We'll talk more about it next time." She took another bite and grimaced. "We can get excited all we want, but until I witness a piece of metal flying faster than sight, I'll have reservations."

The conversation quickly drifted onto more mundane topics around being a craftsperson in Gemore. There was a guild called the "Crafter's Guild" which oversaw the various artisans of Gemore. Aunt Herdin had stepped down from the role of Guildmistress a few years ago and been replaced by a man named Vint Anisal, a stonemason. Both Poppy and Beatred complained about the taxes that he'd allowed to be levied on the crafters in the past few years.

That led to a discussion of the governance of Gemore, which was a topic Nathan hadn't had a chance to learn about. He'd heard of the Council, and apparently it was their lead governing body. There were seven guilds and each guild had a Guildmaster who sat on the Council. Nathan asked about the guilds and got a quick rundown from Beatred.

Four of the guilds were focused on the city of Gemore – the Adventurers, the Guard, the Crafters and the Traders. Nathan was a little confused at the overlap between the Crafters and Traders or the Adventurers and the Guards. He asked, and Beatred's response was rather simple. The Guards and the Crafters were responsible for most things *inside* the walls of Gemore, while the Traders and Adventurers managed safety and kept everybody *outside* of Gemore's walls linked together.

The three other guilds were centered on the villages that surrounded Gemore, which farmed and gathered raw materials for the city. The Village

Guild was almost more of a sub-council, with one leader elected as representative and heavily overseen by the council of village heads. They were primarily concerned with what happened inside village walls.

Meanwhile, the Farmer's Guild oversaw... farming. And herding, apparently. Finally, the Gatherer's Guild oversaw collection of mundane raw materials that *weren't* crop or livestock related. Mining, quarrying and lumber, primarily.

Every guild had its own way of selecting a guildmaster, but many of them seemed to run on personal connections. From Beatred and Poppy's description, you'd never become Guildmaster of the Crafting Guild without being a crotchety old mastercraftsman who'd been around for longer than anybody could remember.

Beatred wanted to stay and go over some details with Poppy. Nathan was starting to feel like a third wheel, so he bowed out to return to the Adventurer's Guild.

It was dark outside, and as Poppy let Nathan out the front door, he realized that he was alone and far from the safety of the Adventurer's Guild. Nobody was escorting him. If there were agents of Giantsrest in Gemore that wanted to capture him, this was their chance.

Chapter 41

Can You Teach a Mage Multivariable Calculus?

Nathan didn't think he was being paranoid. Taeol would *definitely* be looking for him. Nathan wasn't sure if the archmage would be able to convince Giantsrest to throw their whole weight behind the maneuver, but he'd definitely seen that one sketchy guy on the day he'd Developed [Magic Resistance] into [Magic Absorption].

And here he was, about to walk through Gemore in the dark, *begging* to get ambushed.

He almost turned around to knock on Poppy's door. He could ask Beatred to walk him back to the Guild, since her shop wasn't far away. *But.*

Not only was Nathan loath to interrupt what seemed to be turning into a date, but if he was ambushed, how could Beatred help? She had a crafting class, not a combat class. And if Nathan was seen with her too much, then Taeol might draw conclusions and order her kidnapped to learn whatever Nathan was teaching her.

He sighed. He was probably overthinking this. If they'd followed his every move, then they would have been waiting for him here, outside Poppy's shop. Nathan glanced around. The street was dark, without many people around. But nobody seemed to be waiting for him. If they *were* waiting for him, it was probably on the path back to the Adventurer's Guild.

The way you avoided people looking for you was to switch up your schedule and not be predictable. So, Nathan would take a very weird path back to the Adventurer's Guild.

He started by moving *away* from the Adventurer's Guild, going along one of the streets that cut diagonally across Gemore. He climbed a block up the hill before turning around and taking the next cross street back towards the Guild. Gemore wasn't organized in a very orderly fashion – the steep streets with stairs that climbed the hill weren't always parallel, and the streets that crossed them tended to do so diagonally. That meant the city was a mix of quadrilateral blocks mixed with some more triangular shapes where roads joined or split.

Nathan kept going across the hill until he was past the Guild. Only then did he start descending the hill. He kept a careful eye out for anybody paying attention to him or tailing him but saw nothing. He spotted the Guild below – it had a large, open area not too far from the gates. The main entrance was easy to spot, so Nathan snuck around the back, entering an alley that dead-ended against the back wall of the Guild. Nathan knew that there was a pretty big drop on the other side, but from this side it was just an eight-foot wall.

He took a run-up and launched himself into the air, flaring his Rage to boost his strength for the jump. He'd show these *assholes* tracking him. Let them wait all night in ambush somewhere, suckers. And it wasn't like this dumb wall was going to stop him. Who did they think they were keeping out? An eight-foot wall of stone wouldn't even keep out people from Earth, much less people who had assistance from Davrar.

As Nathan's momentum brought him over the wall, he noticed two things. First – there was a line of faintly glowing runes carved into the top of the wall, invisible from below. They dimmed slightly around Nathan's hand, but nothing else happened.

Probably an alarm spell. Not a big worry for me.

Second, the drop on the other side was a *lot* longer than Nathan remembered. The Adventurer's Guild was cut deeply into the hill, and Nathan looked down at a roughly seventy-foot drop below him. And he'd leapt *over* the wall, not *onto* it.

Shit.

The wind whistled past Nathan. He'd been cliff jumping. And skydiving. But this was *different.* It was probably watching the ground coming up at you and knowing that you were going to hit it. Hard.

Nathan landed on his feet, knees bent. His legs cushioned his fall slightly. Then his ass slammed into the sand of the private training yard he'd spent so many hours in with the Heirs shortly before his head made its own little crater in the sand. His Rage was still activated, and it spiked with the injury. This time, Nathan was angry at *himself.*

Goddamned yeeting myself off a cliff. Bad Nathan!

He looked up at the curving sky overhead. There were faint clouds that made it harder to make out the blue-green world above him, but Nathan spent a minute appreciating it as bones *clicked* back into place. He had a headache, even through [Juggernaut's Wrath].

A pair of blue boxes appeared before him.

Pending Talent: Low-tier Slow-fall
You have survived a very long fall without magical assistance. This Talent will turn a risky proposition into a sure thing, slowing your fall.

High-tier Regeneration Rank 4 achieved!

He lay in his impression in the sand for a moment longer, staring at his "reward." Then he dismissed the box. It didn't look useful enough to be his third Talent, unless Nathan made a habit of cliff-jumping. And he could probably get it back by jumping back off the wall again if necessary.

That was kind of fun. But I'm not taking a Talent for that reason.

He got up and surveyed the Nathan-sized crater. It was... pretty obvious. He tried to kick sand into it, but he'd compressed the earth underneath the sand too. There was going to be a depression in the training ground no matter what he did. Maybe he'd tell the Heirs tomorrow... and maybe he wouldn't.

After a moment, Nathan shrugged and went to go find the Heirs.

As he walked into the suite, Stella pinned Nathan with a look. "You! Why are you so late?" She looked pissed, and her eyes were puffy and red. "My parents made me take the *worst* class. I didn't get light or lightning – or anything interesting! I got earth and air. Two of the most useless damned elements around. So, you're going to teach me about light and lightning!"

She looked him up and down. "Why are you covered in sand?"

Nathan sighed, brushing some sand off his shoulders. "I had an interesting time getting home." He pinched his nose between two fingers, willing his headache away. After a moment, it obliged.

Oh, that's handy. Would have killed to do that to migraines back on Earth. Well, not killed. *It's a saying. I wonder if that was [Regeneration] or [Juggernaut's Wrath]. Maybe both?*

Stella wanted to learn about light and electricity. Nathan knew a fair amount about both of those things. And he wanted to see Stella's joy as she explored magic. But how could he explain it? From what he understood of Davrar and its magic, the better you understood something the better your reward. Except for the "Davrar assisted" spells like mind control and healing.

Those were just bullshit. If he wanted to do this correctly, then he'd need to start from the beginning.

He walked over and sat down next to Stella, grabbing a cookie from the plate at her elbow. He picked up a slate from the table and drew a pair of familiar orthogonal lines, labeling one "X" and the other "Y."

"I'm going to have to teach you a lot of math to do this properly. I still don't fully know your notation and writing, and I don't think you *have* a lot of the notation we're going to need."

Stella frowned at him, a bit petulantly. "I'm better at math than anybody else here. No point in me learning any more of it. I can already do mana cost calculations, and those are more complicated than the math you're learning."

Nathan sighed. "I don't think anybody in Gemore, or even Giantsrest, knows the math I'm going to try to teach you. I spent about an hour a day learning math for almost fifteen years. There's more math to teach than you can imagine. At its core, math is a language built to precisely describe the world in details that words never can. I think if I teach you what natural light and lightning *are,* it should help you harness their mana."

I don't think I'll need to get into discrete mathematics, imaginary numbers or Fourier transforms. I'm trying to teach her Maxwell's equations, not circuit design. Multivariable calculus, vectors and differential equations are the goal here. I'm going to need to lean on [Enhanced Memory] for a lot of this, but I think I can get started with the basics without that.

Stella looked at him suspiciously. "Okay. Teach me, oh master of the mountain." Her reply was tinged with more than a little sarcasm. Then she paused and held up a hand to keep him from speaking. "Excuse me. If you can teach me the math to describe the true basis of light and lightning, I will acknowledge that it is a worthwhile Insight. We'll talk about what it's worth when I understand it, but I accept the debt now."

Nathan shrugged. He still didn't fully get this whole "trading Insights" thing. But it didn't seem like a bad thing to have Stella and potentially her family owe him an Insight. They had no end of valuable Insights, and even if Nathan couldn't use them, he might be able to work out a trade for an Insight he *did* want. He made a note to think about that later.

He began his lesson. "Okay, so first we need to have the idea of a *function,* which is an arrangement of variables that describe something. For example, if we throw a rock up in the air, we can make a function where the numbers on *this* line represent time, and the numbers on *this* line represent height. The rock's position over time will look something like this inverted parabola..."

Low-tier Lecturing 4 achieved!

This was going to take a while, no matter how good Stella was at math.

~

Nathan closed his eyes and *breathed*. He was feeling pretty good. He'd just finished meditating and was thinking about the day. It had been a lot of talking, but still a good day. He'd made concrete steps towards empowering his allies, with his gun project being a good first test. He was also really curious if scientific knowledge could help Stella improve her magic.

Yesterday had been a better day for his own personal power, if a scarier one. He reminded himself that he wasn't chasing power for power's own sake. He needed to level, needed to gain powerful Insights to Develop his skills and Talents. Only then could he hope to achieve his goal, of having the power to *do something* about Giantsrest. And any other future goals he had.

In a sense, it's really not that different from publishing on the academic treadmill to get a professorship. Prior demonstration of "excellence" provides more capability for performance. Or something like that. I like this more. I was always dreading the politics of academia. That's certainly something I dodged by getting abducted to Davrar!

But here the important judge wasn't an anonymous "peer reviewer," it was Davrar. Nathan smirked, thinking of the similarities between the inscrutable comments that had determined his academic future and the inscrutable boons that had saved his life. At least he hoped Davrar was unbiased and wouldn't fuck him over because of petty drama.

No, it seemed that Davrar doled out power to those who had the introspection to discover Insights and the courage to capitalize on them. Nathan sighed again. He was being unnecessarily introspective right now.

What he *should* be doing was thinking more about his skills and Talents. What should he focus on? He was already working with his knowledge from Earth to empower his allies. All well and good – he was not only helping his friends, but also gaining favors that he could trade for a potential new Insight.

But he needed to do more to Develop his *own* Insights. [Magic Absorption] needed a lot of rank-ups until it required another Insight, but it would need to be a doozy. Nathan didn't have any ideas right now. What Insight would take the Talent that defined his build in a direction he wanted to go?

[Regeneration] was in a similar situation, but it would probably rank up faster since it was still high-tier and not unique like [Magic Absorption]. And Nathan got injured a lot.

He had some concrete ideas for how to Develop [Regeneration]. One was to control the Talent to allow replicating cells to move away from the standard human body plan encoded in his genetics. Or he could try to take a more direct control of his body on the biochemical level. The first option would let him bulk his muscles to inhuman proportions, or grow bone-claws like Wolverine, or... do some truly gross things like turn into a boneless squid or grow extra limbs.

Nathan was a bit squicked out by that idea. But it wasn't a bad one, and he felt confident he could make the Development stick. However, the other direction appealed more to him. If he had the ability to influence and extend his [Regeneration] to his own biochemistry in the way he envisioned, that could be a game changer. He knew a *lot* about biochemistry, and he spent some time thinking about what might be possible with control of gene expression and biochemical activity in all his cells.

He'd probably be effectively immune to poison. Depending on how far he could push it, he might be able to eat almost anything organic and digest it more quickly. He could try to efficiently pack myofibrils to increase muscle strength. He might even be able to photosynthesize somewhat, though he'd be using melanin instead of chlorophyll – at least he wouldn't need to worry about the reactive oxygen species that process produced. On that note, he'd almost *certainly* be immune to aging if he could apply his knowledge correctly.

Nathan chuckled to himself. You would expect the flesh-monstrosity to be the one immune to aging. And it probably would be somewhat resistant. Cells newly differentiated from stem cells tended to have at least partially reset epigenetic clocks, but adult stem cells didn't have the required telomerase activity to keep that up forever. And he wasn't about to replace his *brain,* so that put an upper limit on things.

Meanwhile, the biochemical control would let him address the issue at the source in all of his cells. Aging was caused by a dozen different forms of accumulating damage and stress, and with Nathan's knowledge, he could address all of them. Epigenetic and transcriptional dysregulation? Gone. Genomic mutations, rearrangements and shortened telomeres? Repaired. Protein homeostasis? Fixed. Autophagy and mitochondrial damage? Crank it up, get that recycling center running. Senescence and the associated secretory phenotype? Annihilated. Metabolic regulation? Back to baseline. General hormonal imbalance? Get that shit out of here. And he'd already dealt with stem cell depletion.

Forget a PhD. With that *Talent I'd get a Nobel prize. The things you could learn with control of your own biochemistry...*

So, Nathan was leaning in that direction. He'd need to consider how he expressed it to Davrar as he ranked the Talent up. And potentially reconsider his objectives on Davrar. If he had more than one lifetime – then maybe his ambitions should expand as well.

Mostly irrelevant. I have my crusade. I might reconsider or complete it later, but I have decided for now. There's all kinds of philosophizing I could do about the potential to live forever, but right now, I'm just excited.

That left two open questions. Nathan had a third Talent slot, and a waiting Development for [Focused Mind]. The Development was something he could do *now*, but he'd put off thinking about the free Talent slot because he hadn't had time before. If he ever wanted to actually Develop another Talent, he needed to put some thought into it.

Besides, he had an idea for the [Focused Mind] Development and would try it out tomorrow in the practice yard. Though it might help if he could remember some Buddhist koans...

Not now. Empty Talent slot time. What was the hole in Nathan's build? Well, what did he intend to do? He intended to fight mages, Giantsrest mages in particular. And if he was going to fight *high-level* mages, what could they do that he couldn't answer?

When asked like that, the answer was obvious. Flight. Dalo and Kullal could fly and carry others with them. Wiam had mentioned that [Flight] wasn't an easy spell, but it didn't seem to be restricted to archmages either. A mage could just hover forty feet in the air over Nathan's head, and there wasn't a thing he could do aside from swearing and throwing things.

Maybe he could try to extend his antimagic into projectiles, or otherwise manipulate its range? Those sounded like goals to keep in mind for the next Development of [Magic Absorption], not necessarily new Talents.

Alternatively, he could try to find another use of Stamina – perhaps turn it into another form of energy. Maybe find a way to make electricity or generate momentum with Stamina? The problem was that he had *no idea* how to get those Insights started. Maybe after the Development for [Regeneration], he could try to make excess bioelectricity. But would it be enough for Davrar to give him a Talent for it?

The problem space is too large. Trim it down. What are the core requirements?

What he really needed was mobility or range. If it was a ranged ability, it needed to incorporate his antimagic or else a flying mage would just use a force shield. Maybe he should ask Sarah if there was an Insight that might let him extend his Talent into a ranged weapon.

If he wanted mobility, it needed to let him reach mages in the sky. A new movement option would synergize with the class skills that rewarded him for having a lot of momentum. He also had [Sprinting] and [Dodging Footwork], and they had been *damn* useful. He decided to ask the Heirs about having overlapping skills tomorrow, since he still had [Low-tier Tumbling] kicking around as an option. But all of those were utility skills and weren't about to let him walk on air.

Kia had it, the ability to stand and push off thin air. Unless it was a divine spell?

He'd seen her kick off of the air to change direction, striding farther than she should've been able to. It had also helped her dodge strikes from the Grave Tangle because she didn't need to be touching the ground to dodge. Nathan was already fast, but he'd only get faster with that Talent. There was a limit on how fast you could be if you needed to wait for gravity to bring you down to the ground.

Kia's ability to push off of the air was what Nathan wanted. If he was unlucky, it was a spell or something specific to her class. If he was lucky, it was a Talent, and he could bargain with her for the Insight. The second seemed more likely, but either way it was worth looking into. He'd ask Kia about it the next time he saw her. Or just ask Khachi to ask her.

Nathan sighed. He hadn't decided anything final, but he'd taken some good steps.

Before he slept, he spent time in his Mind Palace recalling some koans. He'd never been into the Buddhist poem-anecdotes very much, but he'd read some on a tech blog that liked to use them at the start or end of the posts. It didn't seem right to link the ones he remembered to a reagent or lab equipment, so Nathan linked them into some of the reference books he'd kept in his lab's desk drawer.

Mid-tier Enhanced Memory 5 achieved!

Eventually, he slept.

Chapter 42

Skill Combinations

The next day went much like the previous one. A different team of trainees went out, full of braggadocio at breakfast. Nathan silently wished them well. The leader, whose name Nathan didn't know, seemed like a bit of an arrogant jerk. But that only meant Nathan hoped he lived to learn.

Class was more subdued than usual. Jolba wasn't teaching, and they had a farther-ranging geography lesson around a large map spread over a central table. Gemore was in the center of the map, at the nexus of the four cardinal transit roads. The vast ruins of Old Gemore spread around it. Almost directly east of Gemore was Giantsrest, marked with many towers. Between them lay a large mountain range. This map didn't have very many dungeons marked, but Nathan knew the mountains were positively full of them. The map did have a few larger ruins, but they must've been pretty large if none of the ruins Nathan had seen made the cut.

The Giantsrest town of Halsmet was in the mountains about halfway between Giantsrest and Gemore, slightly closer to Giantsrest. Nathan traced his finger north of it, tapping a secluded valley. That was probably where Taeol's Mage Tower was, though Nathan didn't know if Taeol had returned there yet.

West of the mountains, foothills rolled down into plains, dotted with the villages that sustained Gemore. There were almost two dozen of them, spread to the north, south and west of Gemore. Nathan found Pilriden to the north. The village that Sora and Dwoh and the other rescued villagers came from was far from Gemore, one of the farthest. Nathan hoped they were well.

A forest spread along the foothills, following the course of the Drakefish river as it ran down from the mountains. It marked the extent of Gemore territory and had one major bridge across it. Just north of the bridge was what seemed to be marked as an active volcano.

Farther to the south was the trading port of Litcliff, which Nathan had heard very little about.

The plains to the east were dominated by Artha's folk, the Treeborn. They were a nomadic people and knew the treacherous grasslands like few did. The Treeborn controlled trade across the vast expanse of trackless grasslands and curbed the territorial ambitions of the Agmon Empire, the orcish empire that had been mentioned a few times.

The map didn't seem to be quite consistent with scale – Nathan had heard that the plains were much wider than the map portrayed, and that there were a number of smaller cities and rivers on the other side of the plains that weren't on the map. The image of the city on the other side seemed to say, "Agmon this way," more than give a reasonable depiction of what that nation actually looked like.

Past the villages in the north the mountains became brutal – various peoples lived up there, but they were isolated and remote. Only occasionally friendly to the peoples of the Lowlands, they didn't usually differentiate between Gemore and Giantsrest.

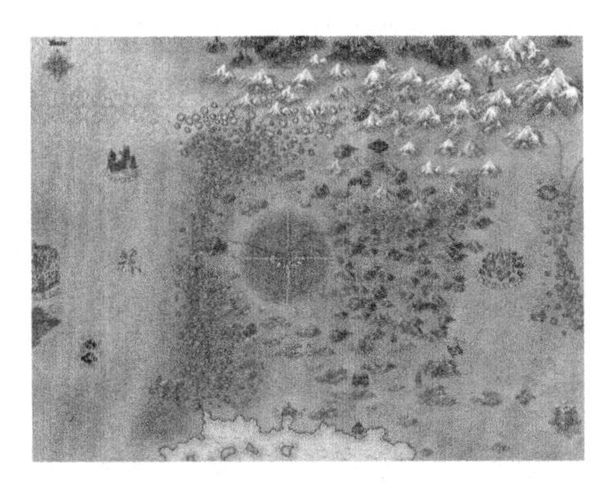

The class ended without fanfare. Next, Nathan had a lesson with Velek. He was starting to get a pretty good grasp on reading. Velek concluded the session with a short comprehension test.

After looking over Nathan's written slate of answers, he nodded. "You're not perfect, but at this point, you'll be able to pick things up from context. I would like to give you a general test tomorrow to see if there are further gaps in your knowledge that need to be rectified."

With that, Nathan headed to lunch and was one step closer to a discussion of skills and Talents with his teammates. Not *at* lunch, of course. Too many listening ears. Lunch itself was good, with the main course made of a pan-fried assemblage of meats and vegetables drizzled with a sweet sauce.

Stella tried to ask Nathan some math questions, but he put her off until the evening, reminding her that he considered that an *Insight*.

Then, they were once again alone in their private training area. Nathan tried to ignore the depression in the sand from the previous night's misadventure, but he found his eyes drawn back to the spot repeatedly. It hadn't even... hurt exactly. Probably due to [Juggernaut's Wrath]. He shivered.

Khachi started out. "We've all probably got some things to talk about, Talent and skill-wise. Levels and Developments all around, I expect. Anybody want to go first?"

Stella stepped forward, looking frustrated. "My parents made me pick [Mage of Elemental Fury]. I got *stone* and *air* mana. They gave me some new spells I need to practice a lot. I'm also supposed to work on channeling a *ton* of mana in short periods of time to get a handle on a new class skill that'll improve my casting speed. I think we can all guess what that means." She pointed towards Nathan. "Target practice."

Nathan held up his hands defensively, half-expecting the annoyed mage to start volleying spells immediately.

Sarah spoke up next. "Nothing new for me, I had already Developed my class. But... I think I'm ready to Develop my mobility Talent. Dad had a few ideas, and I think some of them might involve dodging ranged attacks. But others are going to involve me just jumping around like an idiot, maybe having people throw me to get higher."

Aarl followed his sister. "Not much for me. Weapon practice, weapon practice. I have some skills ready to Develop now, but I don't think I'll need much help for them, except maybe fighting two-on-one a bit for [Combat Awareness]."

Khachi gestured at Nathan to go next. Nathan looked around, biting his lip. All of the Heirs seemed to have such solid plans – likely because they had experienced advisors. To some extent, their builds had been planned for years by their parents. The older Adventurers had knowledge on what worked and what didn't, as well as Insights and the ability to call in debts to get more Insights. It certainly created powerful fighters – but Nathan wondered if Davrar didn't punish the lack of spontaneity somehow.

He didn't have any solid evidence, just a gut feeling. Davrar rewarded *risk*. It rewarded putting yourself out there to achieve a goal you shouldn't really be capable of. If you pulled it off, you leveled and ranked up. If you failed, you died. It seemed philosophically consistent that the same would be true for skills. If you went out on a limb into a situation you couldn't handle, then muddled along somehow, you'd acquire a Talent or skill as a reward. Or Develop an existing Talent or skill that you'd used to salvage the situation.

Regardless, this was a good time to get some answers to firm up his plans. "I've got some plans that you can help with. But I also have some questions that I'd like to ask. First, is it possible to combine utility skills together? Or to make a utility skill a class skill, either when you Develop your class or otherwise? Basically anything where one skill influences another?"

He got a round of confused looks. Aarl answered after a moment. "Why would skills... *combine?* No, that doesn't happen. A utility skill is a utility skill, and it can't combine with other utility skills, or class skills, or Talents for that matter." He shrugged. "I think even Davrar would get a headache from what could be possible."

Khachi held out a hand, pausing to phrase his words carefully. "A detail that should be made clear. Many Insights require other skills or Talents. Sometimes this is obvious – a Talent to shape mana means that mage classes will be among those offered. Additionally, such a Talent will allow utility skills centered around mana manipulation. Some class skills will enable different Talents and skills – especially those centered around the use of a resource.

"In general, skills, classes and Talents are highly dependent on one another. Your build is a *build*, and should be cohesive. Mobility skills and Talents will enhance one another and grant classes that are able to take advantage of mobility. It is not uncommon to gain Insights related to using various skills together in new ways. I will make it clear that it is unusual to be offered skills which overlap with one another too much. It's not supposed to happen unless a powerful Insight is applied in a *dangerous* circumstance. Does this serve to answer your question?"

Nathan, pursed his lips, considering.

Right, I wanted to ask about [Low-tier Tumbling], which I've still got on tap. It overlaps pretty strongly with [Sprinting] and [Dodging Footwork].

"Is having overlapping skills good? If so, what's to stop you from getting two overlapping pending skills and accepting both?"

Khachi shrugged, a bit perplexed by Nathan's metagaming. "You can't do that. When you get a new skill or Talent, Davrar considers all your pending skills as well as your current skills." He raised one finger to emphasize the next point. "Indeed, overlapping skills can be quite potent. If you are able to Develop them to enhance one another, then truly incredible feats are possible. However, if the use of one precludes the other, then some other skill will usually serve you better. Are you comfortable sharing your choices?"

Nathan thought about *that* for a moment. He'd previously gotten a lot of help and advice from the Heirs and their parents on his skills. But it was clear it had been unusual. He'd gotten a lot of critical information on how Davrar worked from them, but he could probably start keeping more secrets if he wanted to.

Beyond – you know – the secret that I'm not from *Davrar.*

On the other hand, *this* wasn't the most critical of secrets. Especially considering the favor he was about to ask from Khachi. So, he told them.

"I have two mobility skills already. One for running quickly, one for dodging. I have *another* pending skill that is also a movement and dodging skill. Some of my class skills benefit from rapid movement, as well. Likely because I already had these mobility skills."

He sighed, then asked the million-dollar question.

"Additionally, I have a Talent slot open, and an idea for how to fill it." Nathan pointed to Khachi. "Your mom can walk on air. I want to know if that's a Talent, and if I can ask for the Insight behind it."

The other Heirs had been paying attention, but not seriously. At Nathan's question, their gazes snapped to him, expressions universally conveying surprise.

Sarah whistled. "You still have a Talent slot free? That's a will of steel." She waved her hand around. "I know it's common wisdom to leave it open, but how many of us truly managed that? Especially with *our* parents throwing around Insights."

The other Heirs all nodded. Then they turned back to Khachi, who was figuring out his response. He spoke hesitantly, spreading his hands wide. "It is not my secret to share. I will tell you two things. This is one of the Insights that my mother guards most closely. And it is a Talent, one that you *might* be able to learn. I have asked her the same question, and she merely told me that I would not survive the Insight." He looked Nathan up and down, eyes lingering on the places where Nathan had regrown limbs. "But you might. I will mention your interest to her. And convey that it would work well with your existing build. She may refuse to speak on the topic at all."

He waved vaguely. "Though I've never been able to convince her of *anything*. But you should consider what Insights you can share, or trade, for it. Or to any of us. I know the Guardians all owe each other old favors, and if you can maneuver to call those in, then it may be *possible*. But don't get your hopes up. It would be impolite to compare Kia to a dragon, but...."

Nathan nodded, understanding. He'd see what he could get.

He considered the pending [Low-tier tumbling]. In some ways, it was underwhelming. But it was low-tier still, and could improve. [Dodging footwork] was a nice skill but required him to stay on his feet. It would still be useful, but this skill would allow him to dodge in more challenging situations. If he ranked up both, then it seemed likely for Nathan to execute some impossible dodges.

Nathan accepted the skill.

> Congratulations, you have accepted the 'Low-tier Tumbling' utility skill.

The other thing Nathan needed to do was figure out how to Develop [Focused Mind]. He had some ideas, and it was time to try them.

Chapter 43

Meditation on the Move

Nathan thanked Khachi, then turned to face the others as he explained the help he wanted to Develop his skill. "Like Sarah, I need to practice getting stuff thrown at me. But it's not dodging practice; I want the things thrown my way to *not* require a lot of effort to dodge. Except for spells, those can just hit me." Nathan made a dismissive gesture to indicate how little he cared about getting hit with magic.

Stella pouted a bit at the implication that her spells weren't even threatening enough to require dodging.

He grinned at her, rubbing it in just a little bit. "It's more about the distraction than anything else, I need to be able to deal with a lot of distraction while I use a skill. I think that's where the Development lies."

Next, it was Khachi's turn. He sighed. "No new class for me, though I have a few Developments related to my shield and armor that I will work on with Mother. As I mentioned before, I need to practice offensive and defensive use of Faith. This will require contemplation, prayer... and a willing target.

Once again everybody looked at Nathan.

"You know, I would like to think I serve another purpose in this outfit other than as a target dummy, but the longer I stick around, the less sure of that I am."

There was a general round of chuckles, and Stella commented, "You're just such a large, durable target. You make it so easy to hit you."

With that, they set to training. Nathan and Aarl helped Sarah work on her jumping, mostly by tossing blunt training weapons at her. After that didn't help, she had them each take a foot and throw her as far as possible, pushing off their hands to achieve some truly impressive airtime. She landed easily each time, rolling smoothly in the sand from the fifteen-foot leap.

She frowned back at them. "That was close... but not enough." She wrinkled her nose, frustrated by the lack of progress.

Aarl had an idea and pointed to Stella. "Maybe *she* can throw you with a platform of conjured earth?"

The red-haired mage was desultorily practicing with some conjured earth. She had a few foot-long jagged blades of rock floating around her and swung them with flicks of her hands. It looked pretty cool, but Stella just looked sad.

When she heard the suggestion, she snorted. "Oh, so I can graduate from throwing fireballs at my foes to throwing my teammates?" After a moment she sighed. "Sorry, I'm just... upset. Air and stone aren't *flashy*. I want explosions, magic that blinds the eye and deafens the ear."

Aarl wasn't entirely sympathetic. "They'll be plenty useful. I'd rather have somebody that can fly than throw yet *another* type of destructive magic around. Or better yet, fly *me* around. Now, about that idea to throw Sarah...?"

Stella waved her hand at him in irritation, then dug in her pockets. She pulled out a thin book, paging through it before studying a page. Still looking at the page, she started tracing her fingers through a spell. After a few moments, a small stone platform appeared before her. It wobbled worryingly.

"Go ahead, hop on."

Sarah jumped on but struggled to keep her balance as the platform swayed unsteadily.

Stella furrowed her brow as she frowned at the page. "And *up*."

The platform jerked up diagonally, sending Sarah pinwheeling as it flew out from under her. It soared over the wall surrounding the training ground and smashed against the roof of a nearby building. Stella frowned even harder. "Hold on. *What?*" She gestured again, and another platform formed. This one was a little bigger.

Nathan stepped forward. "May I?"

Stella looked at him, waving uncaringly at the spell. "Sure. Break it."

Nathan held his hand out and gently stroked the stone platform. It dissolved as his hand touched the surface, but Nathan felt the earth mana that made up the spell. It was more complicated than the conjured stones Nathan had interacted with previously, because the platform was *guided*, not just hurled or conjured in place. He focused on the strands of mana as Stella empowered it, causing the disintegrating platform to lurch upwards before the conjuration finished disintegrating from Nathan's touch.

There were more strands in there than were necessary for conjuration or movement – some of them definitely looped back from the platform to the movement construct. A feedback loop to automatically stabilize it?

Low-tier Identify 8 achieved!

"Hey Stella, you know those four loops which go from the center of the platform to the corners? I think they feed back to guide the direction of movement, automatically preventing it from veering off course. Can you give those loops more control over the platform's movements?"

Stella looked up from skimming the book. "Huh. I could feel them trying to mess with the movement. This book doesn't say it nearly that simply. Let's try it that way." Her next platform didn't wobble. Stella's eyebrows went up. "Oh, that's *easy*. You couldn't do that with force mana, it doesn't flow the same way. Neat."

Sarah had hesitantly watched the whole exchange. She pointed at the platform. "Should I get on?"

Stella nodded, pleased at her new mastery of the spell.

Sarah got onto the platform, then braced herself to jump. The platform zipped upwards again, and Sarah leaped as it moved. She flew high into the air, her arms raised in triumph. Then she looked down and screamed from more than thirty feet in the air.

Nathan and Aarl ran to catch her but ended up colliding with each other.

Stella snorted and waved her hand. A gentle gust of wind kicked up, but it did nothing to slow Sarah's fall.

Nathan was about to activate his Rage to try to scamper under Sarah – when Stella swore and cast another spell.

[Force Block]

A diagonal plane of force appeared under Sarah's body, fifteen feet in the air. She impacted it and bounced to the side before landing with a gentle *thud*. Sarah got up, moaning and brushing sand off.

"Well, that worked! Talent Developed! I'll be able to jump higher and land better now. And at least I didn't leave *that* crater. Where did *that* come from?" She pointed at the depression near where she'd landed, which looked intimately familiar to Nathan.

Nathan scuffed the ground with his shoe. "About that..."

It was time for the Heirs to help Nathan with his own skill Development.

He stood at one end of the training yard, deep in [Focused Mind]. Then, he started walking across the training ground.

The assistance his skill gave him vanished, but Nathan held the meditative state of mind. Everything Nathan saw was in his consciousness, held in his own mind and his model of the world.

That model became rather more complicated as the Heirs began to throw things at Nathan. They were aiming *near* him, not *at* him, so he didn't have to dodge. But he tracked the various projectiles as they flew across the yard. He tried not to *focus* on them, but to acknowledge their existence. And speed. Speed towards *him*.

To distract his conscious mind, he thought of the first koan that came to him.

A monk asked his master, "What is the way?"

The master said, "An open-eyed man falling into the well."

In the moment of incomprehension that happened after the koan, Nathan's mind was blank. He was still *aware* of his environment, and all the things that existed within it. But he was not *thinking* about any of it. In that instant, the skill Developed.

Congratulations, you have Developed the [Mid-tier Focused Mind] utility skill into [High-tier Focused Mind].

Utility skill: [High-tier Focused Mind]
This skill will help you attain a focused and undistracted state under most conditions. Cannot be maintained under stress.

Nathan stopped walking, looking across at the Heirs with his new skill active. They continued to throw things his way, and he had to duck to the side to dodge a blunted hatchet thrown by Aarl. He raised his hands in triumph, and they stopped. Except for Stella who pegged Nathan in the stomach with a spike of rock.

He inspected the new rip in his shirt as he approached. "Well, that worked. But you're [Repairing] this later."

Khachi looked up from where he'd been inspecting his hammer. "You have succeeded in Developing your skill? Congratulations. It seems we have good news all around. As for myself... I would like to try something my mother showed me."

He picked up the hammer and began to chant. "By the power of my prayer, let my blows be empowered! By the strength of this steel, my hammer will strike with the force of Faith! By the glory of Deiman, let my foes be sundered!"

The hammer started glowing with a golden light, reminding Nathan of the glowing blade that had projected from Kia's greatsword while fighting the Grave Tangle. Khachi swung the hammer at the sand in front of him. The swing drew the eye. It *felt* like something you should be paying attention to, like the climax of a battle, where the hero confronted the monster and swung their weapon in glorious defiance.

Nathan felt the mana emanating from the blow. Again, it was the strange, emotion-based mana that he'd sensed before. It prickled with a righteous anger, demanding awe and glory. It didn't seem to be a function of the spell, just a natural effect of the radiating mana. The same way that the death mana from the Grave Tangle had exhausted and debilitated people, this mana naturally wanted to impress and inspire them.

Mid-tier Spellsense 2 achieved!

When the swing impacted the sand, it felt anticlimactic. Sand flew in all directions, and the Heirs were briefly deluged by a gust of windborne particles emanating from the strike. But no monster screamed, no grand story reached its conclusion.

That was strange. Divine mana is weird, *and I don't understand it very well, so I'm not fully immune. I'll definitely want to practice with Khachi more. Not sure I'll want to be the target of that quite yet. Damn.*

Everybody else was silent for a moment as the sand drifted down.

Stella muttered a spell.

[Wind Gust]

The wind wasn't strong, but it was enough to clear the drifting sand. Stella grumbled about how *weak* wind spells were.

Nathan remembered a certain [Wind Blast] from a now-deceased Giantsrest enslavement mage and begged to differ.

They practiced some more, but nobody else had any specific Talents and skills they wanted to work on. Instead, they focused on how their capabilities had changed, and what new Talents and classes they needed to account for.

Through sparring, Nathan learned more about his new skills and their limitations. His passive [Unarmored Resilience] gave him a good deal of toughness, as if his skin was a tough hide. Nathan also knew it gave his bones and organs resistance against crushing blows, because he hadn't been *pasted* when falling 70 feet last night.

It also stacked with the resilience from [Raging Thrill], which increased the resistance of his skin from a tough hide to something closer to metal. However, when not being struck by a blow, his skin still felt like... skin.

Davrar sure is something.

Nathan did a few sparring matches while under the effects of [Raging Thrill]. It wasn't easy to sustain his Rage, and Rage was incompatible with [Focused Mind]. He had to choose one or the other – for now. He had trouble being properly *angry* with the Heirs, and only succeeded by calling up his anger at Giantsrest and directing it at his training. Holding back wasn't easy either, but the increased speed, strength and durability were clearly a potent combination that proved their worth time and time again.

Aarl commented on it after one bout where Nathan clocked Aarl across the jaw hard enough to draw blood. "That Rage is powerful. You'll just ignore my blows, slip through and hit me. There's not much I can do about it aside from physically throwing you away. It does seem to drink Stamina like a parched adventurer."

Nathan nodded, chewing on his second bag of jerky. It was *good*, but at this rate he might get tired of the stuff. He'd also asked Stella for some recharge, and she'd spent some time barraging him with chunks of stone and weak gusts of wind to fill his Stamina.

Nathan had a bit more advice for her on using air magic, but it hadn't seemed to make much of a difference.

Sarah suggested that it wouldn't be a bad idea for Stella to practice throwing the other members of the Heirs with her stone platform, then catching them with her wind spells.

The mage's reply was acerbic. "I mean, I can see that being useful for getting up cliffs and things. But I'll never be able to throw Nathan."

But it gave Nathan an idea. "Actually yes, we should practice that. You can move around non-conjured stone, right? Like, pick up a naturally existing boulder and move it and shape it and such?"

Stella nodded, seeing where he was going. "I haven't looked at those spells much. They're a lot more complicated than magical stone, though they're a bit cheaper on mana. But yeah. I might be able to lift you with a non-conjured stone platform if I can figure out how to hold it by the edges or something. It seems like a complicated solution when we could just throw down a rope."

Nathan shook his head. "But imagine we're locked in a ranged duel with some mages or constructs, and they're on a wall or behind a bunch of fighters with magical shields. If you throw *me at* the mages, then I'll go through their shields.

Everybody looked at him like he was crazy. But Stella's eyes lit up as she clapped her hands together and cackled. "My very own antimagic projectile!"

Skill text comparison:

Utility skill: [Mid-tier Focused Mind]
This skill will help you attain a focused and undistracted state under most conditions. Requires you to be unmoving to use.

Utility skill: [High-tier Focused Mind]
This skill will help you attain a focused and undistracted state under most conditions. Cannot be maintained under stress.

Status of Nathan Lark:
Permanent Talent 1: Magic Absorption 3
Permanent Talent 2: High-tier Regeneration 4
Talent 3: None

Class: Spellbreaker Juggernaut level 43
Stamina: 505/530
Juggernaut's Wrath
Antimagic Momentum
Raging Thrill
Juggernaut's Inertia
Unarmored Resilience

Utility skills:
High-tier Focused Mind 1
Mid-tier Earnestness 3
Mid-tier Sprinting 2
Mid-tier Spellsense 2
Mid-tier Notice 2
Low-tier Identify 8
Low-tier Dodging Footwork 8
Mid-tier Enhanced Memory 5
Low-tier Lecturing 4
Low-tier Tumbling 1

Chapter 44

Introspection on Knowledge

"You should practice your spellwork before you throw a teammate with it." Khachi said, holding out a hand as if to tamp down Stella's excitement.

"Even if he can heal himself?" Khachi fixed her with a steady gaze, and she huffed out a frustrated breath. "Fine. I do need to figure out that spellwork." She reached her hand out to the ground and the sand started flowing over itself, packing down to make semi-solid chunks.

Aarl gestured Nathan over. "Let's practice some dodging."

For the rest of the practice, Aarl helped Nathan get a grip on his new [Tumbling] skill. It helped him roll more quickly and easily, as well as do things like cartwheels. Nathan had never trained at gymnastics before – if you didn't count learning to do a flip on a trampoline when he was fourteen – so he wasn't very experienced. But it seemed like a useful tool in his arsenal. That was especially true when he figured out that the skill helped him regain his feet quickly after being knocked down. It wasn't hard to use the momentum from falling to roll himself up from almost any position.

Low-tier Tumbling 2 achieved!

All too soon, it was time for the private mentoring. Kadid was there, and Nathan walked over to him with a wide smile.

"Heya Kadid, how's it going?" Nathan greeted the older man with a smile and got one in return.

"Freedom 'n brightness, Nathan. I wanted ta ask, do you want me to keep showin' up? Seems like you had some chatter wit' Beatred and Poppy. If you don't need me then there ain't much point in me bein' here." The old man scratched the back of his neck, looking at some of the other adventurers who seemed to share the Bho family look – dark, wide and tough.

"I think I'll leave them be for a bit – though if you could drop by later and ask Beatred how it's going, I'd appreciate it. I think she'll want me to come by at some point, but I don't want to jog her elbow. I also think it might be best if I weren't connected with what she's working on, if you catch my drift."

Kadid looked confused by Nathan's figure of speech but carried on. "A'right, I hear ya. You mentioned Insights the other day, so it'd be important. I'll check in with her later. Anythin' else I can help you with?"

Nathan shrugged. "Don't think so, but thanks for checking. I'll probably be in the Heirs' rooms for the rest of the day. Talk to you tomorrow unless something comes up?"

"Sounds good." The old man waved to Nathan and headed towards the front of the Guild while Nathan turned towards the back.

He fully expected more questions from Beatred and Poppy – if nothing else, about the secrets of metallurgy and chemistry he'd hinted at – but he wanted to minimize the number of times he left the Adventurer's Guild.

I'm still a bit paranoid about being kidnapped, after all.

He got back to the rooms, found a slate for notetaking, and sat down in a comfortable chair. Nathan wanted a few undistracted hours to think.

Specifically, he wanted to systematically go through his knowledge from Earth and make sure he wasn't missing anything else he could use. After all, he knew a lot – about a lot. Was there anything esoteric he could make a skill or Talent out of? Nathan had already used some of his best tricks – memory encoding for [Enhanced Memory], and his biology knowledge for [Regeneration]. Meditation had gotten him [Focused Mind], and what he knew of human perception had helped him with [Notice]. His guess at a nuclear reaction in Dalo's spell had netted him [Identify].

Any other low-hanging fruit that can help me out?

To get a Talent or skill, it seemed that Davrar required you to do the thing *without* assistance. Then, you would be rewarded with the Talent or skill to do it better and more consistently, as well as the potential to Develop the skill or Talent farther than you ever could before. Nathan had gotten [Regeneration] because he knew so much about the biology of the human body, and because

Stamina was a resource that could control and enhance the body. He'd channeled a resource suited to the task with all of his knowledge, and the Talent had been the result.

And then for [Magic Resistance], I somehow came to Davrar with antimagic in my bones. Probably because Earth has no magic. Or Earth has no magic because of some substance there?

So, was there anything Nathan could do, by himself, that might give him a Talent related to physics or chemistry? Probably not. He couldn't *normally* generate light from his fingers or absorb energy into his skin. If he took his [Regeneration] Development and modified his body to innately do those things – maybe that could serve as the basis for a Talent like that.

But that doesn't mean I should discard all that knowledge. Let's go over it.

Nathan considered himself well-versed in general physics, with a focus on optics and some experience with electricity and magnetism. Using diffraction-limited microscopes had been a pretty good incentive to learn about interference and other weird optical effects.

I'd be a lot more capable of using knowledge like that if I had magic. But I don't.

Nathan had taken a few fun electives – some classes on special relativity and quantum information. He was proud that he had a pretty good understanding of what superposition really meant – and why faster than light travel was mathematically equivalent to traveling backwards in time. But that didn't help him with his Talents.

Can I bullshit something about quantum tunneling to let me teleport?

No, absolutely not. Quantum shenanigans happened on the atomic scale, not on the Nathan scale. He had no significant wave-like properties unless he got better at breakdancing.

Moving on... what about chemistry?

He'd done a bunch of chemistry, everything from analytical labwork to biochemistry. His knowledge in those fields would probably let him figure out all sorts of useful skills if he wanted to introduce chemistry here on Davrar. Maybe he should suggest some things to Poppy later. But Nathan wasn't planning on doing a lot of chemistry in the near future.

Though I bet I could get a pretty incredible battle alchemy build. But I'd have to drop everything I've built so far – and I'm not sure that's even possible.

After all – he was planning on doing a lot of ignoring people casting magic on him and then punching them.

All in all, he was happy with how he was using his knowledge. He had a plan to Develop [Regeneration], he was building new weapons for Sarah, helping Khachi Develop his divine mana use, and teaching Stella about electricity. He was empowering himself and his allies, helping protect what Nathan was rapidly considering his new home.

Though now that I think of it, I haven't really done much for Aarl. I can't exactly teach him much about sword fighting. Just gotta look for an opportunity.

With a sigh, Nathan moved onto the next thing he wanted to think about – utility skills. Nathan had ten utility skills already. That was supposed to be the maximum without special circumstances. He wouldn't be offered any more utility skills, even if he did something that deserved one. So, he wanted to consciously decide if there were any other utility skills that would make it worthwhile to drop one of his existing utility skills.

The first step of that was to figure out if there were any utility skills Nathan was okay with dropping. One was obvious – [Lecturing] was just there because it helped Nathan explain guns and math. If he didn't end up doing a lot of teaching in the future, he fully intended to drop the skill. But if he did decide to disseminate more knowledge, then it would be very useful.

Lecturing isn't very helpful for combat, but it would be helpful for other things. What are my long-term priorities? It takes a while to Develop a skill.

If Nathan couldn't use a lot of his knowledge himself, then he'd need to explain it to other people. And [Lecturing] made that process better. But did Nathan *want* to spread more knowledge?

Partially that depended on how his current experiment worked out. Could they get guns to work? Would Beatred and Poppy get attacked by Giantsrest and have their ideas stolen? Arguably it would have been smarter to run this experiment with a less dangerous secret than gunpowder, but guns had a pretty good return on investment and were the easiest thing to implement that Nathan could think of. Especially with the advanced metalwork Beatred had demonstrated.

It was a similar story for Nathan's scientific Insights. Could he really teach Stella to understand light and electricity the way he did? If he could, would she be able to use that knowledge to generate and interact with light and lightning mana? In that case, Nathan was sitting on a gold mine of Insights about the natural world and the mana that was based off of it. He would be able to empower Gemore's mages to incredible heights. So long as he kept them from generating a black hole or antimatter or something *too* destructive.

The downside to that is pretty large, after all. Maybe try to prevent that from happening. Hold on to nuclear and atomic Insights.

Nathan spent a moment feeling sorry for himself. Davrar's magic was *so cool*. He would have loved to spend time experimenting with mana, using scientific principles to pick apart spells and access new mana types. But instead, he was anathema to mana in all its forms. Every step of the way to this point had been reasonable, even necessary. As a [Spellbreaker Juggernaut], Nathan was probably better suited to fighting Giantsrest than he would be as a mage.

I dunno. Nuking people versus punching people. Not equivalent across multiple axes.

Nathan sighed and looked down at the slate, which remained empty. He'd been trying to think about things from Earth he could use here, either for himself or to give Gemore to help them survive.

But what he'd decided was that he *didn't* have any more Insights that had clear applications for either skills or Talents. He also wanted to hold off on more technology until the fallout of guns was made clear, and on more mage-Insights until his lessons with Stella were further along. And he'd hold onto [Lecturing] until that panned out.

And if I do Develop that [Regeneration] upgrade for biochemical control, then I have time. I will take a delayed and more certain victory against Giantsrest over a faster but riskier attempt.

If Nathan decided he wanted to introduce more technology, what kinds of things would make sense? He knew – or could recall – a lot of things. Alloys of metals used for industrial steels. The principles behind an internal combustion engine. Sanitation and basic antibiotics. Electricity.

Let's focus on one of those things. Alloys.

Nathan frowned, imagining the process of trying to walk Beatred through making an advanced alloy. The problem was – there were a lot of details there he *didn't* know. He'd gotten curious at various points about what the elemental makeup of modern metals was and had looked it up.

What he *hadn't* looked up was the treatment processes necessary to *get* to those incredible alloys. How you quenched, tempered and hardened metal was just as important as the exact elemental makeup, and Nathan didn't know much about those details.

He spent a few minutes using [Enhanced Memory] – but Nathan couldn't remember details he'd never looked up. He'd generally been more interested in understanding the basics of how stuff worked over the specific details of how you got there. But knowing *why* alloying helped break up the crystal structure of metals wasn't as helpful to him now as knowing *how* to temper an alloy to achieve that result.

Furthermore, he didn't know that the alloys would be that helpful. They could already make pretty good steel, and a lot of the focus was on enchantments. Maybe fancy alloys wouldn't work well with enchantments, or would be so hard to inscribe that a minimal gain in strength wasn't worth the difficulty of crafting.

Similar problems presented themselves for everything on Nathan's list. Gemore didn't seem to have any signs of sickness or disease – [Curing] took care of disease, and they had had running clean water, and ate a varied diet from the villages.

Nathan didn't actually know how to build a combustion engine – there were dozens of problems he had no solution for, ranging from gas vaporization to tolerances to how you made a crankshaft. All of these had solutions, but they were problems that had taken decades to solve on Earth, with thousands of people working on them. Skills could make up some of that gap like they were doing for guns, but probably not all of it.

Electricity was worse, since a lot of the things you wanted electricity for were already provided by magic in Gemore. Nathan looked up at the glowing crystal in the corner of the room. Making electricity on the small scale to help teach Stella about electromagnetism would be useful. Nathan could probably ask Beatred to whip up a hand-cranked generator at some point, assuming they could find some magnets. But it wasn't exactly necessary to wire Gemore up with lightbulbs.

Even if it was feasible, did Nathan want to unleash an industrial revolution? Not really. Not only would Giantsrest be better positioned to use the technology than Gemore, but industrialization was hard to initiate without rampant exploitation of labor.

Which was why Giantsrest was better positioned, he supposed.

And that's another reason against all of this stuff. It's hard to hide, and I don't want Giantsrest getting it.

Nathan sighed, getting discouraged. Was there anything else, anything he was missing? He cast through his knowledge, looking for relevant fields.

Ah. Yup. Field! Not just fields of study, but also places you grow things in.

One of the heroes of Earth was Norman Borlaug, who had probably saved a billion lives by more than doubling staple crop production between 1950 to 1970. He was one of Nathan's role models, somebody who had used science to save more people than anybody could normally hope to even influence. It'd been a combination of increasing pest resistance, adapting plants to prioritize yield and deprioritize competition with one another, and helping them take advantage of industrial fertilizer.

Fertilizers had developed earlier and been tied to the start of the chemical industry. You needed lots of infrastructure for that – the Haber process ran at about a hundred atmospheres. You also needed hydrogen gas. The alternatives were probably worse – Nathan didn't remember the names, but one of them required incredibly high voltages, and the other required stupid amounts of heat as well as purified hydrogen.

Mid-tier Enhanced Memory 6 achieved!

Those were probably worth considering more. Nathan didn't know much about Gemore's food production situation. It happened in the villages and was heavy on meat. Was food even a limiting resource here? With monsters such a constant threat, food might not be what controlled population size. But being able to produce more food per unit area would mean they wouldn't have to protect as many fields.

Increasing food yield was definitely going on Nathan's list as something to consider going forward. He was leery of making the large-scale changes that came along with starting a chemical industry. There were a lot of hurdles there, and the outcome was... complicated. Once you got started making bulk amounts of sulfuric acid, then the genie was *really* out of the bottle. That allowed nitric acid manufacture, which led to nitroglycerin and dynamite. Or you could start making things like mustard gas. But... not yet.

Nathan was more interested in direct crop breeding. It wasn't something that could be done quickly, and in fact it would take decades to do properly. But it was the kind of project that could make Davrar that much kinder to those who lived in it. Likely without unleashing some horror upon the world.

Don't underestimate Davrar. You'd probably make monster plants somewhere along the way.

He sighed. He wanted to avoid unleashing horrors. If he just started letting knowledge out, then inevitably some of it would backfire. He wanted to introduce more technology to Davrar, but he wanted to do it slowly. Right now, the priority was to help Nathan and his friends get strong. Later on he could put more effort towards Gemore as a whole.

Finally, Nathan wanted to think about trading with Kia for the stepping-on-air skill.

I'm going to have a lot of credit with Stella and her parents if the magical tutoring works out. And same with Stanel for the guns. That'll probably be enough. It better be enough. Should I consider teaching the Insights between [Magic Resistance] and [Regeneration] to others?

After all, people kept mentioning that both of those Talents were incredible. The problem was, he wasn't sure if he could package them up as neat Insights, or if he even wanted to.

[Magic Resistance] was the first one – but the core component of it had been the "magic resistant alchemical ingredients," And Nathan had no clue what those were. Presumably something from Earth that wasn't present here, but what could that be? Plastic? Vaccines? Food additives? Nathan had no idea, and no easy way to figure it out.

With access to even a basic lab, he could take samples of his own body and try to separate out whatever the anti-magic ingredients were. But that assumed they were still present in his body and hadn't broken down, leaving him only capable of antimagic through his Talent.

That seems like a dead end. And I like being unique in my antimagic.

The other Talent was trickier, in that Nathan could *probably* teach somebody to understand biology like he did and guide them to [Regeneration]. But that sounded *hard*. Harder than teaching somebody to understand Maxwell's equations. To Nathan, stem cell biology was built on a vast pyramid of underlying knowledge. Metabolism required an understanding of chemistry and thermodynamics, gene regulation required kinetics and genetics – which required evolution.

If all of his biology knowledge was a pyramid, then Maxwell's equations were more like a tower. Nathan spent a moment reviewing the math he'd need to teach Stella. There was a lot of it – but it was a somewhat straight shot. Nathan had learned most of it by his sophomore year of college, after all.

In comparison, he'd learned stem cell biology, really *learned* it, in his second year of his PhD program while studying for qualifying exams. All for something that was mostly replicated by a [Curing]. Ultimately, it didn't seem like [Regeneration] was worth the time investment for most people on Davrar. Not unless their build was designed around it from the start.

Oh well. I'm glad I at least thought about all of this – I'm more confident I'm not leaving behind anything particularly obvious and I have a plan for when to revisit the introduction of technology.

Chapter 45

Reminiscing and Socializing

Nathan's failure to find new ways to apply his knowledge had made him morose. He reflected on how he'd gotten here, how he was barred off from magic.

If I'd just arrived in Gemore instead of Taeol's damned mage tower, everything would've been better. I could be free to explore magic, without this vendetta against Giantsrest.

Now *that* was an interesting thought. If he'd never met Taeol, how would he view Giantsrest? He'd probably look at it the same way that most people in Gemore did. To them, Giantsrest was an enemy, but one among many. And not the most pressing one – they were farther down the priority list than the monsters and dungeons over the next hill. There were Adventurers like the Giantraiders who made it their mission to fight Giantsrest – but *they* all had lost something to Giantsrest.

And in that sense, so had Nathan. He'd told Sudraiel most of it – but his vendetta against Giantsrest ran deeper than just his lost opportunities on Earth. Nathan had possessed an innocence before. He hadn't truly believed that somebody would just... so casually dismiss him as a person. Taeol hadn't even tried to be particularly convincing. The only reason he'd started out that way is because it would have been *easier* if Nathan had helped him willingly. He hadn't done it because he would have preferred *not* to dominate Nathan. To Taeol, Nathan *was* worthless beyond what he could do for the archmage. And that thought was what repulsed Nathan, what lay at the root of his desire to fight Giantsrest.

He knew about it intellectually, of course. Slavery and exploitation existed in many forms on Earth, and he would have viewed Giantsrest that same way. But when Taeol tried to enslave Nathan, embed him into a golem core, it became personal. Now, the thought that Taeol and the other mages of Giantsrest were acting that same way to hundreds – thousands – of people was a fact that Nathan couldn't ignore. He couldn't just squirrel it away in the back of his head, the way he probably could have if somebody had just described it to him.

It's illogical – the evil is the same whether I have experienced it or not. But it's human nature, and I won't judge hypothetical-Nathan for not declaring a vendetta against Giantsrest. But I am who I am now – I'm different than I would have been without that experience. I'm going to be on a hair-trigger for that sort of behavior for the rest of my life, unable to move on until I've done *something about it. I don't think that's a bad thing – Taeol's tower was a formative experience for me. More trauma than I've experienced anywhere else in my life.*

Nathan hadn't really been *angry* that much on Earth. He hadn't had that much to be angry about, at least personally. And now he did. The ember of Rage that smoldered in his chest even now had been born of Taeol's treatment of him, and Nathan's introspection on what it meant for a whole society to center around the horrifying power to completely dominate people's minds.

It's not something I can ignore now that I've experienced it.

Nathan sighed, then poked his head outside. He was early for dinner, but none of the other Heirs were around. So he walked down the corridor to the dining hall.

He exchanged a few words with the cook, who hoped Nathan would enjoy the food. Nathan responded that he always did before he grabbed a plate and walked back to the Heirs' table to eat.

A few minutes later, somebody slid in across from him. It was Simla, the black-skinned guy who was on a different team. The one who'd been arguing with Khachi on the Nathan's first day. The one who thought Sudraiel's changes were bullshit and tended to disagree with Jolba in class.

"Nathan, yeah? Seems a time to get acquainted. You're from far away, it seems. Inscribe the meeting 'n all. I'm Simla."

Nathan took the offered hand, shaking it over the table. Simla had a firm grip and stared Nathan straight in the eyes, somewhat challengingly. He wasn't bad looking, with golden eyes and jewelry adorning his temples and jaw. The pieces were gold and silver and contrasted beautifully with his skin.

It was a striking look, and the shaved head and well-defined muscles certainly didn't hurt. Simla wasn't a hulk, but he gave off the impression of a corded whip, ready to snap out in any direction. The young adventurer wore a light breastplate and elaborate vambraces. A shortsword balanced on each hip and a shortbow peeked over his shoulder.

As Nathan examined the young adventurer, he imagined what Simla saw across the table. Nathan was wearing cheap but tough clothes, meant to be ruined in a fight and repaired later if possible. He'd left his new spear back in the room, since it wasn't his primary armament.

Simla's lips quirked up. "Funny seeing you on a team with those adamant statues. They're all coasting on their parents' money and Insights. But you've come up the hard way, yeah? No backers, just grit and steel." He held up his hand, clenching his fist in front of his face in a gesture of solidarity.

Nathan frowned. It seemed like Simla was trying to butter him up, establish some camaraderie. Nathan wasn't opposed, but he didn't want to be roped into shit-talking the Heirs and his other supporters. So he took a middle path and nodded to the young man across the table.

"Indeed. But I've had a lot of support – the Giantraiders got me into the Guild, and Sudraiel and Jolba gave me the chance to prove myself. You can't deny the Heirs are powerful teammates to have."

Simla shook his head, grinning with shockingly white teeth. "Yes, they're some real young dragons. But you come in and prove yourself their equal in so short a time. It's inspiring to see somebody raise themselves up, to stand an equal to the Heirs of the greatest Adventurers in Gemore."

He paused for a moment, then launched into the second part of his spiel. "But, you aren't committed to them. You can follow your own path after you swear the Adventurer's Oath – escape these new practices the Guildmistress is laying down."

Oh, I get it. Recruitment pitch time!

"People change teams all the time – if you want more freedom with what you do, with the jobs that you take on, you might consider other teams. Not just mine, though we'd take you. We're planning on diving dungeons as soon as we can. Focusing on dungeoneering, a quick way to earn the metal jangle."

Simla cocked his head, waiting for a response.

Nathan picked his words carefully. No need to make enemies – and honestly, he was happy to learn more about other Adventurers and how they did things. He knew that there was a faction that was opposed to Sudraiel's changes. Simla seemed to represent them among the trainees, and Nathan was interested in hearing the other side of the argument.

"I'm interested. As you say, I'm from far away. There's much I don't know about Gemore and the opportunities for Adventurers. If I stay with the Heirs, what will I be missing out on?"

Simla chuckled, leaning back in his chair and giving Nathan a secretive smile. "Well, that's the question, isn't it? I won't claim that you'll find people more powerful than the Heirs, at least at our age. But what you will find are people willing to make sure the rewards get distributed equally. Suppose you get into a dungeon and find a *blasphemously* bright sword, a real relic of the past. If you're with the Heirs, that'd get reported to the Guild, and if the Guildmistress decides it's important, it might get snatched away from you with just some coin for your trouble." Simla waved his hand as if dismissing an unfortunate possibility.

"But if you're with another team, then there's no need to talk so much about it. Keep what you earn. We're *Adventurers.* We're the ones who take the risks, the ones out there making life-and-death decisions. Here in Gemore the only thing that matters is *victory*, and sometimes that means not following all the rules. Do you read what I'm writing?"

Nathan nodded, inspecting the table. "I get the reasoning. What about the villages? Seems like that's a big part of the job, keeping the roads open, the fields clear and the mines working."

Simla shrugged. "Yeah, and they're jobs that need to be done. But those aren't the jobs that made Gemore Adventurers into what we are, no matter how the Guildmistress has us hopping to every whim of jumpy villagers."

He shook his head sadly, continuing. "My great-granddad made a name for the Bholas clearing dungeons around Old Gemore. He'd not be pleased at the trouble you have to go to just to get *into* a dungeon these days. Used to be you just let people know, then you went on your way. Now, if you don't get *approval,* you'll get other teams sent after you to bring you back." The young man sighed regretfully.

"Gemore Adventurers are going soft, worrying about the villages more than the roving monsters and dungeons. If we want to keep leveling, we gotta challenge the big dangers, not just help some *farmers* cowering behind their walls. They need us, but we don't need all of them so bad – there's way more villages than Gemore needs to stay fed. We could get by with *eight*, not the twenty-two we got." The young man had gotten into a groove, easily recalling some familiar arguments.

"Eldred says it right. Cut back the protection of the villages. Let Adventurers go hunting, delve for some relics of the past – wherever that might take them. We got the strength to do it, and to survive things goin' wrong. Then once we got the levels, we got the loot – we can crush Gianstsrest. Make Litcliff drop their tariffs. When you got the magic sword you get to dictate the terms. And there's magic swords lying all around us." Simla spread his hands wide, indicating Gemore and the ruins beyond.

Then he tilted his head inquisitively, gesturing for Nathan to pick up the conversation. After a moment the young adventurer got impatient. "Well, what do you think?"

I mostly think you're full of crap. You need excess food as a buffer against things like a village losing a harvest, or slavers coming across the mountains. And letting people freely delve into dungeons seems like a bad *idea for a dozen reasons. Sure, you might end up higher level at the other end, but you'd end up with ten adventurers where you started with a hundred. With more villages, you get more Adventurer levels* without *having to risk the dungeons. It's not as glorious, but it's safer. I think Sudraiel's building for the future, and you're dreaming about the past.*

Simla was obviously a firm believer in what he'd said, and if Nathan was earnest with him, he'd probably make an enemy here. An enemy with connections and support among Gemore's Adventurers. So Nathan once again tried to take the middle path, but found his scorn for Simla's suggestions sneaking through. He was *angry* at what Simla's suggestions would mean.

"Yeah, I get your point. We gotta get *stronger*." He lifted his arm and tensed it. Nathan was himself impressed at the resulting flex.

Damn, did I get swole? [Regeneration] at work!

"And the dungeons are a good way to do that. But the dungeon I saw? That seemed like a quick way to die, not to level. It killed dozens of Adventurers before by encouraging them to look away while constructs snuck up on them from behind an illusion." Nathan looked around the mostly-empty room. There were a few teams sitting along the walls of the cafeteria. They seemed like teams that were from the villages, who were in the dining room now because they didn't have any local tutors to guide them.

"And how many of the Adventurer trainees are here from the villages? Seems like at least a few teams. Wouldn't have as many of those without as many villages."

Simla scoffed. "Not real Adventurers. No real Insights to their name, just here to learn and go home to farm, maybe feeling a bit safer with the sword they take back." He scowled and scanned the room, daring anybody who overheard him to take issue.

Oh, now that wasn't a comment fit to endear yourself to me. But let's try one more time.

Outwardly, Nathan shrugged. "Maybe. But I'll take a team of village

Adventurers over no team at all. And in thirty years, if those Adventurers protect their homes and get some levels? If we have thirty villages and twice as many Adventurers as we have now? I think that'd give Giantsrest pause the same way twenty Adventurers at level 500 would. You end up stronger if you help other people and then rely on them to help you instead of enhancing solely your own power."

Mid-tier Earnestness 4 achieved!

Simla scowled and got up. "You're welcome to think so. Keep my offer in mind though. We'd be happy to have you for some dungeon delves. Rumor is that you're the only reason the Heirs are still walking around. We'll see whose *help* is worth more."

Nathan spoke to Simla's back as he walked away. "Good to talk to you."

I won't be getting any [Earnestness] experience for that comment, that's for sure!

After eating, Nathan went back to the Heirs' suite. He was trying to think about more skill options – but he was just pissed. Simla had demonstrated that *people* didn't change, no matter if you were on Earth or Davrar. Taeol had been a monster, somebody who didn't deserve the benefit of the doubt or a chance to improve. He wasn't really a person to Nathan, just a monster with all the capabilities of a human. It had taken Nathan some time to reconcile with that, but if he ran into Taeol today, he'd go for the kill without hesitation.

On the other hand, Simla was a person, and he meant well. Nathan had no doubt he'd put his life on the line to protect Gemore. It's just that he thought things were better in "the golden age of yore," when the first generations of escaped slaves had established the city. They'd become Adventurers by clearing out the dungeons of Gemore. They'd risen in levels and established Gemore against impressive odds.

But Nathan would bet that if those famous Adventurers heard Simla's arguments, they'd slap him and tell him to be thankful he had a safe roof to sleep under and food on the table. They'd be proud that Gemore was spreading, the city powerful enough to defend twenty-two villages that would themselves grow and eventually be able to support themselves.

Nathan gave up and meditated for a while, using the enforced calm of [Focused Mind] to break through his frustration. He had noticed that anger was cropping up more now that he had a Rage class. It wasn't too hard a problem to control, so long as he managed it. Meditating each day helped –

Nathan made sure he didn't have any simmering anger left over from the day that might be set off by the smallest trigger.

Well, except for at Giantsrest. But that's not so much a time bomb as a part of me at this point. I'm determined to harness that anger. Let it be the fuel for my ascent, not the explosive for my destruction.

Nathan opened his eyes, feeling better now that he'd put his finger on that worry. He *would not* let his anger hold him back.

Stella skipped back into the suites, returning from her lessons much earlier than usual. Nathan gave her an inquisitive look.

She grinned at him. "Can you teach me more math?"

I guess I'm happy to have an attentive student. I *would certainly have paid more attention if I thought understanding math would let me shoot lightning bolts.*

Chapter 46

Correspondence from Afar

The next several days passed in an atmosphere of suspense as more trainee Adventurers went out on their Blooding Patrols. One Adventurer died when their team was charged by a siegeboar and he tried to face it instead of getting the hell out of the way. They'd been in a built-up section of the ruins to the south, and the rest of the team had killed the boar *properly*. They'd spent half an hour baiting it from multiple directions, forcing it to turn in tight streets and exhaust itself chasing people around corners of buildings it couldn't simply knock down.

Eventually, the boar had been exhausted and bled dry by dozens of wounds. It wasn't a threat that *should* be killing Adventurers, which Jolba made respectfully clear. That team was still a functional unit, though they now lacked a heavy frontline fighter.

The other teams were sympathetic, though Nathan saw some veiled derision. At least they weren't mocking the dead trainee or his team, but it showed a level of competitive viciousness that Nathan wasn't entirely pleased to see.

The Heirs made no overt comments, showing sympathy from a distance. Nathan was glad they weren't dismissive or critical. Instead, they privately discussed how *they'd* deal with a siegeboar.

With Blooding Patrols well underway, the training course would only run another month or so before they all became official Adventurers of Gemore. There was another set of missions out in the villages before the graduation ceremony, an event which would be held on the summer Solstice.

Their classes proceeded – including Nathan's general knowledge test with Velek. With some explanations of notation, he proceeded to *crush* every test on mathematics and the physical world that Velek gave. Unsurprisingly, he had problems with the sections on monsters, history, and geography of Gemore, and so Nathan was taught more on those topics, as well as general knowledge on the wildlife that existed around Gemore.

The background of Gemore was interesting – it had started as a colony of Giantsrest a few hundred years ago, focused on delving into the dangerous and rich ruins of Old Gemore. They'd had a legion of slave soldiers to do the delving – and the dying. The mages wanted the secrets and wealth of Old Gemore but not the dangers that came with it.

It had been an unpopular post for the mages of the Ascendent Academy, and there'd been a point where several assigned mages had refused to come. There hadn't been enough mages to keep the mental spells active on the slaves who delved the dungeons, and they'd risen up, butchering the remaining mages and fortifying the town against easy reprisal.

A state of war had existed ever since. Nathan asked how Gemore had managed to survive against the might of Giantsrest in the early years. Velek gave a few overlapping explanations.

The first was that the freed slaves had managed to prevent a [Message] from being sent out, and then kept the uprising secret for some time. That seemed unlikely to Nathan, but possible.

Another idea – one that struck Nathan as the most likely – focused on the fractious nature of the Giantsrest Ascendent Academy. Any archmage could have probably crushed Gemore in the early days. However, it had become a political issue where no archmage wanted another to get the credit for such an action. They had eventually settled on a compromise where lesser members of the Academy were sent in their stead. Velek had sneered at the small-minded competition of Giantsrest as he explained.

The last suggestion of how Gemore had survived was that the distance from Giantsrest and the difficult terrain made it difficult for a larger army to approach, and that Giantsrest was more capable of managing slave raids than conquering armies.

Some or all of those things had bought Gemore *time.* The early Adventurers had been quick to reap the rewards of the numerous dungeons and monsters in the surrounding area. They'd earned a lot of levels and ancient magical loot at the cost of a catastrophic casualty rate. Even when Giantsrest did march armies against Gemore, they faced not the newly freed slaves they'd expected, but the precursors to the modern Gemore Adventurers.

As soon as Gemore could produce Adventurers capable of slaying an archmage and had demonstrated that fact, they'd settled into the current simmering cold war that was underway to this day.

The continued lessons were interesting – Nathan was happy to get more context for Davrar, though Gemore's short history meant their history books didn't go back very far.

Beyond his classes, Nathan continued to teach Stella calculus and physics. It was going slower than Nathan had expected, but it wasn't Stella's fault. There was just *so much* to explain. Nathan had forgotten what the underlying mathematics of differentiation were and was having some trouble properly explaining it. He tried explaining the details of limits and epsilon-delta proofs, but they got stuck in that confusing rabbit hole for a few days before Stella got frustrated and asked for examples.

What really got them through was Nathan drawing side-by-side graphs of position-velocity-acceleration-jerk with tangent lines as an example of differentiation. They backtracked a bit until she understood what limits were before moving on. The whole process was good for skill ranks for the both of them, especially when Stella started seeing how conjured bits of rock followed calculated trajectories. She could carefully control how much mana she used to propel them, then link that to how fast and far the projectile went in order to include mana costs in her calculations.

Mid-tier Enhanced Memory 7 achieved!

Low-tier Lecturing 5 achieved!

The Heirs continued to adapt to their skills, and Nathan was somewhat surprised to find himself actively looking forward to fighting by their side again. He had made good progress mastering his new skills, and so had they – it would be great to see what their efforts and levels had earned them. They were all becoming even more effective individually and as a group. Nathan wanted to see how their new coordination stacked up against a *real* foe.

And one appropriate to our level, not a damned high-level dungeon. I am not a big fan of fights that are so risky, even if they are good for levels. I am kind of hoping Taeol tries to jump me the next time we're out of Gemore. I think my perspective on risk is still a little different than the locals.

He'd practiced his own skills, but there seemed to be a limit on what he could get from practice. You could practice to get used to your skills, and maybe get a few ranks in the low-tier ones. But Davrar required risk, Insight, or novelty to advance high-tier skills and Talents.

Low-tier Tumbling 3 achieved!

Low-tier Tumbling 4 achieved!

Low-tier Dodging Footwork 9 achieved!

In working with Stella on magic and math, Nathan got the distinct impression that she was something of a magical genius. Her skills were certainly built for it – like [Magical Intuition], for instance. But Nathan got the sense that she would have fit right in at an elite university on Earth. She was figuring out her new mana types at breakneck speed, and at Nathan's advice, was practicing combining air into her fire spells to give them more *oomph.*

Dalo had also advised her to do it, but Nathan had a unique perspective on fuel and gas mixtures that helped Stella out. They talked a bit about different gasses in air, and Stella started practicing to see if she could use air mana to separate oxygen from nitrogen. The answer seemed to be yes, but it wasn't simple, and it was hard to move or control the effect. Nathan mentioned the idea of suffocating somebody by drawing away their oxygen, and Stella said she'd look into it. But it might only be applicable in enclosed spaces where the Heirs had a separate form of protection from the effect.

Diffusion is a bitch like that.

Sarah tested the use of her new mobility Talent, and had adapted to using her ranged weapons even in closer encounters. It involved continually leaping out of melee range and usually releasing a weapon in midair.

Aarl had *definitely* Developed some skills and maybe a Talent while being mentored by his dad, though he was tight-lipped about it. The wiry young man could become an absolute whirlwind of blades if he so chose. The biggest change was that his blows carried more weight behind them, even attacks from lighter weapons requiring Nathan's full attention to block. He also became capable of swinging even very long weapons with only one hand, apparently no longer needing to use two hands to exert a lever-action on the hilt of his favored greatsword.

Khachi meanwhile was practicing with his new uses of Faith, guided by Nathan's input. The divine magic was squirrely, possessing a sort of adaptive motive force that made it more effective and harder to block. Nathan guided

Khachi to emphasize that aspect, since it seemed inherent and unique to divine mana.

Khachi's biggest focus was decreasing the time it took to summon his Faith, as well as properly enunciating the prayer to make his divine magic work in a fight. He could quickly enhance his now-repaired shield with his Faith to boost its already formidable protection – except against Nathan. His Faith-boosted attacks were also becoming quite scary, empowered with enhanced momentum that released an explosive resonance when a target was struck. With some trouble, they worked out that the Faith was especially effective against magical constructs and defenses, such as Stella's force magic. Kia had confirmed that it would be *extremely* effective against constructs and undead.

On the note of Kia – she'd asked Nathan to accompany Khachi to tutoring in a few days, so they could talk about the air-walk Talent. Nathan was excited about that. Khachi told him to calm himself, for Kia was unlikely to easily agree to teach him the Talent.

Nathan was keeping up with his daily meditations – where before he'd had trouble with anxiety, now Nathan felt like he was having trouble with anger. It wasn't entirely easy to control his Rage in and out of combat. Nathan had never been an incredibly angry person, but now getting angry was *fun*, and addictive. It filled him with a thrilling rush, a feeling that could easily guide him toward bad decisions.

In their previous conversations, Artha had said that Nathan needed some tool to prevent his Rage from consuming him. He'd walked Nathan through the basic tools of his clan, but they had seemed like less-developed versions of meditation to Nathan. He found that meditation plus [Focused Mind] was helping him control the issues.

Nathan wasn't able to check in on his *other* project very much. He was pleased when Beatred left a message with Kadid that she needed to talk to him. He hadn't visited since he'd first talked to her and Poppy, so he quickly followed up, curious to see what she'd been up to.

Nathan felt slightly apprehensive about leaving the Adventurer's Guild on his own, but Beatred's shop was close by. Additionally, Nathan didn't intend to do this regularly or keep a schedule that would let somebody lay out an easy ambush.

When he entered the shop, he saw Beatred helping another customer pick out enchanted arrows – which Beatred churned out by the bucketful. Once the buyer left, she closed the shop and waved Nathan back into the secured workshop.

She brought him to a corner hidden behind some wooden panels, where there lay a few semi-recognizable shapes. The first was just a simple tube a couple of feet long. One end could be sealed with a clamp, and Nathan saw a large block of scarred wood placed in front of the other end. It was scorched and blackened, with some clear bullet holes in the center.

The other shapes looked to be a dummy revolver and a rifle chamber prototype. Off to the side was what looked like a bare-bones revolver handle. It was lying in two halves, showing the spring-assemblage inside.

Nathan surveyed the work. "Wow, this is really impressive. You've done a lot of work quickly."

Beatred rubbed her hands together with gusto. "I've got the skills and the tools. I wanted to show you what we've got and ask a few questions." She held up a loaded brass casing, with a bullet set far back into it. The tip barely stuck out of the front. "We haven't tried to make many of these, still getting a handle on the bullet size and the amount of powder. Poppy's having trouble making powder that's the same from batch-to-batch."

Nathan took the round, examining it. It looked like the back held just a small hole, with a thin disk of paper preventing powder from spilling out. The bullet was set way too far back. He poked it and looked questioningly at Beatred.

She shrugged. "It's easy for the bullet to get pushed back, squishing the grains back into powder. Then the bullet gets stuck halfway down the barrel because the powder's been crushed and there aren't grains anymore. Or so we think."

Nathan thought about it for a second. "I don't think I know how to deal with this problem. You might just need to crimp the casing around the bullet tighter to prevent it from sliding. Maybe a small ridge in the bullet to hold it in place?"

Beatred nodded. "I thought of that, but I'd need to make a specialty tool. I was hoping there was some clever solution you knew."

Nathan shook his head in the negative before examining the prototype cartridge again. "This is very precise. How do you make the casing?"

Vhala pointed to a bench where a few brass pipes were laid out. "Draw a pipe the right size, then cut 'em up and bend down one end. Not hard with a proper blacksmith class."

She then directed Nathan's attention to another barrel that didn't look particularly straight. "I tried cutting some grooves into a barrel, but it didn't work very well. How's it done?"

Nathan furrowed his brows in thought. He'd seen something on this... at some point. There were things called "rifling benches" that had been built specifically to cut those grooves – the rifling – into guns. But Nathan didn't remember how they worked. "Give me a moment."

He sat, immersing himself into his Mind Palace once more. He thought about the process, pulling up a historical article on civil war gunsmithing he'd read at one point. He'd heard the reference to a "rifling bench," and looked up what it was. There was a picture – and Nathan needed to remember it. It took some time, effort and the assistance of his skill, but after a few minutes, Nathan had it.

He opened his eyes and grabbed a slate and some chalk. "It looks like a really big horizontal vise, or lathe, and you need a cutting head with a really hard piece of metal to cut grooves as the barrel rotates. I think it's much easier to only do one groove at a time, and cut several times to get it deep enough. It doesn't need to be *really* deep, but you still need to go over each groove multiple times. The trick is that the barrel has to rotate at a constant speed as the cutting head gets pulled down the barrel, so you need a gear sort of thing *here...*"

Beatred was unconvinced but shrugged and thanked Nathan for the ideas. They chatted a bit more about various problems and opportunities around the guns, and Beatred asked if Nathan could come back in a few days. She'd drag Poppy down, and they could talk over what was working and what wasn't.

Nathan left the shop with high hopes. The assistance given crafters by Davrar made a big difference, and it seemed more likely than not that they'd have a functional metal-cartridge gun before the Heirs graduated from the Adventurer's Guild.

I wonder if they do graduation presents around here?

He was a street away from the Adventurer's Guild when somebody called out to get his attention. "Nathan Lark, I will inscribe our meeting! I have a letter here for you!"

Nathan turned and found himself walking over to meet the man politely extending a rolled up scroll. His [Notice] twigged, and he saw a few people filing out of an alley in his peripheral vision. But he wasn't about to be *rude* and not take and read the scroll, was he?

I think that's a skill working on me. Like that slave master yelling "Halt."

Nathan took the scroll and found himself unrolling it. He ignored the text to read the signature at the bottom.

Signed, Grand Dimension Archmage Taeol dho Droxol, ninth finger and fourth researcher of the Ascendant Academy of Giantsrest

Hah. He got demoted. Before he was the seventh finger and second researcher.

Chapter 47

Consequences for Treason

Nathan was holding a letter from Taeol in his hand. Something pushed him to do the *polite* thing and read the entire letter. But *fuck that*. This letter was from somebody who didn't deserve to be treated as a *person*, much less given their polite social due.

Nathan spun on his heel and took off towards the Adventurer's Guild, leaving the man who'd given him the letter open-mouthed in his wake. He heard somebody else behind him swear.

"Harpy's tits! Net him, Tessa!"

Nathan glanced over his shoulder and saw a woman raise a large, crossbow-shaped device and fire it. A net unfurled and flew at him.

Too late, idiots.

Nathan turned sharply, putting the corner of a building between him and the net. He just needed to make it down the block, round another corner and he'd be at the Adventurer's Guild. He'd show Sudraiel the letter and describe their faces. These assholes were *screwed*.

Then the net *curved* around the corner and caught him. Nathan stumbled and refused to fall for a few steps until the net tangled his legs. He hopped for a moment until a sharp jerk yanked his legs out from under him. He fell forward into a roll, throwing the momentum of his body against the rope connected to the net. The rope slackened, and he heard more cursing from behind as he vaulted back to his feet, making it half a dozen feet farther down the street.

He could only hop or roll, and rolling covered more distance.

I will roll to the Guild if I have to.

Low-tier Tumbling 5 achieved!

Nathan made another roll down the street. On the next roll, the rope jerked backwards much more violently than before. Nathan slammed against the cobblestones as his feet were yanked backwards. He yelled as loud as he could, pushing Stamina to his lungs.

"HEY! HELP! I'M BEING ABDUCTED BY GIANTSREST! HELP ME!"

"None of that now."

Nathan twisted around as he took another breath, looking through the net. The same man who had spied on him with Stella and her parents stood over him, blackened chainmail complementing his dark hair and stubbled face. He threw a thin blanket over Nathan, and all sound cut out.

Nathan could vaguely feel the magic in the blanket – it must've been enchanted to block sound. He focused on sucking the magic out of it, but he was separated by the rope of the net.

Well, this is fucking dumb.

Nathan felt his Rage start to flow. He squirmed, trying to free himself from the net. It resisted, twisting with his motions to bind him tighter. The net wasn't magical – a skill or Talent maybe? He wormed his fingers through the net and tore at the blanket. He managed to get a strand of the net in his teeth and bit down. It was tough rope, coated with some sort of nasty pitch. Nathan didn't give a shit and started wearing down the rope with his teeth, tearing with his hands and thrashing his feet.

Somebody kicked him hard in the chest, but Nathan barely felt it. He was *not* going to be easily captured on the street like this. His Rage burned, and he tore harder at the blanket. He felt the magic faltering, catching snippets of sound.

"... Out of sight... random adventurer..."

He was sliding over the cobblestones as they dragged him away. Nathan kept tearing at the blanket, the sounds becoming clearer. A new voice sounded from some distance away. It was... familiar.

"Hail to the Pack... do you have there, Naghmen?"

Heavy, metallic boots clattered against the street, and Nathan focused his efforts on the blanket. He had touched enough of it to feel for the weave of the enchantment – a simple layer of mana that dampened vibrations. He tore viciously at one particular point, trying to tear a hole in the blanket. More sounds leaked in.

"... Your concern Eldred. I'll buy you a..."

Nathan spat out the netting he'd been chewing on. It was frayed, but far from parting. He leaned into his Rage, tearing with his fingertips into the blanket in front of his face. It tore.

He shouted as loud as he could, pushing Stamina into his lungs. "ELDRED! It's NATHAN! They're kidnapping me for GIANTSREST!"

There was a beat of silence. Nathan could see through the tear, and he saw the big bald man in platemail standing in front of Nathan's dark-haired captor. That was likely Naghmen.

Eldred looked down at Nathan, and Nathan could see a moment of calculation pass through his eyes. His face lit with a grin, and the big plate-armored man looked back up at Naghmen and stepped back.

Naghmen held out his hand placatingly. "Hold on, we can work something out."

Eldred unlimbered his enormous mace. "I don't think you can. VANGUARD, ASSEMBLE! Take down the Pack Leaders!"

Naghmen swore and tore his shortswords from their scabbards. Somebody Nathan couldn't see shot a crossbow bolt at Eldred, but it broke against his armor. The bald man swung his huge mace at Naghmen, who jumped back and then darted in to attack while the enormous weapon was out of position. But Eldred had expected that, and the butt of Eldred's weapon followed through to catch Naghmen in the jaw.

The would-be-kidnapper was tossed aside by the blow, blood and teeth spraying in an arc. Eldred's face was one of glee as he ran past Nathan towards the other members of Naghmen's team. Nathan heard swearing and the sound of feet on stone as they retreated in the face of the one-man assault.

More members of Eldred's team swarmed around the corner, following their leader into the fight. It didn't take long. Eldred's team was big and surprisingly quick. Whatever Naghmen's team was, they weren't specialized in fighting a larger group of armored Adventurers. Nathan didn't see most of the fight, but after less than a minute, a few of the Vanguard were untangling Nathan from the net.

Eldred walked up to Nathan, grinning. He leaned on his mace, both ends of which were bloody. The big man put out a hand and hauled Nathan to his feet, laughing as he clapped a hand down on Nathan's shoulder.

"Well then! I call this second meeting worthy of the memory, Nathan Lark. Let's get down to the Guild and get this all sorted out. Come on boys, bring 'em back to the Guild. I think this might just be the easiest payout we've ever pulled. Drinks on Nathan!"

There was a cheer at that, and the Vanguard grabbed the prone bodies of the Pack Leaders and hauled them back to the Guild. Nathan made sure to grab the letter off the ground.

They made quite a stir as the Vanguard loudly busted into the Guild carrying Naghmen and the rest of his team, who were all injured in various ways. They dropped them in the center of the room as a clerk hurriedly ran out from behind the desk, already yelling at Eldred.

It was Hisla, the same clerk who'd brought Nathan and the Heirs up to the Guildmistress after the Blooding Patrol.

She snapped. "Eldred! What in the Muckgrabber's blighted asshole is going on here?"

He pointed at Nathan, shrugging and handing off responsibility. "They had Nathan wrapped up, and he said they were trying to abduct him for Giantsrest."

A hush spread through the hall, and Hisla's face twisted into a grimace. She hurried back to the desk and spoke into the device that blurred her mouth.

Meanwhile, Nathan was practically dragged over to the bar, where he arranged to pay the Vanguard's tab for the rest of the night. The bartender quoted him a price that made Nathan wince, but he shrugged and handed over the coins.

I'd pay a lot more than that to not get captured by Giantsrest.

A door at the back of the room slammed open, and Sudraiel stormed in. If Nathan had seen her mad before, this time she was furious. Her expression was truly thunderous and her spear was tightly clenched in her hand. She surveyed the room, noting the pile of beaten Adventurers and the celebrating Vanguard.

Nathan approached her, with Eldred not far behind. The bald man already held a tankard of beer and slurped it as he walked over.

"Nathan, you claim they were working for Giantsrest? Do you have any proof?"

Nathan handed her the letter with Taeol's signature. It had been trapped under his body and torn a bit as he'd been dragged, but it was still legible. Nathan himself didn't know what it said yet.

Sudraiel scanned it, then snorted and looked back at the prone forms. "Naghmen, you absolute fool." She handed the letter back to Nathan. "Put that away." She walked towards Naghmen, who was starting to stir.

The Guildmistress snapped her fingers at the silent crowd of adventurers. "Kuzro, get over here. We need to heal Naghmen to hear what he would say."

A mousy figure detached herself from the crowd, scampering up to Naghmen. She leaned over him, then looked back up at the Guildmistress in consternation. "I can't… not quickly. Or cheaply."

Sudraiel waved her hand. "I'll have the Guild pay you. Just get him talking, no need to make it permanent. I'll pay for a better heal if necessary."

Kuzro hesitated for a moment, then looked up at Sudraiel's iron-firm face. The mage bent over the moaning Naghmen, casting magic for nearly thirty seconds. After that, she handed him a flask and helped him sit up. Then the short and hunched mage moved to the other slumped forms, ensuring nobody would die.

Naghmen washed his mouth with the flask, wincing in pain before spitting out blood and another tooth. He looked around and then up at the Guildmistress. She was standing above him like a god ready to pronounce judgment.

His voice was slurred and uneven. "Well, fuck."

Sudraiel spoke. "You, an Adventurer of Gemore, were hired by an archmage of Giantsrest. And you took the job. Tell me everything, and it will inform your punishment. I will be able to tell if you lie or withhold information."

Good to know she's got a skill or something that can determine truth or lies. I've been worried about that kind of thing. I haven't felt any specific magic, but that doesn't rule out much.

Naghmen took another drink of water to stall, then breathed out raggedly. "Somebody got in contact with Tessa and told her that an archmage of Giantsrest had a job for us. An easy one, with a bucket of jangle and contacts for reward. Said we could come and go freely from Giantsrest cities, get help huntin' around there if we did it." He sighed, unable to meet Sudraiel's eyes.

"Job was to deliver the letter to Nathan and escort him to Giantsrest. The contact said there was a good chance he'd come on his own after he read the letter, and that we should grab him if he didn't. Said he'd be low-level, under 27. We thought it was worth the risk to get to hunt around Giantsrest."

Now I want to know what the hell the letter says, if Taeol thought it would make me willingly go to Giantsrest.

Sudraiel was still pissed, but it was mixed with… sadness. And pity. "And the contact?"

Naghmen shook his head. "Never showed themselves. You know the Giantsrest agent routine. Black cloak, masked face. Got the seal of an archmage to show they're a true agent. Free with coin. I didn't try to find out more." He shrugged, looking up at the wrathful Guildmistress. "So, what'll it be?"

All of the whispers in the room went silent as Sudraiel considered. A few of the other members of the Pack Leaders watched with haggard expressions. After a moment of silence, Sudraiel raised her hand with all the gravity of a bishop leading a sermon. Her spear rose to point directly at Naghmen's face.

He was heaving deep breaths, his eyes fixed on Sudraiel's spearpoint an inch from his eyes.

"The penalty for this crime should be death, executed by me, *now*. But you have told all that you know without lie or guile. And before this shameful day, you served Gemore long and well. You will be stripped of all belongings other than clothes, struck from the Adventurers of Gemore, and exiled from the city as you are, with one item each. I would recommend a weapon."

Sudraiel lowered the spear, and Naghmen's frame shook with tears of relief. But she wasn't done. "Go to Litcliff or Agmon. Now that you've failed Giantsrest they won't treat you kindly. They're not keen on independent adventurers, and you can expect a [Dominate] as your only reward. Beware, if you strike at Gemore or the villages I will send the Seven Fools after you, with instructions to be merciless."

She turned away from the terrified Adventurers, quickly delegating.

"Hisla, go tell the Guard of the exile. Provide instructions that the Pack Leaders are to be gone by nightfall and killed on sight if they should return. Eldred, the Vanguard may keep the gear they have on them, the rest of their belongings will go to their families or beneficiaries. Allow them their choice of an item from their equipped gear."

Then, the elderly woman heaved a sad sigh, before turning and walking over to the bar for a drink.

Chapter 48

A Long-awaited Letter

Back in the Heirs' suite, Nathan sat at the table in the common area, the letter in front of him. Everything had gone fairly smoothly after the hubbub in the Guild Hall. Nathan hadn't gone to watch the newly exiled Pack Leaders be ejected from the city. It hadn't been personal. He'd been a job for them, a job that entailed betraying Gemore.

The letter sat on the table. With a sigh, Nathan bent forward to piece together the torn text.

Nathan Lark, dimensional treasure.

I have been following your progress, and I ask you to reconsider your decision to leave Giantsrest. There is so much to accomplish, and I have so many plans that you could be a part of if you would only ask. Your skills and your otherworldly knowledge are wasted in Gemore, a town full of monsters and barbarians that lack the resources and education to draw out your potential. Moreover, you have selfishly held the knowledge of your own world close to your breast, a decision which all those in the Academy are paying for indirectly – and myself directly.

For I remind you, all the potential you have is due to me. I have gone to considerable effort and expense to bring you to Davrar, that your knowl-

edge might be used for progress and the triumph of civilization! You owe me, and you owe Davrar, to use your potential.

Together we can grip Davrar in our fist and bring it to our breast. With your knowledge of non-magical wonders and my magical acumen, we have only to join forces. We will rule Giantsrest within five years, then the region in ten. In twenty, we can change the face of Davrar with the strength of our fist! Bring the marvels from your world to this one, and people will no longer die from monsters, but live without fear on the face of Davrar!

And if there are things about Giantsrest you find objectionable, we can discuss it, and learn from one another. When we control it, we can make of Giantsrest what we want. Join me in my tower, for I will be eagerly awaiting you.

Signed, Grand Dimension Archmage Taeol dho Droxol, ninth finger and fourth researcher of the Ascendant Academy of Giantsrest

Nathan tossed the letter onto the table with a dismissive flick before leaning back and rubbing at his eyes. He didn't even know how to feel.

Just... what the fuck *man. I was half-expecting some kind of [Dominate] enchanted into the letter or something. But no, you're just* so *egotistical that you think you can convince me to come back to Giantsrest. And that I'll "forget" that you tried to stick me into a golem core if you don't mention it.*

Nathan glared at the letter.

I guess this is proof that you don't need to be smart to use magic. Maybe Taeol's just really bad with people. High IQ, low EQ. Rock-bottom EQ. With a superiority complex. At least if he's so desperate to get me back it's less likely he just summoned some other poor schmuck from Earth. Probably that "expense" he was talking about.

Nathan thought back to when he'd first entered this world. He'd been disoriented from a trip through vacuum, confused by the unfamiliar surroundings, and then given the mother of all headaches by a spell that let him speak the local language. But, if he leaned on [Enhanced Memory], he could remember everything he had seen.

Taeol's room-sized dimensional magic contraption had been really complicated, and Nathan wasn't going to understand how it worked. But he *did* remember that some important-looking multicolored magical orbs had seemed to power the apparatus. And after Nathan had been summoned, most of them had shattered and broken. Maybe Taeol was desperate to convince Nathan to return because he *couldn't* try again.

And he did get demoted. Interesting.

Anyway! Nothing that Nathan could do about that now, except not get captured by Taeol. Sudraiel had already seen the letter, so she would probably be taking any necessary precautions. Nathan sure as hell wasn't about to go after the archmage, not until he Developed past level 81.

Or farther.

Stella came through the door, looking around curiously. "Nathan, you okay? I heard..." She saw him staring at the letter. "Is there a problem?"

Nathan grabbed the letter and stuck it in a pouch, making a note to burn it later. "Yeah, things are fine. Some adventurers tried to kidnap me earlier, but Eldred Vanguard saved me. Not fun to be attacked *inside* Gemore."

Stella frowned at him and the letter he'd stowed, but she didn't ask about it, just sitting down across from him. "That does not seem like a good experience. The Pack Leaders, yeah?"

Nathan waved his hand vaguely. "Yup. I hadn't heard of them before. They caught me pretty easily."

Stella shrugged. "They're a harvesting team. Been around for a while, well-respected. Sometimes they capture local monsters alive and ship them down to Litcliff, so I'm not surprised they could catch you. I guess they *were* a harvesting team now, and *had* respect. I'm surprised that Sudraiel let them live."

Nathan honestly wasn't sure what to think of Sudraiel exiling the Pack Leaders instead of executing them. Nathan wasn't pleased that they'd tried to kidnap him, but he was also glad he hadn't seen a half-dozen people executed in front of him. He was trying to get used to the violence here on Davrar, but it would be a while before he was truly cold-blooded enough to want heads to roll before his eyes.

He'd have fought them without hesitation – and been willing to kill if necessary. But when they surrendered and were cooperating on the floor of the Guild – he didn't have it in him. They'd taken a job, and the job had made them Nathan's enemies. But that didn't mean he had a great personal enmity for them. Nathan supposed Sudraiel felt that they weren't blood-enemies of Gemore, and wanted to show that there were rewards for giving up information freely.

Nathan sighed, then grabbed a slate and started sketching out a basic Riemann sum. Now that he'd gone through limits with Stella, integrals shouldn't be too bad.

Low-tier Lecturing 6 achieved!

~

The next day passed quickly – classes happened as normal. The highlight was a member of the Delve Scholars named Mathin who lectured about the history of the dungeons of Gemore. Apparently there'd been a big celebration thirty years ago when the previous "Last Dungeon of Old Gemore" was cleared. That was part of why it was significant to find a new dungeon in the ruined city – they'd thought there weren't any left.

Gemore was *built* by clearing the dungeons of Old Gemore. They knew a lot about how Old Gemore had built its fortresses, guard posts, research labs and various other secured facilities before it was overrun in some calamity or other. They knew how the wards were designed, what kinds of constructs guarded them and so on. Mathin was of the opinion that the dungeon the Heirs had stumbled upon had been a stronghold for the Old Gemore Watchkeepers, a secret police force. It might have even been their headquarters.

Secret police. Fun.

Somebody asked if there could be other, similarly hidden dungeons scattered around Gemore.

Mathin waved his cane around in a "who knows" gesture and continued in a gravelly voice. "Very well could be. We'll be lookin' at the signature of the illusion and tryin' to find the bypasses to the look-away spell. It's built different than the standard Old Gemore pattern, seems the Watchkeepers got some secrets yet. One of the big things that the people who crack it will be lookin' for will be a map of their places in ta city. If it's anywhere, it's there."

He gestured again with the cane. "That and the big ol' self-destruct enchant. The Watchkeepers liked to include those, and they tend to be poised on a hair-trigger. I don't run fast enough for that shit anymore."

~

At team practice Stella tried to throw Nathan from a stone platform. She was using him because he was the most likely to be fine if she messed up and dropped the stone platform on top of him. Nathan promised to be *very mad* if that happened, so that his Rage would protect him.

It didn't go well – Stella was still figuring out how to move non-conjured rock, which was harder than moving conjured rock. Trying to do so against Nathan's disruptive influence was even harder. It was good practice for Stella, but Nathan mostly stood on a stone platform that jumped up, diagonally and sideways at unpredictable intervals.

It's good for practicing balance, at least!

At first he stood with feet planted, shifting his body weight to deal with the unsteady footing. After a few jerks that deposited him on the ground, he started moving with the platform, trying to keep his center of gravity stable.

Nathan realized he had a skill for this. He started incorporating moves from [Dodging Footwork] to help him keep his balance. It was tricky, but it worked. After all, the skill read, "This skill will help you move your feet to more easily keep your balance and dodge attacks." And Nathan was sure as hell using it to keep his balance!

Low-tier Dodging Footwork 10 achieved! Congratulations, you have maxed out this utility skill! It cannot be improved any further. You must achieve Insight into this skill to Develop it to mid-tier.

After one especially chaotic series of movements, where the platform rotated up at a forty-five degree angle before spinning around in a horizontal circle, Nathan felt like he was on the brink of Developing the skill.

The movements became steadier as Stella figured out how to balance the spellwork on each corner of the platform. It wasn't throwing him yet, but it was moving predictably up and down.

He looked over to Stella. "Hey, can you make it jerk around some more? Especially those circular motions, I think I might be near a skill Development?"

Stella raised her eyebrows at him. "Just remember, you asked for this."

What followed earned Nathan several bruises, but he focused on the feeling of lightly moving back and forth on the platform to keep his center of gravity from picking up too much momentum.

High-tier Focused Mind 2 achieved!

It took nearly another half-hour for Nathan to engrain the exercise into his muscle memory. Stella had the platform swinging back and forth in a broad arc, and Nathan was dancing from one end to the other to keep himself on it. The arc was slowly getting broader and deeper, and Nathan pushed with his toes, legs and core to change his momentum enough to stay on the platform. It was *more* than just his feet. These were whole-body motions.

Congratulations, you have Developed the [Low-tier Dodging Footwork] utility skill into [Mid-tier Dodging Footwork].

Utility skill: [Mid-tier Dodging Footwork]
This skill will help you move yourself to more easily keep your balance and dodge attacks.

Neat.

He wasn't surprised to see Kadid waiting for him after the group training. Kia was also there, but she gave Nathan a shooing gesture. So, he walked towards Kadid.

However, somebody intercepted him, holding out a hand to bar his way. Nathan vaguely recognized the blonde-haired human as somebody from the Vanguard, under Eldred.

Nathan hazarded a guess. "Theo, right? What are you here for?"

Theo gestured toward the main hall. "Eldred wants to talk to ya. Come on." He turned to leave.

Nathan turned towards Kadid, who was walking up towards them. "Eldred wants to see me. Should I go with him?"

Theo turned around. "Well, we saved your silly arse from getting kidnapped. You ain't gonna let that go unacknowledged, are you?" He raised an eyebrow mockingly.

Kadid shrugged and waved Nathan on. "You'd be doin' Eldred a disservice to leave him waitin' after he did somethin' like that for you. Go, see how he plays this debt."

I owe him a debt? I mean, I guess he saved me, but like... it seems crass to call that debt in. I guess it's not too different from what happened after I saved the Heirs from the Last Dungeon.

Nathan followed Theo to the guild hall in awkward silence.

Inside, Eldred was monopolizing a table in the corner, and Theo steered him straight there. Eldred was drinking a beer, and handed another to Nathan as he sat down. He waved Theo away, leaving them alone. There were some other Adventurers in the room, but nobody particularly nearby.

Eldred wiped his lips, then spoke. "So, I seem to have saved one of the best Adventurers of the next generation from a kidnapping. And might've made an enemy of an archmage in the process. That 'bout complete?"

Nathan gritted his teeth. Eldred was milking this for all it was worth. He was clearly leaning on social pressure and expectation to make Nathan follow the script. "Sounds about right."

He wants something. I can always just tell him to fuck off. I think I've got enough "macho man" social credit around here after the Last Dungeon for that to not be a giant problem. I need to try not to give him an opening to challenge me to a duel. I don't think I can beat him, and if he beats me he'll have even more leverage. If he does that I'm totally gonna try to disenchant all his shit though.

Eldred leaned forward, frowning as he gazed into Nathan's eyes. "I'd ask if you'd join the Vanguard. We've got a place for you, and I just *know* we'll get good distance with what you've got goin' on with magic. Able to bypass a lookaway not even the Delve Scholars knew about? That's somethin' I can use."

I played off my resistance as a "magic interaction" when he asked about it before the Grave Tangle. I don't think he knows squat. He's fishing for a response that'll tell him more.

Nathan said nothing, simply glaring at Eldred. Eldred gazed back, and they were locked in a staring contest. Neither was willing to back down.

Nathan used [Focused Mind]. His eyes were drying out, but he wasn't worried about it.

Well, this is idiotic. Staring contests are for middle schoolers and horny teenagers. And I'm neither. Anybody's guess as to which Eldred is. But it's the sort of stupid macho contest my build will actually help with.

A few minutes later Eldred broke the standoff first, taking another drink of beer and slapping the table. "Well, if that's how it is, that's how it is. I can respect a man who won't leave his teammates, even if they're spoiled pups. They've got potential, nobody can deny that. I'd probably make the same decision in your place."

Then he unhooked his massive mace and laid it on the table between them. "But there's a debt between us, Nathan Lark. And if you mean to run off without paying it, I'll demand a turn in the ring. So, tell me of the Insights that'd be worth saving your life, and I'll take my pick."

Well, shit.

Chapter 49

Introduction to Witchcraft

Nathan looked at Eldred Vanguard over the table and thought quickly. Eldred had just demanded Nathan lay his Insights out so he could pick one. Nathan had a *lot* of Insights, some he'd used and most he hadn't. Some were his and some weren't. He'd sworn to Vhala to not share the Insight behind [Notice]. The same was true for when Artha had set his feet upon the Path of Rage.

Eldred did *save me from getting captured by Giantsrest. But he pushed hard for me to join his team, as if I didn't have plans of my own. And he's generally been a pushy asshole. The Heirs didn't seem to indicate they owed me a debt after I saved* their *lives, so I'm questioning if I really do owe as big a debt as he claims. I'm not in a position to push the issue, but I don't think I want any more to do with this guy than I have to. Him demanding a list of my Insights seems pretty scummy.*

Nathan had to figure out which of his Insights would buy Eldred off. He had to offer up something tempting enough that Eldred took it without forcing Nathan to spill every skill and Talent he had.

I don't think I'll convince him with [Spellsense] or [Dodging Footwork]. Or Earth scientific knowledge – that seems less useful to a straight fighter like Eldred. It would be more useful to mages and crafters. I also don't want to let out dangerous information to the wrong person.

What are the Insights he'd think are valuable? Probably the ones for [Magic Resistance], [Regeneration], [Focused Mind] and [Enhanced Memory]. I prob-

ably can't *share [Magic Resistance], though he might* demand *I start figuring out how to share it if I tell him anything about it. Shit, and that's the one he has hints about already. Maybe I should just say it requires being injected with something alchemical that I don't know how to make? I need to operate as if he has a skill to tell if I'm lying.*

Eldred watched Nathan closely, waiting for him to answer. He started tapping his finger impatiently on his mace, which lay on the table between them.

Nathan spoke. "I've got four real Insights that I can share. Two of them... are probably not useful to you."

Eldred leaned back, luxuriating in the power he had here. "I'll decide that."

Nathan swallowed. His *least* favorite part of this was that he was letting out information on his capabilities. He didn't trust Eldred not to sell that information later on. But if he didn't...

Nathan looked down at the mace on the table. Eldred was an excellent one-on-one fighter. He'd beaten Artha in a duel and had absolutely demolished Naghmen in a real fight. If he beat Nathan in a duel *and* claimed his debt, he might have enough social capital that most of the Guild would think Nathan should join the Vanguard.

Again, stupid macho bullshit. But I'm part of their society now. If I want to use Gemore as a base in the future, then I'll need to play by their rules.

Nathan wasn't sure what happened if you didn't honor a debt for an Insight or a favor in the Gemore Adventurer's Guild, but it was almost certainly a social shunning of some sort. The Heirs probably wouldn't completely abandon him. But it would make everything else harder and might have more consequences Nathan didn't know about.

And that's the problem. Maybe I get exiled without my belongings. Maybe nobody will talk to me. I almost certainly don't keep my "Adventurer" status that guarantees room and board.

So, he continued. "The best one for you is a utility skill. The big advantage is that it helps me discover other Insights and Develop Talents and skills more easily. It's also helped me resist and break mental spells and debilitating stuff like the Grave Tangle."

Eldred frowned. "Sounds like some mage shit. [Mental Discipline] or something like that? Though Developing things better is interesting."

Nathan shrugged. "Not that. It's been very helpful to me."

Eldred waved it away. "We'll come back to it. Next?"

With a sigh, Nathan continued. "If you don't like that one, I doubt you'd be interested in one that makes your memory better?"

Eldred pursed his lips, tilting his head back and forth. "That's a bit better, I might be interested in how it works. Keep going. I wanna hear the one that lets a trainee not die from a surprise dungeon to the face."

I guess I just gotta be vague.

As Nathan was trying to phrase a description of his [Magic Resistance] that didn't hint at how broad it was, a woman slid into the bench next to him, scooting up close enough that their elbows touched.

Eldred looked peeved and waved her off. "We're talking Insights here, so I'll ask you..." He took a closer look at the woman and gulped audibly. He slid down the table to get farther away from her. "Faline?"

The woman laughed like a crystal bell, sharp and piercing. Her voice was pitched high, but with a cruel and polished intent behind it. "*You* were demanding information you have no right to, Eldred Vanguard. Play your games elsewhere and count yourself lucky I don't take you to the ring right now for this. I've been gone a while, and sometimes I find myself looking for somebody to *bleed*."

"But... I saved Nathan from kidnapping. He owes me."

Faline raised one dark, picturesque eyebrow. "I was tailing the Giantsrest agent who issued that job. He was going to reach out to you next with a *very generous* offer. But..." She laid a dagger on the table next to Eldred's mace, looking small besides the larger weapon. One detail made the dagger seem much more dangerous – the blade was red with blood along its entire length. "I found evidence that you spoke to that agent of Giantsrest last month. You haven't done any jobs for him, or else this would be a *very* different conversation." She tapped a finger on the hilt of the dagger, flicking a drop of blood in Eldred's direction. "You forfeit Nathan's debt. Begone. Now."

Eldred grabbed his maul and left with unseemly haste.

Nathan turned to appraise his savior. She was a beautiful woman, tall and lithe. Her clothes were a set of dark robes, loose in most places. Black leather bands wound around her forearms, shins and midriff. Nathan's eyes were drawn to a necklace holding a large and elaborately worked piece of silver and gems nestled just above her bosom. Her hair was long and dark, falling unbound around her face and past her shoulders. It had a few streaks of green, blue and purple scattered through it. Her skin was pale, with a dusting of freckles scattered over a classically beautiful face with high cheekbones and bright green eyes – which glowed slightly.

She winked at him, and the winking eye flickered pink for a moment.

Nathan regarded her warily, unsure what to say. After a moment he ventured, "Thank you. He's not my favorite person."

She let loose another peal of sharp laughter, this one less cruel than the last. Then she focused on Nathan, inching closer to him. "Too true. He's not my favorite person either. Demanding an Insight after saving somebody's life is just crass. Much less a whole *list*. He's competent enough, but Eldred will never topple Giantsrest, or clear a *true* dungeon. He's more of an annoyance than somebody worthy of real animosity. Who do *you* think is worthy of true animosity, Nathan Lark?"

I like her. Maybe she's using a skill on me, but maybe just because she's a goddamn bombshell who has apparently assassinated the person who arranged my kidnapping.

Nathan replied without thinking about it too hard. "Taeol dho Droxol, ninth finger and fourth researcher of the Ascendant Academy." He twisted his mouth in disgust. "And all of the mages of Giantsrest. I'll see their 'empire' torn down and their filthy mental magics gone with it, by my life or death. Nobody who casts that magic on people deserves to live."

Mid-tier Earnestness 5 achieved!

Faline's grin sharpened to something nearly vampiric.

Does a human mouth normally have that many teeth? Jeez.

"You got his letter then. His demotion was hilarious to watch in person. Very humiliating, you'll be glad to hear. I like your skill. It's very straightforward. Truth for truth, a fair trade if there ever was such a thing."

She knows about [Earnestness]? How?

Nathan looked up at her, trying to figure out how to respond. He settled for the more interesting part of her statement. "You were in Giantsrest?"

Faline tilted her head sideways, looking around the room. "Yes. I travel here and there. Spying. Assassinating." She picked up the bloody knife and wiped it on a cloth that came out of a hidden pouch on her arm, before sheathing it in a separate hidden pocket.

Nathan followed her gaze, wondering if anybody knew that somebody who *had just committed murder* was sitting in the guild hall. The few adventurers who'd been close by had drifted away, and nobody seemed to be paying Nathan and Faline any attention.

Faline noticed his look and waved her hand towards the rest of the room. "Nobody'll pay attention to us. Trust me." She winked again, and again her green eye flickered pink.

Nathan floundered around for something to say. He wanted to impress her.

After a moment, he dug into his pouch for the letter. "Do you want to read the letter?"

She took the letter with a flourish. "Thank you indeed. I was wondering what Taeol spent his remaining funds on, and why he would bother with a letter." She bent to read the torn paper, chuckling after the first paragraph. By the end she was nearly in tears, her shoulders heaving from laughter.

"Oh, he's so utterly *fucked*. Out of friends, out of cash, and *begging* his target to come back to him. He's let the prize of a decade of research slip through his fingers and has to *ask* for the knowledge he considers his due. That must rankle. I should get this copied and scatter it around the Ascendent Academy, he'd be the laughingstock of the place for a year. I'd need to remove the part about your valuable knowledge though." She gave Nathan a playful – yet penetrating – look.

Nathan swallowed, his mouth suddenly dry. He'd... forgotten about that part of the letter.

She handed it back to him, dextrous fingers brushing against his knuckles for a second. "You shouldn't worry about Taeol for some months, now that his fate is in the sewers." She paused, tapping her lips with a finger. Her nails were painted a dark purple. "You may attract the attention of other archmages who manage to discover the product of Taeol's research. The worst case would be if Taeol decides to partner with another archmage and offers to share your knowledge. But! I will be residing in our lovely little town for a little while, and the plots which escape my notice are rare."

Faline shrugged, tossing her hair back over her shoulder in a dismissive manner. "It was good to see what the fuss was about and meet the man Sudraiel brought to my notice. I believe I'll be seeing you again, Nathan Lark. I hope that our meeting will be inscribed across the heavens." Her playful voice evened out, and she gazed straight into his eyes as her tone became deadly serious. "For I too wish to kill every single mage who has ever trained at the Ascendent Academy. You can help me, if you level up. 81 is a good start."

Then she stood, stretching in a way that Nathan was *sure* was intentionally demonstrative of both flexibility and body shape.

"I believe I have an appointment with my good friend the Guildmistress. If I told you we were sisters, would you believe me?" She grinned mischievously, then slipped away.

She vanished from Nathan's attention as soon as she left the table, and he *focused* on paying attention to the room. She wasn't using any magic he could detect, and he couldn't track her movement. He did notice the door leading upstairs open and close, even as his brain tried to pretend the motion didn't happen.

Mid-tier Notice 3 achieved!

Nathan sat there for a moment longer, blinking.
Uh. So that happened. She's scary. And hot.

~

He was still puzzling over the strange encounter when Sarah and Aarl returned to the Heirs' suites. It hadn't been long since Nathan's meeting with Faline, so he was surprised to see them. They usually had dinner with their father, at least.

Nathan put down the slate that he'd been using to figure out a lesson plan for Stella. They were moving through his planned math curriculum quickly, spending three and sometimes four hours a day plowing through concepts on their way to multivariable calculus. Stella had figured out Nathan's preferred algebraic notation pretty fast, and he was glad he didn't have to translate things into the bare-bones mathematical notation Gemore used.

He looked up from his work at Aarl and Sarah, who both wore thoughtful expressions as they barged through the door.

Sarah spread her arms. "Stanel got called in for a meeting, so we're back early. And before you ask, we don't know what it was about."

Nathan connected some dots. "I... think I might know. I just had a strange meeting in the main hall. Somebody named Faline? Eldred knew who she was, and he was scared of her?"

Aarl's eyebrows went up. "The Witch is back? Dark hair with colored streaks? Has a complicated silver amulet?"

Nathan looked at him, nodding. "Yeah, that's right. The Witch?"

Aarl shrugged. "It's a nickname, and better than the one some Adventurers use. Stanel told us that we'd never see her coming. He told us to listen to whatever she said carefully. Then decide for ourselves if what she asked of us was too risky. She's been known to lead people to their deaths if it gets her what she wants. But he *also* said she's probably done more to protect Gemore from Giantsrest than anybody living. What did she want of you?"

"She told me to level up. I'm pretty sure that's the *third* woman from Gemore who's told me to level up before I would be able to do anything."

Sarah sat down across from him, grinning as she pulled out a knife and some wood to whittle. "Welcome to the life of a trainee. We'll be doing routine jobs for a while until we're high enough level to really make sparks fly."

"What's high enough level? Faline mentioned 81."

Aarl sat down next to his sister, picking up the history book he'd been reading. "Depends on your class and build, and how your Talents and utility skills are doing. We all probably need to wait until 81 for the class Developments we're preparing for. Weapon generalists truly need the nine class skills. After that we should be set for a while since we've been building up our skills and Talents from the start. I wouldn't be surprised if we started taking bigger jobs at a lower level than anybody else because of our advantages. But if we want to even approach our parents, then 243 is required, and most of them are over 729."

Both Stella and Khachi walked through the door as Aarl finished. Their parents had likewise been called away, and Nathan grew more certain that Faline had returned to Gemore for more than just him. She had *something* that required the attention of Gemore's top adventuring team.

Well, it seemed this was who Sudraiel had meant to introduce Nathan to. He hadn't expected to meet that person so quickly. Regardless, Nathan was sure he'd see her again.

Maybe next time she won't have to rescue me.

Chapter 50

Divine Upbringing

The next morning a guard stopped by to check in with Nathan, making sure he hadn't unleashed a soul-eating monster that had been hiding within him for the past few days. The Heirs assured the guard that he was doing no more soul-eating than usual, and Nathan went on with his day.

That afternoon, Kia beckoned him over along with Khachi. Kadid was also there, and threw up his arms as if to say, "Oh, come on!" Nathan shrugged apologetically, but he wasn't about to pass up an opportunity to talk to Kia.

Today she was wearing something closer to full plate, but without the gorget, thigh or shoulder pieces. Nathan bet that those pieces were stowed in the slim fanny pack resting below her enormous greatsword. The fiery-haired Adventurer was still intimidating as hell, but Nathan had interacted with her enough to know that she wasn't crazy. Just... zealous. Committed, not insane.

Nathan followed her and Khachi to an obscure corner of Gemore, the foot traffic on the street dwindling away.

As they walked, Kia spoke, turning her head to look at him. "Faline's in town again. She's taken an interest in you, Nathan Lark. She has said she won't try to remove you from the other Heirs' company, but you will be entangled in her plots going forward." She grimaced. "None else can play politics in Giantsrest and return unscathed, and she is an invaluable source of information on their doings."

She sighed and turned to address Nathan directly. "But I mislike her ways. They are brutal, and she slits throats without a pause for thought. There are depths to her that none can gauge, least of all me. And I am used to being able to judge what lies in the hearts of others."

I honestly don't see a problem with that, as long as she slits Giantsrest throats. They can rot in hell as far as I'm concerned.

"Thank you for the warning. She told me to level up before I could help her."

Kia's brows furrowed. "Then I suggest you take that advice. The more powerful you become, the more likely you are to survive whatever her plots entail. It is another thing for me to consider in my decision on this Insight you ask for."

The three of them had arrived at Kia's home. It was a rather ramshackle house tucked against the the stone wave that arched over the upper regions of Gemore.

Not far away was a small stone fortress built into the ridge. Nathan knew it was a shelter, a bunker for civilians to hide in when Gemore was seriously threatened.

Kia pushed through the door, which wasn't locked. The home was bare bones, with only a few rooms. The furniture was rough, bulky and cheap. Past the entryway Nathan saw a large area had been cut out of the rock of the ridge, forming an open room not unlike the practice chamber under Kullal and Dalo's mansion, though with a much higher ceiling.

Kia waved Nathan to a seat at the crude table, while Khachi stood awkwardly to the side because there weren't enough chairs. Kia addressed Nathan directly. "You ask after the Insight that allows me to walk upon air as if it were solid ground. To confirm the lay of things, you have a free Talent slot and wish to use this Talent for yourself? You do not wish to trade it to others?"

Nathan nodded. "If I can use your Talent, I think it will make me much more effective at Adventuring, and especially at fighting mages. I'm very willing to swear to never pass it on to another. I just want to be as capable as I can be."

Kia pursed her lips. "Yes, I can see your reasoning. Do you not worry it will provide you no benefit inside a building? Or underground? Most dungeons are enclosed, and the monsters that Adventurers must kill are often found in underground lairs."

"I think its value is hard to overstate," he said, spreading his arms wide. "From what I saw, you can use the Talent in the middle of another motion, to exert force and reorient in midair. With practice, it seems like it could enable running faster and dodging attacks while moving or airborne."

Kia pointed at him with a gauntleted hand. "Yes. Not many who ask understand the advantages to normal motion. And the fact that you do speaks that you would use this Talent to its full potential. I am glad you understand the value of what you ask for, and I also believe you are one of few who could survive gaining this Talent." She clasped her hands, studying Nathan.

"We come to the question of what Insight you would trade in return. I have all the Talents and skills I wish for. I appreciate you saving the Heirs' lives, but it is expected to do so for the members of your team. Unless you have something of great worth to offer Khachi or the other Heirs, an agreement is unlikely."

Nathan had a response to that. "I may have some useful Insights to offer Khachi, but I don't think they'd balance the scale." He nodded to the armored cleric, who returned the nod but didn't speak, letting Nathan continue. "I have also been teaching Stella Insights that I believe will allow her to master lightning and light mana. If you owe Dalo or Kullal any favors worth your Insight, they may call them in if I succeed in helping Stella gain two mana aspects *without* Davrar's assistance."

Kia's eyebrows arched in mild disbelief, but Nathan plowed on.

"Furthermore, I am attempting to build a new kind of weapon that I believe will be of great interest to Sarah and Stanel. I believe it likely they have never seen anything like it before. It is possible that they would believe it worth an Insight as well."

Mid-tier Earnestness 6 achieved!

Kia's face now bore the faintest trace of a smile. "An Insight worthy of lightning? A weapon unknown to Stanel?" She glanced at Khachi, who gave her a slight nod.

She shrugged slightly. "Regardless of practicality, those would be worth something. However, I do not hear any certainty in your statements. I will acknowledge that *if* either or both of your efforts succeed, I would consider trading favors with my peers to teach you the Insight.

"However, there are certain things I want to ensure are clear as flawless gems before we continue. This Talent is not quick to acquire. It will require many rank-ups before you are able to use it as you desire. The early Developments are dangerous. The later Developments are difficult, and those are the Insights that are of true value. I would set your feet upon the path, then let you walk until you need future Insights to Develop the Talent correctly. I do hope that your plans come to fruition soon, for you will need the time to rank up this skill before it sees serious use."

She paused, then fixed him with a stern look. "I only consider this because you have shown yourself to be on the Righteous Path, and a valuable friend of the Heirs."

That all sounds pretty reasonable. I should check in with Beatred and Poppy, and hopefully get a prototype revolver to Sarah soon. That'll turn Stanel's head. Unfortunately, I think I've got a ways to go with Stella, and we might need some practical demonstrations before she can connect theoretical understanding with magic.

He nodded again. "Sounds good to me. I'll ask again when my plans pan out. Is that all? Should I go?"

Khachi laughed, standing. "You didn't think you were getting away that easily, did you?"

Kia stood and started buckling on more pieces of armor. They seemed made specifically to allow her to armor up quickly and without help. "No. I would see your ability before you go, and train you as recompense for what you have done for Khachi. I also wish to test out your resistance to magic for myself. If that is amenable?"

I did want more experience with Divine magic. Khachi's seems incomplete somehow.

They went into the practice room, and Kia placed her greatsword on a rack before picking up a duplicate. It looked nearly identical but without the enchantments or razor-sharp edge.

Nathan gestured at the swords. "Do you ever grab the wrong one?"

Kia grounded the tip of the sword and leaned the crossguard against her shoulder as she used both hands to negotiate her braided hair under her helmet. "No." Then the tall woman in full plate grabbed the sword and bounded across the room at him.

Ah!

Kia rained blows down upon him, and it was all Nathan could do to survive the torrent of steel.

Mid-tier Dodging Footwork 2 achieved!

Ow.

After a little while, Nathan ran out of Stamina from healing the bruises and cracked bones Kia had given him thwacking his bare arms. She wasn't using magic, but she was *strong*, and hit significantly harder than the sentry constructs.

He wiped his bloody mouth with the back of his hand. "Can you start using magic on me?"

In response, the holy warrior muttered a short prayer under her breath, so quickly and quietly that Nathan barely caught the words *blade* and *strength* mixed in. The sword took on a golden glow, which extended out to nearly a twenty-foot length. Nathan suddenly realized why the room was so large.

She pointed the sword at him, and the tip flicked towards his chest.

Nathan leaned backwards, but Kia merely stepped forward and jabbed. The glowing image of a sword impacted his chest. The tip sizzled apart into motes of light, scorching his skin. Just like when he was healed after the battle with the Grave Tangle, Nathan felt Kia's mana as warm prickling needles.

I'd be a Nathan-kebab right now if I didn't resist her magic.

This spell *clearly* wasn't a healing spell. The spell Kia had cast when she healed the villagers had carried a component of righteous anger, but the emotion in it had primarily been a soothing feeling, inspiring the recipient and encouraging them with courage.

This spell was trying to cut Nathan apart. It felt simpler than the complex knots of mana that mages normally used. Instead of being woven together in a defined shape, the mana flowed in a looser configuration. If this was normal mana, it should've been spilling everywhere and fizzling out.

But instead, the mana in Kia's divinely blessed sword coursed with a feeling of righteous wrath. The will to cut and burn infused the spell, every part of it radiating the sheer power of its intended purpose. The spell knew its function, and attempting to constrain and bind the surging fury in a more complex weave would only have obviated its terrible agency. If normal mana was a powerful flow of water that needed to be carefully guided, divine mana was a water elemental that only needed to be pointed at its target.

Mid-tier Spellsense 3 achieved!

I can feel *[Identify] working on this, but it's not ranking up. I wonder if I can get Kia to cast more spells for me to pick apart for practice. That skill is* hard *to rank up.*

Nathan opened his mouth to ask. "Can you cast more..."

He didn't get any further before Kia muttered another prayer and the glowing intensity of the sword doubled.

The feeling of Divine wrath on Nathan's skin intensified, and he backed away from the blade quickly, leaving a raw and bleeding mark on his chest. It wasn't trying to cut him anymore. It was trying to *disintegrate* him. The spell had become more complex, switching functions to something similar to Taeol's [Disintegrate] spell.

What the shit—

He frantically dodged as Kia swung the enormous blade at him. She advanced, and Nathan had to lean into more and more acrobatics to dodge the truly *stupidly* sized sword.

This is like fighting Yhorm the Giant from Dark Souls. Can hit me from across the goddamn room. Roll!

He recognized that Kia was going easy on him, giving him just enough time after each blow to regain his footing to dodge the next one. The blade annihilated Nathan's clothes and left angry red marks on his skin that wept blood, giving him plenty of motivation to keep dodging even as the magical blows refilled his Stamina. Nathan got faster, optimizing his movements to return him to the ground quickly so he could redirect before the next strike came.

Low-tier Tumbling 6 achieved!

Kia sped up as he did, mixing in more divine spells. Her armor flashed with blinding light. Nathan had already seen that spell from Khachi, but this time it was much stronger. The mana itself tried to stun him into inaction. It fought his absorption like a living thing, attacking his eyes and ears with bursts of sound and light.

Maybe I really do need to think of it like a living thing.

Next, Kia raised her sword vertically, almost scratching the ceiling of the chamber. She spoke another quick prayer. "I command you, *be still.*"

Mana pulsed from the raised sword, washing over Nathan and trying to lock his limbs in place. It was like Taeol's [Paralysis] spell, but more active, responding to his attempts to resist. After Nathan broke the hold on his muscles, the remaining mana tried to construct force barriers to keep him still.

Can I prevent it from adapting?

Kia thrust a free hand to unleash a loose orb of light at Nathan. It struck like a whirling disk of blades but failed to find purchase on his skin. Nathan reached out to the spell, feeling for the motive behind the loose weave of writhing mana. There was *something* there. The spell had been cast with a core purpose, and that purpose was what allowed it to continue attacking Nathan even through his [Magic Absorption]. He needed to *break* that purpose.

Low-tier Identify 9 achieved!

He thrust a hand into the ongoing spell. The spell was already changing to a burning radiance that dried his skin. But Nathan followed the threads of agency, wrapping his hand around something insubstantial at the core of the spell. He closed his fist and felt the spell shatter. There was still power there, but without direction or a stable weave, it dissipated without effect.

Magic Absorption 4 achieved!

Divine mana: understood. Hell yes. Pun not intended.

They ramped down the training soon after, eating a plain but filling dinner of savory porridge. Nathan looked to Khachi. "Do you usually train like that?"

The armored wolffolk snorted, watching his adoptive mother. "That training would kill me. But yes, Kia is good at pushing people to their edge. It helps with ranks."

No kidding. I got four ranks from an hour of training. That's never happened to me before. Of course, that training would have killed most people. Or left them requiring some pretty extensive healing. I suppose Kia's positioned to provide that.

They chatted about Adventurer politics for a bit longer before Nathan and Khachi returned together to the Adventurer's Guild.

More tutoring with Stella ensued, and Nathan felt like he should be *really* sore. But – [Regeneration]!

~

Status of Nathan Lark:
Permanent Talent 1: Magic Absorption 4
Permanent Talent 2: High-tier Regeneration 4
Talent 3: None

Class: Spellbreaker Juggernaut level 43
Stamina: 530/530
Juggernaut's Wrath
Antimagic Momentum
Raging Thrill
Juggernaut's Inertia
Unarmored Resilience

Utility skills:
High-tier Focused Mind 2
Mid-tier Earnestness 6
Mid-tier Sprinting 2

Mid-tier Spellsense 3
Mid-tier Notice 3
Low-tier Identify 9
Mid-tier Dodging Footwork 2
Mid-tier Enhanced Memory 7
Low-tier Lecturing 6
Low-tier Tumbling 6

Chapter 51

Clandestine Operations

Weeks passed. All the trainees finished their Blooding Patrol. No teams were wiped out, though one lost three out of five members when a stalker ambush drove them into a building which collapsed. The survivors were folded into the team which had lost their frontliner to a siegeboar.

Lessons continued, and Nathan learned more details about Gemore and its environs. They had a whole lesson on common enchantments – what you could get enchanted, and what you couldn't. Apparently Gemore's enchanters were of a high level, both because there was a lot of demand and a good supply of materials – and an abundance of ancient artifacts to learn from.

Now that he wasn't as worried about being kidnapped in the streets, Nathan spent more time in the afternoons with Beatred and Poppy. The short orc was in the process of moving his shop next to Beatred's, and Nathan got the sense that they had meals together daily, discussing the firearm project and trying out new designs for cartridges and chambers. He shared some meals with them and would have felt like a third wheel except that they spent much of the time poking and prodding him about technical problems with gunpowder, cartridge and firearm manufacture.

Nathan helped out as much as he could – but he'd already shared everything he'd read in various history books and Wikipedia articles. At this point, he was just helpful as another viewpoint on the problems, since the crafters couldn't bounce ideas off the people they were used to relying on.

Despite some remaining issues, their reported progress was very promising.

Poppy was making a good amount of reliable black powder, and together with Beatred had devised a device to quickly and safely pack the casings. She had *also* figured out rifling and built an effective trigger mechanism that dropped an enchanted hammer to spark the gunpowder through a thin disk of paper without requiring primer.

I am so glad I farmed all this work off to people who can actually make shit.

The first real surprise came when Nathan was called to celebrate them finalizing the cartridge design. When Nathan entered her workshop, Beatred proudly displayed a few of the assembled cartridges to him, ready to be loaded and fired. They were *beefy* – almost half an inch across – and clearly carried a large powder load.

Nathan blinked at the giant round of ammunition, then looked up at Poppy and Beatred. "Why is this so big?"

Both crafters shrugged, and Poppy explained. "If you're shooting at a siege-boar, or at [Mage Armor], do you want your bullet to go through it or not? A bigger bullet also means more room for enchantments."

The rifle bullets were the same *enormous* diameter as the revolver bullets, but the rifle bullet itself was longer and had a larger, tapered cartridge that held significantly more powder.

That's like a 50 cal. Damn.

"I'm shocked that the chambers can handle that much power. I'd expect the metal to break if your powder loads are that large," Nathan said, pointing at the rifle bullets.

"I've got skills to strengthen the metal I work. And enough enchanting knowledge to trace some basic durability into the structure." Beatred was trying to be humble, but her pride showed through the explanation.

Nathan was impressed and didn't hide it. "That's awesome. Well done. If you want armor penetration, you could try putting a steel cap or tip on the bullets. That might be hard to make, since the sides still need to be lead."

Beatred noted down the idea to try another day. "Any other suggestions?"

After a moment of thought, Nathan gave a quick summary of everything he could recall. He explained steel-jacketed bullets and how a bullet could be hollowed out for various purposes. Beatred listened and took notes. She had a few ideas and mentioned buying a slab of meat for testing.

After they'd tapped out that topic, Beatred brought up another. "We're having problems with residue left inside the barrels after a shot. Just a few shots and the next bullet will get jammed. I'd fix this with magic, but I wanted to ask if there were other ways to do it."

The real answer is better powders. Smokeless powders or cordite wouldn't have nearly as much fouling. But that's not really doable with the resources we have. And I do want to see what magic can do for a gun.

"It would be pretty hard to fix without magic. How would you use magic for that?"

Nathan's question was directed at both of them, but it was Beatred that answered. "I can do small stuff, but nothing like this. Probably need a cleaning or anti-stick enchantment on the inside of the barrel. We'd need a real enchanter for something like that. I'll ask my aunt Herdin – she's the best in Gemore. She's been retired almost a decade and made it clear as clean water she won't work on just anything, so it's no sure thing. But I think she'll be interested in guns."

Keep it in the family. Makes sense I suppose.

Nathan tilted his head back and forth, trying to think over the idea. "And she'll also be good at making a foolproof self-destruct, right?

Beatred nodded. "She's the best. She'll probably figure out a hand's worth of ways to improve them as a weapon. There are some other people I would ask, but only after Herdin says no."

Her argument made sense, and Nathan found himself agreeing – keeping it in the Bho family seemed like a great way to maintain a layer of security. He eyed the way Beatred's hand was almost touching Poppy's.

Keep it in the family indeed.

"She'll need to be sworn to secrecy of course. Same terms as the Oath we all swore. So you can't tell her the full details before that. Do you still think you can convince her?"

Beatred was visibly excited by the idea. "I think so. I'm the favorite niece, no matter what Vhala says. Some good enchantments will solve a barrel of problems."

Hopefully they can still make a magic-free version that I can use. I doubt it'll be my primary armament, but it's a hell of a surprise weapon if somebody like Eldred tries to jump me. Or maybe I shouldn't be angling to use a gun at all. I don't have skills to improve a gun like Sarah and Stanel probably do. Furthermore, my Talent would probably break the self-destruct mechanism and that would be bad. Lastly, given what happened to my first spear, there's a good chance a gun wouldn't survive my fighting style. And it looks like they're going to be goddamn expensive.

Over the meal that night they hashed out the rough price – in coin – that Nathan would pay for two revolvers and a rifle for Sarah, as well as several hundred rounds of ammunition for each. It wouldn't be cheap, but it also wasn't nearly as ruinous as it should have been for the amount of time and materials the two skilled crafters were putting into the project. That was because of the Insights Nathan had shared and promised to keep sharing, even if they wouldn't be able to sell guns to most people.

Nathan fully expected Stanel to want one once he saw what they'd come up with, and *he* could certainly pay the necessary price. Nathan would probably need to have a talk with him to ensure he didn't arm the entire Gemore Guard with the weapons.

The whole deal took almost three-quarters of the cash Nathan had gotten from Stanel – but that was what it was for.

Now that it looked like the guns were going to work, Nathan realized he was on a different sort of timer. He'd put in firebreaks to prevent Giantsrest from getting the Insights behind guns. But the knowledge would spread within Gemore, even if the weapon's manufacture was guarded by oath and Insight. Nathan probably had years before the technology would get out. If the Bhos could hold up their end of the deal, then maybe he had decades. He almost certainly didn't have more than that. It was his goal to ensure that Giantsrest wasn't a problem by that point.

Later on the same evening, Nathan found himself discussing a few other Insights with the blacksmith and alchemist couple. With Poppy, he started with fertilizers and painkillers. When the alchemist figured out it would require huge amounts of material to improve farm yield, he got less interested.

However, Poppy was quite interested in non-magical painkillers. They discussed it but concluded that it would be hard to get something like acetylsalicylic acid without a known natural source of it. Nathan sure hadn't seen any willow trees around.

The discussion was winding down, and Nathan was debating sketching out a periodic table and diving into the basics of chemistry when Beatred interrupted him. "You carry any Insights for me, or just for the alchemical arts?"

Nathan turned to address her. "How do you make steel?"

She cocked her head and answered. "Mixing basic ore-cracked iron in a large crucible with charcoal, sometimes other metals. Keep it magically heated and mixed for a time. It works well enough, though the quality depends largely on the skills and class of the smith removing the scum from the mix." She grimaced. "I usually buy my steel from that bandit Helmug, he's got the skills to do it pretty well. My focus is more on turning good steel into good weapons, so I can't make the good stuff."

Nathan was sure there was a twinkle in his eye as he grinned. "Well, I think there might be a better way. Try blowing *air* through the molten metal after you mix in the charcoal. It'll help heat up the metal and should remove a lot of the impurities. They'll either come out as a toxic gas or float to the top as a crust that you should be able to scoop away."

Beatred gave him the weirdest look. Then, she closed her eyes and shook her head in resignation. "Okay, I'll try it out."

Low-tier Lecturing 7 achieved!

~

Eventually, the Giantraiders returned. They'd been bouncing around the hills on various missions. Their latest had been to intercept a slaving raid headed towards the northern villages.

Their ambush had managed to kill one enslavement mage, the second mage retreating within a powerful bubble of force. But the Giantraiders had hounded her until she'd run out of mana, allowing Artha to run her down.

Nathan was glad to have them back. These were the only people other than Sudriael who knew he came from Earth, and he especially wanted to talk about his class Development with Artha. He spent time hanging out with them all as they relaxed from their mission.

Unfortunately, they were heading out on another mission early the next morning. This one was more of a routine scouting mission, ensuring that Giantsrest wasn't building any new strongholds in the mountains that would extend their grip towards Gemore.

Nathan debated trying to get them a gun or two, but he didn't think he could justify it for a number of reasons. So, he just didn't mention it.

He enjoyed spending time with the Giantraiders. He'd had a lot more experience with Adventurers now, and he recognized that the Giantraiders were a bit of an odd group. They were all quite different from one another, with different backgrounds. And while they were friends, that seemed like a *consequence* of their team rather than the driving force behind it. They worked together because they shared a mission to oppose Giantsrest. The friendships and treasure were incidental to them. Important, but not the reason they worked together. Even in relaxation they seemed more focused, more professional than the often-lax Guardians of Gemore.

Regardless, it was good to spend time with them again. In the Giantraiders' private suite, Nathan listened as Wiam described how their newly acquired weapons had been able to crack a [Mage armor], though they had failed against the reinforced force sphere the second mage had used.

In return, Nathan described the Adventurer training. Vhala made appreciative noises when Nathan described the curriculum of the classes, and they all wanted to hear the story of the Heirs' Blooding Patrol.

Emerald in particular seemed enthralled by Nathan's description of dodging through the sentries to reach the bunker. Their feet half-danced on the floor during his description, as if physically playing out dodges and retreats.

When Nathan mentioned that he'd taken his level 27 Development during the fight, Artha's face grew stony. They talked for some time about other things, but it was clear that Artha wanted to discuss Nathan's class Development in private. He didn't kick the other Giantraiders out, but they excused themselves pretty quickly. Nathan made a note to try to catch up with them individually next time they were in town.

Eventually, an ebullient Wiam left to go find some other mages from the Tower of Trickery, leaving Artha and Nathan alone.

Nathan gazed at Artha, once again appreciating the wild majesty of the Treefolk. His silver-maned face and bare chest swelling with muscles were such a picture of statuesque beauty. It was like looking at a sculptor's masterpiece.

The big elk-centaur's voice rumbled at Nathan. "So. Tell me of your choices, and your Choice. I hope my lessons were helpful. Even brief as they were."

Nathan bowed his head, then recited his list of class options and the description of each, thanks to [Enhanced Memory]. Artha's brows furrowed when Nathan mentioned [Magebane Berserker], but then his face smoothed when Nathan described [Spellbreaker Juggernaut]. Then Nathan got to [Antimagic Monk], and Artha looked surprised.

After taking a moment to collect his thoughts, Artha spoke. "Which class did you take?"

Nathan didn't pause. "[Spellbreaker Juggernaut]."

Artha nodded, relieved. "Good. And what does your Rage skill say?"

Nathan recited [Raging Thrill]. "You can voluntarily enter and exit a Rage state, where you will be immersed in the thrill of combat. This will rapidly consume Stamina, but will increase your strength, speed and resilience to damage."

Artha's face fully relaxed. "This is good. Classes which explicitly name 'Berserker' tend to have uncontrollable Rages, which are unable to distinguish friend and foe. They are the strongest in direct combat, but it becomes hard to fight with allies or act strategically. I would have guided you away from that path, had I been present. Your [Raging Thrill] seems similar to my own [Crushing Animosity], and that is good. It should empower you physically without crippling you mentally. Have you had problems controlling your anger outside of combat? Issues thinking clearly when presented with an obstacle? Your [Focused Mind] seemed a good tool for handling these things when we spoke last."

Nathan nodded. "It is. I've been meditating on my anger and the reasons behind it daily. It feels like a deep part of my personality, but not my entire being."

"What of your other skills? Did your Stamina Develop into another resource?"

Nathan shook his head. "No, it's still Stamina. If it did Develop, would I still be able to use my [Regeneration] Talent? It specifically says it uses Stamina. Would I be locked out from my ability to heal?"

Artha's silver mane rippled as he shook his head. "Davrar will not deny you the use of your Talents. When a class resource Develops, then Talents and skills that depend on it will change appropriately. Developed class resources tend to be more powerful, but more specific. For example, Stamina may have Developed to Rage if you had become a Berserker. It would be more efficient at fueling a more powerful Rage, but it would not have allowed you to enhance normal physical movements. It is a trade-off."

Good to know.

Nathan went on to describe all his new class skills, and Artha listened attentively. He nodded through the list, only grimacing when Nathan described [Juggernaut's Inertia].

Then he spoke. "That is a good list. I am glad you received [Unarmored Resilience]. Such a skill is enormously useful, and one of the prized Insights of my clan. The Development of [Brawler's Indifference] and [Antimagic Blows] into [Juggernaut's Wrath] and [Antimagic Momentum] are also excellent. Your skills have become more general, more useful. If you only use a class skill in one way, then future Developments will often specialize in that use, locking your tactics into one path. The trick is to use your class skills in multiple ways. Future Developments will then enhance your versatility, allowing more powerful uses as you level.

"For if you reach the heights of levels, then you will need to use your skills in new ways. If a swordsman can only walk at a normal pace and strike within reach of his sword, then levels past 81 will not help very much. No matter how skilled, how would such a fighter fare against the Grave Tangle?"

The question was rhetorical, and Artha took a second to consider before continuing. "I am not sure of [Juggernaut's Inertia]. It seems only useful during a limited set of circumstances, though I am sure mages will not appreciate the additional difficulty preventing your approach. And I suppose that if *all* of your motions carry greater momentum, it will improve the weight of your blows." He thought for a moment.

Then, the man's craggy face cracked open into a smile. "I am pleased for you, Nathan Lark. You have become a fine fighter, and I am proud to have guided your first steps upon the Path of Rage. I do not think you need more guidance, and I am not able to give you much more help, for I myself have not reached the heights of level 81. Though after the last two missions, I approach it." His smile grew wider still.

Nathan grinned back, and it was a nice moment. "Yeah, I really appreciate your advice and Insights for my path. I like where I've ended up. Though I wonder about [Magic Suppressor] and [Antimagic Monk]. Both seem like they could have been good."

Artha inclined his head a fraction. "Yes. Both sound like they hold potential fit to wake giants. Do not fret your choice overlong. A different Nathan would have made those choices and done well with them. I would only remind you that you had nobody to teach you the details of those skills. You may have received powerful skills. But we *planned* for a class like [Spellbreaker Juggernaut], and our planning has been rewarded."

Nathan nodded. It was late, and probably about time for him to return to the Heirs' rooms. Artha had an early morning tomorrow. But he had one more question before he left.

"Artha, what are the Endings?"

With a sigh, Artha rubbed his forehead. "The Endings. Yes. You come from beyond Davrar, so you would not know."

A small *huff* of exhaled breath drew Nathan's attention to the door of the suite. It was a quiet sound, the sort of sound you might make if you heard something surprising.

Mid-tier Notice 4 achieved!

The door was cracked open, and Nathan looked into the dark hallway. Somebody stood there, their profile unclear. Nathan stepped towards the door, and they spun and *ran*.

Nathan ran after, throwing the door wide and giving chase. Whoever had been spying on them was fast, and Nathan barely caught a glimpse of them disappearing around the next corner. He charged after them, [Sprinting] for all he was worth. He didn't know what he would do if he caught the person, but step one was *finding out who they were*.

The figure ran down some stairs that led outside. Nathan followed, busting through the doors and looking around to see where they'd gone from there. He didn't see anybody and was about to activate [Focused Mind] when a voice spoke from next to him.

"Looking for something?"

Nathan spun and saw Eldred leaning against the side of the building. He was smoking a stubby pipe, his face lit by the bowl as he gazed levelly at Nathan.

It wasn't him. The person at the door was smaller, and their steps didn't clank as they ran.

"Eldred. Did you see somebody run out of this door a moment ago? Who was it, and where did they go?"

Eldred met Nathan's eyes and smirked slightly. "I don't know what you're talking about."

Shit. He's covering for them.

Nathan eyed Eldred and curled his lip with disgust.

The big man placed a hand on his maul, which leaned against the wall next to him. His gesture was clear. *I won't start shit if you won't. But if you start it, I'm ending it.*

Nathan thought he *could* challenge Eldred in a duel for this and demand the name of the person who ran if he won. But Eldred *couldn't* challenge Nathan to a duel because of Faline's warning, so he was clearly trying to bait Nathan into one.

Prick. I wonder if he came up with the plan to spy on me.

Chapter 52

An Unexpected Exercise

Artha emerged from the building a moment later and saw the standoff between Eldred and Nathan. His expression grew thunderous. "I understand." He paused and pawed the ground aggressively. Nathan tensed, expecting the elk-centaur to attack Eldred at any moment.

Eldred shifted, closing his hand on his mace and crouching slightly as he spoke past his pipe. "Remember how this ended last time, Treeborn."

Artha snorted dismissively but stopped pawing the ground. "Eldred, your actions are a transgression." The big centaur's voice rumbled like an advancing storm.

Eldred relaxed, leaning back against the wall and smiling sweetly around his pipe. "I don't know what you're talking about. Now, unless either one of you would like to challenge me, I think I'm done here." He shook out his pipe onto the ground and turned to walk away.

Nathan watched him go. "Could I ask Stanel to challenge him? I think I'll have a favor from him soon enough."

Artha snorted loudly and started laughing. "I would greatly enjoy seeing Eldred stare the ghoul in the eye in such a way." Then he stomped the ground again. "However, that is not how it works." He gestured Nathan back inside, sighing. "An Adventurer of Gemore is expected to stand on their own and can be challenged if they have given offense but not committed a crime within the remit of the Guard. There are no formal rules to the duels of Adventurers. It all works on opinion and judged fairness. In general, you are only expected to fight people of about the same weight as you – if you were wronged by Gale Shullet, the leader of the Seven Fools and the Tower of Trickery, then you could ask Dalo or Kullal Caxol to stand for you. If they had a reason to help that could be understood by those watching."

He shrugged as they walked up the shallow stairs. "In this example, it could be as simple as Dalo's grudge against Gale, though it is old and clotted, or you being friendly with Stella. The Guild as a whole must accept the duel's premise, the reason the fight is occurring, and the fairness of the match. The first battle is one of opinions, that a duel is appropriate. Stanel would never be one to fight Gale since one is a fighter and the other is a mage."

They entered the room as Artha continued explaining. "If Wiam wronged you, then you could ask Stella to challenge him in your stead. Or if Eldred wronged Stella, then you, Khachi or Aarl could duel him. If the offense was terrible, then it might be possible for Stanel to fight, since he is well-known as a family friend. But that would be only possible if most believed Eldred had committed a great wrong, since all know it would be a one-sided beating. Kia is well known to ignore duels, though her displeasure is never to be desired.

"We have no evidence of Eldred's wrongdoing, so one of us would have to fight him personally. Eldred is a good fighter in the ring, and he would use victory to extol his innocence and claim a small favor of us." Artha looked tired as he spoke. "I do not like how Gemore settles these things, and I do not think Sudraiel likes it either. She is working to change it, but this is how things are done." He paused, looking annoyed. "In my clan these disputes were 'settled by the elders,' who knew all involved and could choose the wise path. Most of the time." He waved a hand horizontally, dismissing the thought.

That's complicated. Trial by combat but mediated by the court of public opinion. Gross. Gonna need to keep considering this, it changes the social dynamic pretty dramatically.

Nathan looked up. "Do you know how much they heard? Obviously when I asked about Endings, but did they also hear about my class skills?" Nathan felt he was understandably nervous about people knowing the details of [Spellbreaker Juggernaut].

Artha responded slowly. "I do not believe that the spy overheard the details of your class skills. I glanced at the door while you were describing them, and it was firmly shut, as Vhala left it. I do not know what they can do with the knowledge of your origin."

Okay, so it's not as bad as it could be – they might have heard that my class was [Spellbreaker Juggernaut], but not much more about my abilities. Taeol already knows that I'm not from Davrar, though he seems to be keeping the secret to himself. But he could start spreading it at any time. And whoever the person who spied on me was – they don't know anything about my world. What can they do with just the knowledge that I'm not from Davrar? Make a public stink about it? Sudraiel already knows and is fine with it.

Artha sighed, placing his hands over his eyes. "Nathan, I apologize for all of this. You will learn of Endings at the Solstice ceremony, when Sudraiel tells the Tale of Endings. Then you will swear the Adventurer's Oath at your graduation ceremony. I do not think I can explain it appropriately, here and now. It is late, and the Endings... are not a small topic. But it is not a topic where ignorance will hurt you. You will swear your Oath, the same as any other Adventurer."

Nathan thought about protesting, but Artha had a point. It was late, and they were both shaken from the spying incident. Nathan made a note to have sensitive conversations with more protections. Maybe he could ask Stella to put up force walls to block sound or something.

And I guess I'll have something to look forward to at the graduation. I need to keep an eye out for Eldred from now on. I actually don't think I can do anything to him – I can't beat him in a straight fight for now, and I don't want to get caught doing something shady when I don't understand the lay of the land.

~

The next morning, Jolba showed up in the dining hall. He strode up to the Heirs, who were having a somewhat slow breakfast after their morning exercise.

Nathan just felt resigned, wondering if some stupid Adventurer politics shenanigans were about to cause problems. That just seemed to be the way things were going recently.

Instead, Jolba gestured to encompass all the Heirs. "Mission for you. Come on. Now. I'll brief you as you go."

The Heirs looked around at each other for a moment, and Jolba clapped his hands together. They grabbed their gear and went to deposit their plates, but Jolba clapped again. "Leave them. We're in a hurry."

They all followed their teacher out of the building, and he explained as he walked. "This is another training exercise. We're sending you out on a job in the villages without much time to prepare. You have rations for a few days?

Khachi nodded. "Yes, we do."

Jolba hummed appreciatively. "Good habit. Stay in it. I'll give you this anyway." He pulled a heavy pouch from beneath his jacket and almost handed it to Nathan, before reconsidering and tossing it to Aarl. "Dried oats and a few bowls. A good lesson for Adventurers who don't prepare. Don't tell any of the other teams."

That's one way to teach people to keep food on hand. Make them survive off just dried oats.

Stella broke in, impatient. "So what's the mission? Or is that a secret too?"

Jolba shook his head forcefully. "No, that would be stupid. We're giving you full information on the target. A small tomb appears to have opened up between Stonefall and Thop. Here's a map. It shouldn't be too dangerous. A few shepherds saw some zombies chasing sheep and tracked them to a hole in the ground. Clothing on the zombies looks either Old Gemorian or from the Sklias Dominion. No ghouls or any higher undead so far. *If* that's all, then you should be able to go in, destroy the source of death mana and get out.

"If it's too much, learn what you can and *get out*. Don't do anything stupid, and if you find *anything* indicating a Quaz linkage get out *immediately*. One Grave Tangle is enough for this decade."

He glanced back to check on their reactions, and all of the Heirs nodded at him in response. Jolba seemed satisfied, and they arrived at the gates a moment later.

This feels so... sudden. One moment we're eating breakfast, the next we're planning on going up against a bunch of ravening dead things. I suppose that's part of the training. Off we go!

Jolba gave each of them a handshake, then turned to walk back to the Guild. The city gate guards rolled their eyes as Nathan left, telling the Heirs that they'd need to do another round of questioning when they returned. And probably check on Nathan after a few days to rule out soul-parasites.

Note to self. Watch out for greyish worms hanging in doorways or on walls. Nope nope nope.

They took the north transit road once again, passing quickly through Old Gemore. It really didn't take long to cover the dozens of miles to the outer curtain wall which marked the outskirts of the city.

To Nathan's surprise, the transit road's effects didn't end immediately, and they walked another few miles on the road before the effect began to fade. It was *extremely* disconcerting, and Nathan almost threw up as one step carried him thirty feet and the next was... just a normal step.

He clamped down on his bile and stepped off the road, followed by the rest of the vaguely green Heirs. Aarl did end up throwing up on the side of the road, wiping his face afterwards on a cloth.

Khachi shook his head. "Kia always said that I'd know when to get off the transit road. I guess that's what she meant." He pulled out the map and looked it over. After a moment he waved the Heirs over. It was a crude map of the villages north of Gemore, which Nathan recognized from the larger version he'd seen. There was a spot marked with a red X about equidistant between Stonefall and Thop to indicate their goal.

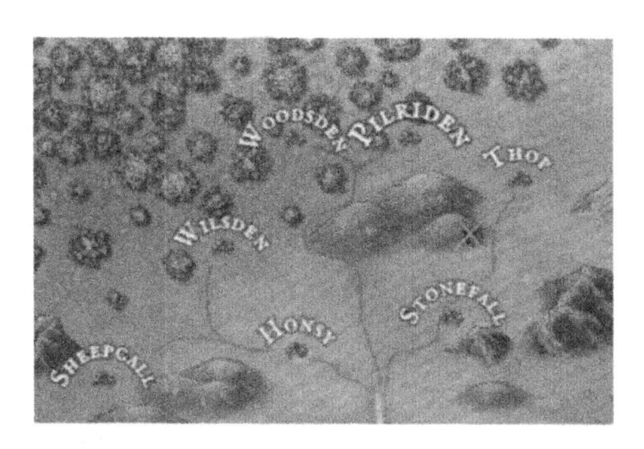

A few paths branched off from the end of the northern transit road, one heading to the right towards Stonefall, while another continued the course of the now-nauseating transit road, likely leading towards Woodsden and Pilriden. A third path went to the left towards the village of Honsy.

The terrain was fairly flat grassland, with low rolling hills stretching off into the distance. To the right some foothills climbed up into large mountains, growing taller and more snow-capped as they marched off into the north. Directly north of them the hills grew larger, with some steep crags visible from their path.

The Heirs set off down the path that led to Stonefall, chatting as they walked. Nathan listened in, reflecting as to how this was different from his last experience walking around the countryside of Davrar. Back then, he'd been in the company of a crowd of villagers with Adventurers escorting them. The atmosphere had been tense, and Nathan himself was still reeling from his experiences with Taeol. The near loss of agency. The violence against the slavers... he hadn't really processed it and hadn't appreciated *Davrar* as much. He'd been lost, unable to square his life on Earth against his new crusade against Giantsrest.

Now, he'd figured a lot of that out. It felt more like he was on a hike with his friends, exploring some wilderness. Actually, that was a bit weird.

Nathan jumped into the conversation. "Why aren't the towns closer to Gemore? Seems difficult to ship food so far. Wouldn't you want them closer?

Sarah looked back at Nathan. "Old Gemore is dangerous. The town locations are picked for being defendable, not transport. Dimensional bags, remember?"

Right. I thought before that those would really change the normal way things worked. It's harder to move people *around Davrar, but easier to move* things. *I'm pretty sure you can't put people in a bag of holding, or else people would like, live in them. You wouldn't need land to build a city on, just a defensible cave with a bunch of dimensional pockets for everybody to live inside.*

Nathan joined the Heirs in conversation as they walked away from Old Gemore. They were hoping to pass Stonefall by the afternoon and make camp when they were relatively close to the tomb, so they could reach it in the mid-morning and have most of the day to clear it without worrying about the sun setting.

It was tempting to stay in Stonefall, since all of the villages maintained barracks where Adventurers could stay. But it would delay their arrival by another day, and Aarl speculated that part of the test was seeing if they could tolerate the discomfort of camping in the open or if they would plan their travel around the villages.

So, they kept on, talking about everything from food to Adventurer politics.

"I am not a real big fan of how duels work. It seems like an awful way to resolve disputes." Nathan declared, glancing around to see if any of the Heirs would argue.

Sarah frowned, responding defensively. "It works out. Far better to have Adventurers fighting each other in the ring than in back alleys, or worried they'll take a sword to the back during a delve."

Nathan gave the argument his full attention, speaking slowly to be sure he didn't give unintentional offense. "You're saying the alternatives are worse, not that the duels themselves are good. What if you had an alternative that addressed the tensions without creating the problems of the duels?"

Aarl stepped into the conversation, defending his sister. "I'm not sure what another alternative would be. The duels came from the early Adventurers, when there wasn't another way to solve a problem. The traditions of respect and limiting conflict have done the Adventurers well."

Nathan quirked his lips, not satisfied by their comments. It seemed more like they were defending the way Adventurer duels worked because Gemore was their home, and they instinctively got defensive when it was criticized. As far as he could tell, they hadn't stopped to *think* about if duels were a good way to resolve disputes or not.

Changing your views when somebody points out you're wrong is a skill, and not an easy one. But the first step is engaging with your own beliefs and picking apart why *you believe them.*

Oftentimes, he forgot that the Heirs were still fairly young. They had trained rigorously for life-or-death combat for years, and been raised to be decent, thoughtful people. But sometimes Nathan was reminded that they were on average around twenty years old. Like when they defended a system of *social-pressure guided duels as a way to solve problems!*

Jesus. That worked out so well *for Galois. Maybe this is something I should try to talk through in more detail.*

So, he approached the problem differently. "The duel system seems like it can easily be abused – if you're stronger than somebody, then you don't have to worry about causing them problems."

Khachi responded. "If you clearly abuse the system, then the Adventurers will see it and stop your abuse. A stronger friend of the abused party will challenge the abuser. If the problem is severe enough, then many may do so. Adventurers take care of their own."

Nathan struggled to hold onto his temper at the even response. "I can think of a half-dozen ways that could go wrong – what if the person being abused isn't popular? Or the person being abusive *is* popular, and generally liked? Popular people punching down is core part of how most social structures *work.* Maybe somebody has skills for manipulating other Adventurers, and makes the situation seem fair when it's not. The court of public opinion is easily swayed."

Sarah was the one to respond, twisting her mouth in disdain. "Social manipulation skills are viewed with disgust. You won't be totally shunned for having one, but it'll make everybody *far* more distrustful of you. And word will spread if you have one."

I guess [Earnestness] does technically count, even if nobody except Faline has picked up on it. I don't think she'll spread it around, given I'm pretty sure she's got multiple social manipulation skills of her own.

Regardless, Sarah's argument didn't convince Nathan. "Okay, so you have to be clever – people hide their skills anyway. I bet it's common to accuse people of having a manipulation skill to discredit them."

Aarl and Khachi tried to speak at the same time, and after a glance, Aarl was the one to reply to Nathan. "Higher-leveled, more competent adventurers *should* have more social pull than anybody else. They are more capable of defending people and solving problems than anybody else, so they've *earned* the right to place the targets."

Nathan couldn't stop the next words from slipping out. "Well, you're on top of the totem pole because of your parents. Would you think the same way if you were from the villages, without your inherited Insights?"

He took a deep breath. "I know that came out accusatory. I don't mean to say you're taking advantage of the unfair social structure, but try to look at it from the perspective of others. What happens if you're unpopular for a reason that isn't your fault? Like, for example, I got into an argument with Simla the other day. He could probably tell bad stories about me, shift the narrative so that people would think *he* was in the right in any future conflict? I'm insulated from that because of being friends with you, but without that social weight I'd have to be wary of getting unfairly abused, because my only recourse would be to challenge him to a duel."

The Heirs were looking a bit conflicted, with Khachi especially wearing a thoughtful frown. None of them seemed ready to speak yet, so Nathan continued.

"I think it would be helpful for everybody to spend a few weeks as a social pariah at some point in their life. It's pretty awful, but that's the *point*. To really judge a social structure you need to be at the bottom of it."

It also does wonders for empathy and emotional toughness.

Nathan realized his temper was running away and took a moment to tamp it down and reflect on his past words. But he didn't feel like he was wrong and wanted to keep talking about issues with the dueling system. "To take another angle, half of the Adventurers in the Guild support Sudraiel's training course and the other half think it's discarding valuable traditions. What happens when those two camps disagree?

"Can the duels resolve *that*? It seems too big to solve with one or two duels – it's a dispute between groups, not individuals. Without a legal, formal means to resolve differences, enmity might keep building until you get something like a *civil wa*r, especially since the duels encourage violence as a way to solve disputes. I don't want to see Adventurers fighting one another in the streets over what's better for Gemore. It's good that the duels are explicitly nonlethal with very few exceptions, though I think it encourages some dumb posturing."

The Heirs continued to listen and Nathan thought he might be getting through to Khachi and Stella, though Stella hadn't said a lot and might just be getting bored of the whole conversation – mage duels were quite rare after all.

Khachi spoke next. "My mother has expressed some similar views, though not as loudly. She has managed to ignore dueling by being strong enough that nobody is willing to court her anger." He chuckled slightly. "I remember a few years ago when Kozar was complaining about her refusing his challenge, so she killed a Castlebear single-handedly within sight of the city walls."

Aarl spoke quietly. "Stanel was a prolific duelist. Said it was the fastest way to make enemies into friends. He met our mother that way." He gave his sister a quieting hand gesture.

It didn't work. Sarah seemed to have reached a boiling point, and she yelled at Nathan. "You're talking to us as if *we* would abuse these rules! Don't imply that, even as a game, or we might *really* have a reason to duel. Nathan, you know us, do you truly think we would do such things?"

Nathan stopped walking and looked at Sarah. He tilted his head a bit. "If a system relies on the people within it to be good, then bad people will use the system to abuse the good people. I don't think you are bad people, I just think the way Adventurer duels work is bad."

Sarah threw her arms wide, and Nathan noticed her eyes were wet. Tears of frustration? "But then why are you telling *us*?"

Nathan spread his hands gently. "Change has to start somewhere. We are the best of our generation of Adventurers. If we want to, we can change how things work. We can refuse duels to set an example, if nothing else. We have some power and we *will* have more. A famous quote from my home says that, 'With great power comes great responsibility.' It's up to us to determine how to use our power and influence. We can change something, but that means thinking about what we want to change. Whatever causes you champion, decide on them deliberately. Don't spend your life supporting something just because it's what has always been done."

Mid-tier Earnestness 7 achieved!

That comment shocked the conversation to a halt for a moment. The other members of the Heirs paused to parse Nathan's words.

Good. I got them to think.

They'd always been the promising young adventurers, the *Heirs* to their parents. They might not have considered themselves as independent agents, capable of looking into the world and saying, "I think that should be different than it is."

Maybe now they would.

Chapter 53

A Light Touch of Undeath

They passed the village of Stonefall in the mid-afternoon, and Nathan saw why it had that name. The small collection of houses were built atop a steep crag of rock, with a switchbacking road leading up to the village. There were a few watchtowers but no wall around the village, and Nathan saw why – anything capable of climbing the hundreds of feet of sheer rock would be able to scale any wall. There was a sturdy gatehouse at the top of the road, and it looked like multiple large spherical boulders were braced such that they could be rolled down the steep incline. There were more rocks piled along the ledge above the road ready to be dropped on attackers, ranging in size from Nathan's torso to his head.

Stonefall indeed. Anybody coming up that road is either friendly – or paste.

Off to one side were a few more crags of the gray stone, which looked like they were being quarried along specific veins of darker stone. The other side of Stonefall was marked by clay pits – even if Nathan didn't see any rivers or other water features. He wondered how they got water up there.

Magic, probably.

The land grew rockier after passing the village and as they approached the large hills where the tomb was located. It was still a ways off, and the Heirs picked a secluded campground within a small dell where they had good visibility of their surroundings.

A few games of sword-axe-spear later, they'd divvied up the watch schedule.

Nathan was amused that it was basically the same as rock-paper-scissors, but with Fire Emblem rules.

Nathan ended up on middle watch, which was no fun. But he'd been better rested in the past weeks than any time Nathan could remember from Earth. The combination of good exercise, no computer screens and easy meditation meant Nathan wasn't having trouble falling asleep. He was also in the best shape of his life. He figured he could handle one night of interrupted sleep.

Granted, it was sleeping out in the open, with only bare camping supplies.

Nathan had to correct that opinion as the Heirs started pulling supplies from their bags of holding. Stella didn't have a tent in there, but she had a large blanket and several padded bedrolls that would be far more comfortable than sleeping on the solid ground.

While Aarl cut firewood and Sarah set up a cooking pot, Khachi was setting up tripwires around their campsite. They were nothing much, just cords tied tightly at ankle-height between bushes or trees with a bell in the middle of the cord. Nathan helped Khachi surround the camp with them, covering the easy approaches with a double or even triple layer of tripwires after just fifteen minutes of work.

Stella looked over at Nathan apologetically. "I think you need to stay off the blanket. It's enchanted to be self-cleaning, and I don't want you to break it. You can sleep here though?"

She flattened a section of bare earth with a combination of force and earth mana, then laid a bedroll atop it before throwing a blanket over the makeshift bed.

Man, I am sure glad I'm not doing this on my own. And that the Heirs' parents saw fit to properly equip them for this. I wonder if the Heirs appreciate the value of all this preparation. Probably, since they knew what to do. I'll need to figure out how the hell I'm traveling if I can't use dimensional storage.

Soon enough there was a small fire cracking in the center of their camp, a savory stew bubbling above it. Day became night with all of the suddenness of a light switch, revealing the spread of continents overhead.

Nathan accepted a bowl of stew from Aarl. It wasn't up to the standards of the Adventurer's Guild, but it was savory and filling after a day of hiking. When they were done, Sarah scrubbed out the bowls with a magical cloth.

The Heirs weren't quite ready to go to bed. Instead, they spent some time watching the world displayed overhead while chatting.

Nathan pointed upwards. "Do you ever want to go there? See that continent there, with the white patch invading the black? Don't you want to go see what that is?"

Khachi answered after a few seconds. "No. Gemore is the place I will live and die protecting." He paused to gesture around the dark plain. "I may venture from the walls, but I will always return. I wish to learn of my father's people eventually, but I will never leave Gemore behind."

There was a brief moment of silence before Aarl spoke next. "I want to see what's out there. Explore beyond where the maps lie. But going somewhere where I can see Gemore above my head is too far. I want to be able to return to what is familiar, to hold that lifeline close."

He looked over at his sister, and she elbowed him before responding herself.

"I think my brother speaks for both of us. Though that might change."

There was another minute of contemplation before Stella answered. They didn't pressure her; it wasn't that sort of gathering. Everybody was watching the sky, appreciating the gentle light of the lands above. When Stella did speak, it was quiet and somewhat uncertain.

"I want to go as far as my magic can take me. Dalo told me that you cannot expand your limits without pushing them. I want to keep pushing the limits of magic until I can travel above my head, to the world on display up there. I want to see what causes that blight we see in the sky. I want to have the power to fix it – if it needs fixing. I want to see Gemore above my head, then come home with new secrets and Insights that can't be found here."

Nathan propped his head on his arm to look over at Stella. Her eyes were fixed overhead, burning with firelight both internal and reflected. "I want to see all there is to see, learn magic undreamt of in the Ascendent Academy. Gain access to every type of mana there is and learn how Davrar *works*. I think I'll need to leave Gemore behind to do that. But it will always be the place I started, and no matter how far I go, I'll want to return some day."

There was another moment of silence as people processed that. Nathan was half-expecting somebody to chime in with a sarcastic comment about Stella's overreaching ambition. But this was a serious moment, a moment to bare your heart. They all respected each other too much to spoil it.

Stella spoke again, looking towards Nathan. "What about you Nathan? Gemore isn't your home. Do you want to return there? Do you know where it lies, or can you only point it out overhead?"

Nathan looked up again, searching for any familiar continents on the off chance he could spot the Americas up there.

Nope.

"I can't point out my home overhead, and I don't know how to get there. But even if I did, I'm not sure I would return anytime soon. I have found a purpose here in opposing Giantsrest. And... I find myself wanting to explore. I want to see more of what Davrar has to offer. There are so many mysteries here, waiting to be discovered."

I can make a difference *here, probably a greater one than I could ever make on Earth. I knew of a hundred scientists who could step into my role on Earth, but I'm the only person with antimagic that I know of on Davrar. I need to see what I can do with that.*

Nathan *almost* told the Heirs about Earth at that moment. But he held back, in the end.

~

Nathan grumbled about being woken up to take the middle watch, but he soon forgot his complaints. The sky was clear and beautiful above him; the night was quiet and serene. He sat there meditating with his eyes and ears open for hours. It was incredibly calm and tranquil, only interrupted on the hour by the faint trill of the enchanted rock they used to keep time.

When it was time to wake Khachi and Sarah for the third watch, Nathan almost regretted it.

I wonder if I can Develop [Focused Mind] into something that replaces sleep. I don't understand the biological need for sleep, so I probably can't cover it with [Regeneration]. It's probably better to Develop [Focused Mind] into something that can be used during Rage though.

With those thoughts, Nathan fell asleep for the second time.

~

The next morning Nathan awoke to the smell of roasting meat. After a wonderful breakfast of thick-cut bacon, they set off for the undead tomb.

It wasn't far, and their first signs were a few wandering zombies. They weren't fast or particularly dangerous. Sarah took them out with headshots from several hundred feet away. Even when there was a cluster of zombies, the undead didn't figure out where the projectiles were coming from until they all dropped to the ground missing some critical, cranial component.

It wasn't hard to follow the concentration gradient of zombies to find the tomb. It was a rough hole in the side of a hill, clearly dug out from the inside. As Nathan watched, a few more zombies spilled from the opening and started walking around aimlessly.

Sarah sighed and reached into her dimensional bag once more, but Nathan held up a hand.

"Hold on. I want to see if my antimagic works against the necromancy animating the zombies."

Nathan handed his spear to Aarl for safekeeping and walked towards the zombies as they ambled down the slope. He was curious about the spell that animated the undead – it had to be pretty complicated, but apparently it could happen naturally? Nathan wasn't worried about being bitten; these weren't the kind of zombies that could infect you. If they killed you, you'd probably become a zombie due to the presence of ambient death mana that undead gave off. But Nathan felt confident that normal zombies could only threaten him if there were at least dozens of them.

He got pretty close before they noticed him, and he used the time to study them. The zombies were wearing the remains of some kind of wrap. The colors had been vibrant, once, but time and decay had spoiled the clothes and much of the body underneath. The bodies looked like they'd been badly mummified, with patches of extreme decay and others that seemed surprisingly well-preserved.

The zombies let out a low *moan* and trudged towards him. He moved so they'd approach him one at a time.

I can experiment on the last one. Let's see how quickly I can take out the first two.

He took a few steps forward and speared his right hand into the neck of the first zombie. His fingers punched through the slimy skin, releasing fluid all over his hand. Nathan's hand was covered in stinking gore, and he yanked his hand back. In the moment before he did so, the slithering feeling of death mana brushed against his skin.

Ew, ew, ewww!

The zombie lurched a few more steps towards him, head lolling. It was slower than it had been. Nathan drew back the same hand, clocking the zombie in the face. More gore sprayed, but Nathan absorbed more of the mana, and it fell over and lay still.

The next zombie lurched forward teeth first, trying to grapple and bite. It had a small body, though the face was thankfully degraded enough that Nathan didn't really see it as a person. He moved quickly to avoid its grab and laid his fouled hand on the zombie's head. Nathan focused on the feeling of the mana animating the corpse, figuring out what he could about how the mana worked.

Weird. It's kind of like a spell, but it doesn't follow smooth lines. Like water flowing through natural channels instead of straight canals – like it's following natural pathways in the corpse.

The third zombie was approaching, so Nathan closed his right hand around the second zombie's neck and *squeezed*. The slimy mana flowed into him like it was being sucked through a straw. Nathan shuddered at the feeling.

I think my limit on fighting undead is going to be my stomach.

He quickly knocked the feet out from under the third zombie, then stepped on its arms before running his hands over the immobile corpse. It was a struggle to *not* absorb too much mana from the undead as he examined it. Nathan focused on the clinical nature of his examination as various secretions covered his hand and flakes of dried flesh stuck to them.

I think my immune system is boosted to hell and gone with [Regeneration], which is probably a good thing. Damn this is icky. There's a reason *I decided not to be a med student!*

However, he got a pretty good idea of the mana flows in the zombie's body. The nexus was in the head, and mana circulated out from there into the limbs to provide motive force. He'd been right before in that the death mana flowed naturally through the body. Each path wasn't particularly complicated, but the fact that the pattern spread across the entire cadaver in delicate flows made it more intricate than most of the spells Nathan had encountered.

Following a hunch, Nathan felt around the ribs and spine again, following pathways from the chest muscles back to the spine and into the head. It seemed to follow the nervous system with some degree of precision. Nathan mapped the death mana, following the nerves between the ribs.

Huh. Death mana naturally follows nervous system pathways. I bet I could give a necromancer some juicy Insights about how the nervous system works.

Low-tier Identify 10 achieved! Congratulations, you have maxed out this utility skill! It cannot be improved any further. You must achieve Insight into this skill to Develop it to mid-tier.

Neat. But this whole process seems really inefficient. The mana is sluggish and seems blocked in a bunch of places. I wonder if...

Nathan absorbed mana from a blockage in the corpse's left arm. The mana started flowing more smoothly, and the arm spasmed, nearly throwing Nathan off as the zombie flexed its arm with new strength.

Okay then. I bet that's the difference between a zombie and a ghoul. A lack of mana blockages. Given that this seems self-sustaining and not that *hard to work out, I bet necromancers are scary buggers.*

Mid-tier Spellsense 4 achieved!

"You gonna kill it or kiss it?" Stella's voice was disgusted as Nathan stayed bent over the corpse.

"I learned a lot from it. I think I understand how necromancy animates corpses now. It's pretty interesting. One more test..."

Nathan tried absorbing mana from a few different places on the zombie, looking for the easiest way to take it down.

Most of the mana was concentrated in the head, but he had trouble sucking it out quickly through the skull. The neck was a conduit to the rest of the body, and Nathan found he could suck the zombie dry almost instantly if he grabbed it around the neck or touched its spine.

Weak spot is the neck. You know, like it is for living people.

Nathan stood up from the corpse and rubbed his hands together to get some of the corpse-goo off of them. "I can absorb mana from undead, it's just real gross. I think I'll ask you to keep my spear for this one."

Aarl regarded him warily. "Sounds good to me, so long as you stand over *there*."

The Heirs looked up at the tunnel together for a moment, visibly steeling themselves to enter the foreboding space. It looked like a ragged mouth in the side of the cliff, with broken rocks guarding a dark gullet.

Chapter 54

A Somewhat Heavier Touch of Undeath

"I think I should go first," Nathan said. "I've got perception skills, as well as resistance to magical traps and healing for non-magical traps. And it seems I'm pretty good at taking on undead in close quarters." Nathan gestured to the corpse he'd just finished sucking the necromancy out of. "After me, probably Aarl, then Stella, Sarah – and with Khachi bringing up the rear in case any come at us from behind?"

Khachi had been prepared to speak but closed his mouth. He'd been about to suggest their ordering, and it was probably about the same order. The big wolfman looked confused more than upset, as if he hadn't expected Nathan's suggestion.

There was a moment of awkwardness as everybody looked at Nathan, then Khachi. The cleric had been acting as the unofficial leader of the Heirs since before Nathan had joined. And this wasn't Nathan trying to take over so much as get the Heirs used to listening to him in tactical situations. Nathan liked Khachi, and he trusted Kia's son with most things. But he didn't want the Heirs to settle into the pattern of listening to him on everything, especially when Nathan had skills and knowledge that might give him unique insights into tactical situations.

Nathan nodded his head towards Khachi. "Do you agree that it's best for me to be in front, calling out directions? I have perception skills and can't be fooled by magic. For now, I believe my suggestion is the best one?"

Khachi slowly nodded, and the rest of the Heirs fell into the suggested order.

Cool. I hope this doesn't lead to confusion as to who gives orders. I do think this party order is best, and if Khachi can't see anything, he'll have trouble calling plays. When I get yeeted into the middle of an enemy formation, then he'll be the one calling the shots. Like where to throw Nathan.

They entered the tomb. The first thirty feet looked like they'd been clawed out of the packed earth by bare hands. The ceiling was low, and the walls were covered with finger-marks. There were signs of multiple cave-ins that had been cleared by hand from the inside. Nathan saw a zombie ahead blindly staggering towards them. Khachi's boot scraped on a stone, and the undead quickly raised its arms, lurching in their direction and opening its mouth to bite.

Nathan seized it by the throat, dumping the inert corpse to the side a moment later. He shook his hand in an ineffectual attempt to remove the squishy gore and the cold, slick feeling of death mana.

That zombie's hearing was better than its eyesight. Huh.

Stella conjured a pair of glowing orbs and hovered one over each of her shoulders. The paired lights prevented any one object from throwing sharp shadows, diffusing more light around the dark tomb. The lights revealed that the bare dirt had transitioned to a worked stone floor. Only a few steps farther was a stone door thrown wide, beyond which the ceiling and walls also became smoothly joined stone blocks.

Looks like an entrance that got covered with dirt over many years, and the undead had to dig to get out.

The tunnel blossomed out into a larger room, decorated with dirty reliefs. An altar of some kind stood in the center of the room, and three passages led deeper underground. Another zombie was wandering out of the rightmost passage, blinking at them in the light. It opened its mouth to moan, and Sarah nailed it in the face with a javelin, dropping the zombie with a wet sound.

Nathan took a moment to study the altar and the stone reliefs. They definitely *weren't* Quazian, and looked vaguely Mayan to Nathan. That likely meant Sklias dominion, which was a snakefolk empire from long ago. They didn't tend to leave the most dangerous or impressive dungeons, so they weren't prioritized in the Gemore Adventurer education. Most Sklian dungeons were tombs of the Sklian mage-lords, who'd had an obsession with legacies. They'd been high on magic, but low on the sort of long-term enchantments and constructs that could make dungeons truly nightmarish.

And this is probably one of those. But not a very rich mage-lord, apparently.

Not enough decoration for that. Anyway, time to follow the right wall. I want to see wherever those zombies are coming from.

Nathan gestured toward the right passageway, then stepped forward. He looked around carefully for traps or signs of magic. Nothing happened as they crossed the room and entered the rightmost passage. In the rear, Khachi swiveled and started walking backwards, shield up and watching their backs.

Nathan moved forward cautiously, looking for more traps and details. He saw some reliefs of a naga-like creature standing on a pedestal overlooking many bowing figures.

The corridor turned sharply to the right ahead, and another zombie stumbled into view around the bend. Nathan grabbed it quickly, laying the now-still body against the wall of the tunnel to prevent any noise.

Then Nathan turned the corner and took a few steps forward into a larger space. He motioned Stella forward to give him lighting and see what was ahead.

It was an ossuary. A long room stretched out, two rows of stone on either side arranged like bookshelves. They were heavily decorated with bones. The shelves held bodies, stacked three-deep. Higher shelves held *more* bones, many of which were non-humanoid. Central tables held *yet more* bones, and Nathan saw a dozen stalker skeletons, carefully laid out on a row of tables that sat between the shelves. Their third eyes were still present, and glistened with a black mist that absorbed the light cast from Stella's spells.

Most of the bodies and skeletons were inert, though Nathan saw one of the stalker skeletons twitch slightly. As he watched, a human corpse jerked, falling from the shelf onto the ground. It lay there for a moment before unsteadily getting to its feet.

Nathan took a moment to kick his shoes off, gesturing back to the Heirs to stay put. He ran forward on the balls of his feet, doing his best to stay quiet on the bare stone floor. He seized the newly mobile zombie and rendered it *immobile*, again laying the body down quietly instead of letting it fall.

Nathan looked around the room again, and noticed another detail he hadn't seen before. He'd thought the black mark on the ceiling was a trick of the light. But it was a black crystal which seemed to absorb the scant light. From this close, Nathan could feel a suffocating *pressure* from it, not unlike what the Grave Tangle had unleashed. But instead of a tide of overwhelming mana that sapped his strength, this mana was insidious. With his new understanding of death mana, Nathan realized it was trying to *animate* him, even as it was absorbed into his skin. He laid a hand against the zombie he'd recently drained, and found that more mana had slithered inside of it in the brief moments since he'd last touched it.

Okay, so that crystal is slowly animating all of the corpses in here. There's a lot *of them. Time to break it I guess? Especially before it gets those stalker skeletons moving, those things look* nasty. *I don't wanna know what those eyes do.*

Nathan hopped up onto the table, avoiding the six-legged skeleton stretched across it. He glanced back to the Heirs, who stood only twenty feet away. They watched him cautiously as he stretched up to grab hold of the crystal.

What he felt surprised him – there was definitely a spell in there, built to shape the mana as it passed through, guiding it into a form that would be better for animating corpses. But the mana was passing through the crystal from somewhere else. This crystal was a conduit for the death mana, not its ultimate source. Nathan got a sense that the mana was conducted through the rock. As far as he could tell, it was coming from farther into the hill.

I'm glad we tested what happens if I absorb mana even when I'm already full of Stamina.

Nathan pulled on the mana in the crystal, siphoning a lot out of it very quickly. His Stamina was already full from all of the zombie-draining, so the excess Stamina manifested as an urgency to move. Nathan felt ready to sprint a mile, leap down a flight of stairs and fight whoever was in front of him. From his past experiments with Stella, Nathan knew his every movement for the next few minutes would be empowered with the excess Stamina. It was a surge of energy that energy drinks could only aspire to in advertisements.

Nathan used [Focused Mind], pulling his attention back to the crystal and the spell inside. As Nathan siphoned mana, the crystal lightened slightly, showing a smoky-quartz nature instead of matte, light-absorbing black. With an effort of concentration Nathan reached past the torrent of mana flowing into him, breaking the spell that guided the diffusion of the mana. Then, he released the crystal and studied it warily for a moment.

High-tier Focused Mind 3 achieved!

The crystal quickly darkened back to black and resumed spilling mana into the air. It was undirected now, more like what the Grave Tangle had released. But it would still probably raise the corpses. Now it would just take longer because the mana was undirected.

Nathan looked around the room from his new vantage point. From here he could see more doorways that led to other rooms. The light wasn't great, but Nathan could see the same ossuary-type rooms, and he assumed that they were similar body-storage-and-reanimation setups, each with their own crystals.

He *also* saw a set of stairs he hadn't noticed before leading down through a gap in the corpse-shelves. The steps were hidden from the entrance where the Heirs still hunkered. A zombie stumbled up the stairs, thirty feet away. Its head focused on Nathan, and as its mouth opened, he realized it would be impossible to silence in time.

He hopped down from the table and ran back towards the Heirs, hearing a deep *moan* from behind him. It was shockingly loud in the enclosed space, seeming to echo back and forth from rooms above and below.

Nathan realized that those weren't *echoes*; those were other undead repeating the noise.

He reached the Heirs and spoke quickly. "Back into the corridor, we need a choke point. The mana source isn't in here, I think it's a straight line from the central corridor, that way." Nathan pointed in the vague direction he'd gotten from the crystal. "Fighting retreat, we decide if we're leaving or going for the mana source based on how bad this is. We've got a straight shot at the exit if this is too much."

Aarl and Stella nodded quickly, moving to put some distance between themselves and the open space. Sarah and Khachi were already farther down the corridor, watching the route back to the exit. Nathan was rearguard, and he ran to catch up while looking over his shoulder. The Heirs were moving faster than the zombies, and Nathan was trying to decide if they should hole up in this corridor or go all the way to the entrance to make their stand. Then, a swarming crowd of agile figures overtook the shuffling zombies trailing them.

They were still humanoid corpses, but they moved with a speed and power totally unlike the slow awkwardness of the zombies. The bones of their fingers had extended and sharpened, giving them a set of awful claws. Their teeth were elongated and split into a jagged mess of sharp enamel and bone.

Ghouls. Oh Joy.

Nathan turned and counter-charged the tide of undead, trusting his team to back him up. He activated his Rage, imagining the social setup that would allow a mage-lord to fill a tomb with this many bodies. It was tyranny that reached beyond death, that spoke of an ownership that could never be escaped. How many of the bodies charging him would have *chosen* this fate?

He was going to *break* this monument to long-dead arrogance.

Thank you Artha, for teaching me to call true Rage within a moment. The secret to this class is that your anger must be deep and true, but never mindless.

Nathan was faster than the ghouls, and his momentum slammed into the tide of flesh and stopped it. His hands snapped out, aiming for necks. His right hand was on-target, and a wave of death mana flowed into him as that ghoul went slack. His left hand was met with a gnashing maw of jagged teeth. The jaws clamped shut on Nathan's hand, breaking skin in a dozen places.

Mid-tier Sprinting 3 achieved!

Nathan ripped the ghoul's lower jaw off. He punched out at another ghoul attempting to grapple him. He had a better understanding of the way death mana flowed through the undead, so when he punched his fingers into a rotting shoulder and sucked out mana, the ghoul's arm went slack.

A dozen ghouls surrounded Nathan, burying him under a press of clawing fingers and biting jaws. He was being dragged down bit by bit, absorbing mana from the disgusting press of bodies but only finishing off a few. Clawed fingers and jaws broke his skin in a dozen places, and Nathan strained to stay upright.

Any time now...

A fireball impacted the ceiling above Nathan's head, exploding out in all directions. He weathered the explosion without problems as the ghouls closest to Nathan were blown apart, while the ones farther back merely toppled like bowling pins.

Exactly what the doctor ordered.

Nathan leapt forward, taking advantage of the fireball's disruption to quickly draw mana from three more ghouls before they could regain their feet. There was only a dozen left and Nathan engaged them hand-to-hand as Stella landed a pair of fireballs farther down the corridor, blasting apart the crush of zombies that were slowly catching up. Body parts pelted Nathan as he vaulted on his hands away from the still-mobile ghouls.

He skirmished with the remaining ghouls, trying not to let them surround or grab him again. It was a truly unequal fight since Nathan's every strike disabled a limb or completely drained a ghoul, while they had to work to even pierce his skin. And those injuries healed in moments.

The only equalizing factor was that they had him outnumbered, but that changed quickly. Nathan heard another fireball go off behind him but didn't stop to look around. He leaned into his acrobatics, kicking off a wall and planting one hand on the floor to aerial away from three ghouls about to surround him. Then, he grabbed one ghoul around the neck, casting the spent body at the other undead.

Nathan was absorbing an incredible amount of mana, and his every motion was suffused with power. Despite Raging, despite [Regeneration], despite spending Stamina to enhance every one of his motions, he was *still* gaining more Stamina than he spent. He rolled into a ghoul and knocked it over, then sunk fingers into a different foe's eye socket before planting a bare foot on the prone ghoul's neck to drain its mana.

Low-tier Tumbling 7 achieved!

Before Nathan knew it, no more ghouls remained. Zombies still staggered towards him, but in a trickle instead of a flood. Their numbers had been vastly reduced by Stella's fireballs, and they were stumbling over the organic wreckage littering the corridor. Nathan moved forward quickly, leaving a trail of newly-motionless corpses behind him.

He reached the ossuary room again and saw no more incoming undead, so he turned and ran back into the corridor to see what was happening with his teammates. It looked like a few ghouls had gotten past Nathan but had met Aarl's greatsword and come off worse for the experience.

Past that, the Heirs were battling another tide of undead that had come from behind them. Nathan almost leapt to assist, but it didn't look like they needed the help. The best thing he could do was ensure no other undead hit them from this side. Like if one of those bone stalkers finished animating, for example.

It looked like the undead coming from the direction of the entrance were more spread out than those who'd engaged Nathan. A few ghouls at a time came around the corner, then charged towards them.

Khachi was planted in the middle of the corridor like a rock, his shield glowing with golden light. It burned to the bone any undead that touched the radiant surface. The big wolfman swung his hammer methodically, crushing the ghouls as they approached and flinched away from his shield. Stella was steadily volleying spells past him at targets of opportunity. She saved fireballs for clusters of ghouls, but Nathan saw her carefully aiming spikes of conjured rock at single targets.

Sarah wielded her favorite bow and was steadily planting arrows through the eyes of the approaching undead. Meanwhile, Aarl stood behind Khachi with a mace and hatchet, taking care of any who slipped past.

Two groups of ghouls surged down either side of the hallway, and Khachi yelled, "Target left!"

He pivoted right, stopping that group cold while Stella shaped a quick ankle-height barrier of force that tripped the other group of charging ghouls, leaving them easy meat for Aarl.

They're pretty good. Almost as if they've been training at this for years.

Nathan turned his back on the slaughter but called out "Watching our backs, call for help if needed!" He heard the steady sounds of under-control combat behind him.

Then, Khachi called out a new command. "Slow retreat!"

Nathan glanced over his shoulder and saw a *mass* of zombies pushing down the corridor. The Heirs were slowly backing away as Stella carefully volleyed fireballs at them, blowing enormous holes in the press of bodies.

Nathan was tempted again to take the stragglers, but Khachi had taken back command of the fight since it had switched directions, and Nathan didn't want to yell, "Mine!" and run past him to steal the last kills while a bone stalker snuck up behind them.

So, he watched the rear as he listened to the Heirs cleaning up the last of the zombies.

Chapter 55

Just Some Really Heavy Undead

When the sounds of combat faded away, Nathan turned back around, examining himself as he did so. He had no idea where his shoes were, and his shirt was *once again* torn to shreds. At least his pants had fared better this time; he'd only lost the bottom half of the left pant leg. However, he didn't think his clothes would be long for this world because he was *covered* with blood and corpse-goo, except for his head.

Nathan clamped down with [Focused Mind] to keep himself from dancing in place to get the gunk off. He took a moment to flick the worst of the pale gore from his hands before swiping the most egregious bits from his arms and chest.

He looked up to see the Heirs examining the recent battlefield. Just like after the stalker fight, there was a look of elation on their faces. Nathan found himself smiling as well, half sharing in their glee and half proud of them. They'd survived another trial. They'd dedicated themselves towards being Adventurers and spent months training to live up to their parents. Now they had *proof* that they could, in fact, be competent Adventurers.

Stella looked over towards Nathan and wrinkled her nose before flicking him a cleaning cloth. "I've got your shoes."

"Thanks," Nathan drawled, "I appreciate it. My clothing budget is high enough as it is." He swiped the rag to get rid of the worst of the chilly goo, tucking it into his belt since he fully expected to get re-gooed later.

He nodded at Khachi. "That worked well, I think? One of us in front, the other behind, the one closer to the danger calls the fight?"

Khachi returned the nod. "Indeed. You suggested the mana source was down the central corridor? Let us go there. I believe you should lead the way once more."

Nathan frowned. "We should at least *discuss* retreating. I think there is more here than Sudraiel expected. Mass animation of ghouls, and whatever those other bones can become? The right decision might be to retreat."

The Heirs all adopted frowns. They didn't want to retreat, and Nathan understood. But they were *thinking* about it.

It's like teaching undergrads again. Half the battle is getting them to think *about things.*

After a moment, Sarah spoke up, gesturing to the piles of corpses around them. "Yes, and we handled it without trial. These dead are not animated yet. We should deal with this *before* it gets worse. Break the mana source and they'll never animate, instead of being a danger to a follow-up team."

Nathan nodded. "Yeah, I agree. Let's go."

Aarl cocked his head, before quietly asking a question. "Didn't you say the right decision was to retreat? Why ask if you weren't going to argue we should return?"

Nathan spoke over his shoulder as he clambered over the piles of shredded and motionless undead to get back to the entrance room. "Because we need to get in the habit of asking the question aloud, instead of making assumptions that might get us killed."

The Heirs reached the entrance room and proceeded down the central corridor, towards the probable source of death mana animating all of the undead in the crypt. This corridor was nicer. The stone was cleaner, the vaulted ceiling higher. The reliefs on the walls were higher quality – though the themes were the same. Lots of figures bowing religiously before a naga, or the naga leading an army of humanoids, or observing them building a grand structure.

After several hundred anxious feet, the corridor let out into a much larger room. The Heirs slowed down, creeping forward cautiously.

They emerged from the corridor, and Stella's light spilled out into the cavernous chamber beyond. It reminded Nathan of a cathedral. There was a wide central nave that stretched into the darkness. Rows of thick pillars marched on either side, beyond which were aisles with displays that recalled reliquaries he'd seen in chapels.

Stella's lights didn't spread as far as they should. The slick feeling of death mana permeated the air, strong and invasive. It curled against Nathan's skin, seeking to invade his body.

Khachi chanted a quiet prayer from behind. "Deiman, shield us from this darkness. Safeguard us through our trials. With your holy light, we will banish this Evil."

A golden glow shone from Khachi, pushing back the invasive death mana. Nathan took a few extra steps forward to avoid interfering with the spell protecting the Heirs from the negative effects of the darkness. The divinely generated mana spread further, revealing a towering but motionless form at the other end of the room. Nathan looked back at his teammates and reflected on the picture they cast.

Four adventurers, striding into darkness. Fire flickered from Stella's hands, and Aarl's greatsword glinted in the golden light shining from Khachi's armor. Sarah had a javelin drawn, and her eyes flicked between potential targets. It was impossible to miss their beacon of light, and so they stood straight and strode ahead resolutely, their footsteps ringing across the underground space. They looked like a *proper* adventuring party, equipped with all of the magic and tools needed to cast down the ancient foes before them.

They're drawing a lot of attention, but it's the only option with this miasma. I'm immune and can probably be our hidden ace if the guardians of the mana source are intelligent. Hell, maybe I can sneak past and disable it.

He hissed quietly to get the Heirs' attention, then signaled his intention to creep up ahead and to the right. Khachi nodded, and Nathan slid off into one of the dark aisles on the other sides of the pillars. Close enough to be within easy rescue distance, far enough to be outside of the bright light radiating out from the Heirs.

I bet if I dropped [Lecturing] right now, I could pick up a [Quiet Footfalls] or something. Probably not worth it – stealth is useful, but only situationally and not something I'm focused on. I know how to walk quietly with bare feet on solid stone. Balls of the feet, don't slide.

Nathan stayed ahead of the Heirs, straining his ears and eyes for signs of motion or hints as to the locus of mana. With his back turned to the light from the Heirs, his eyes quickly adapted to the darkness. He sunk into [Focused Mind], peering towards the far end of the room. Past the death mana in the air, details emerged from the gloom.

The space normally occupied by the altar in a Catholic cathedral was dominated by a gray marble statue. *Surprise, surprise* – it was a giant snake man. The naga's lower body was all coiled snake, while where the head would be on a normal snake a humanoid torso emerged, holding an enormous staff. The statue was colossal, reaching two thirds of the way to the sixty-foot ceiling, its face lost in the darkness.

On either side of the statue were a series of shadowed alcoves where the aisles angled towards the central space. The death mana clung to those alcoves especially closely, hiding what was within. Nathan squinted past the magical darkness, seeing shadowed shapes within. Something about those shapes struck him as important.

As the Heirs advanced and gave the light a better angle, Nathan could make out the figures inside. They were suits of blackened full plate, each holding a bared longsword against their shoulders while a shield rested against their knees. One of the heads turned slightly, following the Heirs as they walked towards the giant statue.

Mid-tier Notice 5 achieved!

Nathan plastered himself against the wall and scooted forward with alacrity, trying to stay out of the armor's line of sight.

Bet there are undead under the armor. I dunno, some sort of disciplined ghoul. Draugr? Grave guard? Bone knight? Whatever – grave guard for now.

The Heirs could see the giant snake clearly now and were examining it from twenty feet away. Nathan scooted around the corner where the first armored figure lurked and grabbed it around the neck with both hands to yank off the helmet, activating Rage as he did so.

Not gonna ambush my friends today. Get counter-ambushed, nerd!

The armor was enchanted somehow, and it resisted Nathan's Rage and Stamina-enhanced strength for a moment before some critical part of the enchantment gave way. He tore the helmet from the armor to reveal a grinning skull carved with delicate symbols. The body started to move, raising the sword to strike at Nathan. He stuck his fingers through the eyeholes of the skull and pulled both physically and with his antimagic.

Nathan absorbed a torrent of concentrated death mana as the armored skeleton lurched forward, taken off balance by Nathan's firm grip on the inside of its face. It tried to bring its sword down, but Nathan ducked close and almost hugged the figure, feeling its movements weaken as he continued to drain the mana. The head was still the focus of the necromantic mana, even without a brain or remnants of a nervous system.

Good. Time to collect some skulls, and maybe look for a skull god who needs a few!

Nathan should have carefully lowered the suit of heavy armor to the ground, but he was too immersed in the thrill of imminent battle to care about that. The other guards crept from their alcoves, advancing on the Heirs while they examined the statue. The grave guard Nathan had ambushed was falling to the ground when Khachi snapped out a quick command.

"Shield up!" The wolfman stepped forward while chanting rapidly.

The *clatter* of the grave guard's armor hitting the ground was drowned out by the sound of impact as the statue struck out with its staff. The blow was enormous, and Stella's quickly formed force shield only slowed the blow before it impacted Khachi's upraised shield, which already glowed with golden light.

The cleric bent under the blow, but he did not break. Sarah's javelin shattered against the statue's face as it bent down from above, smiling cruelly at the Heirs.

Nathan yelled out, "Foes from the sides!" He ran towards the exposed backs of the armored undead as the Heirs began a hasty retreat from the giant *and apparently mobile* statue.

I really don't know what else I expected. Looks fun as hell to fight though!

Nathan tackled the closest grave guard, slamming his shoulder into its backplate so they both went down in a tumble. He grabbed at its helmet, repeating his trick of tearing it off to get at the juicy death magic. The armored figure struggled under him with incredible strength, catching Nathan in the side with an elbow that cracked ribs and almost tossed him away. His death grip on the undead's spine kept him attached, and Nathan held on as the Guard's motions quickly stilled. It was extremely satisfying to literally *drain the motive force* out of your enemies.

Then, another grave guard brought its sword down on Nathan's back. It held the enchanted blade in a two-handed reversed grip, and the blade tore through Nathan's spine and into the ground below. He was pinned like a bug, cut off from all feeling in his lower half.

Fuuuck.

"Help!" he screamed out, desperately reaching back to push the undead off of him. He had no leverage, no ability to push with his legs. His Rage flared white-hot, and his Stamina dropped precipitously as Nathan struggled, feeling his [Regeneration] fail to heal around the metal object embedded in his spine.

The enchantments in the blade flickered and died as he absorbed the mana, but they'd already done their job in allowing the blade to shear through reinforced bone and body. He pushed himself up with one arm, reaching back with the other to grab at the hands holding the sword that still pinned him to the ground.

Stamina: 422/530

He looked towards the Heirs, hoping for salvation. Aarl was a veritable whirlwind of blades, holding off four grave guards that had appeared from the other side of the chamber. He'd taken down one in the initial exchange, leaving an enormous ax embedded in its helmet. Stella was busy fending off magical attacks the statue was firing from its staff, using wind to blow aside a broad spray of darkened needles, before conjuring another shield to deflect a strike from the giant staff's full reach. She retaliated with a fireball that didn't faze the statute in the slightest. Khachi had his hands full blocking bolts of darkness flying from the statue's eyes and defending against two *more* grave guards.

But Sarah... Sarah turned towards Nathan's yell. Khachi's shield flashed with golden light, and when she saw what had happened her whole body sharpened. She reached into her pouch and pulled free a hammer. A heavy mallet, really. She wound up and took a step forward, hurling the hammer overhand in Nathan's direction like a pitcher delivering a fastball.

Nathan braced, ready to push and roll as the hammer spun twice and smashed into the undead holding him down. It lurched back, letting go of the sword. Nathan pushed up with both hands, rolling his torso to free the sword from the stone beneath him. He reached back and grabbed the blade, ripping it out of his back. The grave guard loomed above him. Its helmet was mildly dented courtesy of Sarah's hammer.

I will rip you apart with my teeth if I have to.

It stepped forward to stomp on him, and Nathan flopped towards it to grab the upraised leg, pushing up with both hands. The heavy undead toppled backwards with a clatter, and Nathan grabbed onto its feet, using every muscle he could control to lever himself closer as it sat up. He gained the faintest bit of motion in his legs, and used that to worm himself up the undead's body until he was almost sitting in its lap.

Low-tier Tumbling 8 achieved!

I guess that counted as an unorthodox movement.

It punched him in the side, causing another white-hot flare of Rage as more bones broke. In return, Nathan pounded at the undead's helmet and shoulders without leaving a mark on anything but the enchantments. He felt helpless, his Rage useless against its armor and overwhelming strength.

Focus. Don't flail. Don't panic. FOCUS!

High-tier Focused Mind 4 achieved!

Nathan moved closer, hugging the armor under its shoulders and denying it easy leverage to strike him. He couldn't strike it, but he could still absorb mana. He focused on the sensation of mana flowing in smooth elegant lines through the armor. He drew it out, guiding the flow into his own body. Then, he reached deeper into the undead that lay beneath the armor.

Slurp slurp, motherfucker.

It was a slower process than when Nathan had direct physical contact with the skull or spine. But this time Nathan had *surface area*. He drew mana through every inch of his body that was in contact with the suit of armor. Its movements grew weaker and then tapered off to flopping as Nathan drew out more and more of the animating death mana.

Magic Absorption 5 achieved!

The grave guard had never stopped pummeling Nathan and had broken bones and given him bruises aplenty. But the mana he'd drained had kept it from being an *entirely* losing battle.

Stamina: 359/530

Full feeling had returned to Nathan's legs, and he sat up to look over the battle. The Heirs were still being harried back towards the entrance. Another three grave guards had been rendered immobile, leaving four to continue harassing the Heirs as the giant statue slithered after them with the grating of stone against stone.

I wonder...

Nathan stood up, sparing a moment for the now-empty dais on which the giant naga statute had rested. There was a black crystal there, but it wasn't the source of the death mana. The flow of mana in the room pulsed away from the statue pursuing the heirs.

So, Nathan shrugged and began sprinting towards it.

Let's see how easy it is to climb a giant moving statue.

Mid-tier Sprinting 4 achieved!

Chapter 56

Building a Church to Yourself

It turned out not to be very easy to climb a giant moving statue. The serpent part of the enormous statue was covered in rough stone scales that slithered against each other as the creature slowly advanced on the Heirs. Nathan leapt over the creature's tail and landed on its back. He ran across the uneven footing, trusting his skills and excessive amounts of Stamina to keep him upright. The lessons learned from Stella's Nathan-juggling bore fruit, allowing him to skip across the rough surface even as it rotated and twisted beneath him.

Mid-tier Dodging Footwork 3 achieved!

The statue positively *radiated* death magic. It wasn't in the concentrated and overwhelming waves that the Grave Tangle had unleashed, but it was like every inch of the creature was a fog machine for slimy black mana. Just being near it had Nathan's Stamina steadily ticking up.

He reached the vertical part of the snake, and Nathan's job got a lot harder. He tried to grab hold and pull himself up the body to reach its head, but it was all he could do to hang on as the body above him twisted and shifted. He plastered himself to the snake's body, feeling scrapes accumulate as the rough stone moved beneath him.

Okay, that's a sensitive spot, ouch. On the other hand, I'm drawing out a lot *of mana. Hundreds at least, probably thousands if I stay here for any length of time. Behold, my most dangerous battle strategy against animated statues, leech mode!*

Stamina: 398/530

The body above him twisted alarmingly, and Nathan looked up to see the naga's stone face staring down at him, a look of perplexed annoyance on its marble face. Twin bolts of dark mana lanced out from its eyes, and Nathan grinned back as they impacted him to no effect.

Gonna have to try harder than that, you dumb piece of rock.

Then, it reached its free hand down and plucked him off its body.

I think I deserved that one. Do your worst, you metamorphic idiot!

The giant hand holding Nathan started squeezing with the strength of an industrial press. Recently healed ribs re-broke, and Nathan felt blood rush into his lungs. He coughed out a red froth.

Beyond the statue, he saw Khachi gesture and shout. Aarl stepped forward to block him from most of the remaining grave guards. Khachi knelt down and whispered a prayer to his hammer, lips nearly kissing the weapon. Sarah nailed a grave guard approaching from Khachi's other side with an arrow to the eye-slit. Stella held out her hands, casting a spell on the carved flagstone Khachi knelt atop.

Khachi's hammer ignited with golden flames that shone across the room. The remaining grave guards shielded their eyes and staggered backwards. Stella threw her hands skyward, throwing Khachi into the air as the stone he was kneeling on followed her gesture.

The statue turned to face the new light, flinging Nathan aside with its hand as it hissed. Nathan spun through the air wildly, catching a single image of Khachi descending on the giant statue, swinging his divinely-empowered hammer down upon its head.

Then, Nathan impacted the back wall with a horrible *crunch*, falling twenty feet to the stone floor a moment later.

He was out for a bit after that. He didn't fall unconscious, but there were definitely a few moments of unconnected thoughts.

I'm... please, that it... not hurt. Dark here.

Nathan's cheek pressed against the stone of the dais that the Naga statue had occupied. His eyes were out of focus, but after a moment, tuned in on the smooth expanse of gray stone. He coughed blood onto the surface as his lungs shifted back into place. Veins of dark crystal radiated out across the stone. Their source was a man-sized crystal in the center of the dais that seemed to soak in what light there was.

Wait, that's...

He deactivated his Rage and sunk into [Focused Mind], almost losing the focus as pulped flesh and broken bones made themselves known. [Juggernaut's Wrath] was still active, but now that Nathan wasn't Raging, it was harder to ignore his wounds. He *focused* past the innumerable discomforts, needing to clear his mind and get himself healed as quickly as possible.

Nathan squirmed his body over to the nearest veins of crystal, his broken bones clicking as he moved. His thoughts were clearer and his body was getting progressively more mobile as [Regeneration] restored his body. However, his Stamina continued to dwindle from the full-body healing.

Stamina: 125/530

High-tier Regeneration 5 achieved!

The veins of crystal looked like the same material as the one in the ceiling of the ossuary room, just smoothed down to the surface of the dais. As he touched the vein, his hypothesis was confirmed. He siphoned off some mana from the vein, but the majority flowed underneath the surface of the rock. He looked towards the protruding blacker-than-night crystal in the center of the plinth and crawled towards it. His movements were becoming easier, though his left shoulder and ribs were still a mess and he didn't trust his sense of balance. The blood covering his arms and legs smeared the stone with every movement, leaving a red trail on the rock.

Stamina: 81/530

I think that statue is the source of death mana. It was curled around that large central crystal, propagating the mana through these crystal veins and all over the tomb. The crystal conducts death mana really well, so that's how it was spreading death mana around to animate all of the undead. This seems like the hub of the network. I bet I can suck the mana out of the entire tomb from here. Stop any more undead from animating and heal myself up.

Congratulations, you have Developed the [Low-tier Identify] utility skill into [Mid-tier Identify]!

Utility skill: [Mid-tier Identify]
This skill will help you interpret complex cues to understand strange objects and effects, as well as give you clues on how to manipulate

them. Will not reveal curses without obvious clues, and will not help you identify types of mana or spellcraft.

It's nice to know Davrar agrees with my assessment.

Nathan reared up and clapped both hands on to the spike of crystal, feeling the roiling sea of death mana inside. It wasn't spreading out from the crystal into the room, and there seemed to be a spell on the crystal that guided death mana *into* the crystal. If Nathan's guess was right, it then flowed out to other parts of the dungeon.

So, Nathan broke the spell and drew deep on the mana held within the crystal.

It was like being under a spiritual firehose, deluging Nathan with cold and slimy gunk. Nathan's Stamina skyrocketed as he endured the torrent of disgusting death mana. He stared into the crystal as it paled from light-sucking black to something ever-so-slightly lighter. Nathan leaned into [Focused Mind], reciting an impromptu catechism to maintain his mental state.

This is merely a sensation, like any other. It has no inherent positive or negative traits. It will pass, leaving only a memory.

High-tier Focused Mind 5 achieved!

Nathan stayed that way for a few minutes, staring into the crystal as he sucked mana from the entire dungeon's reanimation network. Within the first minute he was completely healed, his Stamina back to full. After that he just sat there, jittering with pent-up energy as more and more mana flowed into him and was neutralized.

I feel like I'm violating the conservation of energy here. This is like... more than ten thousand mana. Enough for hundreds of fireballs. And all that's happening is I'm shaking uncontrollably. It's not even hurting *me.*

Magic Absorption 6 achieved!

Nathan's fingers spasmed and the crystal cracked, fissures spreading through the now-gray surface as his hands dug into it with incredible strength.

Okay, it's not doing nothing.

Slowly, the flow of mana ebbed and died. Nathan exhaled a long breath, shaking out his arms.

Oh right, I wonder what happened to the giant boss monster that threw me over here. I can't believe I completely forgot about it. I blame head trauma and being dropped next to the biggest mana source I've ever seen.

Nathan stuck his head around the crystal, almost overbalancing from the speed and jerkiness of the motion. "Hello. Anybody out there?" His voice was fast and a little slurred, reflecting the nervous energy flooding through him.

The Heirs were standing at the edge of the plinth, waiting for him. Stella relaxed from her tense pose, and Aarl gave Nathan a weary salute. Khachi was the farthest forward, surveying the dais with his arms crossed over his gleaming breastplate. He frowned slightly as Nathan came out from behind the crystal.

The room was significantly lighter without the cloying death mana spread through the air. Nathan could see the fallen form of the giant statue behind the Heirs. Its head looked crushed and burnt, while the section where the snake part met the humanoid body was shattered.

Nathan stumbled towards the Heirs, eliciting expressions of concern. Stella spoke first, stepping forward and holding out a hand. "Are you alright? What did you *do*?"

Nathan gestured to the crystal as he came to a stop in front of the group, swaying slightly. "Sucked the death mana out of it. I'm pretty sure it was connected to all of the ossuary rooms, and the statue was feeding mana into it to fuel the entire place. There shouldn't be any more undead coming out of this dungeon, no siree. I'm just a little Stamina-drunk, I think." He paused for a moment. "How can a statue generate so much death mana, anyway?"

Aarl responded as he examined his nails. "It wasn't just a statue. It was the true sarcophagus of the mage-lord. Khachi crushing the head blinded it – so we cracked open the coffin in the midsection, and Stella burnt the lich inside to a crisp. That killed the problem pretty well."

Khachi stepped up and clapped Nathan on the shoulder. "It was a good fight, and if you've drained the crystal then our mission is achieved. We should debrief the action on the road home. For now, you should rest while we finish examining this room. We haven't leveled yet, so I expect a few more foes or a trap. Nathan, can you shape your eyes for that?"

Nathan took a deep breath, trying to quiet the jitters that still ran through him. "Sure." His Stamina still read 530/530, but the real number had to be *far* higher than that.

I bet all this Stamina could be used to great effect to improve my body if I had the unique version of [Regeneration] I want. Oh well. Just gotta get in more fights I guess. This extra Stamina is bleeding off pretty quickly, anyway. Maybe I can figure out a use for it before it's all gone.

Nathan held up a hand to Aarl, who tossed him a cloth to wipe off some of the sticky, crusted gore covering Nathan's body. At least most of it was *his* this time, which made it less gross for some reason.

I mean, it's just my own blood, not ancient undead guts. So yeah, less gross.

The Heirs separated to examine the rest of the church-like room, calling out to Nathan or Sarah when they wanted somebody to take a better look at things. Aarl probed around the alcoves with a long wooden pole while Stella examined the now-gray crystal in the center of the pedestal. She whistled, and everybody turned to look at her.

"You sucked the mana out of this? This is conductive quartz, blasphemously useful for all sorts of things. Especially to me. Hard to get without mana in it already though, and doesn't tend to react well to having more than one mana type in it at once. And death mana *really* doesn't react well to other types of mana."

Nathan walked over, laying his hand on the crystal again. There were still traces of death mana in there, and Nathan tried to extract every last trace of it. The crystal lightened from a smoky gray to a colorless translucent around his hand. Unfortunately, the crystal was still connected to the network spread throughout the dungeon, and traces of death mana flowed back slowly from the network.

He sighed. "It's still connected to the network, and it might take me days to perfectly purge every part of it. It's a lot slower when there's not much left."

Stella wasn't deterred. "Aarl, break the crystal. Keep the pieces big, please."

Aarl shrugged and pulled a two-handed pickaxe out of his pouch. He swung it at the base of the crystal, which reverberated with the sound like shattering glass. A few more strikes and the crystal was fully separated from the dais, falling into a few large shards and a multitude of smaller chunks.

Stella directed Nathan to pick up one of the smaller chunks and absorb the mana from it. After the crystal was free from all color, she snatched it from him and examined it carefully. The mage wrapped a careful bubble of force around the crystal and injected fire mana into it. The crystal started glowing a dull red, casting light like a crackling torch.

The red-haired mage cackled, holding the crystal up and gazing at it like a mad scientist holding a super-soldier formula. She held the bubble of force around the crystal aloft for a moment longer to be sure it wouldn't explode, before dismissing the bubble and tucking the glowing crystal into a pocket.

Then, she looked at the pile of crystals and threw her hands wide. "*More!*"

Nathan shrugged and got to work, carefully extracting the last of the death mana from the conductive quartz crystals scattered around the dais.

After a few minutes Nathan was interrupted. He was sitting cross-legged on the dais, draining one of the bigger crystal chunks when Sarah called for him. He put down the crystal, and Stella pouted but followed him to one of the alcoves where Sarah was standing. It was on the opposite side of the chamber from where he had snuck up, so he hadn't seen this particular area before.

Sarah pointed to the back of the alcove, at the back wall. "Do you see anything back there?"

Nathan looked into the recessed space. It didn't take much exertion of [Notice] to see that the back wall was misty and insubstantial, like a fog wall from Dark Souls. "Looks like an illusion to me."

"Yeah, though I bet it's easier for you to spot than me. You want to deal with it? I'd bet dragon bones to stalker teeth there's a trap behind it. We don't have any illusion specialists."

"I'm an all-magic specialist. Might want to clear the line of fire." Nathan carefully approached the wall as the Heirs backed to the sides, ready to support him if need be.

Nathan sidled up to the edge of the illusion and stuck a foot into it.

Yup. Definitely an illusion. Mix of death and darkness magic, not really all that fancy. Weird to see death mana integrated into an illusion, but I bet it helps when there's death mana permeating the air. And there...

As Nathan broke the spell, the alcove was revealed to extend further back into the stone, holding a small storeroom. Of more immediate importance was *another* illusion on the ceiling, more subtle than the fake wall. Nathan squinted past it, his familiarity with the previous spell allowing him to pick out what it concealed. It looked like a set of blades, ready to slice downward. They were long and thin, bubbling with an oily darkness that was almost certainly some kind of death mana spell.

Nathan looked around for the trigger and saw a long plate set flush with the floor just past the illusion. His foot rested inches away from the trigger.

Nathan had no idea how to go about disarming the trap, so he turned back to the Heirs. "Hey Aarl, can I borrow your ten-foot pole?"

Aarl gave him a weird look. "It's nine feet long. You mean to trigger a trap?"

Nathan nodded as he took the pole. "Yup. Some blades coated with death magic. Pretty long."

He edged farther away and to the side, gesturing the Heirs around the corner before he poked the pole against the panel. Nathan had to lean on it a bit, but when he did, the blades snapped forward faster than he could have hoped to dodge, cutting through the pole near the tip. The caustic mana sprayed forward, tracing parallel lines across the floor of the entire room and onto the opposite wall. The stone bubbled where the fluid landed.

Nathan caught some of the spattered liquid on his legs. It was a nasty spell, combining a powerful magical acid with something that infiltrated the body to cause mass cell death and provide the poison with more fuel, all wrapped together with death and darkness mana. Nathan neutralized the spell carefully, picking apart its component parts as he healed what damage got through [Magic Absorption].

Mid-tier Spellsense 5 achieved!

The whole process reminded Nathan he *wasn't* immune to poisons. But this was a spell, and he was stuffed to the gills with Stamina, so it wasn't a big problem. But if it had been a non-magical poison, he might be feeling very sad right now.

Again, gotta rank up that [Regeneration]. I am 99% sure that Davrar won't let me just chop off my hand and then grow it back to train it up. I have to use the power in a new way, or in a truly dangerous situation. Speaking of which, I have a pretty dangerous and novel opportunity right here.

The blades were starting to retract into their illusion, but Nathan jumped forward and grabbed one in each hand. The edges cut into his hands, and the leftover magical poison ate into his flesh, but Nathan used his jittery strength to twist sideways and snap the blades off at the base. He didn't know if he could have done that normally, even with [Raging Thrill]. But with this much excess Stamina, it was an easy feat. He repeated the process a few more times until the trap was completely disabled.

There were several deep cuts across his fingers, with tendrils of darkness reaching up his arm as repeated exposure to the concentrated magical poison tried to eat him from the inside. He sunk into [Focused Mind], holding off on absorbing the mana from the spell. It was just as much of an effort to hold back his [Magic Absorption] as it was to pit his [Regeneration] against the corrupting magic. His unenhanced body was helpless against the magical toxin, and Nathan's [Regeneration] struggled to replace dead and damaged cells as quickly as the magic killed them and used the death as fuel to keep going.

Khachi spoke from behind him. "Nathan? Are you well?"

Nathan ignored him, watching as the black rot fought its way past his elbows, spending Stamina by the bucketful to hold back the tide of encroaching necrosis.

If it touches my shoulders, I kill the spell. It's not getting to my heart or brain.

High-tier Regeneration 6 achieved!

Nathan released his hold on [Magic Absorption], purging the toxic spell and allowing his regeneration to heal all of the damage. Dead skin sloughed off his hands and fell to the floor with wet *plops*, and Nathan winced at the smell.

He turned back to Khachi, who had been watching him with unease. "Yeah, trying something out. All good, I got what I wanted."

Nathan reached up and disabled the illusion, ensuring that what was left of the blades weren't resetting and that more of the vicious magic wouldn't drip down. There didn't seem to be a way to replenish the horrible magical poison, which was just as well. It was likely a one-off trap that couldn't renew automatically.

Nathan stepped aside, waving Sarah and Aarl into the storeroom. Magical items gleamed on the shelves. "All yours. I don't want to break anything. Be careful of curses. This seems like a place to expect them."

Aarl put on a thick pair of enchanted gloves as Sarah pulled out a separate bag of holding to hold the possibly cursed loot. They were excited but moved with care and precision into the room.

Nathan went back to scrubbing death mana from the pile of crystals, thinking about his role here.

See, it's interesting. I'm providing some valuable services here that I don't expect to see much benefit from – I almost certainly can't use any of the magical items from that room, and this conductive quartz is useless to me. Unless....

Nathan tried to push antimagic into the crystal, seeing if it could contain Nathan's special Talent like it could normal mana. It didn't work at all, not giving him the faintest hint that such a thing was possible.

Yeah, it's not mana. Not surprising. Anyway, all of this will help the Heirs. Maybe they'll give me more money in return, maybe they won't. But their friendship and improved capability is more important than the physical rewards here.

They are my friends, and I want to help them be successful. I hope they'll want to help me with stuff down the road. You don't build a ride-or-die friendship transactionally.

Chapter 57

Random Road Encounters

It took a bit longer for the Heirs to finish cleaning out the dungeon. The giant cathedral-like room that had held the mage-lord's stone sarcophagus-mech hadn't held any more surprises. They discussed digging into the sarcophagus, but decided it wasn't worth the trouble or risk of a potential final trap (or fuck you spell) that collapsed the dungeon or whatever.

They spent a while scouting out all the ossuary rooms for any other unpleasant surprises. All they found were a lot of bodies and bones. A *lot* of bodies and bones. A few more newly raised zombies made themselves known, and one very annoying ghoul that tried to jump onto Stella from atop a shelf. Nathan noticed it first, but Sarah was the one to pin it to the wall with a javelin mid-leap.

Nathan kept his eyes out for any more potential fake walls, but all they found were multiple long rooms full of an army's worth of corpses and bones. This Mage-Lord had prepared for their return very one-dimensionally.

"What do we do with all the bodies?" Nathan asked the Heirs. "Especially the stalkers. Those things are creepy as hell."

"We don't touch them," Khachi answered. "Especially the stalker skeletons. They're probably worth something, but we don't want them to melt a hole in a dimensional bag. We'll get a share of anything pulled out of this dungeon by the scavenge team that'll follow us up. They're definitely sending one after hearing our report, and I bet the Delve Scholars are interested. This is a pretty weird Sklias Dominion tomb. Most of them have some undead but aren't nearly as death-mana-centric as this one. And they'll have the authority to decide what to do with the tomb. Either they seal it back up or go to the effort to cremate all the bodies."

That sounded like a plan to Nathan! He'd dealt with enough of the corpses in here; he didn't want to spend several days carting the rest to a pyre. Especially since the excess Stamina was finally wearing out, leaving Nathan feeling mostly normal. It was almost strange to *not* be full of excess energy and strength.

Eventually, they left the dungeon.

> **You have leveled up to level 52!** Congratulations, you have defeated the Tomb of Hruli Evijas, the Sklian Mage-Lord of Necromancy!

They all cheered, and Khachi made sure to write down the name of the Mage-Lord before they left.

Nathan was just glad to be out in the sun again, even if it was early afternoon now. They beelined for a nearby brook and sat on its bank to eat lunch, as Nathan bathed himself in the stream before accepting new clothes from Stella. Her cheeks were faintly pink as she handed him a new set of clothes to replace his torn and ripped ones.

It's funny how I don't feel very self-conscious about running around bare-ass naked when it really wasn't my fault I ended up that way. Having rockin' abs now also helps.

He accepted some fresh pastries from Stella next, alongside his shoes. He was quite appreciative, and mentioned it, his voice tinged with sarcasm. "Thank you from the bottom of my heart, my most wonderful teammate, for saving me from a terrible existence without food or dignity." Then he let his voice grow more serious, meeting her bright eyes. "But really, I appreciate it."

Her cheeks flushed pinker as Nathan bit into what was probably the best danish he'd ever eaten, for hunger makes a fine sauce. The meat pie that followed was equally delectable. Nathan just sat for a minute, watching the clouds stream by overhead as the Heirs basked in the afterglow of surviving yet another life-or-death situation together.

He looked over at Khachi. "I think we did pretty well trading off who was calling the shots back there. Switching over from when the wave was coming from the front to when it came from the back was great. You guys also took down that giant necro-statue very well."

Khachi's mouth was full of his own meat pie. He wiped his mouth before responding. "Yes. We must not grow complacent and encourage confusion, but both of us are suitable for leading in different situations. I must point out that my own strike against the necromantic statue was only possible because you distracted it greatly."

Aarl spoke up, raising an eyebrow. "We all pitched in. That's how it works, yeah? We're a team. We might have managed without any of us, but it went well because we all did our part." He held out a fist, palm towards the ground. "We inherited the seeds of greatness, but it's up to us to see them flower. I'd say our feet are upon that path."

Sarah put her fist next to his. "We keep fighting smart, we try not to fight things above our level, and we'll walk that path straight."

Nathan put his hand in wordlessly.

Khachi followed suit. "This would be an appropriate time for a team motto, but I must confess that none come to mind."

Stella stuck her hand in last. "Neither do I. But let's not be satisfied with what was given to us. We started high, but we should try to climb higher than our parents could ever lift us. Let's end up above them, so that we are known for *our own* deeds, not those of our parents."

It was a nice moment, but soon devolved to people wanting to finish lunch.

They started back toward Stonefall shortly afterwards, running through the fight as they walked, to be sure that everybody knew *why* they'd all made the decisions they had. It was an excellent way to ensure they could understand each other in the future while in the midst of combat.

A short time later, Nathan spotted another party on the path. There were a dozen or so people walking toward the Heirs. Nathan noticed the sun shining off a bald head.

Oh, you gotta be kidding me.

It was, in fact, the Vanguard, led by Eldred. They stopped about a dozen feet away and waited for the Heirs to approach. Eldred threw his arms wide and gave the Heirs a broad smile.

"Ah, if it isn't the most promising team of Adventurers in the young generation! What brings you young dragons out here? I thought you all were still busy with Sudraiel's training course?"

Khachi stepped forward, which Nathan was thankful for. He didn't want to have to talk to this asshole any more than he had to.

The big wolffolk was also taller than Eldred, which the bald-headed fighter seemed annoyed about.

"We were sent on an assignment to clear a small tomb of undead not far from here," Khachi explained "It was a training mission, to accustom us to the other kinds of missions that Adventurers must undertake."

Eldred's face fell a bit. "Ah, the place spewing out zombies not far from here? We caught wind of that and thought we'd check it out. It's unfortunate to hear you were sent first." He shook his head sadly. "If only there were more coordination among the Adventurer's Guild, it would avoid this sort of confusion."

Now he's just sniping at Sudraiel because he wanted to take on the dungeon.

Eldred's smile was back in an instant. "Tell me, did you vanquish the tomb? Or will we, the veteran Vanguard, swoop in and save the day?"

Khachi glanced back at the Heirs, pride in his eyes. "We have defeated the dungeon. There is no need."

Eldred looked vexed, but he recovered. "All the same, I think we'll go check the area out. Don't want any leftover zombies roaming around and causing problems for the poor villagers, do we?"

Nathan spoke up, a sudden suspicion in his mind. "We're sending in a salvage team later, with a full report. If there's anything missing, we'll tell them to ask *you* about it."

Eldred's face darkened as he turned to Nathan. "Ah, Nathan. Well, we wouldn't dream of touching *your* loot. Which the Guild *assigned to you* by sending you to the dungeon first. That you say we would do so is insulting enough that it might be worth a challenge. I don't take insults like that lightly, no matter how unfamiliar you find Davrar."

He spat on the road and took a threatening step forward as he unhooked the mace from his back, resting the head on the ground in front of him.

The Heirs were startled by the rapid change in the tone of the conversation, but they didn't backpedal. Khachi stood in place as Nathan and Aarl stepped up next to him, readying themselves to fight. Stella and Sarah took a few steps back, spreading out slightly.

Nathan replied. "It's not an impingement on your honor. Just letting you know that there'll be a team coming after us, and what remains in that tomb is spoken for." He hadn't missed Eldred's mention of Davrar, and Nathan was desperately trying to steer the conversation *away* from that topic. And also away from a fight between Adventurers.

Unless they're actually trying to capture us to deliver us to Giantsrest. Well, if I accused him of that he would certainly duel me. And we're ready for combat anyway. None of them are mages, so my biggest priority would be to keep them off Stella as she takes them apart with magic. That would be bloody. I don't actually want *to kill a dozen people, a dozen protectors of Gemore. Even if Eldred is an asshole. But I won't let them walk all over me.*

Nathan raised his eyebrows and flexed his arms as he continued. "If you mean to start a fight here, you should *all* be willing to follow it through. People may die, and you know who will be looking into it. We won't be cowed, so make your choice with a full understanding of the consequences."

Mid-tier Earnestness 8 achieved!

Eldred frowned like a thunderhead but made no aggressive moves. The Vanguard behind him shifted uneasily. One of them spoke quietly, but Eldred raised a fist and the voice cut off.

Khachi raised a hand placatingly. "This does not need to come to blows, inside the dueling ring or out of it. You are certainly welcome to clear the zombies that escaped the tomb before we arrived. We will mention it in our report and ask that you receive some of the compensation for the job. If you agree to enter the tomb and ensure it remains dormant, then we will also mention that."

Eldred relaxed slightly, relieved that Khachi was giving him a way out without violence. "Ah yes. Sudraiel's *reports.* We'll take... forty percent?"

Nathan's eyes boggled and he opened his mouth to complain, but Khachi held out a hand to silence him. Nathan shut up as Khachi spoke.

"Twenty."

Eldred sighed, tightening his grip on the mace again. "Thirty."

Khachi nodded, stepping forward and holding out his hand. "Deal."

Eldred's smile grew wide and he stepped forward to clasp Khachi's hand. He whispered loud enough for all to hear. "Just a bit of personal advice – watch out for people you trust keeping secrets from you."

Oh my god. What an ass.

The Vanguard's body language made it clear they weren't about to step aside, so the Heirs stepped off the path to let them pass. It struck Nathan as such a stupid display that he just rolled his eyes.

As Eldred passed, he met Nathan's eyes with a glare. It was clear that he wasn't about to let his dislike of Nathan go.

The Heirs continued on the path a bit in silence, until the Vanguard was out of sight. Then Sarah spoke up. "What made you fart ice at them, Nathan?"

Nathan blinked, parsing the saying. "I told you that Eldred saved me from the Pack Leaders when they tried to kidnap me? Well, he also tried to use that 'favor' to get me to join his team. When I refused, he threatened to duel me unless I gave him a weighty Insight."

The Heirs blinked as one, surprised. Khachi spoke up. "Kia told me of him and his ilk. They must be handled carefully, and must never acquire leverage over you. Did you part with an Insight? I would like to know which one, for some of the ones you carry could impact Adventurer politics."

Nathan sighed, rubbing a hand through his hair. "Faline arrived, and told him to fuck off. He fucked off, but I think he's still trying to get back at me for 'what I owe him.' But he knows that Faline will slit his throat if he doesn't come up with a damn good reason to duel me."

He looked around, feeling bad. "Sorry about that. I feel like my problems with the guy have spilled over to everybody, and now we'll get paid less."

Khachi harrumphed. "They were out here to sneakily take on the tomb, and I doubt they got official sanction. It is good we got to it first, but I expect he would have insisted on his 'share' regardless. It is another conflict over Sudraiel's reforms of the Adventurers. We avoided conflict, and them taking more than their share will not reflect well on them. Though I'm sure Kozar will cheer him on." Khachi looked over at Nathan. "Kozar Bhola is the leader of the Traditionalist Adventurers, and Simla's uncle. Sudraiel took his mastery of the guild and he's been trying to reclaim it since."

The big wolfman shook his head. "We are reaching a point where duels will be fought over this split. I hope Kozar does not manage to challenge Sudraiel – it would be a bad match-up for her."

Sarah spoke up, smiling crookedly at Eldred's back. "Besides, with Nathan's abilities to get us into that trap room we got some good loot anyway. Between that stuff and Stella's crystals, the official jangle for the tomb is gonna be small fry. I bet Eldred's going to be right pissed that he can't disable the traps himself and swipe the *real* treasure."

Her brother picked up the thought. "And if he decides to mess with the necromantic statue and it blows up, that's on him. There's nothing in that dungeon anymore that can cause issues for Stonefall or Thop, so it's not our problem."

A quiet but clearly fake cough interrupted them, and they looked over at Stella, who was watching her own feet and sidling nervously. "So, about that conductive quartz? I'd prefer not to sell it, if that's okay. It's probably best if it doesn't get mentioned too much either. I'm going to keep it because it'll help me get stronger." The last words came out all in a rush, and she looked up for their approval.

Nathan shrugged. "I don't think any of us are hurting for cash. It's not like I need to buy magical items or even healing potions. And I don't think you guys need to either?" He raised his eyebrows.

The Heirs looked at one another and shook their heads.

"Why didn't your parents buy you the conductive quartz if you needed this much of it?" Sarah asked.

Stella shifted uncomfortably again. "Well, it's not really my secret to share. But they do buy a lot, they just try to keep it quiet. It's *really* expensive to get a lot of it aligned with the right mana types. And getting it mana-free is even more expensive. I might tell them to get even the tainted stuff now, if Nathan will agree to purge it for us."

Nathan nodded. "If they keep feeding me the same way as when I came over the first time, then I'd love to. I'm trying to build up favors to get Kia to teach me her Airwalking Insight, anyway. It seems like a valuable one, but I've got a lot of irons in the fire for that." He turned to Sarah. "Speaking of, your new weapon is getting worked on. Maybe seven days until you can have it? It's probably better if we test it somewhere private. Maybe in the Caxol's basement?"

Sarah shrugged. "If you say it's worth the time, then sure."

Alright, cool. Seems like we averted a problem here. I'm just glad that Khachi seems so adroit at Adventurer politics. A bit surprising of somebody raised by Kia.

They walked a bit further down the road, chatting lightheartedly and making jokes at Eldred's expense. But Nathan found himself mulling over another issue.

It's clear that Eldred now knows that I'm not from Davrar and is trying to use that as a wedge to break me off from the Heirs. The right *thing to do is clear the air. I want to be sure it can't be used as a weapon against me in the future. That's exactly the sort of secret that is a bigger problem the longer it festers.*

He waited for Aarl to finish telling a crude joke about what kind of Old Gemorian buildings stalkers preferred to pee on, and then spoke up.

"So, folks. I've been keeping a secret, and I think it's time I told you about it."

Chapter 58

A Crisis of Faith

It was time to tell the Heirs of Earth. That Nathan was from there, and not from Davrar. He was primarily doing it because he didn't want Eldred or any of the other Adventurers who opposed Sudraiel – like Simla – to use it to drive a wedge between them. But he had also come to trust them more and more and wanted to share this part of himself.

His perception of the Heirs had come a long way since they'd first met. His first impression hadn't been great, but they really weren't spoiled children. They were smart, reliable, and willing to face down death at his side. They were his comrades, siblings-in-arms, and that wasn't a bond that Nathan wanted to treat lightly.

So, he launched right into it. "I told you a bit about the United States of America, the place I come from? Well, that place *isn't* on Davrar. It's not some place I can see overhead. There *is* no Davrar there. No Talents. No classes. No magic. No monsters. No dungeons. We have advanced machines that do amazing things without magic. Taeol dho Droxol, Archmage of Giantsrest, kidnapped me to learn about my world – which we call 'Earth.'"

The Heirs all walked on in stunned silence for a moment before Stella wryly replied. "I suppose how you know all this math makes sense now. But I can't imagine a world without magic. It would be... so dark. No lights. No healing." She shivered.

Nathan grinned. "That's where you're wrong. We tamed lightning with the same knowledge I'm working to teach you now. By running it through metal wires, we use it to make lights glow. We have doctors, and very advanced knowledge of the body to aid in natural healing. I was studying to be a scholar, to push that knowledge forward. That's how I was able to Develop my healing Talent."

There was another moment while the Heirs digested Nathan's words. He noticed Aarl and Sarah shooting each other complicated looks.

"I suppose that's a secret and a half," Aarl finally said. "Got any more you feel like sharing in the meantime?" The question was asked half-sarcastically, half seriously.

In for a penny, in for a pound. This seems like the time to be totally honest, so that I know this alliance is solid come hell or high water. I don't want there to be any gaps.

Nathan sighed. "When I got abducted to Davrar, I didn't have any skills or Talents. I picked up everything that would help me survive. The other classes I could have picked..."

He shook his head, remembering the [Scientist] and [Student] classes he'd turned down for [Antimagic Brawler] in his frantic desire to get the hell out of Taeol's tower.

But that wasn't the secret he wanted to reveal. "I also picked up a social manipulation skill, to help me try to placate Taeol, the archmage who kidnapped me."

I want to make more excuses, but I think that would be counterproductive. I think my best path here is to be honest and say as little as possible. Make it clear I'm not *influencing them. This is a big issue, and I want to let them work through it without worrying that I'm pressuring them.*

The Heirs tensed. "Do you still have it?" Stella asked in a low voice.

Nathan nodded, afraid to look at the expressions on the Heirs' faces. "Yeah, I do. It's always active. I used it when I first met you, and back there with Eldred. I think I'm using it now too."

The Heirs drew back from him, as if the distance would shield them from his words.

Stella's voice was small and sounded hurt beyond words. "You're using it on us? And hid that you're not from Davrar? For this long?"

Nathan couldn't help but look back at the short, ever-enthusiastic mage. There were tears in her eyes, and she bore an expression of hurt and betrayal. Her hands shook, fire flickering in her fists.

Aarl and Sarah were also looking at Nathan with concern. Aarl in particular had backed away and had one of his hands in his pouch ready to draw a weapon.

Khachi frowned at Nathan, but his expression was as thoughtful as it was upset. "Peace. Remember Nathan's actions, not just his words. He admitted his temptation to leave us to the Last Dungeon, but he did not. He has stood by us over and over and helped each of us. We should not react without thinking."

Then he turned to Nathan. "But this is concerning. Nathan, I know this is against tradition, but can you please tell us the nature of your social manipulation skill? It may be hasty to judge before we know what it *does.* [Adept Convincing] is a more insidious skill than [Clear Conversation]."

I'm so glad you asked. I think this is better than if I just volunteered the information.

Nathan called up the description of [Earnestness], reading it aloud. "This skill will help you portray your intense conviction and honesty when you speak to people. This skill will encourage people to be honest in return. Cannot fool truth spells or skills."

Khachi relaxed even more. "Ah, yes. That is not a bad skill. It encourages honesty. Have you used it to lie to us? Aside from where you were from, which was rather a large lie."

Aarl and Stella nodded along with Khachi's final words. They had also relaxed some but were still regarding Nathan with suspicious gazes.

Nathan considered, shaking his head after a moment. "I think it doesn't work very well when I lie. It's best when I tell the truth – which I've mostly done. Except for lies of omission like about my homeland. I told you the truth about what I wanted, and my own legacy." He spread his hands. "Taeol kidnapped me because I was from another world, and I have unique and powerful Insights. I want to control how those are used, and not let those like Eldred or Taeol use me for their own gain. That's why I was so confrontational with him earlier."

There was a moment of silence as they stood there on the path. Sarah spoke up, slowly. "And that's why he made a reference to you not being familiar with Davrar? How does he know?"

Nathan sighed. "The Giantraiders know, because they were the first people I met after escaping from Taeol's tower, and they told me most of what I know about Davrar. I was talking to Artha about it and somebody spied on us. I tried to catch them, but Eldred stopped me."

Now the Heirs were pissed all over again, but at Eldred this time.

"We don't know if that's actually true," Aarl pointed out. "Nathan might be using his skill to convince us of something that looks best for him." He turned to Nathan with flinty eyes. "Would you be willing to permanently rid yourself of the skill and swear, upon your class, that you have just told us the truth?"

Nathan nodded and opened his mouth but was cut off by Sarah.

"That is unnecessary, though I appreciate your willingness to swear." She turned a sharp look towards her brother. "Nathan has saved my life and I have saved his. His actions are how I will judge him. He has treated us with dignity and begun sharing his Insights with Stella.

"When we first met him, he told us he was heir to a tradition as weighty as they come, and none of us weighed those words heavily. After all, *we* are the envy of Gemore for the Insights we inherited, and are called the Heirs because of it. But many times it seems that Nathan's Insights are greater than our own. Can you imagine coming to a new city, knowing nobody, and worrying what might happen if they learned who your parents were?"

Stella blew her nose, the sound incongruous. She scrubbed her eyes with a handkerchief and looked up at Nathan, taking a deep breath. "Yeah, she's right. Sorry I reacted badly. It's just the thought that you were manipulating us this whole time... it hurt. A lot. I shouldn't have made that assumption. Sorry."

Nathan smiled at her. "Thank you. I'm sorry I kept secrets." He looked around to the rest of the Heirs. "Is it okay if I keep the skill? It's been very useful, especially for dealing with Eldred. I think it let me call his bluff back there, which probably kept him from pushing harder."

The Heirs looked to Aarl, who had been the one to ask Nathan to drop the skill. He sighed and scrubbed a hand through his hair. "Yeah. We'll talk about it later if it's a problem. Thanks for telling us. Just, don't be a muckgrabber about it? Keep it firm in your mind that we're your teammates, not people you can manipulate to get what you want."

Sarah and Stella *both* punched him in opposite shoulders, but Nathan just smiled. He held out a hand to Aarl. "Deal."

Aarl shook it, looking a bit wry. "Teammates unto the future."

Stella also held out her hand. "I still want to learn more about lightning, if you'll teach me. Even more so now that I know why you know so much! Putting lightning into metal? That sounds interesting."

Nathan went through and shook all of the Heirs' hands, getting a quick comment from each of them. Khachi asked what the gods were like in Nathan's world. Nathan told him that there was religion, but no godly powers, just as there was no magic.

Sarah asked him what kind of weapon she would be getting, showing excitement and expectation that it might be useful for the first time. Nathan just grinned and told her to be patient.

It felt a bit like a second introduction. And it was, in a way. They were meeting Nathan Lark – of Earth.

They spent the rest of the walk to Stonefall asking him questions about Earth, and Nathan did his best to answer without giving away any great secrets. They were boggled by the number of people on Earth, and it took some time to wrap their heads around a place where neither monsters or magic existed.

It was such a large paradigm shift that it was hard to explain how many things worked differently. "How do you deal with dungeons?" was answered by, "We don't *have* dungeons." That led to, "What do your fighters *do* all day?" which prompted Nathan to describe how few people on Earth truly specialized in violence, and that the primary purpose of standing militaries was to deter foreign aggression, not actually fight.

Stella piped up with an insightful point. "Ah, so that's why the system of duels offended you so much. Not very many people know how to fight, and there are so many people that personal reputation is less important. How do you manage disputes? Just rules for *everything,* like how the guard handles crimes?"

Nathan nodded. "Basically. The law is complicated because there are so many people and so many rules. When there's a conflict you each hire somebody who is trained to interpret the law and then they argue about it. They're called lawyers and we make a lot of jokes about them."

"Uh-huh." Stella didn't know what to say to that. "That sounds expensive. And rough. So if somebody falsely accuses you of things, you need to spend a bunch of money to hire a lawyer and prove yourself innocent?"

"Yup, exactly. There's a problem where rich people will sue people – that's the term for that kind of dispute – not with the intent of winning, but with the intent of costing them a lot of money by making them hire a lawyer. But at least they don't have to fight and submit to somebody who might be wrong but is a better fighter than they are."

Aarl looked over at him, cocking his head. "Well, the more capable Adventurers are treated with more respect because they've earned it. They have more Insights, they can protect more people. They know more. The better fighter is more valuable and *should* win those disputes. But in your system that's whoever has more money, no matter how they got it. Who even makes your laws anyway?"

Nathan shrugged. "Supposedly an elected council of the people. But at the scale of a nation of hundreds of millions it gets... complicated." Nathan took a mental step back. He didn't want to get embroiled in a discussion of American politics versus the ol' buddy system Gemore seemed to have. Governance was hard, and Nathan didn't want to pretend he had answers. "We can talk more about this later, it's a pretty darn difficult topic. Do you want to ask me more questions about Earth?"

Over the next few hours, Nathan found himself talking about the natural history of Earth and his universe. He explained what a star was, and how plate tectonics and the solar system worked. It was tricky because the Heirs had no frame of reference for what he said, but they accepted it at face value. The idea of a planet as a sphere was bizarre to them. If he lived in Davrar, the idea of the planet as a sphere wouldn't have occurred to him either.

Is Davrar a sphere? The easiest way to find out would involve a long and still body of water, especially since the sun doesn't move across the sky.

All in all, they were shocked at how small Earth was compared to Davrar. On Davrar, there was no limit to the horizon. You could keep going and going, and always expect to find new things. As Sarah put it, "There is always another danger over every horizon."

"Nathan, what were you doing in that world?" Stella eventually asked. "Not violence, based on what you said. Though you seemed reasonably capable when we first met you."

Khachi pitched in, grinning slightly. "Not very good, really. Not terrible, but not good."

Nathan snorted at Khachi's reminder of their first duel. "I never had a real fight before I came to Davrar. I trained to fight as a hobby, to get some exercise. I never expected to use it."

Then he answered Stella's question. "I was training to be a *scientist*, to push forward the knowledge of our world. Allow us to do new things without magic or classes. It's a job that takes twenty years of schooling to learn, and I was about done. And then Taeol kidnapped me. I'm pretty pissed at him for that, because so much of what I learned is useless on Davrar."

Sarah raised her eyebrows. "Some of it seems pretty useful. What were you learning about?"

Nathan's brows knitted, trying to parse down all of his academic research and goals into a few pithy sentences. He had a practiced patter on his research, but that required an understanding of things like DNA.

Instead he spoke in generalities. "I studied how life works at its most detailed level. How a baby grows into an adult, and why offspring get some traits from their parents and not others. Why scar tissue forms, and what the healing process is like."

He shrugged. "It's all pretty complicated. Like I said, twenty years of school. And all I got from it was this stupid [Regeneration]!"

They don't even know about t-shirts.

The joke triggered a round of laughs regardless, and then they asked more questions as night fell. Nathan found himself describing the barest bones of the World Wars, and briefly skating over the thousands of years of history before. The Heirs were enthralled by the idea of ancient epics, and Nathan promised to tell them about *Beowulf* and the *Iliad* later. Maybe even *Le Morte d'Arthur* and *The Song of Roland*.

I wasn't much of a fan of the Epic of Gilgamesh. I never actually read the Edda, but I know most of Norse mythology from various sources. I know snippets of the Mahabharata too, but that one's just dang long.

Mid-tier Enhanced Memory 8 achieved!

Low-tier Lecturing 7 achieved!

Finally, they arrived at Stonefall. It was late, but Stella used a flame to signal they were coming up the rocky hill. A nervous villager standing in front of the gate questioned them, and Nathan noticed a few more people had positioned themselves to drop rocks on the Heirs if they made threatening moves.

Khachi managed the whole thing adroitly, and they were soon given a space in an empty bunkhouse, along with some fatty stew. Stella thanked the man who'd brought them the food and pressed a few coins into his hand, before turning back and setting a fire flickering over all of the bowls for a few minutes to warm them up.

Nathan could see the temptation to ask him more questions, but by unspoken rule, it seemed that the Heirs weren't going to talk about Earth around other people. He appreciated it.

Instead, they talked about what lay ahead in the training course. They were pretty sure that this was the last real-world adventuring trial they would face before graduation in several weeks. It was time to consolidate their gains, learn the limits of their newly Developed skills and work on a few tricky Insights. Nathan was looking forward to Sarah trying out her new firearms and Stella getting to the interesting bits of electricity and magnetism. If they spent a few hours a day going over it, Nathan thought they could get there before the graduation.

They went to bed early, tired out by a long day of Adventuring and crises of faith.

Chapter 59

Fruits are Borne

They returned to the city with little fanfare and no further drama. There was no interview with Sudraiel this time, though they submitted a detailed report on the tomb. They got a decent monetary reward, but Nathan was reminded that it was thirty percent smaller than it *could* have been. There was also the promise of more after the salvagers went through the tomb.

They had to declare the loot they'd picked up – though it seemed like the Adventurer's Guild was more concerned about cursed or dangerous items. Stella's parents showed up and helped the Heirs through the process. Kullal advised the Heirs not to use the Guild-offered appraisal service, instead opting for a Knuld named Neverin. The old and bent orange-skinned man operated out of a small and intricately decorated shop near where Dalo and Kullal lived.

Neverin confirmed that two of the items from the storeroom *were* cursed, a set of swords holding an enchantment that would continually erode the flesh of anyone who touched their hilts. Except Nathan of course, but he'd break the *entire* enchantment in the swords, rendering them non magical and cutting their value tenfold.

It was a shame, since they were the fanciest items of the lot, and Neverin commented that they were likely the personal weapons of the Mage-Lord. However, he judged the curse too dangerous to attempt a standard curse-breaking on, and recommended that they break down the swords for their quite valuable raw materials.

Their remaining loot was an assortment of useful combat items – weapons, amulets, rings, torcs and smaller artifacts capable of a variety of effects, ranging from automatically making force shields to shooting bolts of death mana. But no utility items like portable tents, cooking equipment, climbing gear, or anything like that.

Neverin submitted a report to the Guild and offered to buy a few of the more interesting items once the Guild cleared them to be sold. The enchanter was especially interested in a torc that contained a self-recharging death mana reservoir. It was an uncommon item, since it was hard to make and usually harder to cast spells with mana that wasn't your own.

The conductive quartz was mentioned in the report, but Dalo and Kullal made sure that its quantity wasn't remarked over. It wasn't hard, since most people assumed death-tainted conductive quartz was relatively useless and was hardly considered a magical *item*. Just a raw material.

The Guild quickly cleared the items, offering a price sheet for all of the items. None of them got marked as "mandatory" to sell to the Guild, and Nathan noticed that the Guild price for the torc was less than half of what Neverin had offered to pay.

It's kind of like eminent domain, but for magical items. I can see why a lot of Adventurers hate this system. But I also understand Sudraiel wanting a list of the items that get found and the ability to take a soul-destroying weapon or an especially nasty cursed artifact off the streets. It's a standard "governing is hard" problem, and I think I'm on Sudraiel's side on this one. And this way when adventurers like Simla hide something nasty and it blows up in their faces, Sudraiel can point to that instance and say, "I told you so."

They sold the items they didn't want to Neverin, including the torc, for a pretty tidy profit. They kept most of the items, distributing them out according to their specializations. The bulk of them went to Aarl and Sarah, since they could actually use the assortment of random magical weapons. Nathan asked to keep the cursed set of swords, an idea germinating in his mind.

The Heirs made it clear they owed Nathan a small favor since he hadn't received much of the loot. He didn't turn it down but didn't feel like it was fully necessary. And he had taken the most 'valuable' pieces of the loot, even if the swords were cursed badly enough to be unusable.

Stella told her parents that Nathan could cleanse conductive quartz. Dalo and Kullal cornered him later to tell him they *also* owed him a small favor for giving Stella so much. Dalo swore at himself for not thinking of the possibility earlier.

His exact words were, "The thought passed my mind, but I assumed he'd just shatter it! That stuff is as much magic as it is rock."

Nathan asked why it was useful to them and they evaded giving a clear answer. Nathan shrugged and decided he wasn't going to delve into their secrets too much. Might have something to do with their insane mana capacities.

Kullal also asked if he'd be willing to cleanse more conductive quartz or similar materials. Nathan agreed. He definitely wanted to keep building up his favor stockpile. He still had his eye on the ultimate prize of Kia's airwalking Talent, and the more favors he could build up the better.

Nathan *also* asked if he could bring Sarah and Stanel to their basement in five days or so to test the new weapon he was cooking up. Secrecy was all well and good, but if Sarah was going to use a gun while part of the Heirs, their parents were going to learn about it. He'd need to get permission from his collaborators first.

So, Nathan made it a priority to talk to Beatred.

He headed out to Beatred's shop the next day, not planning on taking any special precautions besides being on his toes. Not only had Faline suggested he was in the clear, but he'd found staying close to the Adventurer's Guild offered reasonable protection.

As Nathan left the Guild he noticed that Eldred and Simla were sharing a table in the corner, deep in conversation about something. Simla looked up and saw Nathan, then quickly looked away. Nathan was happy to pass the pair by. He was being careful to avoid Eldred, aiming to prevent any more incidents with the seasoned Adventurer.

At least he can't really challenge me to a duel. Though as I prove myself and get more respected that will become less true.

At the very least, Nathan hoped that the *next* time he needed to call for help, the nearest Adventurers wouldn't end up being the Vanguard.

Beatred's store was closed, and so was Poppy's next door. Nathan stood around outside for a few minutes, considering banging on their front door. From how things had been going between them, he was almost worried he'd catch them in a compromising position. Then he heard a muffled *bang* from inside, as well as a cackle.

If that's sex, then they're off the deep end.

Nathan banged on the wall next to Beatred's workshop, yelling, "Beatred! It's Nathan! Can I come in?"

A few moments later she unbarred her front door and ushered him in, waving her hand ineffectually through the smoke that hung inside the workshop. She spoke distractedly, already turning away. "Hello, Nathan."

There were two people already in the room – Poppy and an ancient woman who looked like a bent and twisted tree. Her dark brown skin was gnarled and spotted, and her wispy gray hair cascaded down her back like a whitewater rapid. She had multiple golden rings and tight-fitting bangles on her arms.

She turned to examine Nathan with intense eyes, her voice dry and scratchy. "Is this the one who brought these ideas here? Come closer, and we shall inscribe our meeting, Nathan Lark."

He sat in a spare chair next to the woman and examined the room. There were even more mock-ups than the last time, and he saw Beatred inspect the barrel of a nearly finished revolver. The handle was a bare metal framework, and Beatred had taken off the cylinder to examine the inside of the barrel from both ends.

She frowned. "Still a lot of dung inside. Gonna need to try a different barrel enchantment."

The burly smith idly waved to Nathan, busying herself with scrubbing out the barrel with a cloth stuck to a stiff wire. Poppy watched with a slight frown on his face, handing Beatred a cleaning solution she lathered into the barrel.

Nathan was about to respond, when the old woman sitting next to him caught his hand in a firm – and surprisingly warm – grip. "Here, boy. I know the toy is shiny, but I want to be properly introduced. I am Herdin Bho, and if Vhala hadn't already given you an Insight, I would *suggest* that we offer you one. As it is, I think we may need to negotiate other payment than jangle."

Nathan's mind jumped to the cursed swords that the Heirs had stashed back in their suite.

I want to learn how to break curses.

As Herdin examined Nathan, he noticed that her dark eyes glowed with a faint tracery of thin lines. Her nose and ears were pierced with more golden rings that contrasted with her dark skin. From this close, Nathan could tell that all her jewelry all had the faint tracery of fine enchantments. She wore a stiff robe of thick and heavily embroidered fabric. It looked almost like a Persian rug, tailored quite nicely to fit a person.

"I'd say you're from Kalis before I'd say you're from Giantsrest," she remarked after studying him in turn. "Beatred told me you wouldn't explain where you learned about all this" – Herdin waved her hand at the gun that Beatred was busy fussing over – "so I won't ask. But it's a *mighty* interesting weapon. There's a lot of room for improvements with enchantments to this sort of weapon. Very unique. Just the sort of thing an old woman needs to keep her mind sharp."

Nathan replied carefully. "I'm glad you like the design. I think it has a lot of potential."

She looked over the workbench again. "Same idea as a bolter, but I've built enough of those damned things that I almost threw Beatred out on her ear when that's how she introduced the idea. Damned mana-drainers, those things are. And they'll break when a stalker sneezes on you and take *me* a whole day to fix. But these..." She tapped her finger on a brass casing that lay on the table.

"You don't need to use magic to move the projectile. It's like a crossbow, but smaller, more powerful and versatile. Instead of enchanting the string to be stronger, you enchant the chamber to hold more explosive force! I'm wondering if we can integrate a dimensional pocket to hold ammunition and empty casings. Fill it with as many of these 'cartridges' as you can make and load the weapon automatically." She paused for a quick breath.

"And the bullets themselves – such an interesting enchanting problem. Like an arrowhead, but so much *faster*. If I use a penetrating enchantment the bullet goes through both sides of enchanted plate! I might need to dig up my notes on momentum enchantments... haven't touched those in decades. But whatever you enchant a bullet with, it'll need to be cheap."

Herdin was no longer looking at him, instead gazing off into the distance. She shook herself and smiled self-indulgently. "Divine blessings, it is good to have a *new* enchanting problem. I thank you Nathan, for that kindness to an old woman. And I think these weapons will become a specialty of the Bhos, even if their sale is restricted. *Must* be restricted. I cannot wait to see what kinds of classes could Develop around such things. They might require specialized enchantments and skills to fight the largest monsters, but so does every weapon." She waved her hands, clearly lost in her imagination.

Poppy spoke up, drawing attention away from Herdin and her rambling. "You wanted me to remind you to swear the oath when Nathan next arrived."

Herdin finally let go of Nathan's hand, which she'd been holding this entire time. "Oh, indeed so." She turned to fully face him. "I, Herdin Bho, swear on my craft and my class to keep all information related to guns, gunpowder and the enchantments associated with them secret from all except Nathan Lark, Beatred Bho and Poppy Miri. All four of us together can agree to bring people into this secret. And I'll bend my *considerable* influence to keeping these Insights from all but those we decide. May Davrar revoke my class if I break this Oath." She spoke in a businesslike tone, but the traceries in her eyes glowed with a brighter light than before.

Then she chuckled, low and long. "For how else will we profit from them?"

Nathan felt a little bit run over by Herdin's diatribe. He ventured a quick response. "Yeah, it seems like there's a lot of potential for guns to be improved pretty dramatically by enchantments. Do you think they'll need them to work?"

Beatred frowned at him. "If you want to fire one more than a few times in a row, yeah. The barrel gets fouled with crap, and the bullets get stuck from the damned powder residue. Do you know anything we can do about that?"

Nathan thought for a moment. *I think that was why fancy smokeless powders were developed later. I know how to make a couple of them, but they* all *require nitric acid as a starting point, which is a no-go given the necessary volume.*

Nathan shook his head. "I think it's a problem you might need to fix with enchanting. It looks like that's what you're working on now?"

Beatred had just finished attaching a new barrel to the apparatus and looked over at him. "Yeah. Auntie Herdin demanded I make her a bunch of barrels to enchant to solve this problem. Took me all night a few days ago. Cleaning enchantments and the like. But this crap is *sticky*."

Poppy handed her the cylinder of the revolver, loaded with a single round. Beatred reattached the cylinder, carefully spun it to line up the round with the barrel, and aimed at a scarred wooden block a few feet away.

Nathan winced, expecting the sound to be deafening at this range. But when she pulled the trigger, the sound was muffled, and an enchantment around the tip of the barrel lit up as a cloud rose to join the smoke hovering under the ceiling.

Oh. Silence on the barrel. That makes sense. Sounds more like a suppressed gunshot.

Herdin cackled again, watching the block of wood jerk as it gained a new hole. "I will always enjoy that. It requires so little effort! Pull a little lever and *bam!*" The old woman clapped her hands together gleefully.

Beatred cycled the cylinder out, dumping the empty casing onto the table where it smoked slightly. She looked through the new barrel. "Huh. I think that might have done it."

She held out her hand, and Poppy handed her a clean scrap of white fabric on a wire. She dragged the rag through the barrel, twisting it thoroughly. The cloth didn't come out pristine, but it was only lightly darkened. Beatred looked over at Herdin, eyebrows raised.

Herdin grumbled and snatched at the gun, examining the barrel closely. She leaned back and sighed. "Of course it was the anti-stick enchantment. The *hardest* one to make. At least it's also quite stable." She handed the revolver back to Beatred, who was grinning as she went over the other parts of the gun, quickly disassembling it into a pile of component pieces.

Nathan watched the smith neatly sort weapon parts. He had to face the truth here. He'd given Beatred and Poppy the Insights needed to make a gun, boosting them through *hundreds* of years of firearm development on Earth.

But then they'd taken those Insights and run with them, covering an incredible amount of ground in bare weeks. *They* understood what was going on here better than he did – at least from the practical angle.

And now Herdin was here, taking the project in new directions that Nathan wouldn't have thought possible. They were using enchantments to solve practical problems that Nathan would have expected to pose big issues. And now Herdin was thinking about a dimensional magazine?

Maybe I should explain how a fully automatic mechanism works. Or maybe not. I think I might prefer to keep Gemore weapons at an "Old West" phase, and not a "modern military rifles but with more ammunition" phase. Honestly, they can probably figure that out themselves. At least they're pretty limited on ammunition?

Nathan turned towards Poppy, who'd been quiet throughout his visit so far. "How many rounds can you make?"

The short orc shrugged, scrubbing his hand through his thinning hair. "I made some pretty big purchases, hammered flat a method to make the powder strong and consistent. Had to get a bunch more charcoal and buy out most of the sulfur some traders had, but I've easily got enough powder for thousands of rounds. I'm feeling a little useless now, indeed I am."

Beatred was busy talking with Herdin about the barrel, gesturing toward the longer rifle prototypes that were scattered across another workbench.

Poppy pointed at the burly smith. "She's been working on nothing else almost since you first showed up. It has been wonderful to work so closely on it." He gained a small smile, before his face fell again. "But I've figured out the powder, now there's nothing to do but make more. Ah, it's not worth muck-grabber slime to complain. We're happy."

Nathan nodded. "Have you thought about putting alchemy *inside* the bullets? You can bore out a little chamber into the bullet, put something inside and then seal it back up? I doubt an explosive would survive that, but I bet it would be a good way to deliver poison pretty far into a big monster."

Poppy sighed. "I hear you, we already talked about it. It'll work, but not for the first attempts. I'm back to the job of a normal alchemist for now. But I want to know *more*. So..."

He turned to fully face Nathan. "You've already given us such Insights, I'm hesitant to ask for more. We can't offer to make things for free – we don't have enough for that. But I want to know more about how alchemy works. I will owe you a favor for any other Insights you share."

Do I explain chemistry to an alchemist? Maybe just draw him a periodic table and let him figure out the rest?

Chapter 60

A Solid Phase

Nathan pursed his lips as he looked across the workbench at Poppy. The short alchemist was looking at Nathan with a kind of desperate hope. Nathan thought about what he could teach Poppy, and what made sense to teach Poppy. They probably weren't the same.

He wants to learn more about alchemy and has offered a favor in return. I'd certainly be happy to take a favor from an alchemist, especially one involved in ammunition manufacture. But I don't understand alchemy. I understand chemistry. I could teach him chemistry? Maybe I could come up with something from chemistry he could use in alchemy. I think I need to understand alchemy better, to know where he's starting from and where he wants to go.

Nathan gestured with his head, and they moved away from where Beatred and Herdin were arguing over the placement of the self-destruct enchantment so it would destroy the weapon without interfering with its normal function.

Nathan clasped his hands in front of him, leaning towards Poppy. "I think I need to understand how you do alchemy. I need to understand where you're coming from first, before I figure out what would be useful to you."

Poppy raised his bushy eyebrows "Alchemy is the creation of magical potions and ingredients, usually by extraction of magical components from natural ingredients. Those components are purified, processed, stabilized, and mixed to produce the desired effect. The most difficult part is coming up with new recipes. I'm hoping you can point me in a direction that will give me things to try. It'll help me get a unique product and my level. But more importantly, I just want to *know* more about my craft."

And that's why I want to help him. He just wants to know. Know how the world works, and how he can use the laws of the world to create wondrous effects. Much like me. But it seems like he cares more about learning alchemy than chemistry. Magical versus mundane. And I don't know squat about how magic would work in chemistry – which seems to be what alchemy is? I lack a basis for this.

Nathan frowned, thinking. "Can you describe how you make a healing potion? Pretend I'm a complete novice. I don't need the tiny details, but I'm curious how you think about it."

Poppy shrugged. "It's not a secret. Every alchemist makes healing potions, though most throw their own style at it. In the core recipe, a healing potion has three ingredients. The first is life essence, usually filtered from bone marrow or crushed meat. Any marrow or meat will do, but that from a stronger and more vital creature produces a better product.

"Then you need growth essence, which can be extracted from a few magical plants with different kinds of alcohols. The final ingredient is just crystallized mana made using a standard spellform. Anybody can make it, though skilled mages produce crystallized mana of better quality that doesn't evaporate so quickly."

Poppy was becoming more enthusiastic, moving his hands to describe each process. "Then it's pretty straightforward. You *can* just crush the crystallized mana and mix all the ingredients together before it evaporates, but that tends to produce an inferior quality potion that won't remain stable for long. It's far more effective to vaporize the growth essence and pass it through boiling life essence, agitating medium-sized chunks of crystallized mana in the mixture along with a stabilizer. You need to pull the crystallized mana out at the right time though, or else it'll start moving on its own. Fast enough to break the glass." The orc chuckled, leaning back. "Everybody remembers the first time a basic healing potion blew up in their faces. At least it heals whatever it burns!"

What? Okay, um...

Nathan smiled back at Poppy as he tried to reconcile what he'd just heard with the chemistry Nathan knew. The biggest problem was that he didn't know whatever the hell "life essence" or "growth essence" was. It sounded like a lot of alchemy was extracting, filtering or distilling complex, *magical* mixtures from previously existing magical sources, then figuring out how to optimally combine them for the desired effect. Unless they were extracting some form of liquid "life mana."

Nathan opened his mouth, then closed it again. After a moment, he ventured a thought. "It seems our disciplines approach this problem from opposite ends. With what I know, we try to break things down to the most basic building blocks possible, then rebuild up and understand every step along the way. That lets us generalize to other processes."

Poppy shrugged again. "People have done further purifications on life essence, it's a classic training exercise for a young alchemist. Make them figure out how to distill it down to the Six Primary Fractions of Life. Some are better than others for making healing potions, but they're all helpful and it's not worth the effort for most potions. There's a few specialty potions that use *just* the second gaseous life extract, which is the hardest to properly purify."

Ah. It feels like we're talking past each other. I don't understand what he means by the Six Primary Fractions, and he doesn't understand that I mean pure chemical compounds.

Nathan pursed his lips. "I don't think that's what I mean. I mean like how charcoal is mostly a single *thing*, while I think even the simplest of the Six Primary Fractions of Life are composed from many of those different components."

Poppy cocked his head at Nathan, still confused. "But they're entirely different categories. Essences have an inherent magical nature, and while they can be altered, destroyed and subdivided, they are a different kind of thing than a base material like charcoal."

Nathan shook his head. "My science is dedicated to figuring out how to combine base materials, which we call *elements*. Things that cannot be further reduced or subdivided into more components. You would use several of them to create a more complex and advanced material that has properties that none of the individual components have. It's not a great example, but the way that gunpowder combines different basic material components, none of which explode, to make something explosive. Extrapolate that to more complex mixtures and you have some idea. My discipline doesn't extract complex pre-existing mixtures, we start from purified single sources and make the desired product in greater purity, predictability and yield."

Here I am, taking a giant shit all over the field of natural product chemistry. It's okay, they can't make their own drugs anyway, gotta rely on the greatest chemists to do it for them. Cells! Well, mostly plants. And Streptomyces. Those metabolic clusters might as well be magic.

The alchemist's eyes went wide, then narrowed. "That – sounds hard. But if you could make a magical reagent from base materials! You would have so much control! How could I get started with that?"

Nathan sighed. He was already teaching Stella electricity and magnetism, and they were making fast progress. But he spent a *lot* of time with Stella. He wasn't sure he wanted to spend that much time teaching Poppy basic chemistry. Or that it was *possible* to make something magical from raw elements. Was there such a thing as 'magic' carbon as opposed to regular carbon? Isotopes? He *definitely* didn't have the tools to start figuring that out.

Nathan held up a finger. "Hold on a second, I need to think about this."

What's the right balance here? I don't want to leave this guy with nothing. I want to help, and I'm glad I understand a bit more about how alchemy works. But I don't want to get stuck teaching him atomic theory, the periodic table, electron shells and the rules of covalent bonding, especially when the payoff is unclear. To properly explain it, you need the Schrödinger wave equation. Maybe I give him a few teasers and see where he goes with it? He'd get frustrated if I leave him with abstract knowledge that doesn't quickly go anywhere. And I don't have time *to explain covalent theory properly.*

Is there anything I can give him that would help now? *And help prove my point about using a base material in new ways? There's gotta be* something, *Nathan, think.*

Nathan reached into his knowledge for basic chemical reactions that would be helpful to the orcish alchemist. Maybe just classic acid-base chemistry? But to understand what was going on, he needed knowledge of ions and polarity. That was a whole bag of worms that led right back to covalent theory. Not the *best* starting place. And Nathan would be surprised if Poppy didn't already know a fair amount about acids.

Maybe – it seemed like alchemy involved a lot of extractions. Extracting magical essences from magical sources. He'd mentioned an alcohol extraction, which was a classically mundane way to extract natural products. There were some fancy ways to do extractions that Nathan knew about. He searched his mind for a good example and found one after a few minutes.

Caffeine! They make decaf coffee beans by doing a supercritical carbon dioxide extraction to pull all the caffeine out. I did one with lemon peels in my undergrad chemistry lab; we did LCMS on the limonene left over. I think it's used for a lot of different plant extracts too. You basically need dry ice and a slightly heated, pressure-tight vessel since carbon dioxide goes supercritical above 70 atmospheres and about thirty degrees celsius. 70 atmospheres is a lot, but definitely possible to contain.

Mid-tier Enhanced Memory 9 achieved!

Nathan opened his eyes and looked up to Poppy with a smile. "I have a suggestion for a new extraction method. Or I could give you some general hints as to how this idea of building up from basic materials works. Which do you want?"

The orc looked slyly at him. "Extraction method. I want to *work* on something."

More practical than theoretical then.

Nathan nodded, figuring out how to explain a supercritical carbon dioxide extraction process. "So, this is a bit tricky, but there's a component of *air* that can be made solid. It's only present at low concentrations in normal air. But it's present in higher concentrations in the air coming off a fire. It's heavier than the other components of air, though not by much. If you can pressurize air with a lot of that component and make it extremely cold, then it will become solid. I bet you can do it with enchantments – it's cold enough to burn you, but if they can make cold enchantments strong enough to put on a weapon it would probably work for this. The solid looks like ice, but much colder, and it isn't wet. You'll need to keep it well-insulated."

Poppy looked mystified, but Nathan plowed on.

"Then comes the interesting part. In normal air this special ice will just vaporize – turn to a gas. It'll look like white trails are coming off of it, but that's just because of water vapor in the air condensing. You can't breathe the gas – it'll make you fall unconscious. *But* – when you put it in a sealed container, the pressure will keep going up as the not-ice vaporizes. Eventually, if the pressure gets high enough and the temperature is about at body temperature, it'll turn into something that's like a liquid but also acts like a heavy gas and is *amazing* at extracting materials. The pressure is *quite* high, so you need to do it in a really strong container. Once you let the pressure off, it all turns to gas, leaving behind *just* the extraction, without any solvents. If you put a grate in your vessel then the extraction will be under it, and whatever you've extracted from will be on top. It *does* happen at very high pressure – just need to be careful that your vessel doesn't explode."

Poppy's mouth opened and closed for a minute like a fish. "I – think I understand? I need to try this. If it works – I could try this new extraction method on every raw material I use to see what I get!"

Low-tier Lecturing 8 achieved!

Nathan smiled, seeing Poppy pull out some rough paper and start scribbling down some very small text.

After a moment, the alchemist looked back up at Nathan. "I appreciate this

Insight. I would ask you to wait for any more. I do not want to incur more debt than I can reasonably pay back." He chuckled heartily. "And I expect I will be too busy trying this 'solid air extraction' for some time to brook any thought of additional explorations."

Nathan blinked at Poppy's last sentence, which had veered off into a florid and emphatic accent he hadn't heard before. But he just grinned back at the orc and clapped him on the shoulder. "Good! Now let's see what our betters have come up with while we were busy."

With that, they turned back to Herdin and Beatred. Beatred was holding the revolver prototype and pointing at the underside while Herdin nodded along, considering. Nathan just caught the tail end of the argument about where to put the self-destruct mechanism.

Beatred turned towards him and let out a frustrated sigh before she spoke. "Well. It looks like the self-destruct mechanism needs to take up most of the space in the grip and will thread up into the chamber mechanism. We're currently thinking that it will be heat-based, melting the grip and chamber if activated. Herdin says it's not too hard to manage with a one-shot enchantment."

The old lady sat back down in her chair, a self-satisfied smile on her face as she grabbed the metal panels that would cover the exposed innards of the prototype. From a pouch she pulled out a pair of needles that looked identical to small-gauge knitting needles. Then the enchanter started scratching on the metal interior of the grip-covers.

She spoke, not looking away from her work. "The trigger mechanism for self-destruct is trickier. We're making a cursed weapon here. I've disabled enough of them to know the best ways to do it. The cleanest is to imprint the weapon at the time of purchase, and then trigger the self-destruct the moment anybody else touches it."

She shrugged, never moving her hands away from her work. "At the same time, that can lead to all sorts of accidents, and means you must break the curse for somebody to inherit the weapon or sell it. I'll modify it to only trigger if somebody besides the bearer holds the weapon for longer than five seconds, tries to fire it, or anybody tries to disassemble it. With the runes contained on the inside of the grip, it'll be *quite* difficult to disable the enchantment." She cackled. "It's enjoyable to be the one making the curse, for once. I know all the tricks."

She gave another few scratches, then looked up and pinned Nathan with her gaze. "Ah, boy. I meant to ask you. The better classes of enchanted arrows are made by adding layers of metal and enchanting each one. Is there a reason it wouldn't work with bullets? I was thinking of stacking up little disks of enchanted steel, then melting lead around the outside to stick them together and make the outside softer than the barrel. Any reason that wouldn't work?"

Nathan blinked. He hadn't thought of that. It sounded like a great way to increase the enchantment area of a bullet.

He nodded. "I've only heard of people putting steel in the bullet to increase how much it penetrated, but that sounds like it would work."

Herdin gave an affirmative nod, glancing back down to her freehand engraving.

Nathan peeked at what she was doing. "Herdin, you mentioned owing me a favor. Do you think you could explain cursed items to me?"

She didn't look up, but her voice was acerbic. "Oh, you want to be an enchanter now?"

Nathan shook his head, even though she couldn't see it. "No. I want to learn to break curses. I'm resistant to magic but can interact with it. I figure it's a good skill to have."

The old enchanter *did* look up at that, her eyebrows raised and her gaze intent. "True indeed? Well, come back later and I'll do just that. It'll help pay back the debt for these Insights you share."

Then, Nathan asked everybody to agree that he could share the *existence* of guns with the Heirs and the Guardians. He wasn't planning on describing any of the Insights of how they were made, just the overall functionality in broad strokes.

Herdin chuckled. "The team of any Adventurer who has a gun is going to find out the weapon exists. It isn't blood from our wounds to have some of the best Adventurers in the city want one. I bet you Stanel wants six. I agree, and I vote that we should also sell Stanel whatever he wants, so long as he promises not to give them to anybody else. I'll handle the imprinting process." She pointed at Nathan again. "That means you need to invite me along when you give the weapons to Stanel's kid. It's Sarah now, right?"

Everybody else agreed, and Nathan got the distinct impression that Herdin had kind of taken over the gun project. He was fine with that. She had sworn the Oath and knew how to coordinate something like this. If anybody could figure out the potential of guns while keeping them relatively secret, it was the Bhos. Nathan would not be surprised if he was asked to bring on other Bho craftsmen in the upcoming months, and whether they could share the weapon with the younger generation.

Nathan would need to think about how he felt about that. He didn't want somebody like Simla to end up with a gun. Though Simla *wasn't* a Bho. Apparently his family was a branch that had made a hard split with the main family some ninety years ago.

Then Nathan discussed logistics with Beatred. He wanted to deliver the first set of guns to Sarah before graduation, and it looked to be possible in only a week or two, depending on how many hiccups there were with the final enchantments. In the end, he handed over much of what remained of Stanel's money, feeling more comfortable *not* running around with the equivalent of several thousand dollars in cash.

Nathan also asked Beatred for an additional custom item, drawing out a few diagrams. It wouldn't be particularly simple but should be easy to make with her resources. She shrugged and quoted him a price, making it clear that was "the friends and family" discount. He agreed and left the workshop, almost skipping on his way back to the Adventurer's Guild.

Oh yeah. Everything's coming together. Between the guns and teaching Stella electricity and magnetism, I'll both power up the Heirs and get enough favors to trade for Kia's airwalking Insight. It won't be quick, but we have some time before graduation.

Chapter 61

Flux Across a Surface

Nathan's math lessons with Stella had been going well. They'd started doing two sessions a day. The first was right after lunch, in the training yards. While the rest of the Heirs practiced their weapon skills, Stella and Nathan sat down on a bench and worked through more math.

The second was in the evening, after they'd both returned to their suite. Nathan noticed that Stella was returning earlier than she used to. She was driven in her desire to understand what Nathan had to teach, and to learn of light and lightning.

He just hoped that it would work. That he wasn't giving her false hope. As they advanced through the curriculum that Nathan recalled, he grew less and less worried about that. Stella was finding many uses for this math in her magic already.

Stella had taken to calculus like a duck to water, though at the start they'd kept the practical examples simple. Newton's laws of motion were simple. Vectors and differential equations had been a stumbling block, but as soon as Nathan introduced the idea of a vector field and flux across a surface, it smoothed out.

It turned out that Stella could simulate a vector field by channeling unformed mana through a space, shaping its flow with force constructs. Instead of relying on two-dimensional drawings or vague descriptions of water moving around a space, she could make her own vector field, including point sources and sinks. Getting the math right was a lot easier when you had a visual diagram moving in front of you.

That was the big breakthrough. Nathan had difficulty figuring out what she was looking at without destroying the field with his antimagic, until she figured out how to combine air and earth mana to suspend conjured sand in the air, moving it around in the flow. Once that problem was addressed, they spent some time going through the different kinds of structures and making sense of the various mathematical formulations.

It helped that Nathan was primarily trying to help Stella learn the *ideas* behind this sort of math. The goal was to teach her to understand Maxwell's equations, not necessarily calculate every random line integral known to humanity.

It was already helping her magic. Nathan had learned a few of her skills because she *could not* keep quiet when they ranked up. Her [Mana Manipulation], [Magic Intuition], [Delicate Manatouch] and [Robust Spells] had all seen big benefits. She was in the habit of celebrating and hugging him every time something ranked up, then jerking away as she remembered that he might break the enchantments on her robes.

Thinking in terms of mana fluxes and stable flows had also helped her to make new spells. The most notable was a beam of air, flame and force that shot out from a sort of stabilized fireball that Stella channeled in front of her. She was over the moon after that and named it the [Flame Lance].

The next big Insight Nathan needed to communicate was how to fit electricity and magnetism into this towering house of cards that they were building. He had tried communicating it on faith, but that wasn't going well.

"You're saying that lightning is just this *charge*? And it creates a vector field just like my mana – but I can't see it?"

Nathan sighed. "There are *two* different fields. Electricity and magnetism. They're related, but different. Charged things make an electric field, magnetic things make a magnetic field."

Stella frowned. "Okay, sure. But if I want to create a charge to make lightning, how do I do that?"

Nathan waved a hand vaguely. "The Insight that we're building up to is that a moving magnetic field makes an electric field, and a moving electric field makes a magnetic field."

He spent a bit of time explaining how to think of electric and magnetic fields in the same math as they'd been using – fields and fluxes.

But it wasn't getting across, and Stella was getting frustrated. They were *almost* there, and she was having trouble connecting the math he'd taught her to the reality of lightning and light.

"If I accept this because you say it, it doesn't help me understand what's going on. I've poked magnets before, but that's not the same. I need something I can *feel.*"

Nathan nodded agreeably. Stella was a visual learner, that was for sure. "Yup. Let's take a break for the afternoon and pick back up tonight..."

Stella wasn't done, and she let loose a yell of frustration. "I've spent so much time learning your math, and now it can't help me! I think of these fields as mana fields, but that's *not* what lightning is! So *stupid*."

Nathan got up, holding out a hand to hoist her off the bench. "It's okay. We'll figure it out."

She looked up at him, nose scrunched up in annoyance. "Will we? Because it seems like a pretty big leap to get from the pure math of fields to being able to *make* lightning mana."

Nathan had a sudden urge to pat her on the top of the head, but resisted it, growing serious instead. "Have faith. Faith in yourself to figure it out later. Let's give this a break for now. I'm amazed you've come this far so quickly. Even if we get stuck here for a while, I've got some ideas to help you through it. Believe me – we *will* figure it out. Even if you don't believe you can do it, I do."

Nathan felt his [Earnestness] *flex*, like it had almost-but-not quite Developed. He missed being "disadvantaged" sometimes.

Stella pouted a bit, trying to hide her embarrassment at being praised. She opened her mouth to be flippant, then reconsidered. "Thanks for teaching me. I'm not very good at being patient."

"I've taught worse. It helps that I'm just teaching *you*, and not fifteen others like you. You pick things up quickly, and don't hide it when you don't understand. That's the most important part."

"Nobody else is like me. I always get bored in class because everybody else is slow. You're good at teaching people."

Nathan smiled, remembering his own school days. "There *are* others like you, and I've taught them. Hell, I've *been* the gifted kid in class. You're doing good. We'll get there."

Then they joined the rest of the Heirs at combat practice.

~

That afternoon, Nathan visited Beatred's again. He was trying not to go too often, but he needed to pick up his special order from her. Kadid's great-nephew Erlan was tending the front of the shop and let Nathan into Beatred's workshop.

All the gun paraphernalia was hidden behind some screens that blocked the back third of the room. Beatred stood in front of the facade, putting the final touches on Nathan's order. She leaned over a cylindrical drum, busy fastening some magnets to a stationary plate on one end.

Beatred looked over at Nathan, then back to the hand-cranked generator he'd asked her to build. It was about a foot-and-a-half across, with cloth-insulated wire wrapped around four spokes that stuck out of a rotating axle, almost touching the magnets.

The smith glanced up at him. "This thing looks ridiculous. Nathan, what did you have me build?"

Nathan had based the drawings he'd given Beatred off a YouTube video he'd seen a few years ago where somebody had built a generator for a wind turbine. This looked pretty close to that actually.

He walked over. "It's a way to make very weak natural lightning. How it works is another Insight. I want to use it to help me teach Stella how lightning works. I hope those magnets are pretty strong."

Beatred nodded, gesturing at them. "They're a forge-helping tool, great for picking up iron shavings. Helmug makes them himself. I have extras, just like you asked for. Here." She handed him a spare, and Nathan picked up the strip of metal before tapping it against a few nails in the table.

Yup, magnetic. Pretty strong too. Maybe I should try to find this Helmug if he can just whip out magnets like this. Later – got a lot on my plate for now. I bet you could make some kickass compasses out of this. You know, I just realized I haven't seen a compass on Davrar.

"Beatred, do you have compasses?"

She looked at him strangely. "What's a compass?"

Nathan gestured at the magnet he was holding. "You suspend a small magnet in oil, and it points north."

Beatred blinked. "It does? I don't think that's right."

Nathan frowned. "Can we test it?"

A discussion later, Nathan was staring at a splinter of strong magnet... not spinning. It was suspended in a dish of lubricant that Beatred had lying around, and just sat there. "Huh." He picked up the little dish and spun it around. The magnet spun with the dish, then just... kept spinning.

Weird.

He looked up at Beatred. "How do you know which way north is?"

She looked at him like he had grown another arm and was scratching his crotch with it. "We look outside. North is the direction where the mountains have snow on them."

Nathan shook his head. This wasn't why he was here, but he couldn't resist it. He sat down and thought for a moment.

Either Davrar has no magnetic field, or it's super-weak or something. Maybe the planet doesn't have a spinning ferrous core? I remember that the Earth's magnetic field has switched its orientation, and it might have gotten much weaker during that period. Maybe that's happening now on Davrar?

I dunno man. File under the "cosmology" category. I think that's over in the serological pipette drawer in the new Mind Palace. Along with Endings, the night sky, the sun, Davrar's systems of classes and levels. Heck, magic itself. Hmm. Maybe I should subpartition that drawer. Bigger issues are bigger pipettes. And Davrar itself and all my hints about what it is are the pipette gun.

Mid-tier Enhanced Memory 10 achieved!

Nathan took a second, thinking back over the conversation they'd had before he got derailed learning the planet he was standing on didn't have a magnetic field.

Right, metal filings.

"Do you have a spare bag of those shavings I can have? That would be useful."

The big smith was still giving Nathan an odd look, but eventually she shrugged and moved over to a small pile of rough bags. "Indeed I do. I must admit I'm blasphemously curious why you want them, and *what* this strange device does." She gestured towards the generator. "It's harder to spin than it should be, and I'm not sure why. I've checked the axle, and it's not grinding."

Nathan grinned, checking the magnet orientations with the spare magnet. They *seemed* right. "That means it's working. Well, not entirely. For what I want, there's one more step. It's hard to explain, but you can help me with it!"

They needed a brush that would convert the alternating current coming out of the generator into direct current, which was what Nathan had in mind for his explanations. It took a while to build, but Beatred had enough metal-working expertise that they were able to knock something together fairly quickly.

It wasn't a great brush setup, and the wires made an annoying scraping sound as the generator spun. Sometimes they got bent out of contact and had to be fixed, but Nathan didn't care too much. This was a tool for teaching, it didn't have to be perfect.

Mid-tier Identify 2 achieved!

I guess this counts as a "strange object or effect," and I am manipulating it.

After getting accidentally shocked, Beatred eyed him coolly. "I'd normally ask for the Insight behind how this blasted thing works as payment. But with how much time I've spent on guns, I think I'll just ask you to pay me."

Nathan paid the rather high price without grumbling. At this point, he was spending out of the various Adventurer rewards and not the cash Stanel had given him, but he wasn't worried.

Money is honestly the least valuable currency I have. I get room and board as an Adventurer. I can't buy fancy enchanted weapons. And anything that lets me trade money for respect and Insights is worth it.

With that, Nathan asked for a bag to drape over the crudely built generator before carefully carrying it back to the Adventurer's Guild. It was bulky, and he got a few strange looks. But nobody stopped him, and Nathan got the device into the suite he shared with the Heirs.

Aarl was the only one there. He had various weapons laid out on every piece of furniture in the main room, examining his arsenal of swords, axes, maces, hammers, daggers, spears, staves, chains and pickaxes. A few larger and more exotic weapons were leaned up against the back wall, including a large scythe, a trident and several different variations on a blade-tipped staff. Halberd? Naginata? Guisarme? Nathan wasn't sure of the names, but they were all variations on the theme of "sharp piece of metal on a stick."

Aarl jumped a bit when Nathan came in, clearly not expecting any company as he basked in front of his polished and lethal horde.

Nathan paused in the doorway, examining the room. He looked to Aarl, who looked back with consternation.

After a moment of hilarious awkwardness, Nathan ventured a question. "Uh, can you clear the table so I can put this down?"

Aarl lunged forward to clear the table of its portion of the display, quickly dumping the set of daggers into the large dimensional pouch he'd set on the floor.

Nathan set the generator on the table, glad to put down the bulky object.

Aarl proceeded to clear the room pretty quickly, explaining as he went. "Sarah is with my dad. They're going over an Insight for [Ranged Mastery]. I hope I'll get to do that at some point, when my own [Melee Mastery] goes unique. She makes fun of me when I lay out my weapons like this. I just like seeing them all at once."

The copper-skinned man was clearly uncomfortable and talking to cover it.

They'd started to be more free with their secrets after Nathan had made his own confession. He knew that Aarl was currently a [Master of Melee], Khachi was a [Martial Cleric of Deiman], and Sarah was a [Ranged Specialist]. He'd already known that Stella was a [Mage of Elemental Fury].

Nathan didn't say anything, just pulling the cover off the generator and checking that nothing had broken during the walk from Beatred's shop. It also gave Aarl an opening to change the subject.

"What in all of the secrets of Kalis is that? I hope it's not the weapon you're giving Sarah. I don't think she'll like it."

Nathan grinned, imagining that. It might be a good joke for later. "It's for teaching Stella about lightning. Here." He spun the wheel, watching to be sure the brushes were lining up. He had to speak up over the grinding of the generator. "Touch those two wires together."

Aarl eyed the wide grin on Nathan's face, but went ahead and grabbed both wires to tap together. They sparked very slightly and gave Aarl a light shock. He dropped the wires in alarm.

Nathan chuckled and stopped spinning the generator.

Aarl waved out his hand. "That felt like a lightning enchantment. Is that what you've got in there?"

Nathan shook his head, slapping the side of his device. "Nope. No magic involved. This thing makes really weak lightning when you spin it. That's it."

Aarl grabbed one last hatchet that had fallen between two couch cushions. "I have never heard of the like. That's amazing. Who did you get to make it?"

Shrugging, Nathan explained. "It's the same weaponsmith who is making the new weapon for Sarah."

Aarl raised one dark and delicate eyebrow. "Any chance I can get something like that? You're treating the women to all kinds of gifts, and none for me or Khachi! I suppose you're helping Khachi with his divine magic, but that's really more of being a practice partner. Got any Insights you can throw my way?"

Nathan thought for a moment. *Was* there anything he could get Aarl? He'd been planning to try to uncurse the swords they'd picked up earlier if he could.

But was there anything else he could do? Gemore had some pretty darn good steel already, and it wasn't like he had an innovative design for a new melee weapon. He shook his head apologetically. "I know a few fighting styles from my home, but they're mostly designed for unarmed combat. And you're already better than anything I know. Sorry, I got nothing."

Aarl reached out and punched Nathan in the shoulder, grinning to show there were no hard feelings. "It's okay. Sarah's really looking forward to whatever the new weapon is. I think she's having a hard time not telling Stanel why she thinks it'll be great."

Nathan considered that. He appreciated that Sarah hadn't told her father about him being from Earth. But the secret was out, and Nathan should consider letting the Heirs' parents know himself, so he could control how they learned about it.

Maybe when he gave Sarah the guns? Maybe not. Nathan would have to see if it made sense.

He was about to tell Aarl about his plan to uncurse the Mage-Lord's swords when Stella came back in.

She seemed more centered after spending some time with her parents, sighing and sitting down on a chair. Then, she saw the device on the table and gawked. "What is *that*?"

"*That* is how you're going to learn about lightning."

Chapter 62

A Growing Spark

Stella was immediately engaged, coming over to study the machine in detail. After a minute, she looked perplexed. "Okay, what does this have to do with lightning?"

Nathan pointed to the two wires coming off the brush. "When I spin this handle, those wires will get charged. Not strongly – you would need to touch them together for there to be a spark. But this device is a way to demonstrate the basic principles I was talking to you about."

"*She* merits a warning," Aarl complained from the side of the room. "I understand the lay of the land. *I* just get shocked."

Stella turned and stuck her tongue out at Aarl but turned back quickly. She grabbed the two wires and gestured for Nathan to turn the crank.

He leaned his back into it, spinning up the generator and keeping it moving fast. Stella started tapping the wires together, giggling as small sparks zapped. After a minute, he slowed down and the sparking stopped.

Stella stood up, excited. "Okay! Great. So, tell me how this works!"

Nathan grabbed a slate and sat down. "So I told you before that when you have a moving magnetic field, that creates an electric field, right? That's what's going on here. It's invisible, so you can't see the field. But I can draw about what they would look like. Now, before we start looking at *why* that happens, we need to go over the basics of how electric and magnetic fields work."

Nathan pulled out the two magnets and handed them to Stella. "Have you run across these before?"

Stella blinked, then took the magnets, sticking them together and then pulling them apart with a bit of effort. "Yeah, though they're not used for much. Not magical, and they mess with some kinds of magic in weird ways. My dad has a couple of them, but more as curiosity pieces than anything else."

Nathan pointed at the magnets fastened to the inside of the generator – they were almost touching the spinning coils of copper wire. "They're sources of magnetic fields, but not a simple monopole. Here, let me draw what it looks like."

Nathan started explaining the basics of magnetic fields, sprinkling some iron filings around the magnet on a table to demonstrate how the filings gathered on the magnet. He spent a few minutes spreading them out, showing how they followed the magnetic field lines.

Now we're in the meat of it, but this is still going to take a while.

Low-tier Lecturing 9 achieved!

~

Several days later, Nathan was eating lunch with the rest of the Heirs. He had something to celebrate – he'd been running suicide drills the other day, pushing the limit of what Stamina and Rage could do for his physical abilities and incorporating a single, rapid handspring into each cycle.

Mid-tier Sprinting 5 achieved!

Low-tier Tumbling 9 achieved!

It had been a pleasant surprise, but Nathan supposed the training *had* been pretty intense. Probably beyond anything that a human on Earth could hope to accomplish, as a matter of fact.

He was still thinking about it, and considering if there were more intensive training drills he could do for [Tumbling] when Simla approached. His team had just come back from their own surprise mission and were basking in the praise of the other trainees.

Simla stepped up and addressed Nathan. "No more monsters in our way before graduation, eh? You ready to swear the Adventurer's Oath in a few weeks, Nathan?"

Nathan looked at Simla and cocked his head. "What is the Adventurer's Oath, Simla?"

Simla shrugged. "You're not from Gemore, true enough. It's the oath we swear at the end of training. It used to be sworn at the first Solstice after the Blooding Patrol, but I suppose that's what this is now, hey?"

He ticked off on his fingers. "Around here, the Guildmistress is the one to tell the Tale of Endings, and then we swear on the Endings to defend Gemore. Not too high a bar, is it?"

Nathan looked around at the other Heirs. Aarl shrugged expressively. Nobody seemed to know where Simla was going with this. A few other people in the room were paying attention, but not very many. If Simla was trying to make this a grand confrontation, his stage presence needed work.

Nathan looked up at the golden-eyed man. "I will swear that oath."

Simla clapped him on the shoulder. "Good, I'll see you there."

I have the feeling I missed something.

Nathan turned to the other Heirs. "Anybody know what that was about? Is the Adventurer's Oath a big deal?"

Khachi shrugged. "It is and it isn't. Traditional Adventurers put great stock in dividing the Adventurers who *have* sworn and those who *haven't.* That is how Sudraiel took over the Guild, to raise the past to the present. When Kozar was the Guildmaster, he would prevent people from swearing the Oath if they were not 'traditional' enough. A cruel line to draw."

He shook his head sadly. "Hear me, but a fine fighter does not always make for a fine Guildmaster. It was a good thing when the rest of the council kicked out Kozar and Sudraiel replaced him. She made it into an application. Any who have Adventured for Gemore and protected its interests can climb to the top of Gemore and swear upon the Seal at the Solstice. And any who finish the training process, of course."

Nathan raised his eyebrows. "What's the Seal?"

Sarah answered. "It's an enchanted stone disk at the top of Gemore. Looks like a big stone portal set flat into the top of the mountain. Doesn't do anything but light up on the Solstice. I'd offer to show you, but it's one *hell* of a climb and the guards would probably stop us. One of the duties of the Guard is to protect the Seal. Every day but the Solstice, that is."

Stella chimed in. "I'd ask my parents to fly us up, but, well." She waved at Nathan, sighing dramatically. "Not something you can do. Maybe eventually I'll be able to *throw* you that far."

"Ha ha. Well, I'll see it at graduation."

~

A few days later, Kadid was waiting for Nathan when the Heirs broke from their group practice.

The old man greeted Nathan by muttering something about not enjoying being an errand boy, but with a small grin that suggested he wasn't mad. They warmly gripped each other's forearms and walked towards Beatred's shop.

"Beatred and Herdin have been dangerously quiet about what they are working on," Kadid probed. "When you first mentioned the topic, you said it would involve an Insight, but I didn't realize it would be this big. Something to bring *Herdin* out of retirement. I ask myself, what could have interested that old crone so?

"And I think, it couldn't be a new weapon, no indeed. She's worked on every weapon under the sky and invented some herself. My guess is a way to make alcohol from thin air. That woman is a demon with her infusions."

Nathan shrugged. "We've sworn to not talk about it. So I won't say squat."

Kadid laughed, then shook Nathan's shoulder lightly. "And it seems you won't. I wish you luck, whatever you're doing. It seems you're becoming a true friend of the Bhos. Most of us may not fly as high as the parents of your new friends, but we're the blood of Gemore. Stay safe, Nathan Lark."

With that, Nathan walked into Beatred's shop. Kadid closed and locked the door behind him as Nathan entered the workshop.

Poppy, Herdin and Beatred were all sitting around a workbench towards the back, admiring the items on the table.

Nathan had only been here once since he'd picked up the generator from Beatred, and it had primarily been to learn about curses from Herdin. As part of that, she'd given him a lesson on how enchantments worked. They *weren't* a spell, and the mana flows in spells and enchantments weren't even that alike. An enchantment guided mana so that a spell was cast, but it was like the difference between encoding a function into an operation on a chip, and building the function from component parts of code. That analogy, and understanding the difference, had awarded Nathan with a skill rank-up.

Mid-tier Spellsense 6 achieved!

Then they had moved along to practical curse breaking. The old enchanter had brought along a dagger with a curse that made the handle stick to your hand. There was a mundane sharpness enchantment woven into the weapon, and the challenge was to break the curse while preserving the other enchantment.

Herdin had tried to teach Nathan how to crack open the hilt to get at the enchantments, but he'd just grabbed the hilt and felt out the magic with [Magic Absorption]. He'd tried to isolate the curse from the sharpness enchantments but had ended up breaking both and leaving the weapon drained dry.

Herdin had been surprised, to say the least. She'd grilled Nathan a bit about his Talent, but backed off when he mentioned it was a unique Insight. Then, she'd loaned Nathan a few other cursed items she had to see if he could figure out how to cursebreak them. He'd practiced in both figuring out what the enchantments *did,* and figuring out how to break the curse while leaving alone the useful enchantments.

The items themselves were interesting, representing a range of styles and methods. There was a spear from Agmon that could kick out a powerful blast of force but would turn and cut an unauthorized wielder. A low-tier dagger from a Fortress of the Face had a self-maintaining blade of incredible sharpness, but tried to brand a rune onto anybody who picked it up without thick gloves. Then there were a pair of amulets from some unnamed southern ruins that could generate bubbles of air around the wearer's head, but the curse would make that air toxic. He managed to keep one of those functional and was a bit sad to give it back to Herdin afterwards.

Mid-tier Identify 3 achieved!

Anyway! Nathan was here again and was surprised to see the workshop in a much cleaner state. Many of the prototypes had been cleared away. Sitting on the table were three guns, all beautifully crafted.

On the left side were a matched pair of revolvers, gleaming steel etched with flowing lines that glowed a delicate blue. The handles were made of a light wood that had been inlaid with dark metal to form magical symbols that reminded Nathan of lowercase Greek letters. They were big weapons, more than a foot long. The barrels were wide and extended, with a pair of stubby iron sights rising from the top. Next to the guns lay a set of plain wooden speedloaders, little bullet holders that could be used to reload an entire cylinder at once.

On the right side of the table was the rifle. It wasn't as decorated as the revolvers, though it shared the glowing blue tracery up the barrel, as well as the dark metal inlaid into the grip around the handle. The rifle looked longer and heavier than hunting rifles from Earth, but otherwise had about the same profile – no scope, though. Just another pair of iron sights.

In the middle of the table sat several wooden boxes of different sizes marked with simple labels. Most of them were wide flat boxes labeled "normal revolver ammunition." A few larger boxes said "normal rifle ammunition." Then there was one smaller box each of "explosive" and "penetrating" ammunition for the rifles.

Nathan paused to appreciate the sight. "That's quite a display. Very nice."

Herdin cackled and clapped her hands together. "Indeed it is! A gift to the daughter of Stanel Crusens should be beautiful. And as the first example of a new weapon, it must set the tone! Now then. I will need to be present for the initial imprinting of these weapons, to activate the self-destruct. When is that going to happen?"

Nathan paused, thinking. "I need to set up a time – I'll tell Kadid when I know. It might be as early as tomorrow night. Does that work for you all? It will almost certainly be at the Caxol mansion, where Kullal and Dalo live."

Poppy and Beatred glanced at each other, before Beatred spoke. "Looking forward to it."

They talked about some last-minute details before Herdin started fishing for any more Insights that Nathan might be willing to share. Beatred had described the basics of the generator, and Herdin seemed very interested in the knowledge behind it.

She took a polite refusal well enough, though Nathan had second thoughts as he looked back to the guns.

I wonder if she can make a railgun. Or a coilgun. The problems with those on Earth were always a need for a lot of current at once and material issues. Having seen a good enchanter at work, I bet those issues are surmountable with magic. I would probably need to teach her a good deal of the same math I'm going through with Stella though. Hmm. Something to consider for the future.

Nathan asked for a brief rundown of the ammunition, curious as to the final form factor. Beatred described the regular ammunition, pulling out a few cartridges. The revolver round was big, almost a half-inch across with a dome-shaped lead bullet capped by a steel ball.

The rifle round was enormous, almost as long as Nathan's hand. The bullet was the same diameter but much longer, capped with another ball of steel. Herdin explained that she'd had to strengthen the chamber and barrel to prevent the charge of powder from cracking the barrel, and added force enchantments to dampen the recoil.

Then the older woman took over describing the enchanted bullets, opening up the smaller boxes. There were only a dozen of each enchanted rifle cartridge, with about twice as many revolver cartridges. The two different kinds looked identical in construction, more cylindrical than the normal bullets, though they each had a pointed lead front. The bullets themselves were stamped with a small symbol to tell them apart.

Herdin was excited about these, holding up a penetrating revolver round. "I stacked up nine engraved disks for the enchanted bullets. It easily went through four inches of steel and far into the ground."

Beatred held up a metal ingot, which had a notable bullet hole all the way through. Herdin kept talking.

"The enchantments *are* only one-use, but they should enhance one another. A muckgrabber can eat my foot if the rifle penetrator doesn't go through a foot of steel. We haven't tested it, since *somebody* didn't have a foot of steel lying around."

She held up one of the explosive rounds. "These are based on a one-shot crossbow fireball enchantment. Supposed to stick into the target and then detonate – I had to shorten the time, but when we shot a wood block, it blew it to splinters from the inside. Very exciting."

Nathan praised Herdin, Poppy and Beatred for their work before heading back to the Adventurer's Guild. The crafters would bring the guns to the event Nathan had to set up.

~

That evening, Nathan schooled himself to patience until all the Heirs were back. Stella was the last one – she staggered in looking exhausted.

Nathan popped the question. "Hey Sarah. I think your new weapons are ready. They're downright *amazing*. You ready to see them?"

Sarah twisted to look at him from where she was busy whittling another small wooden figurine. This one looked like a small stalker. "Multiple? I thought you were making me *one?*"

Nathan shrugged. "Plans changed. Stella, do you think we can do it at your parent's place? I mentioned before that I wanted privacy."

The bedraggled mage looked over from where she had collapsed on a couch. "What? Oh. Sure. I'll ask them tomorrow. So long as they don't make me do channeling practice again. Got some more rank-ups though, so it was worth it no matter how scummy I feel."

Sarah was excited. "I would *prefer* it to happen sooner rather than later. I want to experience weapons from another world."

Nathan noticed Aarl frowning. He was bent over a slate, working on more math.

He's really the only one of the Heirs I don't have a plan to power up in some way. I mean, maybe the cursed swords are cool, but I have no idea how they'll stack up against the armory of weapons he already has. Anyway, he's kind of a greatsword-guy. If you know what I mean.

Nathan smirked a bit at his own double-entendre.

I just can't think of anything beyond getting Aarl some new weapons. Maybe I can ask Herdin to enchant a sword? But if it's an enchantment she has, then she's probably already figured out the best ways to use it and I won't be able to contribute much. And if I understand her, she'd refuse to do it because it would be boring.

I'll need to think about whether it's worth trading her an Insight on electricity in order to get a momentum greatsword. Or maybe I can come up with something. Hm. A monomolecular blade would be cool and all, but I have no idea how to make or maintain that kind of edge. Steel won't cut it.

You know, I have no idea why I'm waiting on trying to disentangle the curse from the swords. Let's give that a go.

Nathan stood up, crossing over to the cabinet that held various odds and ends. One of the items inside was a thick sack containing the cursed swords.

He pulled it out. "Hey Aarl, you got a moment? I want to try something, but if you're busy it can wait."

The [Master of Melee] let loose a frustrated sigh, putting down his chalk-dusted slate. "Indeed, Happy to have an excuse to take a break. What are you thinking?"

He saw Nathan pulling out the bag containing the cursed swords and raised his eyebrows. "I was wondering what you were planning on doing with those. Only fair you take them as your claim of the loot, but I thought you couldn't use magical items. Even if the curse on those won't hurt you?"

Nathan set the bag carefully on the table. The generator setup had been moved to his room, so there was space. "I don't think they're for *me*. I cannot use magical items without breaking them pretty quickly. I don't think I want to Develop my Talent to change that. But these swords look fancy. I want to try to break the curse, then give them to *you*."

Aarl was visibly surprised by that, his eyebrows climbing as he looked at Nathan. He tried to refuse the offer. "They seem to be very fancy swords, but that is not necessary." He paused. "I truly was joking yesterday about asking for something."

Nathan carefully tugged the bag off from the swords, careful not to touch them as they clattered to the top of the table, still sheathed. He'd examined them a bit earlier without touching them, trying to get a sense of the enchantments inside. But he had to admit that they really were *very* fancy. They looked like a pair of fine sabers, with impeccable craftsmanship that seemed a cut above everything else they'd salvaged from the Mage-Lord's tomb. Shame about the curse.

Nathan looked up from inspecting the swords, meeting Aarl's eyes. "No, you were right. This isn't about balancing the scales. I have the capability to try and help you, so I will. *Friends don't count favors.*"

Then Nathan grabbed the handles of the cursed swords.

Mid-tier Earnestness 9 achieved!

Chapter 63

Weaponry in Motion

Nathan held onto the hilts of two extremely cursed weapons. On the one hand, he should've definitely tried to break the curses on the swords one at a time, so that if he failed on the first, he could apply any lessons learned to the second. On the other hand, the swords were part of a set, and it seemed wrong to not treat them as such.

Nathan had wondered if the curse would detect him and trigger at all, given that some of Herdin's practice weapons hadn't triggered when he grabbed them. It had made it harder to break the curses, since it was difficult to separate the inactive curse from the other enchantments.

That quickly proved to not be a problem. The swords pulsed some sort of detection magic at his hands. Nathan recognized what kind of spell it was – he'd seen and heard enough about the self-destruct mechanism on the guns to piece together that this was something similar.

The enchantments to enable that magic weren't visible on the hilts of the swords any more than they were on the guns. It was obviously a bad idea to make your security runes visible – though some of Herdin's cursed items had worked that way. Regardless, the appraiser and enchanter who had looked over these swords had decided it wasn't worth the risk to break the curses.

The enchantments checked if Nathan was the proper wielder and determined that he was *not*. The flesh-dissolving spell started to bite at Nathan's hands, but he understood death mana well at this point, and it amounted to barely a tickle.

The spell ramped up in intensity as Nathan drew the sabers from their sheaths. The swords were beautiful, artistic curves of shining metal without any engravings. The single sharp edge seemed to drink the light, steaming with faint dark tendrils.

Are the enchantments inside *the blade somehow?*

Nathan held the swords crossed in front of him as he furrowed his brow, concentrating on the feeling of magic playing around his hands and creeping up his wrist. The sword hilts contained a *mess* of spellwork, and Nathan closed his eyes as he constructed a mental model of what was going on. He tried to keep his antimagic from breaking anything before he understood the enchantments, but he felt the enchantments closest to his hands starting to fray.

There were smoothed crystals of necromancy-charged conductive quartz embedded in the hilt and touching his palms, which linked to more enchantments farther up the blade. Those crystals were full of death mana, and Nathan tried to prevent his [Magic Absorption] from draining them dry just yet – not before he understood more about the overall structure. The Talent wasn't built for fine control, but Nathan focused his willpower on reducing the absorption.

There were spells strung throughout the handles for all kinds of purposes. Some reinforced the handle to make it less likely to break. Others prevented the blade from slipping and... wicked away moisture?

Mid-tier Spellsense 7 achieved!

The crystals are the key. They fuel all the other enchantments, and don't have their own charging mechanism. This weapon has only a limited charge unless you can fuel it with death mana. I bet that's why Neverin wasn't interested, because the crystals integrated into the sword are death-aspected, so that would be impossible to change. For anybody that's not me. But if I just rip the mana out, it'll probably break all *the enchantments.*

Mid-tier Identify 4 achieved!

Man, analyzing spells while they try to eat me is great for skill ranks. I'm taking a risk to solidify new knowledge, so that's helping.

Nathan kept the drain on the crystals low, but constant. He tried not to give the enchantments any sudden shocks. After that was established, Nathan focused on disentangling the magic that was trying to eat his hands. It was a race against time as his antimagic fractured and absorbed the other spellwork in the handle. The entire structure of the interlocking spells quivered, and

Nathan's lips pursed as he tried to stabilize the structure and target *only* the spellwork that was directing the death mana into a disintegration field – that now reached nearly to his elbows. It was like trying to stabilize a Jenga tower when the only tool you had was a pickaxe.

He heard the Heirs moving around, but he didn't spare them any attention. The crystals were almost drained of mana, which meant Nathan was nearly out of time. He recalled how he'd broken Taeol's early spells and latched his Talent onto the threads of destructive power that were wrapping around his flesh. Then he gave a metaphysical *yank*. The spellwork in the sword quaked, but Nathan followed the propagation of his pull on the disintegration spell.

Mid-tier Notice 6 achieved!

Got you.

Nathan pulsed his antimagic into the hilt of the sword, targeting the specific flows of mana that likely made up the security curse. That part of the spellwork fragmented, and Nathan cast the swords away from him. The crystals were out of mana, but he'd destroyed the curse. And he guessed he'd only broken one or two additional enchantments along the way.

High-tier Focused Mind 6 achieved!

Nathan opened his eyes to see that the Heirs had vacated the room. One of the swords had sunk into the table in front of Nathan. Though it wasn't exactly a whole table anymore – it seemed that the disintegration spell hadn't just focused on *him*, but tried to get at everything nearby. It had eaten the sleeves of his shirt back to the elbows and taken a large chunk out of the table.

The second sword had clattered to the floor after Nathan released it. The edge was shinier than before. Without the death mana empowering whatever enchantments were on the blade, it no longer sucked in the light.

"Did it work?" Khachi spoke from the side of the room, looking in with some exasperation.

Nathan reached down to grab the sword, then thought better of it. "I think so. I'm almost certain the curse enchantment is gone, but I don't know if the rest of the enchantments still work. Either way, I completely emptied the mana reservoir. I think it can be recharged with another kind of mana now? Maybe?"

Stella poked her head around the corner now that the fireworks were over. "Oh, that's weird. I'd be surprised if the spells all still worked if you charged it with a different kind of mana. But if they were built well... maybe?"

Aarl walked forward, looking excited. He poked at the sword that was sticking out of the table tentatively. When nothing happened, he slid it out without effort. He admired the blade for a moment, before delicately placing it on the table and bending to pick up the other sword of the pair.

Stella walked over, looking at the swords. "Yeah, definitely uncharged. I think I can charge those with mana, though you won't be able to change the aspect – unless Nathan drains them again. I don't know exactly how the enchantments work though, so I don't know what different kinds of mana would do."

"Well, there should be a good enchanter around when I give Sarah her new weapons," Nathan said. "We can probably ask her?"

Aarl picked up both swords, feeling at their balance for a moment. "It would be nice to have weapons that have specific magical effects. Most of mine have durability and sharpness enchantments. But Stanel has made it clear that he won't just gift us any of the *truly* potent weapons. Those we need to earn."

He slipped the swords into his dimensional pouch. "Or be given by a teammate. Thank you, Nathan. I will think about what mana I wish to put into these weapons. I am leaning towards a different type in each, but I will wait to speak to this enchanter first and see what is compatible."

Both he and Sarah looked towards Stella, who was yawning. The mage jumped at their attention, realizing they were waiting for her response. "Right. I'll ask my parents if we can invite everybody next time I see them. Stupid [Message] spell – I'd just ask them now but I still can't cast it. It's really hard to cast with air mana. Would be a lot easier with shadow or dreams, or one of the other silly and insubstantial mana types. The ones I don't have."

The next day, another team returned from their surprise mission. The rest of the trainees had started to wise up, acquiring rations and camping gear in case they were sent out into the wilderness at a moment's notice.

The latest team to return was a group of trainees called the Dusteaters: a few humans and catfolk from the southern villages. They were telling the story of their mission in the dining hall, and Nathan scooted over to listen.

Their leader was somebody Nathan had met in passing before – a young human man named Nornan. He was a bit of a jokester, and a large group of trainees were listening to him with smiles on their faces.

"... And then, Inarl tripped over a rock and started a small rockslide," Nornan declaimed, recounting how they'd tracked a group of Ashblood cobras to their lair. "It was like the opening of a dragon's maw! All dozen serpents turned towards us and *hissed* – fit to make your grandmothers' bones shake. Hear me, but I was sure they'd swarm us!"

Nathan stepped up to the group, smiling. This guy had *flair*. "Did they swarm you?"

The pale-skinned man turned towards Nathan, blonde mop swinging. He raised a finger. "Aha! You would think so, but we'd prepared. We were on the steeper of the slopes, and the slope was covered with loose scree, so they couldn't simply slither up to us. After I gallantly helped Inarl to her feet, we beat a hasty retreat to the top of the hill, peppering them with poisoned arrows!"

A catfolk to Nornan's left swatted at him. "By my memory, you screamed like a piglet and shot them a dozen times without helping me at *all*."

Nornan turned on her with a radiant smile. "But that *was* helping you up, since they were slowed by my incredible marksmanship. I got one arrow right down one's throat. Must have given it *terrible* indigestion!"

Everybody was laughing at Nornan's incredibly bombastic story, including his own team.

That guy's great.

Nathan hung around, meeting some of the other Adventurers and learning their names. The Dusteaters specialized in ranging the drier desert region to the south of Gemore, and Nathan wasn't surprised to hear that Nornan had been the one to choose the name.

It didn't take long to set up another small dinner party at the Caxol's place. Stella made it clear that not nearly as many people were invited this time. It was just going to be Dalo, Kullal, Stanel, Kia and whoever Nathan brought in addition to the Heirs.

"It won't be Cantas' cooking," Stella had informed them apologetically, "but we'll have some good food."

Nathan wasn't worried about food. He was worried about presenting a gun to the famous [Weaponmaster] of Davrar. What if he didn't find it very interesting? Nathan told himself that it had been impressive to Beatred, Poppy and Herdin, so it *should* be impressive to Stanel.

Nathan had asked Kadid to inform Beatred and Herdin about the party. He was expecting the older man to complain about being asked to pass a message, but Kadid had taken the request in stride.

Then, he'd said something interesting. "It appears that you are making valuable connections between my family and the most powerful Adventurers in this city. I thank you for this, Nathan."

~

Nathan met up with all three crafters at Beatred's shop before they set off to the Caxol estate. Nathan ended up carrying a stack of unenchanted ammunition boxes – *carefully*. Poppy carried the rest of the ammunition, while Beatred toted the guns in a cushioned sack.

On the way, Nathan mentioned that he'd uncursed a pair of swords and wanted Herdin to take a look.

The old woman sniffed disdainfully. "Eh, get another enchanter for that. I've spent enough of my time hunched over old enchantments, trying to figure out how they work. What's the source of the swords?"

"They're Sklian dominion, we think they were the personal arms of a mage-lord. Found them in a hidden treasure room right off where he was buried."

Yeah, buried as the power core and intelligence of a giant naga-mech.

Herdin shook her head slightly, sending her mane of poofy white hair shaking. "Sklians were shit enchanters. Those swords are probably packed with rare materials used poorly. Might get more selling the raw materials now that the curse is broken."

Hmm, she still doesn't seem interested. Well, time for a bit of bait.

Nathan grinned at the elderly enchanter. She looked back with narrowed eyes. "I know that look. You think you have something interesting. I will decide that, indeed I will."

"Well, the swords were loaded with death mana," Nathan explained, "but I think they're unaspected now. We want to know if they can be recharged with a different kind of mana and if the enchantments will still work."

Herdin sniffed. "No. The aspected nature of whatever they were using as a mana storage will make the whole thing blow up. Basic shit, boy." She paused and glanced at him again. "Unless the storage material was prismatic diamond. But if it was, then it would be a *crime* to leave that material in a Sklian sword. It wasn't a prismatic diamond, was it?"

Nathan's grin didn't slip. "No. It was high-quality conductive quartz. But what if I told you that the quartz doesn't *have* an aspect any longer? No trace of death mana to be found. Ready to be charged with any other mana. And we want to know if the enchantments on the sword will still work with other mana types."

Herdin frowned in thought. "Right. Whatever weird magic stuff you do, I'd have to take a look. It's not many enchantments that could cope with that. But the Sklians tended to build their enchantments *sturdy*. If stupid. So maybe." She paused, then swore. "Harpy's tits, Nathan. Fine, I'll take a look at this sword. And if you've managed to remove the aspect from a mana storage, I might call in this favor one day for a project of *mine*."

The old woman was moderately grumpy for the rest of the walk to the Caxol's mansion, but Nathan could tell it was mostly an affectation. She didn't want people asking her about enchanting all the time, so she acted grumpy about it. But she *liked* enchanting and couldn't help getting involved when somebody presented her with an interesting problem.

They approached the front gates to Stella's house. The gates and walls sparked with lightning, just like last time. But as they walked up, the gates opened and they could pass inside to the garden.

Nathan spied Dalo and Kullal sitting inside on a bench set to the side among the lush growth. Kullal was sprawled idyllically against Dalo's chest, and they were both admiring the verdant beauty around them. They both stood as Nathan and the crafters approached.

Dalo nodded in their direction. "Herdin, I haven't heard from you for long enough I assumed you were dead."

The old woman snorted. "Retired, not dead."

Dalo stroked his beard in her direction. "It's hard to tell the difference. Your activities were loud enough that their sudden absence invoked a death."

Herdin just glared at him. "At least you're not like Kozar. Damned fool bothers me every week to make more shit for him. I told him to go lick a muck-grabber's asshole last time."

Dalo chuckled, stroking his beard in a dignified fashion. That lasted until Kullal leaned in and licked his ear, making him start.

"Dear," she said. "Let's invite them in, let them put down those heavy boxes."

The old man snorted. "Nathan's got Stamina. He'll be fine."

Regardless, the crotchety man turned and walked towards the front door. Kullal stayed behind in the garden to let other people through the front gates.

Everybody else followed Dalo, and he led them downstairs to the practice room in the basement. They set everything down on a table in the viewing area, then sat around to wait for Stanel and Kia, and the other members of the Heirs.

Stella joined them after a few minutes. "Sorry I missed you arriving. I was busy reading in the library. Is this it, then?" She gestured to the clutter of boxes on the table.

Nathan nodded. He almost moved to open the bag when Beatred stopped him. "Let's wait until all are present, yeah?"

It didn't take long before Sarah clattered down the stairs and popped into the basement room. She looked excited. Stanel was close behind, his heavy tread and bemused expression signaling that his expectations weren't as high as his daughter's.

Then again, she knows these weapons were invented on another world, while he does not.

Aarl walked in behind, followed by Khachi and his mother.

And the gang's all here. Well, except for Leska and Xarian. They're Guardians but don't have kids in the Heirs.

Beatred looked over to Nathan, silently asking if he wanted to start. He shrugged and stepped out into the practice area, turning to address the gathered Heirs and Guardians. It felt a bit like giving a lab meeting.

Not really that different in a way. I've been working on something new for a while, and now it's time to explain to an audience of my peers what I've been spending time and money on, and convince them it was good and worthwhile. Then ask for their input and hope they find it useful.

Chapter 64

Guns and Blades

Nathan stood in front of the majority of the Guardians of Gemore and the Heirs. He rubbed his hands together, psyching himself up to introduce their presentation on *firearms*.

"Let's get started. We're here to present a new kind of weapon that I've been working on with Beatred, Poppy and Herdin for a while now. It's something from my home, and I think it will be a valuable weapon in Sarah's arsenal that will complement her build well. This weapon is the *primary* armament in my home, to such an extent that other kinds of weapons are comparatively rare."

He paused to ensure that he had everybody's full attention, then gestured towards where Beatred and Poppy stood next to the table of guns. "Of course, I only had the Insight of this weapon, I didn't have the skill or *skills* to make it. Beatred Bho and Poppy Miri did all the hard work here, and Herdin Bho handled the enchanting. I must say, they did a fabulous job recreating something that I only remembered. Much of the credit should go to them. At this point, they can make more by themselves – though they will need my permission."

The dark-skinned enchanter heckled from the audience, where she was already sipping on a dark blue cocktail. "Blasphemously lucky of you I was bored."

Nathan raised an eyebrow at her. "I seem to remember you *thanking* me for a new challenge. Anyway, Beatred's the one who's done most of the testing, and

I don't want to touch the weapon because it's enchanted, so she'll demonstrate."

He waved Beatred forward, and she grabbed the bag of guns. Poppy hoisted cases of ammunition for both the rifle and the revolvers before following.

Nathan sat down in the viewing area, next to Stella. Sarah was in front of them, paying rapt attention. Stella leaned in and whispered to him. "After all this, it better be a weapon fit to wake the giants."

Nathan smirked as Beatred put down the bag and fished out a revolver. She turned towards them. "Can I get a target? Something sturdy for practicing ranged attacks on. And with a backstop."

Kullal gestured, and a man-shaped mannequin of dark wood flew out of a closet, settling on the far side of the room. An inclined plane of force materialized behind it.

Beatred looked nervously at the target. "This weapon is hard to explain, so I will demonstrate." Poppy had popped open the box of revolver ammunition and handed her six rounds before backing up out of the way.

Beatred loaded the rounds quickly, almost dropping one. Then she turned to the dummy, aimed down the barrel and pulled the trigger. There was a muffled *bang* and a cloud of smoke, but the burly blacksmith didn't stop. She pulled the trigger again and again in rapid succession until she'd emptied all six bullets into the dummy. It was only thirty feet away, and she didn't miss a single shot.

There was a moment of silence, then Dalo waved his own hand, dispelling the smoke. The dummy shot across the room, coming to rest before the audience. One bullet had made a mess of its head, while the rest had impacted the center mass and turned it into a cratered ruin of kindling. Nathan was surprised the bullets hadn't penetrated all the way through the wooden dummy.

Stanel spoke up quietly. "That's Everoak, isn't it?"

At Dalo's answering nod, the [Weaponmaster] looked impressed. "Can I see the weapon?"

He held out his hand, but Beatred shook her head jerkily. "We're not done."

Then she pulled out the rifle, and Stanel's gaze intensified as she loaded a single round. Kullal summoned another dummy while Beatred aimed down the length of the long gun. She leaned forward into the recoil as she fired, but still staggered slightly at the sharp *crack* of the big cartridge.

The dummy's head *exploded*. The bullet ricocheted off the angled plane of force and left behind a crack in the spell. It bounced a few more times before burying itself in the solid railing that separated the arena from the viewing area. Nathan winced. He was glad that ricochet hadn't hit anybody.

Stanel's jaw dropped, and he breathed out a single word.

"Extraordinary."

Stanel was staring in rapt fascination at the rifle in Beatred's hands. Then he turned to address Kia. "Good bet." He pulled out a wide, flat disk – about nine inches across – and flicked it towards the tall woman.

She snapped out a gauntleted hand to catch the disk with a snort. The tall woman turned to display the object to Nathan. The surface of the disk was intricately enchanted, with a large gem glowing white in the middle. Seven crystals were spaced along the outside edge, each glowing a different color.

She explained briefly before tucking it away. "It's a recharge disk. A Kalis Conclave item that can recharge near any enchantment."

Nathan blinked. "Did you bet that Stanel wouldn't know the weapon?"

Kia nodded. "Yes. You have the sharpness of a good blade. I did not think you would be wrong with this."

Nathan turned to Stanel. "You gave me the money for this project! You didn't think I could do it?"

Stanel had a slight grin on his face. "I figured you'd come up with something useful to Sarah, and that a gift from a friend weighed differently than a gift from a father. Besides, I thought I might be wrong! And I was!" He gestured to the rifle, then stepped towards the arena with his hand outstretched. "How does it work?" he asked Beatred.

The copper-skinned man's advance was blocked by a hand like a gnarled branch.

Herdin stood in his way. "Now that you're all lit and flaring, it's time for me to dump some water on the fire. These weapons have some *true Insights* behind them. We'll tell you the basics of how they work, but not the details. And I'll imprint the weapons to your daughter here, with a curse activating if anybody else wields them or tries to take them apart.

Sarah had also stood and was stepping towards Beatred. "Yeah, *Dad*. These weapons are for me, not for you. Thank you Herdin, Nathan, Beatred, Poppy. I look forward to holding them in my own hands."

She brushed past her father, who was looking forlorn. His hands made little grasp-y gestures at his side.

Herdin's stern expression cracked into a broad smile at Stanel's expression "We can do the imprinting *later*, after you get the chance to weigh them in your own hands. Then you can order some of your own. We've already agreed to make you some if you want them. For now, let your daughter try out her new toy."

Kullal frowned as she inspected first the bullet embedded in the railing, then the crack in the force wall. She dismissed the force wall and sat for a moment before turning to Stella. "Stella, can you figure out an appropriate backstop that won't send pieces of metal flying back at us?"

Stella looked a little blindsided. "Uh..."

Nathan was sitting in between Stella and her mom. He turned so the foxfolk could only see the back of his head and mouthed a word at Stella. *"Dirt."*

Stella caught his silent motion and narrowed her eyes in thought. Then, she snapped her fingers and spent ten seconds working through a spell before casting. A mound of conjured earth appeared on the other end of the arena. It only covered about a quarter of the back wall.

Dalo seemed to think it was a good idea, and with a wave of his hand, more conjured dirt showered down to cover the entire back wall.

Beatred had been explaining the operation and terminology of the revolvers to Sarah. She showed her how the mechanism worked and gestured at the cartridge and the enchanted hammer on the back of the gun. She loaded one revolver and had Sarah load the other one, before showing her the speedloaders and demonstrating their use. Beatred had Sarah keep the guns pointed downrange at all times with her finger off the trigger, which reminded Nathan of something.

I just realized we never built a safety onto those things. Hm. At least Beatred's got the rudiments of gun safety and trigger discipline already figured out.

Sarah was extremely focused on the instruction, not missing a single detail as Beatred explained with occasional interjections from Poppy. After just a few minutes, Sarah was smoothly handling the revolvers as if she'd been using them for years. She loaded and unloaded the cylinders, then aimed and mimed firing with an empty chamber. She examined the box of bullets to see how many rounds she could afford to play with.

Then, she carefully loaded each revolver and took one in each hand. She stood in the center of the room. Kullal conjured some small targets, some of which bobbed back and forth. They looked like small, colored [Force Blocks], but... almost insubstantial.

Sarah took a deep breath and raised one revolver. Her first shot cracked apart a stationary target, and she paused to assess the shot, frowning over the feeling of recoil.

She raised the gun again and fired quickly, hitting a target with every bullet.

As soon as the gun in one hand was empty, she raised the other hand and resumed firing, quickly tearing her way through the targets.

I guess that answers the question. Her class and skills definitely apply to guns.

She'd holstered the first revolver while firing the second. As soon as the second gun ran dry, she flipped out the cylinder and shook out the empty casings. Her other hand came up and tried to slap a speedloader home, but she fumbled it and sent the rounds falling to the ground.

Nathan winced, hoping none of them went off. None did.

Right. No primers. You need to stick something thin and hot through the paper to set them off – and basically only the enchanted hammer fits the bill. That probably makes them a lot less likely to discharge accidentally.

Dalo repeated his trick to get rid of the smoke, and Sarah stuck the guns into her pouches, beaming.

She turned to Nathan and bowed deeply. "This is a true gift, Nathan Lark. I will treasure this day until the Ending."

Nathan didn't know how to respond and just nodded back with a broad smile on his face.

Everybody else seemed thrilled with the display. Nothing else would suffice but for Sarah to try out the rifle.

Nathan explained that it was meant for longer distances. Beatred chipped in that she hadn't been able to properly calibrate the sights in her workshop, since she hadn't wanted to go into Old Gemore to properly test the range. She showed Sarah how the front sight was actually clamped onto the barrel and could be moved around slightly to properly calibrate it.

Zeroing? Ah, whatever.

But Sarah didn't seem worried. She had skills that enhanced accuracy and power of ranged weapons in general, and they seemed to apply to guns too.

She squeezed off a few shots, getting the feel for the recoil. Nathan advised her to pull the trigger smoothly, not jerk it and throw off her aim.

Eventually, Stanel got his turn. He took a revolver in each hand and sighed, closing his eyes as he simply held them.

"Oh yes. This is a good weapon. I think I will want several of these. They're so *quick*, I don't even need to draw my arm back. Just track from target to target."

The [Weaponmaster] swept the guns across imaginary targets in a complex pattern. "I wonder if... well. Time will tell how compatible these are with my skills."

Then he picked up the rifle, repeating the process where he closed his eyes. "Indeed, truly a weapon worthy of a Questor. This rifle might make me put down my Edrani sharpshot bow." He hesitated. "For some things." He cracked his eyelids open and looked to Herdin. "I see some enchanted rounds over there. May I ask?"

Herdin smirked, the expression looking very natural on the crotchety old woman. "Indeed. I could guess that *you* would ask for enchanted ammunition. You'll like them. Explosive and penetrating. The explosive should only explode inside the target, and I think the penetrating rifle round would go through a siegeboar the long way. *Before* skills are applied."

Stanel rubbed his hands together. "I'll be dropping by the shop tomorrow. Should I come to Beatred's place?"

At her encouraging nod, he looked down at the weapons. "And I think I'll place an order of more ammunition for these weapons, for Sarah."

Finally, his attention turned to Nathan. "And Nathan, I think Sarah, and I, owe you a *favor* for this. For the gift of a new and powerful weapon to my daughter, and for teaching the crafters of Gemore a new type of weapon, however restricted it must be."

Nathan nodded, looking to Kia. His implication was obvious. She tilted her head from side to side, then spoke.

"Stanel and I will speak of this later. I am inclined to agree, but I recall you mentioned another possibility?" She gestured towards Stella with a questioning look.

Stella looked flustered. "I-I don't know yet. It's helpful, but we aren't done yet."

Kia made a thoughtful noise. "Then we will speak more after the graduation ceremony, when you *are* done. I have not shared my Airwalking Insight with any, and I would wait for the Adventurer's Oath."

After that, there were a few more things to take care of, mostly involving Herdin. She imprinted the weapons to Sarah, warning everybody not to touch them. It would take a good bit of handling to set off the self-destruct, but better not to risk it.

Additionally, Herdin looked over the swords that Nathan had broken the curse on. She was surprised by whatever she saw and called over Dalo and Kullal to take a look as well. After looking over the sword, Dalo shot Nathan a gauging look. Aarl hovered nearby, clearly anxious for the verdict.

While Herdin, Dalo and Kullal conversed over the swords, Nathan looked around for the other members of the Heirs. Sarah was talking to Poppy, but Stella and Khachi came over. They chatted about the new weapons. Khachi schemed about having a *truly* long-range option for the team, and wondered if they could force most foes into attacking them. Stella seemed relaxed and pleased, glad that her friends were upgrading their firepower.

Then Herdin came forth, holding the swords. "The primary enchantment on these swords are still intact. It's an impressively simple but powerful mana channeling enchantment. The basic strengthening enchantments on the blades are also still active. Most of the grip-specific enchantments are dead – but they were stupid ones anyway. What kind of fool needs to burn mana to hold onto their sword? Or keep their hands dry?" Herdin shook her head, seemingly disappointed in the sweaty-palmed long-dead Mage-Lord.

She returned back to task. "The swords are ready to use, and the craftsmanship is... acceptable. Especially for Sklian blades. The materials are excellent, and the edge itself is made of manaforged mithril for the enchantment to work through. I would almost recommend breaking them down for component parts to get a new pair of swords made, but this channeling enchantment is surprisingly versatile."

She paused, offering the swords to Aarl. "However, you should choose what kind of mana you want imbued. They don't come with a self-recharge, so you will need them manually recharged by a mage with the appropriate mana types."

Aarl took the blades, and Herdin gestured towards Stella. "The channeling enchantment is best with non-elemental mana, though less-substantial elements like fire or air would work. I would not recommend water, earth, wood or life. I think air mana would just send a gust of wind with every swing, pushing everything away from the blade. Fire would heat the blade and burn all it touches but would do little for its penetrative power. Shadow would mimic the original death mana but would be better for destroying armor and worse at disintegrating flesh."

Stella frowned at the swords that Aarl was busy examining. "What about force, or lightning? Or light?"

Herdin looked surprised at Stella's question. "You are young to have all those powerful mana types." Then she shrugged. "But it is not my role to question your secrets. Force would be good – it would extend the weapon with a blade of force which would cut like a high-tier force spell. The sword itself would become nearly impossible to break. Lightning would give a strong shock and blast back any target the blade touched. The effect would be strong, as all lightning spells are, but it would drain the mana storage of the blade quickly. The mana storage is expansive, and as long as it could be recharged frequently, that might be very effective."

The old woman paused and frowned. "As for light... I have not worked with many light enchantments. It would likely let off a blinding burst of light with every strike and might duplicate some of the burning effects of a fire imbuement. I am not sure."

At that, Kullal got everybody's attention with a quiet but very clear flashing chime. "This has been very exciting, but we are late for dinner. Let us go eat!"

~

The rest of the dinner was a lot of fun – Nathan enjoyed hanging out with the Guardians. They were self-confident and cool, and the mood was celebratory. Nathan got toasted a few times, along with Beatred and the other crafters.

Stanel seemed in a grand mood, mentioning multiple times that he expected Sarah and Aarl to start making their names now that they had worthy weapons.

Sarah made a joke about potentially angling her level 81 class Development to focus on guns. It was the kind of joke that tested the waters, probing for a response. Stanel looked thoughtful but didn't shoot down the idea.

Huh. Interesting.

Chapter 65

A Frustrating Field

Before too long, the Heirs were on their way back to the Adventurer's Guild. The new weapons were all stowed away in Sarah and Aarl's dimensional pouches, and they strolled down the hill chatting and being cheerful. There hadn't been any alcohol, so Nathan was completely sober.

They arrived back at their suite of rooms in a celebratory mood, with Aarl especially not wanting to sit down and relax. He pulled out the twin swords again, examining their shining curves in the main room while the rest of the Heirs lounged on the various couches.

Sarah asked the obvious question. "What mana types are you thinking of having imbued?"

Aarl looked up from the swords and turned towards Stella. "It seems best to have mana types that could be recharged by Stella? I realize I am assuming your willingness to help me."

Stella blew a raspberry and waved her hand at him. "Truly the most difficult task." Her expression sobered. "I would agree to charge your weapons for as long as we are on the same team."

Aarl nodded back seriously. "In that case, I believe force would be an obvious choice. An unbreakable blade that extends the size of the sword and cuts with such a fine edge would be powerful." He looked down again, considering the swords in his hands.

"But I don't believe that I should do that to *both* swords. I should limit myself to mana types you have available, so that recharging is easier.

"Fire seems a lesser choice, but better than air. Herdin made it sound like air would be actively harmful to the weapon unless we're worried about poison gas. Earth mana does not seem like an option. I find myself hoping that your Insight of lightning is going well." Aarl grinned expectantly at Nathan and Stella.

Stella rolled her head around, flipping her braid over her shoulder. "Fine! *Fine*. Let's get on with it. Nathan? It's time to teach me of Lightning. *Again*. Hear me, but I am feeling like this Insight is forever around the next corner."

Nathan nodded agreeably and cracked his neck as he sat down next to Stella. He spoke to the other Heirs. "Fair enough. We're close, might get to it as soon as tomorrow. This probably won't be too interesting to y'all, so you might want to find something else to do."

He focused the lesson on electricity and magnetism. They had already gone through some practical exercises with the generator, and Stella understood that things were more complicated than they seemed. She'd messed around with magnets and charge enough to accept that there were invisible, hidden forces moving things around.

And it was up to Nathan to explain what those forces were. He needed to connect the math he'd been teaching Stella to the evidence before her eyes. He'd been taught to do a full derivation of all of Maxwell's laws, and he wanted to instill at least a bit of the logic of those processes into Stella, if not necessarily walk through every aspect of the math.

But math was just a language for describing the world precisely, and Nathan was going to take it as far as he could. His [Lecturing] was certainly helping out – concepts were easier to explain than they should have been, and Stella was likely to interpret Nathan correctly when he made things ambiguous. Honestly, Nathan wasn't sure how much of that was his skill and how much of it was Stella being smart.

Regardless, Nathan wanted to start with describing how electric and magnetic fields were generated. Over the evening, Nathan walked Stella through the first two of Maxwell's laws, which governed how electric charges created electric fields and magnetic dipoles produced magnetic fields. Nathan was glad to revisit the ideas and go through the math behind them.

He'd always found it elegant that under Gauss' law, static electric fields were created by imbalances of charge, while the law for magnetism basically meant that there were *no* imbalances of magnetic sources and sinks. If you broke a magnet in half between the two poles, you created new poles at either side of the break point.

The math was almost supplementary to helping Stella create the right kind of field simulation with her magic. They went out to the practice field, where Stella placed a few glowing orbs in the air to illuminate the darkened area. Nathan was sure to close and latch the gate before they moved to the far side of the practice area, under the 70-foot drop that Nathan felt so well-acquainted with.

Then Nathan helped Stella understand how a charge moved in the presence of electric and magnetic fields. He used his spear to write out the equations in the sand. He had Stella conjure up some simulated fields and traced how a charge would spiral around magnetic field lines via the right-hand rule. Electric field flow was a bit easier, since a charge would follow electric field lines towards an opposite charge, or away from a similar charge.

Part of the trick was to explain how most fields were not simple. In the real-world, multiple contiguous sources tended to complicate things enough that applying the math was hard.

This is really so much easier to explain with a 3-dimensional model. I'm jealous. I had to learn by drawing X's and bullseyes on paper.

Low-tier Lecturing 10 achieved!

Yay.

They left off there for the evening, though Stella wanted to keep going. She was starting to see the elegance of the way electricity and magnetism worked together, orthogonal yet complementary to each other. And she was *hungry* to complete the puzzle.

Oh, I can't wait until I get through Ampere's law and Faraday's law and show her that light is a combined electromagnetic wave. That realization is mind-blowing.

But it was getting late, and Nathan reminded Stella that they still had time. After all, he wasn't planning on running off into the wilderness anytime soon. He'd prefer to come back to this tomorrow when they were fresh. She looked frustrated, but acceded to his request.

~

The next morning, Stella was anxious. They did their exercises and she managed to keep her peace, though she kept shooting Nathan impatient looks.

She kept silent over breakfast, sullenly glaring at the other teams around them. Finally, as they were leaving class, she asked Nathan if he'd skip class to teach her math.

Okay, that's just hilarious. I've skipped class for other things. But never to do math. Well, I think I was late to class a few times because I was busy doing math, but that's different.

The rest of the Heirs teased her about it, and Stella just pouted and murmured, "But I wanna learn about lightning."

Nathan raised his hand respectfully. "That's a pretty great argument. Still, after lunch. We have time."

Nathan was glad they hadn't skipped class – they were learning more about Giantsrest and what forces they would deploy on the field. The military might of Giantsrest was primarily in its mages, who had an almost feudal-like structure, with the archmages of the Ascendent Academy standing at the peak.

Then there were various tiers of researchers, lecturers, and proctors beneath them, owing their loyalty and education to their high-ranking sponsors. The pattern continued on down to the lowest of students, who typically were the children of existing mages. It was common for male mages to have a lot of kids in Giantsrest, which sure didn't diminish his hatred of the place.

The more Nathan heard about the Ascendent Academy, the more he felt it exemplified the worst excesses of academia back on Earth. People fought tooth and nail to climb the pile. Once they were atop it, they had ultimate authority over those below them, bordered only by others of the same authority. It seemed a life of polite violence, with brutal politics that could get you demoted, killed or mind-controlled at any misstep. You trod on those below to ascend, wary of being backstabbed by those at your side or squashed by those above.

Apparently the enslavement mages were considered "lesser" mages, since they needed to leave the Academy to pursue riches or recognition. The highest calling for a Giantsrest mage was to ascend an archmage, rich with magic and wealth. The "best" way to do this was by demonstrating magical genius with your learning and original projects, leveling from displays of magical might. That would let you catch the eye of somebody above you, who would count on your support once you rose in power.

And that was because Giantsrest fought duels, just like Gemore. Many of their duels weren't dangerous, focusing more on judging magical power and control with only reputation on the line. Of course, when a low reputation could result in somebody [Dominating] you with no consequences, their duels were hardly without stakes.

What a damn snake pit. And it's all based on magical might.

Nathan found the discussion of the structure of the Ascendent Academy helpful to understanding his enemy. However, this lesson was focused on what made up the military might of Giantsrest.

Almost every Giantsrest mage would know [Mage Armor], and most of them had force mana as well. In contrast to Gemore style of force mana, Giantsrest force constructs tended to be invisible, but smaller and somewhat harder to pierce. Most Giantsrest mages could cast basic mental spells like [Paralysis] and [Daze], with spells after that depending on the specific build and mana types of the mage in question.

Enslavement mages with [Mass Daze] or [Dominate] were fairly common in Giantsrest forces, and they tended to have several spells focused on controlling enemies and preventing them getting close enough to attack.

Aside from mages, Giantsrest didn't have much of a formal army. They had no standing forces – not even of slave soldiers. Instead it was all just the personal possessions of various archmages and the mages below them. The relevant "possessions" being slave soldiers and golems.

Golems were expensive, and usually required one or more people to be sacrificed to empower the golem core with motive force. But they were strong, hard to kill, and their bodies could be further enchanted. Excellent guards, but their lack of flexibility and mobility in rough terrain tended to be a problem in the guerrilla wars that Gemore liked to fight. Kill the person directing the golems, and they would revert to the simplest of orders.

The slave soldiers were mostly uniform – they weren't supposed to win fights against high-level Gemore Adventurers, they were supposed to prevent anybody from running up to the Giantsrest mages while they were casting battle-winning spells. They tended to be drawn from lower-performing servants or artisans who were considered expendable. That meant they didn't tend to have specialized martial classes.

Slave soldiers were usually armed with a big shield and a spear. But the mental spells used to control them were brutal and left fairly little in the way of autonomous thought. A slave soldier wouldn't break until the mage commanding them was dead and the fight was obviously lost, at which point they would lie down and die.

I know enough military history to know that being unbreakable is incredibly important to large-scale conflicts. "Morale is to the physical as three is to one" and all that. No wonder Gemore doesn't fight Giantsrest in the open.

Giantsrest did have specialized slave soldiers – different mages had their personal forces trained in different ways according to their whims. Some archmages had cadres of specialized archers, assassins, heavily armored linebreakers and more. They were trained from birth, guided towards specific classes, and could be terrifyingly potent.

I think those guys are going to be my biggest weakness. I probably stand a good chance against an archmage in a confined area right now – if they don't already know to use non-conjured elemental magic against me. And I'm only going to get stronger. But one of those elite slave soldiers could probably take me apart. Something to watch out for.

Finally, there were the slavemasters. These formed what middle class there was in Giantsrest, and were the middle management and overseers for when more initiative was required, but a full mage wasn't justified. The overseers weren't often seen in combat situations except for slave raids, where their specialized classes helped get new captures organized and moving quickly.

I don't think I'll have a problem with killing them either.

After the lesson, Nathan had to spend a few minutes controlling his anger. It had been an enlightening lesson, but it had reminded Nathan of what was going on across the mountains while he lazed around in Gemore.

Over lunch Stella encouraged everybody to eat quickly so they could get to the practice fields as soon as possible. Aarl and Sarah went back for seconds, then thirds that they didn't really eat while Stella glared. They still left the dining hall earlier than most, and beelined for the private training area.

There, Nathan finally turned to the derivations and logic behind Ampere's law and Faraday's law. From seeing the generator, Stella had accepted that a moving magnetic field could move a charge to make current, but unifying all of it and describing the surface integral so that she *got* it was taking a little while.

It was the nice part of tutoring somebody one-on-one – you could ask questions Socratically and be sure they understood everything, and weren't just nodding along to get to the next part of the lesson.

Meanwhile, the rest of the Heirs were doing various kinds of weapons practice or running drills. Sarah had made some dummy cartridges from spent casings, and was practicing rapidly reloading the revolvers, as well as incorporating them into her usual cycling of weapons. The more she practiced, the more Nathan saw that the revolvers were quickly becoming a weapon of choice, even if she wasn't live-firing them very often. Nathan knew Stanel planned to take Sarah out into Old Gemore with Beatred later to practice privately and at longer ranges with both types of firearms.

Khachi was working on quickly summoning divine mana to enhance his shield and hammer without requiring a lengthy prayer. He had gotten much quicker with the shield but was having trouble imbuing the divine power into his hammer as rapidly.

Aarl was going through sword drills with the new sabers, getting an exact feel for their weight and also working out the best ways to draw them from his pouch and trigger the enchantments nearly instantaneously. They weren't empowered yet, but it didn't stop Aarl from practicing.

Finally, Nathan was satisfied that Stella had understood Faraday's law, and why changing magnetic flux caused a voltage over a wire.

Then it was time for the Heirs to break and go to individual tutoring. Stella walked toward her parents but looked back at Nathan with a twinkle in her eye. "I'll be right back."

She exchanged a few quick words with them, pointing back at him. Dalo looked like he was about to argue, but Kullal raised her hands placatingly. Then, Stella stormed back towards Nathan while Dalo shot him an admonishing look.

The short, red-haired mage waved to her parents without looking back, dismissing them. She gestured back to the practice area. "Let's keep going. I want to figure this out *today*."

Chapter 66

Very Very Frightening

Nathan looked over at Stella's parents. Dalo had a peeved expression on his face while Kullal merely appeared curious. Dalo almost started striding in their direction before Kullal grabbed his sleeve and pulled him back. They had a short conversation before taking to the air and flying back to their home.

Doesn't seem like my place to get involved with family discussions. If Stella wants to keep learning about electricity and magnetism instead of her parent's magic tutoring, I'm not gonna say no. We'll deal with it if it becomes an issue.

They moved back to the practice field, and Nathan launched into the topic of Ampere's law, which described how a moving charge created a rotating magnetic field. He didn't go into special relativity and the concept of reference frames but was able to communicate the idea well enough.

It felt like [Lecturing] was pushing at its boundaries, ready to Develop but awaiting an appropriate Insight. It was only low-tier, so it made sense that it would be easier to Develop.

Stella examined the latest set of equations as she played with her floating sand simulation of a moving charge.

She looked back up at Nathan. "Okay, I think I understand these forces. Now, how do I use them to make lightning? And what about light? Is that going to require a whole new set of mathematical equations? I'm still interested, but..."

Nathan was lost for words for a few seconds. He'd kind of forgotten the ultimate goal of all of this – allowing Stella to generate new types of mana without having to take up a class skill.

He scratched the back of his head. "Well, it's not too much farther to get to light, actually. Though we'll be missing some of the details..."

Stella shook her head. "I can think of so many amazing things I can do with lightning now that I understand how it works! But how do I *get* there? I need to manipulate charge with magic, but what's the first step? I don't just want to understand it, I want to *use* it!"

She was starting to get frustrated – which was fair. She'd just spent a ton of time learning several college classes worth of math and physics, all with the promise that it would let her shoot lightning.

And now the last leap was the final stumbling block. Nathan thought for a moment.

Natural sources of lightning. Well, there's the obvious one. And Stella has air mana. Not water mana, but static is all about friction between insulators anyway.

Nathan grinned, then turned to Stella. "Okay, so static electricity is what makes lightning. Static shocks are imbalances of charge that are generated by rubbing things that *don't* conduct electricity against one another. For normal lightning, it's usually about collisions between water, but static *can* happen when air rubs against itself too.

"I want you to try using air mana to make a bunch of woven bands of air, which are rubbing against each other. Have two different flows, each moving in a different direction and converging on different points. Maybe make the flows with two different gas compositions, if you can?"

Stella frowned at his description, especially when he mentioned making the streams of air have different compositions. She sighed and threw up her hands. "Why not! Let's try it out."

She gestured for Nathan to step back. The mage spent a few minutes fiddling with empty air, concentrating intently on something invisible to Nathan.

Then she banished the attempted spell with a frustrated gesture. "No. That doesn't work.... How about *this*?"

She fiddled with the spell some more. Nathan would've loved to help, but he didn't understand how to *make* a spell all that well, so he trusted that Stella could figure it out.

The mage turned back to Nathan, digging her fingers into her auburn hair in frustration. "That doesn't work either. It feels like cheating, if all I needed to do was rub some air together, and not learn all of that dumb *math*." Then she paused. "I wonder... force spells can block lightning, but they start acting strange afterwards. I wonder if they build up charge?"

She turned and jogged back to their suite, Nathan following along behind the agitated mage. The sun was setting and people were heading to dinner, but Stella ignored them and went into the main room, where she pulled out the generator and gestured for Nathan to spin it.

He obliged, putting his back into it. He didn't know what Stella was planning, but he was going to let her apply the knowledge she'd learned.

Soon enough there was a faint sparking between the generator wires. Stella stuck her finger into the gap, her face intent. The sparks had to sting, but she left her hand there for a minute. She withdrew her hand and conjured a small pane of force between the two wires.

"Keep turning it. I want to see..." She left the force block there for twenty seconds, then reached her hand back into the device. There was a much larger *pop* this time as Stella's hand approached the pane of force. She jumped and shook out her hand.

I think the force pane acted a bit like a capacitor, storing a charge. Wild.

She examined the construct before dismissing the force pane and making a more complicated force construct with two panes that joined together in a narrow spike. The spike was aimed at her, and Nathan frowned at the force construct.

But she hadn't told him to stop, so Nathan kept spinning the generator. After a moment, faint sparks started to bounce around at the point of the force spike. Stella grabbed a spare magnet in one hand and closed her other hand around the point, hiding the sparks. She moved the hand holding the magnet to be next to the hand covering the sparking spike.

"I understand that this is just a moving charge, a *current*. I know how it's made, by a moving magnetic field. I can guide it with my magic."

Her hair started to stand up. It was still tied in a tight braid, but strands escaped and fluttered around her head. Stella extended the hand holding the magnet away from her and pointed her finger out. Faint tendrils of electricity started jumping from her finger, as if it was a van de graaff generator. She started chuckling, ramping up into a full-blown cackle as the tendrils grew stronger and the distinctive *crackling* of electricity discharge ramped up.

"And if I wrap it with a spinning field from the magnet, I can guide it..." The manifold tendrils narrowed down to a cone, then to a line of crackling electricity extending a foot away from her hand.

The door opened and Khachi walked into the room, turning to ask about the crackling noise in the room. He nearly walked into the faint line of electricity which reached out towards his armor. He fell over on his ass as Stella, still laughing, discontinued the spell with a flourish.

She stood there for a moment, cackling and raising both hands in triumph. Her hands twitched involuntarily and looked faintly burned. She turned to Nathan and gave him a hug, magic robes be damned. Nathan hugged back and was rewarded with a static shock for his trouble. It almost interrupted his attempt to hold back his antimagic as Stella's still-staticky hair climbed up his nose.

She pushed away, beaming ear-to-ear. "I have two new mana types now. One for electricity, another for magnetism! I've never heard of that one before, so I doubt there are many existing spells for it. But that just means I get to invent them!"

She spun, full of excitement, and hugged Khachi as he climbed to his feet. He looked down at Stella and gently patted her on the shoulder.

He turned his attention back to Nathan. "That seems to have gone well?"

Nathan nodded, also smiling. "I think Stella might need some healing though. Please make it thorough."

She blinked, looking down at her hands. "Oh. Ow. Yes please."

Khachi sighed, shaking his head as he bent over Stella's hands, muttering a long prayer to heal the electrical burns.

Those can be scary as hell – getting zapped can leave you with mild skin burns but lethal internal burns.

He urged Khachi to keep going, and he obliged, sweeping Stella with multiple passes of his healing magic.

Stella was having trouble staying still, prancing around the room with excitement. "Electricity! And magnetism! Dragon's breath, that's exciting."

Her enthusiasm was infectious, and Nathan couldn't help but prompt her. "Congratulations, you understand one of the four fundamental forces of reality! And there's one more part to it. Light, remember?"

She turned back, a bit flushed. "One of the *four*? Don't you think we've done enough for one evening?" She stopped talking, mouth still slightly open. "What am I *saying?* Teach me of light, O master of the mountain!"

Nathan grabbed a slate, making a quick sketch. Once you understood Maxwell's equations, it was easy to make the jump to generalized electromagnetic waves. You could figure it out yourself if you just thought about it, and all Nathan needed to do was guide Stella in the right direction.

"This is simple. Say you have an independent magnetic field, without a source. Don't worry about how it started. It just goes from nothing to *this* vector, then dies out again." Nathan looked up, judging Stella's reaction.

She was calming down but looking doubtfully at the slate. "But it can't come from *nothing*."

"Bear with me. Once it goes away, since there's nothing causing it, it's a changing magnetic field. So what does that make?" He prompted her by gesturing with the chalk.

"An electric field."

"Right. Which would be in *this* direction, perpendicular to the original magnetic field, if slightly offset. But then you have an electric field with no source, so *that* goes away. And that makes..."

Stella was looking at the slate with some concentration. Nathan could tell she was connecting the dots. "That makes a magnetic field without a source. Just like what you started with. But farther along."

She looked up at Nathan. "And that's light? Just alternating electric and magnetic fields? It would just keep going until it ran into something. It's not a physical *thing,* just a perpetuating alternating field, traveling perpendicular to the field directions. Just a force...."

Nathan smiled. All it had taken was a little push.

Congratulations, you have Developed the [Low-tier Lecturing] utility skill into [Mid-tier Lecturing].

Utility skill: [Mid-tier Lecturing]
This skill will help you explain concepts in the future, smoothing over gaps and aiding greatly in explanation and understanding. Will not help you convey details you do not know, and will not help you suppress people's doubts about what you are teaching.

Nathan commented on her statement. "Effectively right. Light is electromagnetic waves. And more than that. You can't separate out the two fields in light, and they don't really have a directionality in quite the way that it seems. They're also quantized because it's like a packet of waveforms moving along. I can explain some of that with math, but it gets even more complicated."

Stella barely heard him. She was looking off into the middle distance, her jaw hanging open. "It's. Wait. That's too big..." She sat there, mumbling for a moment.

Khachi squinted at them like they were speaking a different language. Which they essentially were.

Yeah, the language of math, built to describe physical reality.

Stella sat down heavily on the couch. It seemed like the idea Nathan had given her was too big for her to process all at once.

And I didn't even go over the full thing. You kind of need special relativity and frames of reference to properly understand it. Maybe later!

Khachi spoke up, looking concerned. "Stella? Is there a problem?"

She looked up at him, her gaze unfocused. Then she raised a hand in the air, and it flashed with sparks and a flickering light. The sparks were unfocused and jumped back to Stella's own hand. She twitched and pulled her hand back as it was shocked, her hair rising into the air once more.

A scabbarded knife on the table next to her had jerked, and Nathan could feel the magnetism mana from here. It felt like warm wires dragging over his skin. He guessed she'd just poured a bunch of electric and magnetic mana together, trying to make light in the way that Nathan had explained.

Mid-tier Identify 5 achieved!

Khachi looked even more worried. "Stella? This is the wrong time to experiment with even more new mana types. Look at me." He stepped closer, wary of the way her braid had started rising on its own. He shot a desperate look to Nathan, who took the hint.

Nathan stepped forward, burrowing through the aura of charged mana. He grabbed onto Stella's hand as it reached upwards once again. "Stella, hold on. Don't go too quickly. Lightning is dangerous, don't try to make up spells with it on the fly. That's how you kill yourself. You know better than this."

A jolt of mana came out of her hand again, both lightning and magnetism. Nathan absorbed it smoothly, examining the magnetic mana for the second time. Stella's spell was unfocused, as if she'd jammed the two mana types together and hoped they fit.

Mid-tier Spellsense 8 achieved!

He leaned down and yelled in her ear. "STELLA!"

She shook her head, then her eyes focused on Nathan's, just a foot in front of her face. They locked eyes for a moment, and Nathan saw lightning crackling in a spiraling pattern inside her pupils.

Stella sucked in a breath and looked away. "Sorry. I wanted to try it... I think I need to go talk to my parents. They need to know about this."

Nathan nodded, then pulled her up. "Do you mean to teach them the Insight?"

Stella wobbled as she rose, her motions jerky. She snorted disdainfully. "No. I don't know if I *can*. There's so much that they would need to understand... and they both have lightning already. They think of it *completely* differently. It's not just another element like fire. It's a fundamental force. Not a thing. A *field*."

Maybe now's not the time to explain combustion.

Nathan looked to Khachi. "Should we walk her up there?"

The wolfman stroked his chin. "I am glad that this lesson seems to have gone well, but it seems that what Stella needs is advice from her parents on handling powerful Insights."

With that, they escorted their Insight-befuddled teammate up the roads of Gemore to her parent's mansion. She quickly regained her motor control and was soon skipping up the mountain. Nathan made sure to mention to Kullal that Stella hadn't eaten when they dropped her off.

~

Stella did not return that night, and Nathan had to explain to Aarl and Sarah that he *might* have taught her an Insight that was slightly too big for her.

Nathan meditated before bed, as was his usual practice. He was apprehensive about the consequences of what he'd just done. He hoped it didn't end up being a problem for Stella's development as a mage. But with this out of the way, everything *should* be smooth sailing until graduation on the Solstice.

Stella did return the next morning, as they were gearing up for calisthenics. A sleepy-looking Dalo descended from the sky with Stella in tow. He dropped her off, fixing Nathan with a complicated look. Then he broke eye contact and sighed without saying anything. The elderly mage flew away as they started running.

Stella seemed happy and refreshed. She took off immediately, taunting the rest of them to keep up. Khachi looked at Nathan and shrugged before they all followed along.

~

Skill text comparison:

Utility skill: [Low-tier Lecturing]
This skill will help you explain plans and details clearly in the future, smoothing over gaps and aiding in explanation and understanding. Will

not help you convey details you do not know, and will not help you suppress people's doubts about what you are teaching.

Utility skill: [Mid-tier Lecturing]

This skill will help you explain concepts in the future, smoothing over gaps and aiding greatly in explanation and understanding. Will not help you convey details you do not know, and will not help you suppress people's doubts about what you are teaching.

Chapter 67

The Building Charge

Nathan felt more at ease over the next few days. He'd accomplished his goals at empowering the Heirs. They were deadlier than ever, and Nathan felt like his own increasing power wouldn't end up eclipsing theirs anytime soon. If anything, he was the one falling behind!

He looked up from stretching one evening as Sarah returned from the tutoring. It was late out, and Nathan could guess why. "Go outside the city with your dad again?"

She nodded, looking satisfied. "Pistol practice in the Caxol's basement, then long-range shooting outside the city. I can kill a stalker with one rifle shot from half a mile off."

"I'm glad it's going well. I was worried that they would be too different from the weapons you grew up practicing with." Nathan got up from the ground, pleased with his flexibility.

"Stanel trained us to use every weapon, just like he does. But even he recognizes that the guns are something special." Sarah hesitated for a moment before continuing. "I dropped a skill called [Straight Flight] earlier. It would help my weapons fly straight through difficult winds – but that seems less of an issue with guns. I picked up one called [Gunslinging] instead. It improves the speed for drawing and reloading."

Nathan's eyebrows raised. "Can you show me?"

In a flash, both of Sarah's pistols were in her hands, aimed at a couch to Nathan's right. "No need to draw back my arm or load an arrow. Just... aim and fire." She gave Nathan a grin. "These are indeed weapons worthy of a Questor."

At that moment, Stella staggered through the door, collapsing on the couch that Sarah was aiming at.

Sarah holstered her weapons, taking in the exhausted mage. "Practicing new mana types with your parents?"

"Did you need a prophecy to learn that?" Stella's sarcastic response was muted by a yawn, but she also looked happy. "They don't want to teach me many lightning spells. They're costly on mana and very dangerous. But that's the entire point. And they know they can't stop me now that I have the mana types."

"What about magnetic mana? Do they know any spells for that?"

Stella waved a hand dismissively at Nathan's questions. "No. Dalo did mutter about some Kalis conclave spell references, but it seems rarer than a dragon's egg." Her tired face morphed into a satisfied grin. "But it's great for guiding lightning. The most complicated part of lightning spells is guiding the mana – and magnetic mana is excellent at it. I'm building my own lightning spells, replacing the guidance mechanisms with magnetic constructs."

"We'll practice with it tomorrow?" Nathan asked.

Stella nodded. "After I sleep."

The next day, Nathan got to know the humming crackle of lightning mana even better. It was a great way to efficiently recharge his Stamina, given the cost and speed of lightning mana. Stella's growing prowess at targeting meant she could nail him from across the battlefield with a lightning bolt to completely fill his Stamina. Even when Nathan tried to dodge the bolts to give her better practice, he mostly failed. The spell was nearly instantaneous, and Stella's aim was *good*.

They emerged from the practice yard to a number of awed and jealous looks thrown Stella's way by the other Adventurer mages. After all, it was hard to hide that you were throwing around lightning bolts in the practice yard. Only a handful of mages in all of Gemore could use lightning mana – and most of them were over level 243, since they'd gained the mana type from a class Development.

Over the next few days, Nathan helped Stella experiment with magnetic mana-only spells, holding up magnets or chunks of metal for her to throw around.

After a lot of failure, she got frustrated. "The mana's too slippery on its own! I can create spiraling constructs to guide lightning, but a simple flow to throw metal isn't working!"

Picking up the spray of metal pieces, Nathan nodded silently. He didn't have much to add – this wasn't something he had a lot of expertise with.

After a bit more practice, he broached a topic they'd dropped earlier. "Are you interested in trying to get light mana again?"

"No." Stella answered quickly, eyes downcast. "My parents made me promise not to. They said they'd help me with it after graduation, but my dad said it was a undead-brained move to learn another mana type before then."

Later in the week, Nathan did more sparring with Aarl. He was working with sabers more now, getting familiar with the blades now that his new swords were charged. Stella had charged one with lightning and the other with force mana earlier, and they were potent weapons.

He'd demolished a score of even the toughest training dummies, and was forced to spar with Nathan, who could resist even that level of magical firepower. The force-blade extended far enough to rival the reach of his favored greatsword, and the projected edge could take chunks out of mundane steel – though they broke on Nathan's arms.

Meanwhile, the lightning-blade struck like a thunderbolt with each blow, zapping the target with electricity while letting loose a directional detonation of concussive force. Even though Nathan could absorb most of the attack, the concussion was enough to send him skidding back with every blow.

So much power was released with each hit that the sword only lasted for a dozen blows before Stella had to recharge it, but Aarl could deliver those dozen blows in half as many seconds. It was an impressive display of rapidly delivered firepower capable of taking down the toughest enemies.

The last member of the Heirs hadn't been slacking either. Nathan regularly sparred with Khachi as the cleric worked on incorporating divine magic into his fighting style more and more.

"Again."

Nathan shrugged, once again setting himself to charge at his teammate. His legs carried him rapidly over the sandy ground before he threw himself shoulder-first at his training partner.

In the second before impact a golden barrier spread outwards from the shining shield. Nathan crashed through it before impacting the metal. Khachi held him back easily, but Nathan wasn't trying to knock him over.

"It was faster that time. And tougher. More imbued with the will to protect." Nathan's ability to give detailed feedback was invaluable to Khachi, and his magic was progressing by leaps and bounds. The divine power was more potent, quicker to activate and more focused since he'd made the decision to focus more on the magic to the expense of martial ability. Khachi could heal at range now and could wreath his hammer in divine energy in a bare second.

Not to be outdone, Nathan pushed himself to get better at hand-to-hand combat. He focused on getting comfortable parrying weapons with his bare hands. The practice made clear the benefits of his Rage, with the enhanced speed, strength and toughness allowing him to catch a full-strength strike from one of Aarl's unenchanted swords on his outer forearm. He'd stop the blade cold and come away with little more than an easily healed graze.

Those practice bouts with Aarl were quite even – though Nathan had to admit they played to his strengths. Aarl wasn't using enchanted weapons and couldn't run away to gain distance. He'd frantically batter at Nathan, trying to keep him from getting in close to grapple. Every time Nathan managed to grab hold of Aarl, he was able to overpower the younger man quickly.

The spear is a weapon for big monsters. Fighting other people, the speed of my fists is the way to go. I just need to get my hands on them and then my enhanced strength can usually win the day.

Nathan had some free time most afternoons and had been cashing in on his [Magic Absorption] for favors and profits.

Herdin had called him in to help cursebreak a few items she'd had stored away. It was challenging but interesting work, and he'd had to regenerate his hand after a cursed bow ate the original. Literally *ate* it, the weapon growing a pair of wooden jaws and snapping off the limb.

I doubt most people would consider that an "interesting" afternoon.

After a few sessions he'd broken a few items but managed to uncurse some others. Herdin was pleased and paid Nathan in both favors and coin, promising that she'd help him figure out if the *next* item he cursebroke was safe to use.

Mid-tier Identify 6 achieved!

The next afternoon, Stella beckoned Nathan to follow her as she went to meet her parents. "They've managed to scrounge up a pile of contaminated conductive quartz. If you want more favors, this is a way to get them."

Nathan was only too thrilled to follow – though he was expecting to be grilled about the lightning Insight.

Instead, Kullal bowed her head to him. "We acknowledge the weight of the Insights you have given our daughter. Are you willing to do us another favor?"

Dalo looked like he wanted to say more, but Kullal shot him a firm glare, which repeated itself every time it looked like Dalo wanted to bring up the subject of Nathan's Insights.

Instead, they fed Nathan a good dinner, then asked him to purify a pile of conductive quartz contaminated with mana of all kinds. Nathan got familiar with even more varieties of mana, from the shifting strength of metal mana to the sharp-edged slickness of what Nathan could only call *salt* mana.

Maybe just crystal mana?

Mid-tier Spellsense 9 achieved!

After he was done, Dalo inspected the crystals. He looked pleased and turned to Nathan. "I will ask Kia to teach you her [Airwalking] Talent. This favor and the others – they are a heavy burden, and it would go far to balance those scales. She knows how much Stella means to us."

Aw yeah. Next best thing to flight, here I come. Honestly, it might be better than straight flight if it lets me use all of my movement skills.

The other adventuring teams were getting sent out on their own long-distance missions, killing monsters or clearing out lairs around the villages. It seemed to be going well, and it wasn't uncommon for a team to swagger in and brag about the levels they'd earned.

But the Heirs didn't feel the need to keep up. They were *already* ahead and spent a lot of time just hanging out and chatting. The barriers between them were few and growing fewer. Nathan felt at home with them in a way he only had with his closest friends on Earth.

They talked about hopes, fears, and dreams. Their deepening friendships led to discussions of politics, ambitions and what they would do with their growing power. No decisions were made, but they all spoke of ending evils and protecting the people of Gemore in new ways. The Heirs were realizing that they had agency, and the power to back up their opinions with meaningful actions.

~

All too soon, graduation was upon them. On the day before the Solstice, Jolba laid out what would happen. This news was new to most people, since Sudraiel was co-opting a tangle of various traditions for her ceremony.

The Solstice was a day where the sun would not appear. It would vanish one day as it usually did, a dark line sliding across the glowing orb, and then it would not appear the next day. The night sky would grow darker than usual, and wavering lines of light would replace the glowing landscape that usually spread across the sky. The sun would reappear on the dawn of the second day.

It was tradition for Adventurers to trek up to the very top of Gemore to guard the Seal during the Solstice, when the sky was dark. The seal would start glowing, shining brightly enough to light up the sky at noon. Sudraiel would give a speech before having them swear the Adventurer's Oath, next to the glowing Seal.

It sounded like a whole *thing*.

Nathan had another dinner with the Guardians of Gemore, catching up with Leska and Xarian. They seemed very pleased that Nathan was keeping up with the Heirs. Xarian's wife Krisa confided in Nathan that they'd been worried about the Heirs being completely dependent on their parents, and mostly cut off from the broader Adventurer society because of it. They were glad that Nathan was an outside influence.

Though I'm not exactly a great bridge to the rest of the Adventurers.

Some kind of horse-trading went on behind the scenes, and Kia agreed to teach Nathan the airwalking Talent. *After* he swore the Adventurer's Oath at graduation.

All too soon, it was the day before the Solstice. Their classes had wrapped up without fanfare, and Nathan had never seen the Adventurer's Guild so packed. The Giantraiders along with dozens of other teams were back in Gemore for the occasion.

Nathan noticed that a lot of the Adventurers were tense – and wary. He found Vhala. "Why are the Adventurers treating this like the eve of battle?"

The broad dark woman set down her ale and wiped her lips. She looked the same as when Nathan had first met her outside Taeol's tower.

When she answered him, it was with a frown. "Bad things happen on the Solstice. Big monster attacks. Strange magic. People say the Seal wakes it all up, that all the monsters in the world want to break the Seal on the Solstice. So we guard it, and the city people take refuge in the fortresses under the mountain. The villages hunker down too, but they've never been attacked. The monsters go for the Seal." She shrugged. "Most years, nothing happens... but when something does happen, it's always a battle worthy of remembering. On the worst years a few Questors show up to help out. That hasn't happened for decades."

Nathan thanked her, then spent a few hours trying to relax with the Heirs. They were all nervous, both about graduation and the Oath, as well as the Solstice itself. They played some card games to pass the time, conversing about training and what kinds of jobs they wanted to take after graduation.

Nathan didn't fully relax until he meditated before bed. There was a sense of impending doom hanging over everything. But what would come, would come. Nathan had done what he could to prepare himself and his friends for any threat they could reasonably handle. Worrying about it now would only hamper his readiness.

Anything that came at Gemore would need to contend with a city full of formidable Adventurers, ranging from the Guardians of Gemore all the way down to Nathan and the other trainees.

–

The next morning was quiet, as if a pall had fallen over the city. The Heirs woke up earlier than usual but didn't do their normal exercises, instead trooping over to the dining hall in the predawn gloom. The sky was growing darker, with the continents overhead fading as dawn approached. Dozens of faint pinpricks of lights slowly replaced the normal skyscape. They were in various colors, from purple to red, and looked something like stars in the sky, but spaced at regular intervals.

Breakfast was subdued. All the trainees ate in silence, quickly finishing a hearty meal heavy on carbohydrates. Then Jolba ushered them out of the dining hall, and together they started to climb the mountain that Gemore was built into.

The trainees were joined by all the other Adventurers in the city, forming a silent pilgrimage up the steep slope. Every Adventurer Nathan had met was in the procession, from Artha and the Giantraiders to Eldred and the Vanguard and the Guardians of Gemore.

The city was well-lit by magical lights mounted on buildings, and the guard was out in force. Nathan looked back over his shoulder and saw the wall fully manned, with lights shining outwards onto the killing field around the city.

They walked up towards the peak of the city. The sky was even darker now, and Nathan realized how accustomed he'd become to the glowing world overhead. Now it was gone. Nathan felt like he was alone in the wilderness back on Earth, with a black sky pressing down upon him.

The mood was somber as everybody felt the oppressive darkness, with few conversations as they climbed the steep slopes of Gemore.

Nathan saw city folk hurrying past in the dark. They carried magical lights or torches and congregated around the entrances to the bunkers dug into the mountain. The guard was also manning the bunkers, though not as heavily as the outer walls of the city.

They're preparing for a full-scale attack.

They climbed higher than Nathan had ever been, to the council chambers sheltered under the overarching stone. The building was ancient, obviously original to Old Gemore, and possessed of a level of craftsmanship and elegance that reminded Nathan of the Sagrada Família or Hagia Sophia. Nathan spent a moment examining the building, admiring its grand scale, flowing stone architecture and clear defensive nature – before Sarah elbowed him and gestured onwards.

They walked past the council chambers to a grand staircase that cut through the stone. The staircase led into a broad and high-ceilinged tunnel that climbed up the inside of the cresting wave of stone that hung over much of Gemore.

The stairs were wide and shallow, the space dimly lit by magical lights set into the walls. With so many people in the enclosed space, the sounds of boots and hooves on stone echoed loudly, only interspersed by the occasional cough. Still nobody spoke. It was a solemn occasion, full of majesty.

That sense of majesty redoubled when they reached the end of the staircase, which led onto a broad and mostly flat area atop the mountain. The dark sky stretched above, seemingly ready to swallow them in its enormity.

As Nathan gazed upwards, his eyes adjusted, and the distant dots of light came into view once more. Nathan might have imagined it, but he thought he saw threads of light connecting the dots. The lines shifted in color and wavered like a faint aurora borealis.

Nathan tore his gaze from the sky as the crowd of Adventurers pushed through the chill wind of the mountain peak. They were high above the ruined city of Old Gemore, standing on the curved top of the mountain.

The stone underfoot was natural and rough, and there were no railings. The area around them curved down gradually for hundreds of feet on either side of the ridge-like mountaintop. In one direction that slope suddenly dropped away over the city of Gemore, and in the other, it continued down the steep back of the wave-shaped mountain.

They were headed towards the Seal. It had been described to Nathan like a big stone door set into the top of the mountain. Now that he saw it in person, he'd say it reminded him of a vault door from the *Fallout* games. Glowing blue lines traced a pattern like an irising camera lens on the forty-foot-wide stone circle, and a beam of light shot upwards from the center of the Seal. Nathan squinted and could make out spidery symbols glowing on the recessed stone surface. They looked nothing like the enchantments Nathan had grown somewhat familiar with through Herdin's tutelage.

On the other side of the Seal was a wide plinth, supporting an obelisk whose outline was vague in the darkness.

Sudraiel stepped up onto the plinth in front of the obelisk and was lit from beneath by the light from the Seal. She was dressed in a sleek breastplate and fine chainmail, carrying her spear like a staff of office.

Her voice was loud and shocking after the lack of conversation on their journey.

"Take up your assigned positions! Trainees stay here. Scouting revealed no groupings of monsters, so we should be safe. But consider this the start of your final lesson. *Take no chances on the Solstice!*"

Chapter 68

The Tales of Endings

There was a moment of silence after Sudraiel's words, then the creak of leather and scrape of boots as the experienced Adventurers formed a perimeter around the blue-glowing Seal. Several teams took to the sky, led by the Guardians of Gemore as Dalo cast [Mass Flight].

The trainees remained in a large clump next to the Seal, separated by team. They looked around to ensure that they weren't supposed to be doing anything, some talking in quiet voices. Simla and his team were nearby, and Nathan noticed Simla shooting glances at him. Behind them were Nornan and the Dusteaters, laughing at a quiet joke. The trainees stood and muttered for a few minutes before another figure came into view atop the plinth, lit from below by the iridescent light of the Seal.

It was Faline. Her hair blew in the wind, and the light reflecting from the colored streaks looked like a stream of viridian sparks. Green eyes flashed with light and her voice cut through the wind more cleanly than Sudraiel's yell, reaching all of the Adventurers spread around the mountaintop. Her speech was formal, with a ritualistic cadence.

"And now we begin the oldest of the Guild's traditions! The story of the slain and the spinning of their stories. Listen and learn, for the lessons of this lecture are as much a part of our Guild as the ground of Gemore.

"This is a time when we speak of Endings. I begin with the tale of a man known only by deed and legacy! A man long dead, whose shadow looms long upon us all. His name was Istin, and at first he had no other, for Istin was born a slave of Giantsrest. He was no soldier, but a worker who cleaned trash and scrubbed floors. When the slaves rose to cast Giantsrest down, Istin was one of them.

"That day was darker than the sky of today, but Istin stood with his fellows. He fought mages that blasted them with fire and death. He killed one with a broom and was badly wounded by another. His class Developed from that fight, and he was the first of *my* kind. The kind of adventurer who creeps in the darkness and strikes from the shadows. An Assassin of Gemore, who strikes those who think themselves invulnerable in their fortresses. And he chose his name that day, as *Bho*."

Nathan noticed the trainees with the dark skin and broad frame of the Bhos stand straighter as Faline named their ancestor.

Faline proceeded to tell of Istin Bho's Adventurers, how he had delved into the dungeons of Old Gemore and killed Giantsrest mages and their households in the darkness of night. Many of his friends died, but he and a few others achieved a high level. They had families, gathered magical items and protected Gemore from the early assaults of Giantsrest. Faline told how he'd had children and started the Bho clan to follow in his footsteps as an Adventurer of Gemore.

"There were many whose stories are the same, and many are descended from them. Gemore owes its existence to the first generation of Adventurers. But Istin's story is always told first today, on the Solstice.

"And that is because he was the *first to kill an archmage*. The Archmage Gralus raised his faction and marched the streets of Giantsrest with scores of mages, ranks of golems and legions of slave soldiers. His parade was a showcase of pageantry and power, a declaration of his designs upon Gemore.

"Istin Bho killed him before he left the city. He leapt from a rooftop and used an Old Gemore blast disk to shatter the shield of Gralus' platform before butchering him beyond any hope of healing. He cast the would-be conqueror's head toward the other archmages and declared, *'thus to those who threaten Gemore.'* To this day, any archmage who considers attacking our city must consider Istin's Lesson."

Faline raised her arms to the sky, looking upwards towards the lights. Her voice grew more strident, like a prophet leading a prayer. "And on this day, the day of the Solstice, a day of remembrance for those lost, *remember Istin's lesson.* For though Istin killed Gralus, and the invasion was stopped, Istin was slain by the assembled mages of Giantsrest in turn.

"The first duty of an Adventurer of Gemore is to protect its people. The final duty is to be willing to do *whatever it takes* to accomplish that goal. For we must teach Istin's Lesson again and again to greedy Giantsrest. The cost of that lesson is in the lives of the Adventurers of Gemore. We can make them fear the cost of their invasion, but only by being willing to stake our own lives on that cost."

She pointed towards the assembled trainees, and her hand was suddenly filled with a long dagger which seemed to cut the light of the Seal.

"And that is Istin's Lesson. To safeguard our home, we must be more committed to protecting Gemore than Giantsrest is to conquering us." With that pronouncement Faline lowered her hand. Her glowing green eyes stared into the crowd of trainees, and Nathan could swear that she was looking straight at him.

"The Assassins of Gemore teach this lesson. If you wish to hunt mages unseen, to teach them the meaning of *fear*, speak of it. We will find you and teach you to kill all who reside in Giantsrest."

Her mouth curved in a smile and one eye flashed pink before she *vanished*. Nathan focused his mind, trying to see through what was likely a very advanced stealth Talent or collection of powerful skills.

Awfully bloodthirsty... she's gotta be some kind of [Assassin] variant.

With the darkness and the shifting light cast by the Seal, Nathan caught not a trace of the elusive woman.

The trainees broke out in whispers. Aarl leaned into the center of their small circle. "She's scary. I wouldn't want to go into the heart of Giantsrest for any reason."

Khachi spoke a little louder in his response, making heads turn in their direction. "There is reason for all to listen when she speaks."

Kadid was the next to climb to the top of the plinth and be illuminated by the Seal. "Now it's time to speak of those we knew. I'll start with my nephew Tygal Bho, who died this past summer to a Northern Wyvern." He proceeded to tell Tygal's story – who he was, how he'd lived and how he'd died.

Oh. This is a time for eulogies.

Adventurer after Adventurer mounted the plinth, telling the tales of Adventurers past. Not all of these people had died in the past year, with some particularly glorious stories having been passed down from generation to generation. Many of the stories were long, but the trainees stood rapt, hearing the tales of their predecessors. The legends of those who had come before them, as Adventurers of Gemore.

Not all of them had died in battle, and some of the most celebrated were those who had lived through all of their years and raised a new generation of Adventurers. Others had died without witnesses, and there was a lot of, "and then they went into the dungeon and never came out."

One recent example of that was the Gray Moon Order. They had gone into the Monastery of Quaz on the most recent Delve day, the one that the Grave Tangle had come out of. They had been a group of scholars and mages who focused on necromancy and the safe disarming of Quazian ruins.

The one telling their story was an old crowfolk woman named Gale Shullet. She headed the Tower of Trickery, where illusion mages like Wiam were trained. Gale didn't judge the Grey Moon Order. She just seemed sad that experienced Adventurers had died to something that probably wasn't their fault.

There was another lesson there, that was communicated through the stories being told. Sometimes you failed and died, and it wasn't your fault. Sometimes there was an undetectable sensor in a random corridor that set off a bomb, unleashed a magical plague or awoke an ancient army.

Some of the stories were funny, some were sad. All were proud of the legacy of the Adventurers of Gemore. Nathan felt the weight of tradition start to press down upon him. These stories communicated what being an Adventurer of Gemore *meant*. It meant glory in battle, standing against impossible odds, and being willing to die to protect the city. Most of the Adventurers around Nathan were descended from those whose stories they were hearing, and Nathan felt like an intruder in this space.

He hadn't been raised here – he had come to Gemore only a few months ago, and now he was taking part in their most sacred ceremony. Nathan found himself awed at this beautiful tradition, the way it encouraged new Adventurers to feel part of something larger than themselves. Indeed, many of the faces around him were awestruck and wet with tears.

The stories continued and the light of the Seal grew more focused, more intense. Instead of a directed glow, it projected a beam of light up into the air. Enough diffused out to light the top of the mountain, but the beam seemed to thicken and intensify until it reflected off the sparse clouds overhead.

I bet that would be actually blinding to look into from above. We're only seeing a tiny spillover of light from here. You don't see a laser if you're standing next to it, only the reflection from what it's pointed at.

As the night continued the clouds dispersed, and the other points of light in the sky also brightened. The aurora that Nathan thought he had imagined earlier proved to be very real, connecting the lights in the sky with a wavering iridescence that was beautiful to behold.

The day wore on, and the stories continued. Nathan learned of other teams who had died, some recently, some famously, some both. Nathan could tell who supported Sudraiel's agenda and who didn't by the message of their stories, by how they described the deeds of past Adventurers. The event was too solemn and serious for the petty politics to emerge into the open, but the subtext of the progressive and traditional factions of Adventurers was clear.

Nathan was listening to a slightly rambling story about a team called the Sky Spears, who had died five years ago fighting a rock elemental. He found himself watching the sky. The dots of light overhead had only increased in brightness, and the shifting streamers of light coming off them looked like a distant spiderweb, blowing in a cosmic wind. Then Nathan saw another aurora, much closer to hand. It was branching off of the beam emerging from the Seal. The clouds had cleared, and he saw a wavering banner of light stretching off to the north.

Wait, are all *those points Seals? Just ones on the world above my head? That's... big.*

Nathan squinted upwards, trying to use the light to make out the continents above. But he was interrupted by a *thump* from the dais.

Sudraiel stood there, lit brightly by the Seal. Its glow was ramping up faster and faster, casting shadows behind everybody nearby.

Sudraiel brought the butt of her spear down on the dais again with another *thump*, then raised her voice in a yell. "We are blessed by a peaceful Solstice, and so it is time for the Tale of Endings! A story older than Gemore, older than Giantsrest, told across Davrar!"

The faint burble of conversation died completely, leaving only the breeze that soon calmed itself. It felt like the whole world was waiting for Sudraiel to continue.

She spoke slowly, clearly, as if reciting an oral epic. It had a kind of rhythmic meter to it, though it wouldn't carry over to English.

"The Solstice, and the Seal, our oldest tradition.
But older yet is the tale remembered past the Ending of the World.
The Tale of Endings is not something written. It is for times when writing is lost,
times when civilization dies, when there is no priority but survival.
Remember the Endings when cities die and the land breaks.
If you lose all else, if nothing else will survive, preserve yourselves, and preserve the Tale of Endings!
This is the story of how the world Ends.
We record not what was lost, but how it was lost.
The Prophecy will allow survival of the Endings."

There was a moment of absolute silence, and Sudraiel leaned on her spear, gathering herself before launching stridently into the next part of the Tale of Endings.

"The world has ended before, and will end again! The order of the Endings is the only part of the story that truly matters.
"Magic
Gods
Monsters
Undeath
Wrath
Storm
Deicide
Elements
History
Spite
Silence."

Sudraiel paused and continued in a more normal voice. "Those who founded Giantsrest survived the Ending of Elements, and next is the Ending of History. We clear the Dungeons, that History's wrath may pass us by. Now, again, and *remember.*"

Her tone grew formal once more as she recited the list a second time.

This time, the crowd chanted the Endings along with her. Nathan joined in, remembering the order from the first recital. As he spoke, Nathan closed his eyes and came up with a mnemonic story for the Endings, to ensure he would never forget them.

"Magic
Gods
Monsters
Undeath
Wrath
Storm
Deicide
Elements
History
Spite
Silence."

There was a moment of silence, then Sudraiel continued.

"Three pieces of advice follow, three for the essentials of food, water and shelter.
First, make common cause, for the Endings will kill all.
Second, the Ending will last three generations, plan for repeated catastrophe.
Third, survival above all else!"

Sudraiel slammed her spear down on the plinth for the third and final time, gazing at the beam of light cast upwards by the Seal, as if waiting for something. The pillar of brightness pulsed in recognition before the light blazed brighter than ever before. There was a faint cry as the other trainees shied back and covered their eyes.

So that's the Tale of Endings. I swear that I'll keep the story alive, however long I may live. This memory, that mnemonic, is stored in the freezer in my Mind Palace, where it will never change or degrade so long as I exist.

Congratulations, you have Developed the [Mid-tier Enhanced Memory] utility skill into [High-tier Enhanced Memory].

[High-tier Enhanced Memory]
You have a detailed mental construct to aid with memory, and a mental process to help you encode information into it. This skill will help you store and recall memories quickly. This process operates quickly and cannot be interfered with by outside sources. With time and effort you can recall older memories and store them in the mental construct.

Nathan blinked away the box and looked upwards, seeing that the pulse of light hadn't just come from here. The spots overhead had also flared with brightness, and the aurora pattern blazed as the tendrils above Nathan reached up and met those reaching down from the dots far overhead. The filaments of light illuminated the object they were reaching towards – a featureless orb in the sky. It was made tiny by distance and directly overhead, where the sun usually was.

More tendrils came from the sides, joining as the entire world was lit by flowing tendrils of magic. Nathan could feel the power in the light now. It was like every form of magic all at once. Only the barest wisps of it reached Nathan, but it felt like the energies of creation. He tried to separate out the components of what he was sensing, but it was like trying to pull one strand of wire from a twisted cable supporting a bridge that crossed an ocean.

The light was bright enough to illuminate the world overhead, and Nathan saw that the other lights – the other Seals – were almost all placed on continents. Some of them were centered on the virulent patches of white and black, looking like the sources of an infection.

And then, after an instant – or a quarter-hour – of gazing spellbound into the sky, the magic tapered off. It happened smoothly but rapidly as the Seal's magic ramped down. Before Nathan knew it, the Seal was just lighting the top of the mountain once more, no longer illuminating Davrar for miles in every direction.

Nearly forgotten, Sudraiel raised her spear to gather the trainees' attention. "*That* is why we defend the Seal on the day of the Solstice." She seemed to deflate. "I will say a few things on the Tale of Endings before we move to the Adventurer's Oath. Hear my words.

"I believe that only the Prophecy of Endings and the three-part advice is original to the Tale, and all else has changed over time. It is a feeling, that there is a groove worn into the world by this Tale. It has been told for many thousands of years, and on this night it is easier to tell truth than to mistake."

She coughed dryly and took a drink from a waterskin, leaning heavily on her spear. But the old woman's duty was not yet done. "The Adventurer's Oath. You will ascend to this platform and swear to me and the gathered Adventurers that you will protect the people of Gemore from monsters, enemies and Endings with your life. The embellishments of the Oath are up to you, but you *will* swear by Davrar and the Endings."

The other Adventurers had relaxed their vigilance and were grouping around the trainees. They didn't seem to be expecting an attack anymore.

Sudraiel focused their attention. "Let the Heirs start. Come forward!"

Another voice interrupted, young and tense with anxiety.

"Wait! There is one of the Heirs who *should not* swear the Oath. Nathan Lark learned of the Endings this very night. He does not know our ways and we do not know his! He shall not become an Adventurer of Gemore. I heard him say he is *not even of Davrar!*"

Nathan turned to see who had spoken. It was Simla, and his outstretched hand was pointing directly at Nathan.

~

Skill text comparison:

[Mid-tier Enhanced Memory]

You have a detailed mental construct to aid with memory. This skill will help you store and recall memories quickly. Only provides fast recall for memories gained after gaining this skill, or memories stored in your mental construct. With time and effort you can recall older memories and store them in the mental construct.

[High-tier Enhanced Memory]

You have a detailed mental construct to aid with memory, and a mental process to help you encode information into it. This skill will help you store and recall memories quickly. This process operates quickly and cannot be interfered with by outside sources. With time and effort you can recall older memories and store them in the mental construct.

Chapter 69

An Aurora Duel

Simla glared at the bewildered Adventurers with a challenging look on his face. "I speak true! Nathan Lark comes from beyond Davrar itself! He is *alien*, and we should not welcome him into our ranks, nor let him swear our most sacred of Oaths! He did not know of the Endings until just now. How can he defend the people of Gemore against them? Who knows what his ways truly are?"

Sudraiel looked down upon Simla, visibly peeved. "What does it matter from where Nathan comes? The Adventurers of Gemore have always allowed wanderers to join and swear, even those who have lost the tradition of Endings. Be silent, Simla. *I* have deemed Nathan worthy, and that is enough. No matter how others may complain." Her gaze passed across Eldred, eyes hardening.

In reply, a rough voice pitched across the mountaintop. "Do not deny that Simla's words hold the weight of truth. If this boy is not from Davrar itself, then we *will* know more. I do not think I speak for just myself in this. Or do you finally give me reason to challenge you, Sudraiel?"

The source of the voice emerged from the crowd of Adventurers. It was an old man, with a grizzled, salt-and-pepper beard and hair. He was tall and broad, standing like a craggy granite outcrop. He clutched a pair of heavily enchanted javelins in one hand. More poked up from a quiver over his shoulder.

Eldred was standing near Simla and cheered the newcomer. "Speak the weighty truths, Kozar!"

Sudraiel turned to address the old man. "Kozar. You'd use this as excuse to challenge me?"

The man shrugged. "Let the boy speak for himself. We've truth-telling skills enough to know if he speaks true. Your pets should be able to defend themselves, and there have been claims that he acts dishonorably." He tilted his head towards Eldred, then gestured for Nathan to take the floor.

Nathan stepped forward and past Khachi, who frowned and gave him a concerned look.

Thoughts flickered through Nathan's head.

I didn't expect this. It seems like a setup – partly political. The traditional faction of Adventurers is coming after me as a way to get to Sudraiel and the Heirs.

Then Nathan's attention landed on Eldred, who was standing at Simla's shoulders and grinning cruelly.

This is Eldred's scheme. He couldn't challenge me, but he found somebody who could. He helped Simla spy on me, then goaded him to do this. He just doesn't want me to be an Adventurer.

Nathan felt the ember of Rage at his core kindle to life. This was petty adventurer drama *bullshit*, and he was not pleased about it.

I want to make these assholes regret screwing with me. How do I respond? Clearly can't lie. Fuck it, my skill helps me be honest. So it's time to be earnest. *Flip the script.*

Nathan focused his mind past the growing anger and rolled his shoulders as he walked up next to the Seal. He turned and looked over the crowd of Adventurers. Some of the gazes coming his way were hostile – but most were merely curious.

"It is true! I come from beyond Davrar. I was brought here by magic, by the power of an archmage of Giantsrest. He sought to control me, but I escaped. The Giantraiders rescued me and brought me to Gemore.

"The Adventurers' Guild of Gemore has taken me in. Become my refuge against this world, with all of its terrors and monsters of all shapes! Gemore has become my new home, and I *will* fight to protect it. Or would you turn away all who ask for help, and can help in return? That seems a path to a proud and selfish death." Nathan met Kozar's eyes, which studied him coldly.

Mid-tier Earnestness 10 achieved! Congratulations, you have maxed out this utility skill! It cannot be improved any further. You must achieve Insight into this skill to Develop it to high-tier.

Simla stepped up to face Nathan in response, every inch a warrior prince. His sleek armor was patterned with gold-and-silver engravings. His hands rested on well-crafted hilts rising from each hip, and a polished bow peeked over his shoulder. Golden eyes glowed faintly at Nathan as they studied each other.

Simla sneered, then spoke. "You speak a pretty story, enough so that I suspect you have a *skill* to help you. But I wonder, how will you weigh your life when the next Ending comes, when it seeks to choke all life from the land and bury us under the weight of History?"

Nathan seethed at Simla's attack. He couldn't outright deny he had a social manipulation skill, but he'd been right in assuming that accusing your enemies of having one was a cheap but valid tactic.

But he could use his [Earnestness] to respond. Nathan considered his next words carefully, seeking to turn the moment to his advantage.

This reveal of the Endings pisses me off. They speak as if the Endings are unavoidable apocalypses which can only be weathered, not fought. They scheme against each other like crabs in a bucket, not thinking to challenge the bucket.

But they know what the future Endings are going to be, so they're deterministic. Something must be causing them. Whatever that is can be worked against. It's gotta be some kind of magical bullshit anyway. I bet there's some magical crystal somewhere that triggers it all. Maybe beneath this very Seal. I'm antimagic, so I might be able to break it.

Nathan locked gazes with Simla, speaking with a cold fury. "In my birthplace, there is a saying, said with many meanings. *The last enemy that shall be destroyed is death.* To me, it means that no enemy, however terrible, cannot be fought. I will not only protect Gemore from the Endings. I will swear my Adventurer's Oath to prevent the Endings altogether. I will *fight back*, not merely fight to survive!"

There was a moment of hushed silence across the entire mountaintop followed by scattered whispers. Nathan [Noticed] Kozar snort, opening his mouth to speak derisively.

Nathan spoke first to cut the man off. He looked past Simla to the other Adventurers, to the Heirs. "Who will join me in this quest to *End the Endings*?"

Kozar's eyebrows rose and he looked mirthful. Eldred guffawed.

Simla smirked. "Nobody will join you in that stupid dream. I think..."

He was interrupted as the Heirs brushed past him, moving to stand behind Nathan as one.

Congratulations, you have Developed the [Mid-tier Earnestness] utility skill into [High-tier Earnestness].

Utility skill: [High-tier Earnestness]
This skill will help you portray your intense conviction and honesty when you interact with people. This skill will encourage people to follow your example in words and actions. Cannot fool truth spells or skills.

Khachi raised his voice first, his chin high and eyes shining with golden light. "I will stand with Nathan Lark, to challenge the very heavens." He put his hand on Nathan's shoulder, continuing in a whisper meant just for Nathan and the other Heirs. "He was preparing to challenge you. Challenge him first."

Stella placed her hand on his other shoulder, continuing where Khachi had left off. "We are the Heirs to traditions that span worlds. If anyone can do this, it is us!"

Her hand sparked where it touched Nathan's skin, and he glanced at her. Stella grinned back malevolently; her eyes lit with lightning as she silently channeled electricity mana into his skin.

Aarl spoke up, jaw set as he glared at Simla. "We must move beyond tradition, beyond merely embracing the past. We must build upon it, for how else will things be better than they were?"

Sarah picked up from him, just as stridently as the others. "We stand upon the shoulders of the Adventurers of Gemore who came before us! We are the Heirs who inherit their power! It is up to us to use it responsibly, to not just react to the evils of the world but to act against them."

The Heirs stood before the assembled Adventurers of Gemore, having just declared their purpose.

Nathan's eyes fell on Simla, who looked perplexed. This clearly hadn't been part of the script.

Time to throw it off a little more.

"Simla. I challenge you to a duel to submission. Here and now, for seeking to prevent me from becoming an Adventurer. For sullying my name and honor."

I'm mad enough to challenge him to a duel to the death, but that's not how these duels work. And that's my Rage talking anyway.

The princely Adventurer, lit by the light cast from behind Nathan, blinked at him for a moment. Then he grinned a vulpine grin, and his hands tightened around the hilts at his hips. "I accept. I will fight you atop the Seal. It shall be our ring!"

Nathan glanced behind him, at the wide disc of stone. The light cast from it was dimming, but it was still bright enough it would make visibility difficult.

You know, I do remember getting offered that [Blinding Resistance] Talent.

Sudraiel and Dalo yelled in denial at the same time. "No!"

They looked at each other, then Dalo waved his hand, and a thirty-foot wide circle of low flames sprouted from the rock. "Fight here instead. The Seal is not a place for a duel." He eyed Nathan with trepidation.

I was so caught up in how cool it would be that I didn't even think that maybe it would be a bad *thing to drain the magic from the Seal. For now.*

Sudraiel relaxed with Dalo's actions. Then she spoke again. "I declare this duel fair! Do any disagree?" She glared at Kozar, who smirked back at her. "Who will stand for Simla Bhola?"

"I will." Eldred walked forward, putting a hand on Simla's shoulder.

"And so shall I." Kozar's voice rang out across the top of the mountain, though Eldred frowned at him.

Eldred leaned down to whisper into Simla's ear, eyes flicking to Nathan. His hands moved subtly down near his side, Eldred's armored bulk hiding it when he surreptitiously pressed a small disk into Simla's hands.

I wonder what that was.

Kozar ran a steely eye over Nathan and the Heirs. "And who will stand for Nathan Lark?"

Kia fell out of the sky in full armor and *slammed* into the ground beside Nathan. She landed in a classic superhero pose, knee pressed into the stone and greatsword held sideways in one hand. She ripped off her helmet and latched it to her belt as she stood.

"I will." The holy warrior spared Kozar a glare before turning and examining Nathan.

He shivered under the intensity of her gaze, but she merely stepped in and whispered quietly. "The spear won't do you any good. Simla's resource is Precision, and he's got skills for speed. He'll seek to bleed you with his enchanted blades, but he *will* go for a deeper cut if given the opportunity. Watch for the tendons in your legs."

She noticed Stella's hand on Nathan's shoulder, faintly sparking as the mage continued to pour magic into Nathan. Stella had to have dumped thousands of mana into him by this point, *way* more than she was supposed to have in her mana pool. Nathan noted the distinct, jittery feeling of Stamina overload, and was having trouble staying still.

Kia snorted, the edges of her lips twitching faintly before she put her helmet back on. "Humble him, Nathan. It will shame those who stand for him."

Then Nathan stood barehanded just inside the ring, facing Simla from twenty feet away. Kozar and Eldred observed from one side, Kia from the other. As one, Kia and Kozar held aloft their weapons.

"Begin."

Nathan settled into a fighting stance, struggling not to fidget with the excess Stamina and anger coursing through him. He wasn't quite as juiced up as after draining the massive necromancy crystal, but this time he was *very pissed off.*

Simla drew his weapons in a flashy pattern and began walking towards Nathan slowly.

I need to keep my Rage in check. Can't kill him. But I believe I can keep it under control. These duels are as much about public opinion as winning. But god do I want to beat his face to a bloody pulp.

Nathan activated his Rage and sprinted at Simla, meeting him in the center of the arena. Simla's eyes widened in surprise as Nathan threw his body forward, hoping the smaller man would try to block his momentum.

But Simla did the clever thing instead, sliding deftly to the side and striking high and low at Nathan's side. Simla's feet took him farther than they should have, and his blades reached farther than their length would suggest.

Nathan snapped out his arm to deflect the sword going for his gut. He tried to bring his hand down to grab the blade, but the sword cut and was gone in an instant.

A stinging pain shot from cuts in his arm and leg, and Nathan hissed in frustration as the cut to the back of his knee made it hard to bend that leg. Blood dripped, staining the ground of the arena. Eldred cheered loudly.

Those blades are heavily enchanted alright. Sharpness, extra cutting force, and a bleeding enchantment, I think. Nothing dimensional, so I wouldn't be surprised if there's a Talent giving them extra reach and maybe letting them cut more than they should.

The magical signature left by the bleeding enchantment snuffed out as Nathan kept his eyes on Simla. The younger man prowled around him like a puma facing down an elk.

He didn't keep contact long enough for my antimagic to do much work on those swords. But I only gotta grab him once. And he knows it.

Nathan turned, keeping his eyes on Simla as his wounds quickly healed. The smaller man's every step seemed to slide across the stone, moving him deceptively far. Simla lunged to the side where he'd cut Nathan's knee, cutting low at Nathan's ankle. His motions were fast and precise as the swords flickered out.

Nathan pivoted and lashed out with a kick to Simla's torso.

Simla had been expecting Nathan's movements to be slowed by the knee injury, and he pulled his attack as he dodged away from Nathan's blow. But Nathan jumped forward, and the kick struck Simla's chest. There was an audible *crack* as the breastplate absorbed the blow, and several of the glowing enchantments went dark.

Simla was tossed back but unharmed by the rib-snapping kick. Nathan's fury demanded that he follow through, and he chased Simla as the smaller man tried to retreat and regroup.

Nathan didn't give him room, remembering his practice with Aarl. He needed to get in close, to grab Simla and pound the *bejesus* out of him. Nathan was very much looking forward to punching the smirk off that face.

Simla edged away, but Nathan was careful not to build up too much momentum and get baited into overextending. He had movement skills of his own, and when Simla skittered aside, he matched the movements.

Nathan lunged forward and reached out, relying on his movement skills to keep his balance. Simla backpedaled furiously, flicking quick strikes at Nathan with both hands. His movements were fast, but every strike was precisely aimed and scored light wounds on Nathan.

He's got a bunch of movement and weapon skills. A Talent making his steps move farther, and another to make his swords cut deeply. My skin should be as tough as metal right now, but his lightest strike is still spilling blood. Good thing I can make more of that from Stamina!

Nathan kept up with Simla and managed to dodge half the man's lightning-quick strikes. The other half he caught on his arms. A few slipped through, gouging at Nathan's ribs.

Mid-tier Dodging Footwork 4 achieved!

The injuries were deep, but the bleeding stopped and the wounds began healing only seconds after being delivered. His Stamina was still full. *Beyond* full.

Thanks, Stella!

Simla was going all out, his face a mask of concentration as he kept striking at Nathan while skittering from side to side. But Nathan was still closing in and wouldn't let the lithe man break away. Simla wasn't as good as Aarl. In the same league, but not as good.

And while Simla was faster than Nathan's usual training partner, he didn't have weapons with sufficient weight to keep Nathan back, no matter how well they cut. Nathan could just take the blows and keep coming, so long as Simla didn't hit anything vital. And this was a duel to submission, not death.

Nathan slid forward as Simla struck at Nathan's head and chest. Nathan ducked the top blow and caught the other sword in his left hand. It cut deep into his palm, grating over the bones beneath.

Got you.

Nathan clamped his hand on the blade, feeling its magic flicker as his antimagic tore at the enchantment.

Simla yanked the blade backwards, trying to slice open Nathan's hand. But Nathan's hold was too strong and the blade didn't budge.

In the grips of his Rage, Nathan felt triumph. He felt unstoppable. The enchantment fell to pieces as Nathan brought his other hand down on Simla's sword, snapping off the last two-thirds of its length.

He cast aside the fragment of blade, then brought his hand up in front of his face before clenching his fist. Blood squirted out between Nathan's fingers, and he leapt at Simla again.

Simla juked and dodged with inhuman grace, but Nathan wasn't letting him play matador. He picked up a few quick cuts from Simla's single scything blade, but he could tell the enchantment on the second sword was starting to fray.

Simla drew out the object Eldred had given him, gritting his teeth in a snarl as he cast it at Nathan's feet.

Kozar saw the action and threw out a hand. "No!"

Simla dived backwards and laid himself flat. Nathan had only an instant to throw himself into a forward roll before the magical bomb went off.

A wave of heat and pressure buffeted Nathan, and he only partially absorbed the blast. Chips of stone flew past, gouging his flesh. His roll became a flip as the pressure wave carried Nathan over the prone Simla.

Nathan spun in midair and landed on his feet, staggering sideways to avoid leaving the ring of fire demarking the dueling arena.

Low-tier Tumbling 10 achieved!

Blood ran from a cut on Nathan's forehead, but he glared down at Simla as the man got shakily to his feet. The center of their ring was blasted and broken, a crater marking where the explosive item had detonated.

Oh, we're doing killing blows now? Guess the rules of the duel just changed.

Nathan glared his hate as he advanced, yanking a spike of stone from his side. The younger man darted a glance over at Kozar, who looked furious. But the older man didn't interfere.

High-tier Regeneration 7 achieved!

Simla looked back at Nathan and his unhurried gait, swallowing. He raised his sword once again, then feinted and dove low, looking to slice at the back of Nathan's ankles as he rolled unnaturally far with a gymnast's precision.

Played that trick one too many times.

Nathan kicked Simla in the chest mid-dive, sending him spinning into the air. Then he leapt forward and grabbed Simla's ankle right before the man hit the ground. Nathan swung the man through the air like a sack, planning on bashing his skull into the ground *repeatedly*.

He's just an obstacle, not a true *enemy. I won't break my word for* him. *Save that for Giantsrest.*

Instead of following through, Nathan spun in a half circle and threw Simla from the arena, watching him fly over the circle of flames.

That was a near thing. Guess Simla gets a chance to learn not to piss off somebody on the Path of Rage.

Nathan closed his eyes, releasing the gloating thrill of victory. It was made harder when he heard Simla's scream cut out with a *thump* as he impacted against the mountaintop. There was a cheer from the Heirs, and Nathan smiled as he let go of his Rage.

High-tier Focused Mind 7 achieved!

You have leveled up to level 53! Congratulations, you have won a dangerous duel against a rival who sought to discredit you.

When he opened his eyes, Nathan was calm. He was stained with blood from dozens of wounds. But his Stamina was still full, and his clothes were even mostly intact, if cut in a few places, bloodstained and torn from the explosion.

Nathan met Eldred's gaze, smirking slightly as he walked towards the dais next to the seal.

The heavily armored man glared impotently, and Nathan could tell he was thinking about stopping Nathan somehow. But he glanced around, seeing the other Adventurers watching and subsided.

Kozar merely frowned thoughtfully at Nathan, watching him walk up the steps with a vaguely frustrated expression.

As he stepped atop the platform, Nathan looked around. The Heirs were right behind him, and Simla was being fed a healing potion by his team. Kia gave Nathan a single nod, and Vhala raised her fist in support.

All the Adventurers of Gemore watched Nathan as he stood beside the beam of magic emerging from the Seal.

"By the Endings of Davrar and the wonders of Earth, I vow to fight the Endings themselves! I will prevent them from happening at all, if it can be done. May my class be stripped from me if I forswear. I will protect the people of Gemore from that which would assail them, be it monster, person or Ending!"

END OF BOOK I

Full Status

Nathan Lark

Permanent Talent 1: Magic Absorption 6
You have Developed High-tier magic Resistance Talent into a permanent pillar of your being. You are heavily resistant to all forms of magic, and can directly absorb the mana of spells cast on you into Stamina. You are forever unable to cast spells or access magic. Magical items cannot affect you and you will begin degrading them at a touch.

Permanent Talent 2: High-tier Regeneration 7
This Talent will automatically spend Stamina to very rapidly heal wounds. Larger wounds and replacing greater amounts of missing flesh will take longer and cost more Stamina. Regeneration will not prevent you from dying to grievous wounds, and will not protect against poison.

Talent 3: None

Class: Spellbreaker Juggernaut level 53
You have embraced your anger and thrill of battle and used them for unrelenting assaults. This class will make you an unstoppable force, granting skills and modifying existing skills to enable Raging, where Stamina will be spent to become significantly tougher, stronger and faster. Additional skills will enhance your durability, as well as your

ability to disrupt spell effects, especially those aimed at hindering or slowing you. This class may further Develop into classes focused on breaching fortified defenses, extending or enhancing yourRage, or further enhancing your antimagic capabilities while raging.

Stamina: 620/620
You have unlocked the Stamina resource! Stamina will accumulate during periods of rest, and can be spent to improve the speed and strength of your movements, or used for other skills or Talents that utilize Stamina.

Juggernaut's Wrath
You will be unflinching in the face of pain and injury, and serious wounds will enhance the intensity of your Rage. This skill will trigger your Rage without your consent if you are badly injured.

Antimagic Momentum
Motion enhances your inherent antimagic, allowing you to break magical effects with your movements and blows. The greater the momentum behind the motion, the greater the enhancement. Effect is further enhanced while Raging.

Raging Thrill
You can voluntarily enter and exit a Rage state, where you will be immersed in the thrill of combat. This will rapidly consume Stamina, but will increase your strength, speed and resilience to damage.

Juggernaut's Inertia
Your motions carry greater momentum, and it will be harder to stop or slow you, especially with magical effects.

Unarmored Resilience
When not wearing armor your body becomes more resilient to damage from all sources.

Utility skills:
High-tier Focused Mind 7
This skill will help you attain a focused and undistracted state under most conditions. Cannot be maintained under stress.

High-tier Earnestness 1
This skill will help you portray your intense conviction and honesty when you interact with people. This skill will encourage people to follow your example in words and actions. Cannot fool truth spells or skills.

Mid-tier Sprinting 5
This skill will help you run very quickly in the future. Will not allow you to run in circumstances where you couldn't otherwise.

Mid-tier Spellsense 9
This skill will help you identify mana types and spell weaves more easily. Helps you understand what individual elements of spells are accomplishing. Does not grant understanding of how to weave mana together for specific spells.

Mid-tier Notice 6
This skill will help you notice details in the future. Especially useful for detecting concealed magical effects and triggers.

Mid-tier Identify 6
This skill will help you interpret complex cues to understand strange objects and effects, as well as give you clues on how to manipulate them. Will not reveal curses without obvious clues, and will not help you identify types of mana or spellcraft.

Mid-tier Dodging Footwork 4
This skill will help you move yourself to more easily keep your balance and dodge attacks

High-tier Enhanced Memory 1
You have a detailed mental construct to aid with memory, and a mental process to help you encode information into it. This skill will help you store and recall memories quickly. This process operates quickly and cannot be interfered with by outside sources. With time and effort you can recall older memories and store them in the mental construct.

Mid-tier Lecturing 1
This skill will help you explain concepts in the future, smoothing over

gaps and aiding greatly in explanation and understanding. Will not help you convey details you do not know, and will not help you suppress people's doubts about what you are teaching.

Low-tier Tumbling 10

You have used acrobatic tricks to dodge blows from dangerous opponents. This skill will help you use unorthodox movements involving rolls and handsprings to avoid blows in the future.

About the Author

Alexander Olson first knew he wanted to be a scientist when his dad taught him how to capture hydrogen gas with foil, batteries, and water. He grew up in Colorado, got his bachelors in chemistry and biology from a small engineering school in Southern California and his PhD in biochemistry from a larger school in Boston. Now he works full-time in science, the closest thing to magic he can achieve in this world.

His love of magic came from escaping into fantastical stories as a child, where he could explore worlds that stretch to the limits of imagination. He first delved into creating his own stories by running tabletop roleplaying games. Eventually he decided to write the story he wanted to read.

Detalle—Detail: *Birkenau*, 2013 [Cat. 17]

Publicado con motivo de la exposición *Yishai Jusidman. Azul de Prusia* (27 de agosto del 2016 al 12 de febrero del 2017) MUAC, Museo Universitario Arte Contemporáneo. UNAM, Universidad Nacional Autónoma de México, México, Ciudad de México.

—

Published on occasion of the exhibition *Yishai Jusidman: Prussian Blue* (August 27, 2016 to February 12, 2017) MUAC, Museo Universitario Arte Contemporáneo. UNAM, Universidad Nacional Autónoma de México, Mexico City.

Textos—Texts
José Luis Barrios
Yishai Jusidman
Virginia Roy
Andrew Weinstein

Traducción—Translation
Robin Myers
Christopher Michael Fraga
Jaime Soler

Edición—Editor
Ekaterina Álvarez Romero · MUAC

Coordinación editorial—Editorial Coordination
Ana Xanic López · MUAC

Asistencia editorial—Editorial Assistance
Elena Isabel Coll
Adrián Martínez
Maritere Martínez Román

Corrección—Proofreading
Ekaterina Álvarez Romero · MUAC
Ana Xanic López · MUAC
Jaime Soler

Diseño—Design
Cristina Paoli · Periferia

Asistencia de formación—Layout Assistance
Sarah-Louise Deazley

Primera edición 2016—First edition 2016

Río Pánuco 141, colonia Cuauhtémoc, 06500, Ciudad de México
© RM Verlag S.L.C/Loreto 13-15 Local B, 08029, Barcelona, España
www.editorialrm.com
295

ISBN RM Verlag 978-84-16282-90-6
ISBN de la colección 978-607-02-5175-7
ISBN

Impreso y hecho en México—Printed and made in Mexico

YISHAI JUSIDMAN

AZUL DE PRUSIA
PRUSSIAN BLUE

MUAC · Museo Universitario Arte Contemporáneo, UNAM

Delantal—Apron, 2011-2016. Detalle—Detail [Cat. 26]

Fuga y catástrofe

VIRGINIA ROY

Dachau, 2014 [Cat. 19]

Para recordar hay que imaginar.
G. DIDI-HUBERMAN

Azul de Prusia es el nombre del primer pigmento moderno, fabricado artificialmente desde inicios del siglo XVIII. Este pigmento, hecho de ferrocianuro férrico, fue descubierto accidentalmente por el fabricante de colores berlinés Heinrich Diesbach, y tomó su nombre de los uniformes de los militares prusianos, en cuyos tejidos se utilizó el tinte.

Gracias a sus cualidades técnicas, su bajo costo y la limitada viabilidad de azules alternativos, muchos pintores comenzaron a emplear el azul de Prusia pródigamente. Si bien, por una parte se puede asociar este color con el perfeccionamiento pictórico, después de Auschwitz se erige como paradigma de barbarie humana y de nuestros fracasos ético-políticos como sociedad.

Tras la liberación de los campos de concentración nazis, cuando el mundo empezaba a comprender la dimensión del genocidio, se apreciaron unas manchas color azul de Prusia en el interior de algunas de las cámaras de gas. El gas empleado en los asesinatos masivos, Zyklon B, había reaccionado químicamente con los muros de estas cámaras provocando la aparición del azul de Prusia en las paredes. Tales máculas han quedado hasta hoy como los residuos de una atrocidad.

El azul de Prusia, pues, nos remite a actos opuestos del ser humano: por una parte, inventar un color para enaltecer el arte y, por otra, cometer abyectos crímenes contra sus congéneres. Como escribió Bataille: "Desde entonces, la imagen del hombre es inseparable de la de una cámara de gas".[1]

Esta relación cromática actúa como eje conductor de las nuevas pinturas que nos presenta Yishai Jusidman. Con el uso de este pigmento, y desde la práctica pictórica, Jusidman aborda la representación del Holocausto. El artista pinta en color azul de Prusia los espacios y las cámaras de gas de diversos campos de concentración, a partir de fotografías de archivo y de algunas otras tomadas personalmente.

—

1— Georges Bataille, "Sartre" (1947), en *Oeuvres completes,* XI, París, Gallimard, 1988, p. 226.

Las cualidades mismas del pigmento le permiten a Jusidman explotar una contraposición de significados. El tinte, de brillante saturación y transparencia, y que tendía a decolorarse con la luz, es famoso por su acción de veladura, esto es, su particular propensión para superponer capas finas de pintura. Jusidman despliega al límite este potencial del pigmento en sus monocromos de 2014–2015, al llevar la aplicación reiterada de veladuras al extremo de alcanzar una densidad absoluta. De esta manera, el artista obtiene una opacidad que le sirve para aludir a la dificultad intrínseca de representar la Shoah,[2] una tensión presente en toda la serie de Jusidman. Esta complejidad de representación del genocidio guarda relación con dos diferentes acepciones de la palabra "velar"; por un lado, cuidar y custodiar la imagen, protegerla, y por el otro, cubrirla y ocultarla, esconder una imagen que quedaría borrada de la fotografía por exceso de luz.

Desde hace casi 30 años, Yishai Jusidman reivindica la práctica pictórica y su vigencia en el siglo XXI. Igual que en trabajos anteriores, sus nuevas piezas acometen la exploración de las dialécticas entre forma-contenido y técnica-concepto, donde lo pictórico adquiere preeminencia. Obras anteriores como las series del *Astrónomo* (1987–1990) y *Geishas* (1992–1993) aluden ya a esta investigación formal y examinan las fronteras de la pintura desde su materialidad y sus poderes de articulación.

Así, mientras que esta disciplina ha sido asesinada y resucitada en innumerables ocasiones durante los últimos años, Jusidman defiende con su trabajo el sentido de la práctica pictórica hoy día. Su posición parte del entendimiento de la pintura desde una perspectiva que comprende y trasciende lo técnico, más allá de la textura, la composición y el color. La concibe desde su proceso creativo y de configuración; ubicándose en la tensión entre el pintor y sus datos. No se trata de partir del lienzo blanco sino de enfrentarse al blanco mismo, para desarmar así los estereotipos y todo lo que pesa ya sobre el cuadro, incluso antes de iniciarlo. Como apunta Deleuze:

—

2— Shoah, significa "catástrofe" en hebreo, este término se utiliza comúnmente para referir al Holocausto.

> Dicen que la pintura *ya* está en la tela. Encuentra ahí todos los datos figurativos y probabilísticos que ocupan, que preocupan la tela. Hay toda una lucha en la tela entre el pintor y sus datos. Hay entonces un trabajo preparatorio que pertenece plenamente a la pintura, y que sin embargo precede al acto de pintar [...]. Ese trabajo preparatorio es invisible y silencioso, sin embargo muy intenso. Si bien el acto de pintar surge como un *después* ("histéresis") en relación con ese trabajo. [...] Este acto o esos actos suponen que los datos figurativos ya están sobre la tela (como en la cabeza del pintor), más o menos virtuales, más o menos actuales. Son precisamente esos datos los que serán desmarcados, o bien limpiados, barridos, arrugados, o bien recubiertos, por el acto de pintar.[3]

Deleuze aborda la configuración del acto mismo de pintar y la dificultad que adquiere a causa de clichés y expectativas preconcebidas. Y reflexiona sobre la experiencia de la pintura en lo que él denomina la *catástrofe*, aquello con lo que se enfrenta el pintor en el acto de pintar:

> De todas las artes, la pintura es, sin duda, la única que integra necesariamente, "histéricamente", su propia catástrofe, y se constituye desde entonces como una fuga anticipada. En las otras artes la catástrofe no está más que asociada. Pero el pintor, él, pasa por la catástrofe, abraza el caos e intenta salir. Los pintores difieren en su manera de entender el caos no figurativo, y también en su evaluación del orden pictórico por venir, de la relación de este orden con ese caos. [...] El caos es la catástrofe, es el derrumbamiento de todos los datos figurativos, el trabajo preparatorio es entonces una lucha, lucha contra el cliché (tanto más necesario por cuanto no somos "inocentes").[4]

Si el proceso pictórico ya comporta en sí mismo cierta resistencia de la propia representación, la situación se agudiza al abordar un suceso de la magnitud de la Shoah. Frente

—

3— Gilles Deleuze, *Francis Bacon. Lógica de la sensación*, París, Éditions de la différence, 1984, p. 58.

4— *Ibid.*, pp. 60 y 65.

a esta dimensión del horror, ¿de qué manera mostrar lo irrepresentable, lo indecible, lo inimaginable?
La propia maquinaria nazi participó en este proceso de des-imaginación. Ante la barbarie, los verdugos eran conscientes de la dificultad de la dimensión de la aniquilación e, incluso, de creer en sus propias atrocidades. El hecho de ocultar el exterminio formaba parte intrínseca de la barbarie, de no hacerla real: "Aunque alguna prueba llegase a subsistir, y aunque alguno de vosotros llegara a sobrevivir, la gente dirá que los hechos que contáis son demasiado monstruosos para ser creídos".[5]

Ésta dificultad de verbalización y visualización de la Shoah es lo que nos hace plantearnos qué palabras e imágenes nos pueden aproximar a un hecho que es, en sí mismo, impensable: ¿cómo podemos hacerlo visible?, ¿de qué manera evitar simplificarlo, banalizarlo o desvirtuarlo?

El cineasta Claude Lanzmann lo expresó en su emblemática película *Shoah* (1985), cuyo precepto de partida era la imposibilidad de dicha representación a partir de imágenes. Con un claro posicionamiento ético-estético, Lanzmann realiza un enriquecedor ejercicio de memoria por medio de testimonios y entrevistas en las que la imagen de archivo o documental está significativamente ausente en todo momento. Proclama así una prohibición de la representación para evitar cualquier banalización o estetización del horror; la imagen desaparece para dar paso a la palabra.

En oposición a Lanzmann, Didi-Huberman defiende la imperiosa necesidad, y a la vez el deber, de recuperar la imagen. Es preciso volver imaginable y decible la imagen de la representación del Holocausto y trabajar en su recuperación, aun cuando las posibilidades de la representación pudiesen ser sólo fragmentarias y parciales.

Así pues, *pese a todo*, imágenes: pese al infierno de Auschwitz, pese a los riesgos corridos. A cambio, debemos contemplarlas, asumirlas, tratar de contarlas. *Pese a todo*, imágenes: pese a nuestra propia incapacidad para saber mirarlas tal y como se merecerían, pese a nuestro propio mundo atiborrado, casi asfixiado, de mercancía imaginaria.[6]

—

5— Primo Levi, *Trilogía de Auschwitz*, Barcelona, Océano, 2012, p. 475.

6— Georges Didi-Huberman, *Imágenes pese a todo*, Barcelona, Paidós, 2004, p. 17.

En esta tesitura se inscribe el proyecto de Jusidman. En *Azul de Prusia*, el artista aprovecha las posibilidades de la dualidad abstracción-figuración de la pintura para afrontar la dificultad de la representación de la Shoah, en un ejercicio de contrapuntos. Jusidman inicia la exposición de la serie con *Haus der Kunst* [*Casa del Arte*] (2012), la galería de arte de enaltecimiento del régimen y propaganda nazi, esta vez con el espacio vacío, sin pinturas, contrapuesto intencionalmente a *Treblinka* (2012), pintura de un montículo de cenizas del campo de concentración del mismo nombre, descubierto en 1945. Las dos vertientes del nacionalsocialismo. A partir de ahí, el artista nos sumerge en un recorrido donde las pinturas "Cámaras de gas" y "Paisajes" de los campos de exterminio se alternan y confrontan con la abstracción de los monocromos y las manchas de pintura. Estas últimas son el resultado de la disolución del pigmento en el trapo durante el proceso de trabajo del artista, produciendo manchas con texturas y residuos del mismo tinte que crean una sugerente presencia. De esta manera, el color, protagonista también de la serie, pasa por todas las fases de su materialidad en el lienzo.

Azul de Prusia sorprende por la ausencia de toda presencia humana más allá de sus rastros en los edificios y sus ruinas. Un ejemplo es el caso de las cuatro fotografías realizadas clandestinamente en Auschwitz por el Sonderkommando para demostrar la existencia de las cámaras de gas, y de las cuales Jusidman se basa en la única donde no aparecen personas, la más abstracta, para su pintura *Birkenau* (2012).

La inclusión de personas en las representaciones del Holocausto, normalmente mediante el testigo o superviviente, genera en el espectador una empatía que le hace consciente del sufrimiento y la barbarie. En contraste, en la serie de Jusidman no hallamos a la persona, sino únicamente un espacio vacío, frío: sólo la huella. Y el único testimonio que permite el artista es el del propio espectador, ahora convertido en el protagonista que penetra esos espacios. Jusidman nos emplaza a un diálogo entre ausencia y distancia, y a la vez, al testimonio de esa realidad.

Azul de Prusia es un ejercicio de capas que permite imaginar haciendo presente lo ausente. Una dialéctica que resignifica, a través del color, las diversidades de la representación, así como de la propia práctica pictórica. De esta manera, podemos entender el proyecto de Jusidman como una fuga constante, no como huida o escape, sino como composición musical de contrapuntos, una polifonía basada en la reiteración de melodías y consonancias —no imitaciones—, expresadas en diferentes tonalidades y gamas de un azul con un peso más que específico.

Trapo #2—Rag #2, 2011–2014 [Cat. 28]

Fugue and Catastrophe

VIRGINIA ROY

Auschwitz, 2011 [Cat. 4]

Prussian Blue is the name of the first modern synthetically manufactured pigment, produced since the early eighteenth century. This pigment, made of ferric ferrocyanide, was discovered accidentally by the Berlin colormaker Heinrich Diesbach. It took its name from the Prussian military uniforms, which were tinted with this dye.

Due to its technical qualities, its low cost, and the limited viability of alternative blue pigments, many painters began using Prussian blue in lavish quantities. While this color can be associated, then, with painterly advancement, it has also become, after Auschwitz, a paradigm of human barbarism and of our ethical/political failures as a society.

Once the Nazi concentration camps were liberated, when the world began to grasp the magnitude of the genocide, blue-colored stains were noted in some of the gas chambers. The gas employed in the mass murder, Zyklon B, had undergone a chemical reaction within the walls of these chambers, causing Prussian blue to appear on their surface. Today, these stains survive as the residue of an atrocity.

Prussian blue, therefore, gestures towards opposing extremes of a so-called progress: through technological savvy, human-kind comes up with a pigment to exalt art, as well as with a gas to murder millions. In Bataille's words: "The image of man is henceforth inseparable from that of the gas chamber."[1]

This chromatic relationship serves as an axis for the new paintings by Yishai Jusidman. Through emphasizing this pigment in his pictorial practice, Jusidman addresses the representation of the Holocaust. The artist paints the spaces and gas chambers of various concentration camps in Prussian blue, using archival images and other photos he took himself.

The very features of the pigment allow Jusidman to implement a counterpoint between meanings. The color, brilliant in its saturation and transparency, though it used to fade somewhat in time, is famous for its effectiveness as a glaze (*veladura* in Spanish); that is, for superimposing thin coloring layers of transparent paint. Jusidman fully exploits this potential in his monochromes of 2014-2015, taking the repeated

—

1— Georges Bataille, "Sartre" (1947), in *Oeuvres completes, XI*, Paris, Gallimard, 1988, p. 226.

application of glazes to the point where he achieves absolute density. In this way, the artist is able to produce an opacity that alludes to the intrinsic difficulty of depicting the Shoah,[2] a tension present throughout the *Prussian Blue* series. Such intricacies in representing the genocide evoke two different senses of the word *velar* (*to veil* in Spanish): on the one hand, to care for and watch over the image, to protect it; on the other, to cover it up, to hide it, to conceal an image that would fade away from the photograph through an excess of light.

For nearly thirty years, Yishai Jusidman has vindicated the practice of painting and its relevance for the twenty-first century. As in his prior work, his new pieces explore the dialectic between form/content and technique/concept, giving preeminence to the pictorial. Previous works like the *Astronomer* series (1987–1990) and *Geisha* (1992–1993) already allude to this formal investigation, examining the boundaries of painting through its materiality and powers of articulation.

Thus, while painting as a discipline has been murdered and resuscitated countless times in recent years, Jusidman's work secures the purpose of painterly practice in our present day. His perspective emerges from an understanding of painting that encompasses and transcends the merely technical, beyond texture, composition, color. He conceives painting from within the creative and configuration process, which is grounded in the tension between the painter and his *givens*. This isn't a matter of beginning with a blank canvas, but rather of facing the blankness itself, so as to disassemble the stereotypes that already bear down on the painting—even before it begins to exist. As Deleuze writes:

> They say that the painter is *already* in the canvas, where he or she encounters all the figurative and probabilistic givens that occupy and pre-occupy the canvas. There is thus a preparatory work that belongs to painting fully, and yet precedes the act of painting....This preparatory work is invisible and silent, yet extremely intense, and the act of painting itself appears as an afterward, an *aprés-coup* ("hysteresis") in relation to this work... Now this act, or these

—

2— Shoah means "catastrophe" in Hebrew, the term is commonly used to refer to the Holocaust.

> acts, presupposes that there were already figurative givens on the canvas (and in the painter's head), more or less virtual, more or less actual. It is precisely these givens that will be removed by the act of painting, either by being wiped, brushed, or rubbed, or else covered over.[3]

Deleuze addresses the configuration of the very act of painting and the difficulty it acquires due to clichés and pre-conceived expectations. And he reflects on the painting experience in what he calls the "catastrophe," that which the painter confronts in the act of painting:

> Of all the arts, painting is undoubtedly the only one that necessarily, "hysterically," integrates its own catastrophe and consequently is constituted as a flight in advance. In the other arts, the catastrophe is only associated. But painters pass through the catastrophe themselves, embrace the chaos, and attempt to emerge from it. Where painters differ is in their manner of embracing this nonfigurative chaos, and in their evaluation of the pictorial order to come, and the relation of this order with this chaos.…Chaos and catastrophe imply the collapse of all figurative givens, and thus they already entail a fight, the fight against the cliché, the preparatory work (all the more necessary in that we are no longer "innocent").[4]

If the painting process already implies a certain resistance to its own representation, the situation intensifies in addressing an event of the Shoah's magnitude. Faced with horror of such a dimension, in what way can the unportrayable, the unsayable, the unimaginable, be shown?

The Nazi machine itself participated in this process of de-imagination. In the face of barbarity, the executioners recognized the difficulty in encompassing the scale of the annihilation—and even the difficulty of believing their own atrocities. The act of hiding the extermination constituted an intrinsic part of the brutality, of not making it real: "And

—

3— Gilles Deleuze, *Francis Bacon. Lógica de la sensación*, Editions de la difference, 1984, p. 58. (English translation consulted on http://isites.harvard.edu/fs/docs/icb.topic1315975.files/The%20Gathering/Deleuze%20-%20Diagram.pdf)

4— Ibid. pp. 60 and 65.

even if some proof should remain and some of you survive, people will say that the events you describe are too monstrous to be believed..."[5]

The challenge of verbalizing and visualizing the Shoah is what makes us ask ourselves which words and images could bring us into contact with an event that is in itself unthinkable: how can we make it visible? How can we avoid simplifying it, trivializing it, or distorting it?

The filmmaker Claude Lanzmann expressed this concern in his emblematic film *Shoah* (1985), the foundational precept of which was the impossibility of representing the Holocaust in images. With a clear ethical/aesthetic stance, Lanzmann performs a salutary memory exercise through testimonies and interviews where the archival or documentary image is conspicuously absent at all times. He thus proclaims a prohibition on representation in order to avoid any trivialization or aesthetization of horror; the image disappears in order to make way for words.

In contrast, Didi-Huberman has defended the pressing need, as well as the duty, to recover the image. It is necessary to work toward retrieving, to render imaginable and utterable the visual representation of the Holocaust, even when the possibilities of portrayal may be merely partial and fragmentary.

And so, *despite everything*, images: despite the hell of Auschwitz, despite the risks incurred. In return, we must look at them, take them on, try to describe them. *Despite everything*, images: despite our own inability to learn how to look at them exactly as they deserve to be seen, despite a world—our world—crammed with, nearly suffocated by, imaginary commodities.[6]

Jusidman's project is immersed within this arena. In *Prussian Blue*, the possibilities offered by painting's abstraction/figuration duality are employed by the artist through an exercise of counterpoints in order to address the difficulty of representing the Shoah. Jusidman begins the exhibition of the series with a depiction of the empty space, without paintings, of the *Haus der Kunst* [*House of Art*] (2012)—the gallery built

—

5— Primo Levi, *Trilogía de Auschwitz*, Océano, Barcelona, 2012, p. 475.

6— Georges Didi-Huberman, *Imágenes pese a todo*, Barcelona, Paidós, 2004, p. 17.

to showcase Nazi propaganda and art—intentionally placed against *Treblinka* (2012), a painting of a mound of ashes in the eponymous concentration camp, as found in 1945. These were the two faces of National Socialism. From there, the artist takes us on a journey in which the *Gas Chambers* and *Landscapes* of concentration camps, are alternated and confronted with the abstractions of monochromes and stains. The latter are the product of pigment dissolved in rags during the artist's working process, yielding stains with textures and residues that generate a suggestive presence. Thus, color, also a leading element in the series, evolves on the canvas through all phases of its materiality.

The images in *Prussian Blue* are striking for the total lack human presence—aside from the traces left in the form of buildings and their ruins. This absence is especially telling in Jusidman's *Birkenau* (2012), a painting based on one of the four photographs taken surreptitiously in Auschwitz by the Sonderkommando in order to prove the gas chambers' existence; Jusidman chose the most "abstract" photo, the only one empty of people.

To include people in representations of the Holocaust, usually through a witness or survivor, causes empathy in the viewer and thus makes her conscious of suffering and brutality. By contrast, in Jusidman's series we find only cold, empty spaces—only the traces of people left behind can be felt. And the only testimony the artist allows for is that of the viewer herself, now transformed into the protagonist who penetrates these spaces. Jusidman engages us in a dialogue with absence and distance—and, concurrently, in the testimony of that reality.

Prussian Blue is an exercise in layers that engages our imagination making present what is absent. A dialectic that re-articulates, through color, the varieties of representation, as well as of the practice of painting itself. Hence, we can understand Jusidman's project as an ongoing fugue. Not as a flight or escape, but rather as a musical composition of counterpoints, a polyphony based on the reiteration of melodies and consonances—not of imitations—expressed in different keys and ranges of a blue whose weight is peculiarly, disturbingly specific.

Sobre la inminencia de lo insensato o la pintura como aniquilación. Memoria, materia e historia

JOSÉ LUIS BARRIOS

Struthof, 2010 [Cat. 14]

0. La obra de arte desconocida

> ...el infierno del pintor, aquello a cuyo fondo tiene que descender para volver a encontrar la vida, el *mover*, es en principio un color.
>
> GEORGES DIDI-HUBERMAN, *La pintura encarnada*[1]

> Porque ante la muerte, la visibilidad de una tumba hubiera podido reapropiar al extranjero, hubiera podido significar para él una especie de repatriación.
>
> JACQUES DERRIDA, *La hospitalidad*[2]

En la breve novela *La obra maestra desconocida*, Balzac replantea lo que al parecer, en el seno de la historia del arte occidental, ha definido la relación entre pulsión, mirada y representación. Es sabido que esta relación también es, en buena medida, la que en su momento llevara a Paris a decidirse por la diosa más bella del Olimpo: Afrodita; y es que en ambos casos lo que se pone en juego es la relación entre erotismo, belleza y mirada. Más allá del tema —o incluso del canon— que define el sentido y el valor de lo bello en pintura, en la historia de la misma se anuda una cierta intriga en la que el ojo, la cosa y la representación encuentran su "acomodo" o, si se prefiere, su condición de posibilidad en la imagen como "espéculo",[3] como "fantasma". A diferencia de la escultura, sobre todo aquella que cuaja la *vida* en el instante —un congelamiento que quizá sea la cifra que define el estatuto ontológico-estético del ídolo, la idolatría y su consecuente prohibición en religiones monoteístas—, es en la pintura y la poesía donde se plantean los problemas en torno a las relaciones entre representación y verdad. Sin duda la condena platónica de ambas enunció el carácter equívoco de estas artes: la

—

1— Georges Didi-Huberman. *La pintura encarnada.* Valencia, Pre-textos/Universidad de Valencia, 2007 p. 85.

2— Jacques Derrida and Anne Dufourmantelle, *On Hospitality*, translated by Rachel Bowlby, Stanford, Stanford University Press, 2000, p. 133.

3— Es decir como reflejo, como espectro. En todo caso, la definición mecánica de espéculo es una buena explicación para describir esa función del ojo: "Instrumento que se emplea para examinar por la reflexión luminosa ciertas cavidades del cuerpo". *Diccionario de la Real Academia Española*, *s.v.*, "espéculo", en: http://dle.rae.es/?id=GXgjH1m, consultado el 18 de mayo del 2016.

mentira, de la primera; el delirio, de la segunda. Acaso por ello, esta condena platónica significa también un índice radical a partir del cual la pintura y la poesía han intentado escapar del delirio y la mentira con las que se las ha pensado, quizá a pesar de ellas mismas, en la historia de Occidente.

Lo cierto es que, en una primera consideración, algo aparece en "escena" a la hora de pensar la pintura como una *superficie* donde se pone en tensión el juego entre mirada (deseo + cosa = objeto = *fantasma*) y representación (delirio + mentira = engaño). El fantasma siempre nos engaña porque, al parecer, es un nudo entre cosa y deseo que tiende a ocultar la verdad. Esta afirmación, aunque maximalista, abre una de las perspectivas desde las que me gustaría abordar mis consideraciones en torno a la serie *Azul de Prusia* de Yishai Jusidman.

La otra consideración general que me gustaría traer a cuento —allende de que, más adelante, abordaré la temática sobre los campos de exterminio y su núcleo obsceno, la cámara de gas— es la equívoca figura que en muchos ha inspirado cierta lectura sacrificial y sagrada en torno al hecho de que la "solución final"[4] debiera ser leída conforme a la prescripción bíblica de la prohibición de las imágenes. Lo sugería apenas unas líneas arriba: el contexto de la prohibición bíblica se refiere a los ídolos como cuerpo real de los dioses, por tanto a la idolatría de la escultura.[5] No es éste el espacio para abundar esta discusión pero basta asentar, como bien lo observa Georges Didi-Huberman, que, si perdemos de vista que el referente de esta prohibición tiene que ver con la relación entre el volumen, la piedra y

—

4— "Solución final" (Endlösung der Judenfrage [solución final de la cuestión judía]) es el nombre que los líderes nazis dieron al exterminio judío en la segunda guerra mundial.

5— "Para comenzar, debe recordarse que el mandamiento prohíbe construir imágenes 'de todo lo que está en los cielos, sobre la tierra, en las aguas', es decir, de todas las cosas, y en particular, hacer de ellas imágenes *esculpidas*. El mandamiento concierne entonces a la producción de formas consistentes, enteras y autónomas, como lo es una estatua, y destinadas así al uso como ídolo. Se trata de la idolatría, y no de la imagen en tal o de la 'representación'. El ídolo es un dios fabricado, no la representación de un dios, y el carácter irrisorio y falso de su divinidad obedece al hecho de haber sido fabricado". Véase Jean-Luc Nancy, *La representación prohibida*, Buenos Aires, Amorrutu, 2007, p. 22.

la fuerza como campo de inmanencia estética de las relaciones entre vida, figura y forma, entonces lo que perdemos es el carácter mismo de totalidad ontológica del ídolo y con ello la implicación religiosa, política e histórica de la escultura o lo escultórico para la antigüedad.[6] Algo que por lo demás es fundamental tener en cuenta para entender de igual manera cuál es el temple y el carácter estético del arte nazi, un arte pensado en términos de producción de idolatría, tal y como lo demuestran la escultura y la arquitectura del régimen nacional-socialista alemán.

En este contexto, es probable que la primera problemática que se debiera atender, como bien lo observa Jean-Luc Nancy, es cierta confusión presente en la historia de la discusión sobre la representación del momento: la solución final. A saber, la confusión entre prohibición e imposibilidad. Dicho de manera breve: la solución final es irrepresentable porque está prohibida —el estatuto de la víctima es sacrosanto— o, más bien, es irrepresentable porque es imposible hacerlo, porque su estatuto es el del horror y tiene que ver con la estética y la política del exterminio. De acuerdo con Nancy:

> ...la cuestión de la representación de *Auschwitz* con la representación —suponiendo que haga falta mantenerla, en esos términos, como cuestión— no puede resolverse —si puede serlo— en una referencia, ya sea negativa o positiva, a un horror extremo o una extrema santidad. La cuestión debe pasar por este interrogante: ¿Qué ocurrió en Auschwitz con la representación misma? ¿Cómo se la puso en juego ahí?[7]

Puesta en esta perspectiva, la pregunta por la representación de los campos y el núcleo obsceno —y como veremos más abajo, perverso— de la prohibición de la representación está más relacionada con un cierto límite impuesto al nexo entre política, estética y representación, que con un cierto carácter

—

6— Georges Didi-Huberman, *op. cit.*, pp. 127-128.

7— Jean-Luc Nancy, *Ibid.*, p. 33. El énfasis de las cursivas en Auschwitz es mío y lo hago para remarcar el carácter paradigmático de este campo en la historia del exterminio de la segunda guerra mundial.

religioso de la misma. Ésta no es una cuestión menor; entre otras cosas abre la posibilidad de pensar cuál es el sentido, la función y la potencia que la pintura tiene respecto a esta discusión, que sin duda ha atravesado la fotografía, el cine, la novela e incluso la poesía a lo largo de la historia de la imagen y la palabra en los últimos setenta años.

No se trata entonces de un problema genealógico de las causas que hacen imposible o que prohíben la representación de la Shoah, más bien se trata de una pregunta lanzada en los límites de ésta —y que sin duda toca de manera directa el quehacer de la pintura en la historia política y ética de Occidente. Una pregunta que pareciese volver pertinente el trabajo de la pintura, que nos permite repensar su significado de acuerdo con Derrida en *La verdad en pintura*, y que para formularla en términos de la serie *Azul de Prusia*, echo mano de esta observación de Nancy: en términos de la imposibilidad de la representación de la solución final, la cuestión no consiste en saber si es imposible representar el "instante" mortal de la aniquilación, que de hecho lo es; más bien se trata de hacer presente (representar) la ausencia (*absens*, lo irrepresentable en tanto no está) *en* la cosa. Pero ¿qué quiere decir lo irrepresentable *en* la cosa? Esto devuelve a la pintura en la historia de la imagen como nuestra historia, hace de nuevo pertinente la pregunta sobre su potencia fundamental: la representación. Sobre ello habré de insistir a lo largo de las siguientes páginas, baste por ahora entender que el preguntarnos por lo irrepresentable *en* la cosa supone una interpelación irrecusable a la pintura, aun más a la *superficie*, por no decir la tela o el lienzo. Desde siempre, lienzo quiere decir "extensión de un cuerpo a lo largo y ancho" o, si se quiere, el jirón de un plano…

Sin duda, el problema de la representación es el "asunto" fundamental de la pintura, incluso del concepto quizá más debatido de su historia de la representación: la mímesis. Re-presentar significa traer al presente la presencia de algo que ya no está. El mero estar presente no requiere volver*se* a presentar: *re*presentar*se*. En cambio, la *presencia* se representa en tanto que lo que se ausenta del *presente* vuelve a la presencia a través de la representación.

Otro asunto es saber si el volver a traer al presente tiene que ver con la figuración o la abstracción. Un asunto del que aquí no me puedo ocupar, pero que para la finalidad de este análisis importa en tanto que buena parte de la discusión sobre el estatus de la representación o no del terror del exterminio, se resolvió en el binomio figuración-expresión (con Bacon) o abstracción-expresión (con Rothko y de Kooning). En todo caso es importante pensar con la pintura, y en especial con la serie *Azul de Prusia*, qué significa la mímesis en el punto donde el nazismo postuló una estética de la suprarrepresentación como lo propio del arte de este régimen:

> Propongo llamar "suprarrepresentación" —dice Nancy— a ese régimen en el que se trata no sólo de representar a la humanidad triunfante en un tipo [...] sino de una naturaleza o una esencia (el cuerpo ario) en la cual consiste verdaderamente la presencia de la humanidad auto-creadora (y en este sentido divina, pero divina sin ninguna distancia con lo divino, o sin "santidad"). El cuerpo ario es una idea idéntica a una presencia, o la presencia sin resto de una idea: con bastante exactitud, aquello que Occidente pensaba desde hacía siglos como ídolo. [...] El judío, por el contrario, es para Hitler, justamente, el representante de la representación en su sentido ordinario y peyorativo: el único arte en el que el judío tiene éxito es el del comediante...[8]

Acaso esta observación de Jean-Luc Nancy nos dé alguna pista de cómo entender esa frase que Celan deja caer en su poema "Fuga de muerte": "Gritad los unos más hondo en la tierra los otros cantad y tocad/ agarra el hierro del cinto lo blande con sus ojos azules".[9] Quizás sea por ello que Celan escribe a continuación "hincad los unos más hondo las palas los otros seguid tocando a danzar".[10]

—

8— Nancy, *Ibid.*, pp. 43-44.

9— Paul Celan, "Fuga de muerte", en *Amapola y memoria*, en *Obras completas*, Madrid, Trotta, 1999, p. 63.

10— *Ibid.*

I. Medio, historia y representación

> La muerte nos hace sus promesas por cinematografía.
>
> JEAN-LUC GODARD, *Histoire(s) du cinema*[11]

> Una comunidad no se da más que en la muerte, y no precisamente en el cementerio, que es un lugar de espaciamiento, de distinción: sino en la ceniza de los hornos crematorios o en las pilas hacinadas de los cadáveres.
>
> JEAN-LUC NANCY, *Ser singular plural*[12]

Es indudable que la llamada crisis de la pintura no sólo tiene que ver con el supuesto límite que la solución final pudo haber planteado a la representación, sino que es una historia cuya genealogía remonta al momento histórico del nacional-socialismo. Se trata de una historia bien conocida por todos y sabida al punto del cansancio. Tiene su comienzo con la aparición de la fotografía y con el subsecuente desarrollo de las tecnologías de reproductibilidad técnica, las cuales plantearon problemáticas inéditas, aunque conocidas, en la tradición de la visualidad occidental. Pero más allá de esta consideración, desde mi perspectiva existe un nudo más complejo de las relaciones entre técnica, historia y representación y que para lo que aquí importa me permite ahondar en el problema que dicha relación plantea al lugar de la pintura en la estética del terror del siglo XX.

En este contexto quizá podríamos aventurar una afirmación provisoria, a saber, que la verdad no es asunto de la pintura, o al menos considerar que la verdad *en* la pintura responde a otras condiciones de posibilidad de las que se determinan en las relaciones entre representación y reproductibilidad. Esta afirmación me permite postular una cuestión que no abordaré pero que funciona como marco de referencia de los análisis elaborados aquí. Pensar en la verdad de las artes o considerar los regímenes de la imagen supone pensar la verdad *en* las artes: pensar

—

11— Jean Luc–Godard. *Histoire (s) du cinema. Toutes les histoires une seule histoire seule, 1*, Paris, Gallimard, 1998.

12— Nancy, *op. cit.*, pp. 154-155.

sus técnicas, sus soportes, su materialidad, pero también pensar el carácter histórico material de estos medios. Sobre el primer asunto —sobre todo el relacionado directamente con la pintura, al cual volveré más adelante— me gustaría abordar una problemática que es propia del carácter histórico material de los medios mecánicos de reproductibilidad técnica respecto al problema de la representación de la solución final, de la (im)posibilidad de mostrar, de capturar el instante mortal de la cámara de gas.

Jean-Luc Godard (1930) en su *Histoire(s) du cinema* [*Historia(s) del cine*] (1988–1998) afirma que la vocación política del cine fracasó en la historia. Esto lo dice al menos en dos sentidos, el primero relacionado con el carácter equívoco del cine y la fotografía, el segundo con el montaje como operación ideológica. El contexto de estas afirmaciones tiene que ver con el hecho de que durante la segunda guerra mundial, y de manera particular respecto a los campos de exterminio, el cine estaba obligado a dar cuenta de las atrocidades de la operación y administración de la muerte llevada a cabo por los nazis en esos años. Sin embargo, para este director suizo-francés, el cine no dio cuenta de la operación necropolítica de los nazis: llegó tarde a la historia y en contra de su propia potencia política de representación. El cine no estuvo ahí, no testificó la administración del exterminio. Es cierto el carácter constatable de esta afirmación, pero también es cierto que parte de la lógica de la solución final suponía el borramiento y la clausura de la representación. En este contexto, no dio cuenta del exterminio porque estaba impedido para hacerlo. Acaso por ello, en su fracaso político al no poder constar el instante del exterminio, produce la aporía de la representación.

Incluso al lado de las observaciones de Godard, habría que considerar el punto vacío de la imagen del terror que se muestra en las fotografías tomadas por los Sonderkommandos de las cámaras de gas de Birkenau (1944). Era imposible que la cámara fotográfica —al menos las cámaras con las que se contaba en los años cuarenta del siglo XX— pudiera dilatar temporalmente la toma al punto ciego donde el gas se rociaba sobre los presos al interior de los "baños" de los campos de exterminio. En este contexto, sin duda la pregunta planteada por Nancy respecto al hecho de que la representación devenía imposible en Auschwitz, parece no sólo pertinente, sino necesaria. La solución final plantea la pregunta por las condiciones de posibilidad de la representación.

Son muchas las aproximaciones a esta problemática, y no me ocuparé aquí de manera exhaustiva de ellas, pero vale la pena mencionarlas con la intención de precisar lo que se pone en operación en la serie *Azul de Prusia* de Yishai Jusidman.

Circunscritos al medio de reproductibilidad técnica y con la finalidad de plantear la tensión dialéctica en las distintas prácticas visuales que han abordado la aporía de la representación de la solución final, *Nuit et Brouillard* [*Noche y niebla*] (1955) de Alain Resnais (1922–2014), *Shoah* (1985) de Claude Lanzmann (1925) e *Histoire(s) du cinema* de Godard son filmes que de una u otra manera han abordado la contradicción entre representación e irrepresentabilidad del "instante" del exterminio. A diferencia de muchos otros, en estos filmes es el vacío *de* o *como* representación, el punto donde coinciden muerte, tiempo e imposibilidad.

Allende los contextos para y en los que se filmaron estas películas, aquí no puedo más que trabajar sobre lo que estos materiales muestran. A diferencia de largometrajes como *La vita* è *bella* [*La vida es bella*] (1997), *Schindler's List* [*La lista de Schindler*] (1993) o más recientemente *Saul fia* [*El hijo de Saúl*] (2015), en los que cada uno, a su manera, intenta suturar la relación entre imposibilidad, muerte y vacío (ya sea por la fábula como recurso narrativo en la primera, por el hiperrealismo de la segunda o por el juego entre primer plano y rito de la tercera), las películas de Resnais, Godard y Lanzmann tienen algo en común: filmar la posteridad del acontecimiento mortal. Ninguna de estas películas aborda el momento acontecimental (*site* événementiel) de la solución final, ninguna de ellas busca mostrar el instante mortal de las cámaras de gas. Imposible hacerlo en la medida en que ese *locus* sólo funciona como un vacío que señala una operación final; imposible porque el acontecimiento mortal que *yace ahí* no puede producir más que testigos en segunda persona y victimarios. Acaso una objetivación de la muerte en su sentido extremo donde el Yo y el Mí de la muerte, como los hubiera pensado Heidegger, encuentran el punto extremo de su alienación en la imposibilidad del duelo, quizá la forma extrema del terror. En suma, lo que cada uno de estos filmes lleva a cabo es una suerte de *puesta en escena* de la imposibilidad de la muerte. Aquí imposibilidad de la muerte significa la imposibilidad de *mi/su* muerte. Dicho de otra forma, estos directores, al hacer coincidir el punto ciego de la mirada con la clausura de la cámara, hacen de lo irrepresentable la condición de posibilidad del mal radical, lo obsceno en el sentido nietzscheano; no la violencia de lo vivo sino la violencia del terror. Esto no es una cuestión menor, pues estas estrategias cinematográficas enuncian la aporía fundamental de Auschwitz: la ausencia absoluta como condición de posibilidad de la imagen. El vacío *ante* la cámara aparece entonces no como la prohibición, sino como la condición misma de la representación del horror.

Visto así, la pregunta no es si se puede o no representar el núcleo obsceno del terror: la cámara de gas, sino que en tanto inmostrable, la cámara de gas es el punto de anonadamiento, de nihilización tecno-política de los cuerpos. Hacerse cargo de esta forclusión, al punto donde el vacío, la nada y el despojo suponen una pregunta radical al sentido y al significado de la mímesis en la cultura occidental, significa, en el sentido lacaniano, una suerte de retorno de lo real.

Llegado a este punto pareciera entonces que la aporía sobre la representación/irrepresentabilidad de la solución final se produce no sólo en términos de lo visual en tanto tal, sino sobre todo en la condición de la reproductibilidad técnica en sí misma. Si hemos de estar de acuerdo con la afirmación de Godard sobre el fracaso histórico del cine y la fotografía, es a condición de asumir —en un giro benjaminiano— que a este fracaso no le puede ser ajeno el carácter histórico-político que le es propio a su condición histórica-material, a saber: la relación entre instante, verdad y representación. Pareciera que estos medios lo más que pudieron lograr fue definir la aporía de la representación, conducir a un callejón sin salida a la relación entre instante, verdad y representación. Sin duda, y de acuerdo con lo anterior, es cierta la afirmación de que el arte —en tanto medio material de representación— determina las condiciones históricas de la mímesis; en esta medida es indudable que la fotografía y el cine son el medio material de existencia histórico-político de la imagen desde finales del siglo XIX. Dicha condición, además, determina —como fue problematizado desde el siglo XIX en el impresionismo— el sentido y la función de la pintura en la historia de la visualidad y la representación en el siglo XX.

Este asunto adquiere una significación particular a la hora de pensar el lugar de la pintura en el horizonte, la aporía de la representación que significa Auschwitz. Acaso como lo observa Jusidman, la pintura ha estado más bien ausente respecto al problema de la representación de la Shoah. Y esto en algún sentido es cierto toda vez que ni el instante ni el documento ni el testimonio ni la transformación de la reproductibilidad en representación son asuntos que, en la historia, le correspondan a la pintura. En este contexto se antoja endeble, pues es frívola la pregunta por la función de la pintura ante la Shoah como índice radical del terror en el siglo XX. Sin embargo, es factible reformular esto de otra manera, desde la pintura, ¿qué puede suplementar la pintura en torno a la aporía de la representación? O, mejor aún, ¿qué problemas le plantea la aporía de Auschwitz a la pintura y a la representación?

Para formularlo en términos pictóricos: ¿cuáles son las condiciones de posibilidad, ya no de la imagen —algo que se ha planteado en la historia del cine y la fotografía de manera fundamental—, sino de lo pictórico ante la aporía radical en el punto de coincidencia donde el vacío y el despojo conforman las condiciones de representación de la aniquilación?

II. La aporía de la poesía y el silencio *de/en* la pintura

> ¡Tan blanco de nieve son, viento nocturno, tus cabellos!
> ¡Blanco lo que me queda y blanco lo que he perdido!
> Ella cuenta las horas y yo los años cuento.
> Nosotros bebimos lluvia. Lluvia bebimos.
>
> PAUL CELAN, *Amapola y memoria*[13]

—

13— Paul Celan, "Los Jarros", *Amapola y memoria*, p. 70.

¿No está el soñador *convirtiendo* esta pintura, otros dirían pervirtiéndola en pintura religiosa, en sacramento de cierta memoria judía, por otro lado interpretada libremente? ¿No está haciendo que hable, dándole una voz, forzando la voz, arbitrariamente, ahí donde la pintura calla? ¿E incluso ahí donde se trataría de hacer callar a Yahvé?

JACQUES DERRIDA, *Del color de la letra*[14]

NO MÁS ARTE DE ARENA, ni libro de arena,
ni maestros.
Nada que se arroje a la suerte
de los dados. ¿Cuántos
mudos?
Diez y siete.
Tu pregunta — tu respuesta.
Tu canto, ¿qué sabrá?
Hondoenlanieve,
ondinieve
O— i —e

PAUL CELAN, *Cambio de aliento*[15]

Es un lugar común referirse al horror de los campos de exterminio con la afirmación que hiciera Theodor W. Adorno respecto a que después de Auschwitz la poesía era imposible. No hay que dejar pasar esta afirmación tan a la ligera ni subsumirla a los discursos sobre el problema de la irrepresentabilidad de la solución final que se ha dado en las artes visuales, el cine y la fotografía. La afirmación adorniana, desde mi perspectiva, es más cercana a las consideraciones que Benjamin hiciera respecto a las relaciones entre experiencia, narración y enmudecimiento que él observó en los soldados que participaron en la primera guerra mundial.

De acuerdo con Benjamin, el enmudecimiento de los soldados no se explica por el hecho de no poder narrar su experiencia en el frente, sino más bien por el hecho de que estar en el frente suponía una carencia de

—

14— Atlan, *Grand format*, Paris, Gallimard, 2001, pp. 8-27.

15— Celan, *Selected Poems*, translated by Michael Hamburger, New York, Penguin Books, 1990, p. 232.

experiencia. Para este filósofo, el mutismo de los soldados supone una imposibilidad de experiencia: no hay nada que contar.[16] Se trata de una imposibilidad de narrar, en virtud de que aquello que merece ser narrado se relaciona con una suerte de magia de la memoria y la tradición, en la que la experiencia de lo vivido construye mundos. Por el contrario, ahí donde se inscribe la violencia al cuerpo, cierta amnesia, el olvido y la sutura definen una condición del relato que tiene que negociar el recuerdo desde una cierta perturbación del presente de lo vivido.

Como sea, para la "conciencia" europea, la primera guerra mundial supuso algo inimaginable: la barbarie alcanzaba su grado de violencia extrema con el desarrollo de la tecnología industrial en el seno mismo de la civilización moderna. La modernidad encuentra entonces su punto de perversión en la industria del exterminio que el nazismo produjo en el proceso de aniquilación de los judíos. De esto sin duda da cuenta la narrativa de Primo Levi, sobre todo en los relatos que conciernen al mutismo del "musulmán": esos sujetos sumergidos en el pasmo de lo casi muerto, del pasmo erguido y del gesto-mueca de lo que "resta aún" y que para él significó el punto más cercano al que se podía aproximar la narrativa de la Shoah —indudable la importancia de los relatos de Levi en torno a la vida en los campos de concentración y de exterminio. Su literatura introduce una de las paradojas ético-jurídicas más radicales en torno a la industria del exterminio nazi: la paradoja entre el testigo y superviviente que se "encarna" en la figura del musulmán. Este "resto de humanidad", lo que muestra es:

> ...que lo no-humano y el humano, el viviente y el hablante, el musulmán y el superviviente no coinciden; precisamente porque hay entre ellos una división insuperable, puede haber testimonio. Es justamente el hecho de que éste (el testimonio) sea inherente a la lengua como tal, porque atestigua el manifestarse de una potencia de decir solamente por medio de una impotencia, lo que hace que su autoridad

—

16— Walter Benjamin, "Experiencia y pobreza", en *Obras*, vol. II, tomo 1, Madrid, Abada, 2007.

> no dependa de una verdad factual, de la conformidad entre lo dicho y los hechos, entre la memoria y lo acaecido, sino de la relación inmemorial entre lo decible y lo indecible, entre el adentro y el afuera de la lengua [...] Por esto mismo —porque se testimonia sólo allí donde se da una imposibilidad de decir y porque hay un testigo sólo cuando ha habido una de-subjetivación— el musulmán es verdaderamente el testigo integral, por eso no es posible separar al testigo de superviviente.[17]

Aquí el inmemorial habrá entonces que entenderlo en sentido de la vida —la mera vida, la vida desnuda— como aquello que testifica a pesar de la lengua, a pesar del sujeto, aquello que hiere la lengua.

Si la poesía —según planteó Adorno— ya no era posible después de Auschwitz, ¿será entonces que este colapso entre lengua y cuerpo del que da cuenta Primo Levi es la fuga que reconfigura la función política del relato después de Auschwitz? En alguna medida esto es cierto, sin embargo, como el mismo Levi lo reconociera, esto era lo que emergía de la "tiniebla oscura", de una lengua ni viva ni muerta que el autor de *Si esto es un hombre*, reconoció en "Fuga de muerte" de Paul Celan.

De su poesía emerge la lengua herida, es decir, la impronta de una herida en la lengua y de la lengua como herida; una política del poema como crítica material de la historia. Una política del poema, no de la lengua ni de la poesía sin más. Aquí la política del poema, en la obra de Celan, tiene que ver al menos con dos cosas: con el poema como data y con la poesía como crítica política a la modernidad. Si bien no puedo ocuparme aquí de ello, baste con decir que la tensión dialéctica entre estos dos términos tiene que ver con la lengua como acontecimiento material del poema y con éste como potencia de la memoria como data irrevocable

—

17—Agamben postula la aporía del testimonio de Levi de la siguiente manera: "'El musulmán es el testigo integral' implica dos proposiciones contradictorias: 1) El musulmán es el no-hombre que en ningún caso puede testimoniar y 2) El que no puede testimoniar es el verdadero testigo, el testigo absoluto", Giorgio Agamben, *Lo que queda de Auschwitz. El archivo y el testigo. Homo Sacer III*, Valencia, Pre-textos, 2000, p. 165.

de la historia.[18] Acaso por ello, de “Fuga de muerte” emerge el poema como data, emerge el carácter sólo presente de la memoria del pasado como herida: “¡Tan blanco de nieve son, viento nocturno, tus/ cabellos!/ ¡Blanco lo que me queda y blanco lo que he/ perdido!/ Ella cuenta las horas y yo los años cuento”. Pero del poema surge también la crítica a la modernidad: “NO MÁS ARTE DE ARENA, ni libro de arena,/ ni maestros./ Nada que se arroje a la suerte”. En el punto donde todo poema es una data de la memoria del pasado en el presente como extravío y evanescencia, y la poesía un acontecimiento que no se explica por el azar; entonces quizá Celan pautó en una forma del pensar la aporía de la representación justo en el punto donde no hay metáfora, sino metonimia; un resto de algo que sustrae a la poesía de la metáfora, la sustrae de la mitología y la coloca en el lugar, no de la poética del acontecimiento, sino del acontecimiento como poema y de éste como política, aunque ésta sea la de una fuga.

Justo en esta tensión entre una política del poema y de la poesía como crítica a la modernidad es posible pensar en la condición estética de la representación. Me parece que aquí se dibujan las condiciones de posibilidad de la pintura respecto a la aporía de la representación que produce la solución final. Visto así, la cuestión no es que la solución final se resuelva tan sólo por un cierto programa iconográfico, figurativo, abstracto o temático abordado por la historia de la pintura tras la segunda guerra mundial, tampoco sería un asunto de poéticas de la forma o de lo informe que ante la aporía de la representación encuentran en las cualidades expresionistas de la materia y el trazo una forma de traer a la presencia el horror del exterminio.[19] Más bien se trata de hacer de la clausura de la representación una condición estética de la pintura, es decir, repensar cuáles son la condiciones de la mímesis pictórica a la hora de enfrentarla con el

—

18— Al respecto de esta consideración sobre Paul Celan remito al libro de Pablo Oyarzún Robles, *Entre Celan y Heidegger*, Santiago de Chile, Ediciones Metales Pesados, 2013.

19— Antes bien, quizá la representación de la dialéctica del terror de la segunda guerra mundial se materializa en la obra temprana de Francis Bacon, donde la relación entre mueca, terror y cabeza prefiguran las formas de la violencia que producirán los campos de exterminio: una suerte de sustracción de lo humano hacia lo animal.

problema de tener que redefinir, como afirmábamos más arriba con Nancy, qué ocurrió con la representación misma tras Auschwitz.

Como lo he intentado argumentar, la verdad *en* fotografía y *en* cine descansa en la mera indicación que se hace de lo ausente puesta en el intersticio entre el instante, el tiempo y la cosa. Así, el *dictum* de la fotografía define la verdad puramente en la huella que logra imprimir en tanto instante-del-acontecimiento; mientras que el cine, si bien distiende el instante en la toma, lo hace a condición de pretender sustituir el movimiento y el tiempo de la cosa por el de la imagen. Estas consideraciones son fundamentales porque, contra lo que suele pensarse, quizá de manera demasiado fácil, estas tecnologías de la mirada se determinan por su potencia de falsedad, lo que las hace radicalmente distintas respecto al sentido y el significado de la verdad en pintura. Colocado en el tenor dialéctico de estos análisis, habrá entonces que entender qué significa la verdad *en* pintura.

Al inicio de este trabajo adelanté una afirmación respecto a lo que podría significar la verdad *en* la cosa. Para apurar el referente de lo que ahora habrá que entender como cosa, aquí *cosa* significa pintura. Pero no cualquier *pintura*, sino esa que se hace cargo de la aporía de la representación de la que he querido dar cuenta a lo largo de todas estas páginas, la que se hace cargo de la historia de la representación de acuerdo con una cierta *política de la pintura*.

Política de la pintura: esta afirmación, aunque atrevida, resulta de una consideración compleja respecto a la tensión dialéctica propia de la reproductibilidad de la imagen y poesía, tal y como la materializó Paul Celan.

Desde luego han pasado muchas cosas: existe la pintura de Atlan, el cine de Resnais y el de Lanzmann. Incluso, como lo afirmé de pasada, la crítica política-montaje desde el desmontaje de Godard. Pero en todo esto, al menos en la pintura, no había existido sino un cierto silencio y una cierta ausencia a la hora de abordar la clausura de la representación del horror como una de las constantes de los regímenes visuales del siglo XX e incluso del siglo XXI. En todo caso, es en esta complejidad donde Jusidman aborda el problema de la representación, de la mímesis en la pintura.

Sin duda, una primera incomodidad que podría aparecer en estas consideraciones tiene que ver con la pregunta de: ¿por qué un artista tendría que abordar el problema de las condiciones de la representación de la solución final después de sesenta años de haberse mostrado las primeras imágenes de los campos de exterminio, de los cadáveres apilados o incluso de las cámaras de gas? Más aún, ¿por qué es un artista mexicano perteneciente a la generación de los neoconceptualismos de los años noventa en México el que aborda esta temática, tan trabajada por la conciencia histórica, artística y estética de emplazamientos hegemónicos del arte?

Podría ensayar un respuesta inmediata y decir que Jusidman, si bien artista mexicano, es judío, lo cual lo pone en una cierta condición de deuda respecto a lo que significa el mandato de guardar la memoria del exterminio como un mandato talmúdico de preservar la comunidad a través de la "narración", es decir, como una suerte de figura mishnaita[20] que se hace cargo de la ausencia y la testifica en un programa artístico específico. Incluso si esto fuera cierto, me parece que no da cuenta de todo el problema que el artista aborda a partir de la aporía de Auschwitz. Más bien me parece que es al contrario, se trata de hacerse cargo de la historia de esta aporía para replantear el lugar de la pintura en el arte contemporáneo, lo que, a mi parecer, define la especificidad de este trabajo. Visto así, se trata de entender qué preguntas plantea a la pintura la complejidad de la solución final en tanto cuestionamiento donde se producen las condiciones histórico-materiales de la falta de correspondencia entre acontecimiento y representación, un problema que sin duda y por principio intentaron resolver la fotografía y el cine, y que, con sus medios, la pintura busca abordar.

De vuelta a la pintura desde una distancia de sesenta años y a partir de un cierto alejamiento, si no de la historia, al menos de la memoria de la historia, *Azul de Prusia* es una investigación sobre las condiciones de la memoria y la materia como potencias miméticas a partir de las cuales resignificar la relación entre archivo e historia de la solución final. En un cruce entre los materiales de archivo y modos

—

20— La Mishná es la parte del Talmud que obliga a que ésta sea reinterpretada de acuerdo con el presente de la historia.

de circular de las imágenes de los campos de exterminio, Jusidman replantea las condiciones de posibilidad estética de la pintura ante el acontecimiento extremo del exterminio judío por parte de los nazis. En lo que funciona como una declaración de principio, el artista explora el "asunto" de la representación como aquello que le corresponde a la pintura. Una exploración que se hace cargo no sólo de lo que la pintura pudiese o no hacer con ésta, sino de lo que significa hacer pintura de un acontecimiento radical que en buena medida está sobre-expuesto hasta el punto del vaciamiento.

Son varios los registros sobre los que se despliega la serie. Construida mediante un montaje dialéctico, ésta se despliega sobre la tensión de contextos y afectos en los que las imágenes funcionan de acuerdo con una estrategia más propia de la fotografía y el cine. En el cruce entre las "tomas" abiertas (*Haus der Kunst* [*Casa del arte*], 2012) y los "planos suturados" (*Birkenau*, 2012), los dos lienzos iniciales de la serie están concebidos como un prólogo a la narrativa de la obra. Una narrativa que en primera instancia se construye a partir de cuatro motivos temáticos y pictóricos: "Cámaras de gas", "Paisajes", "Memorial" y "Manchas". Sin embargo, este recurso sobrepasa su propia estrategia hacia zonas más complejas de significación estética, de manera que no se trata de un mero ordenamiento temático o formal presente en las pinturas. Sin recusarlos, habría que atender más el formato, el emplazamiento en el espacio y la cualidad háptica de las obras. Se trata de un montaje que se construye en las intersecciones entre la figura y la abstracción, entre la escala y la afección, entre la profundidad y la atmósfera. Así, los cuatro momentos que la componen transitan sobre cierta historia de la "aporía plástica" de la representación: de las imágenes hiperreales de los campos al gesto mínimo del despojo de las telas de trabajo o a la impresión de las huellas de pigmento sobre los muros del estudio del artista; en la tensión entre figura y "expresión residual", se pone en operación cierto carácter afectivo en el que la impronta histórica del exterminio se inscribe en la corporeidad del espectador, en un doble juego entre memoria y afecto. Se trata de un cierto pliegue del documento sobre la superficie-lienzo como memoria presente del pasado histórico en la *re*presentación.

Si *Azul de Prusia* se concibe como la relación entre serie y montaje, entonces es factible pensar su emplazamiento como un espaciamiento: es factible pensarla como totalidad de la memoria y la historia distendida en "espacio", a la vez que es una cita con la historia de la pintura, es un quiasmo entre la memoria y la historia de las atrocidades de la Shoah sobre la materialidad de lo pictórico. Esto quizá sea una de las diferencias fundamentales que la serie posee. A diferencia de otras prácticas de la pintura —e incluso de los grabados de David Olère (1902–1985)—, Jusidman asume la matriz fotográfica y documental como un momento de la propia aporía de la representación de Auschwitz. Esto lo hace en dos sentidos: el primero, en este tipo de documentos visuales, como lo argumenté anteriormente, se presenta un retardo respecto al instante mortal de la cámara de gas; y el segundo, que a partir de esta condición, las pinturas de la serie no intentan suturar ni aclarar esa aporía, sino que asumen el retardo como una condición de posibilidad histórica con la que se conforman dichos documentos. Se trata de un quiebre que se hace a la ausencia y al vacío de esas imágenes desde la pintura. Dicho de otra manera, aquí la pintura se hace cargo de mostrar la clausura de la representación no en función del tiempo, ya sea como memoria o como historia, sino de remontarlo hacia el espacio como huella o impronta, como impronta del terror en la superficie. Asumir entonces la aporía de la representación no significa lo irrepresentable, sino una suerte de búsqueda a través de la pintura de aquello que de una u otra manera el cine y la fotografía —como los medios materiales que definieron el carácter de la imagen y del imaginario de la Shoah— no pudieron dar cuenta. En éstos, el acontecimiento (temporalidad e instante) fue sustraído como condición ontológica de la representación de dichos medios.

Llegados a este punto, la serie *Azul de Prusia* no es un mero ejercicio pictórico sobre un tema o un suceso cualquiera, sino más bien la toma de postura estética, ética, política e histórica de su autor respecto a la solución final a partir del propio medio. Si las condiciones histórico-materiales del cine y la fotografía configuraron un modo particular de abordar la aporía de la representación, si la poesía de Celan se sustrae a las relaciones fundacionales entre mito y metáfora como lo propio de la poesía y a cambio hace de la materialidad de la imagen poética una data en la que se juega el carácter político de la lengua, y asimismo, la imagen poética como memoria política de la historia; el trabajo de Jusidman problematiza en estos mismos términos el quehacer histórico-político de la pintura después de Auschwitz.

El azul de Prusia o ferrucianuro es un color artificial que desde el siglo XVIII acompaña la memoria material de Austria. Como lo observa Cuauhtémoc Medina: "El ferrociaunuro fue el colorante escogido para los uniformes militares prusianos de los siglos XVIII y XIX: fue entre otras cosas el distintivo de los soldados que enfrentaron a los ejércitos napoleónicos. De modo más siniestro, el azul de Prusia ha quedado ligado al exterminio de los judíos en Europa".[21] La apropiación de este índice histórico-material es el punto de partida que define, en principio, la serie *Azul de Prusia* como una data en el sentido en que Celan hace lo propio con su poesía. El hecho de que este pigmento artificial sea la materia prima sobre la que trabaja Yishai Jusidman supone por principio una reconsideración sobre la *grisaille*[22] como *subjectil*.[23] Se adivina de inmediato que aquello que soporta y acoge al mismo tiempo, en una suerte de acción y pasión de la materialidad, es el azul de Prusia en las "pinturas calladas" de Yishai Jusidman.

Habrá que entender esta *grisaille-subjectil* en varios sentidos: primero, como un fondo indeterminado a través del cual los elementos de la pintura emergen; es una suerte de pulsión que permea las condiciones de posibilidad de la figuración en el lienzo. Segundo, como impronta material, y sólo material, de la solución final en tanto vestigio y retardo. Finalmente, como la eclosión del

—

21— Dossier de la serie *Azul de Prusia*, MUAC-UNAM, agosto-diciembre de 2016, p. 4.

22— La *grisaille* o grisalla es una técnica pictórica en la que se utilizan diferentes tonos de gris, blanco y negro, imitando relieves escultóricos o recreando espacios arquitectónicos.

23— Entiendo por *subjectil*, siguiendo a Derrida, como lo que subyace (*subjectum*) y lo que soporta, lo que en pintura significaría aquello que sujeta y acoge la representación o, para más precisión, *lo que yace debajo*.

acontecimiento en la producción material de la clausura y de la aporía de la representación. Vayamos por partes.

En tanto base, fondo, atmósfera y transparencia, el azul de Prusia define el modo de advenir de los planos, los cambios cromáticos, las formas y las figuras en las pinturas. En este sentido, el azul subyace y soporta el "temple" de lo representado en los cuadros. Pero no sólo se trata de esto, sino que el azul de Prusia, tanto en su artificialidad como en el patronímico que lo califica (Prusia), supone de entrada un cierto índice histórico del que no es posible sustraerlo. No se trata de un mero color "natural", antes bien su genealogía lo inscribe en cierta historia de la ciencia (la de la química del siglo XVIII) donde el accidente puede ser articulado en términos de saber y poder de acuerdo con la conocida fórmula postulada por Foucault, que llevada a su extremo, da cuenta de una las formas de necropolítica de la modernidad: la industria de la muerte.[24]

Como sea, la impronta en azul en las cámaras es resultado de la utilización del gas Zyklon B. Se trata del vestigio de un químico que produce una inscripción material de la historia en el espacio, lo que en otros términos significa una suerte de memoria de la materia, que en su propio proceso de reacción ante el medio, funciona como prueba material de un hecho, en este caso: el gaseado dentro de las cámaras. ¿Tiene esto un carácter de prueba forense? Aquí la clausura del residuo material adquiere su potencia política: al mismo tiempo que define una falla en la estrategia de borramiento de cualquier vestigio como condición de la solución final tiene un carácter de memoria material de la historia. El teñido en azul de Prusia, si bien nunca podría ser una prueba contundente del uso letal del gas, en su fallo pone en evidencia lo que era una constante en otras cámaras de gas donde el vestigio se borra: el uso

—

24— Sin duda, es fácil deducir de los argumentos foucaultianos la consideración de que en la modernidad no hay accidentes sino variaciones de probabilidad del valor de la verdad y el conocimiento de acuerdo con el *a priori* cientificista que define el sentido del saber en la modernidad. De acuerdo con ello, producir por accidente el azul de Prusia en realidad está determinado por una variación mínima del modelo de la química del siglo XVIII. Dentro de un rango de experimentación se reconoce el accidente como variable del modelo, nunca como una irrupción del caos o la fuerza de la materia.

de cianuro.[25] En todo caso, aquí el azul de Prusia "amarra" la representación a la facticidad de la historia, ata el significado a la materia, en suma evade el significante como excedencia, imposibilidad y prohibición de la representación o imposibilidad de la Shoah; y a cambio asume una cierta materialidad del hecho, que es donde el silencio vibra en la materia. Esta relación entre materia y memoria es advertida por Jusidman como el elemento que permite reintroducir la pintura en la historia de la representación de la Shoah. Esta serie de pinturas no puede ser leída como una versión, como un relato más, que se suma a la historia de la representación de la atrocidad del exterminio de los judíos. Antes bien, aquí el color define una condición objetiva de cierta historia material del horror, al punto en el que la relación entre materia y forma es reconfigurado de manera radical en el trabajo de Jusidman. Visto a contrapelo de las condiciones materiales de representación del cine y la fotografía (el instante y el acontecimiento), la apropiación que se lleva a cabo en estas pinturas reintroduce dos cualidades fundamentales que le son propias a este medio, y al hacerlo, logra —al menos desde mi perspectiva— una tensión dialéctica entre el vestigio y el retardo. Afirmar una tensión entre el vestigio y el retardo supone una relación, no de causalidad del tiempo del trazo que se soporta sobre el azul de Prusia, sino de la colisión de ambos en el plano pictórico en tanto tal. El modo en que la figuración emerge de la forma, ésta del plano y éste del color, provocan que la matriz documental de las imágenes de donde provienen los motivos de las pinturas sean reconfiguradas en tanto pinturas y no sólo utilizadas de acuerdo con la pretensión de objetividad que suponen poseer. Acaso por ello las cualidades hápticas de estas pinturas, es decir la vibración y la porosidad, no son

—

25— Acaso como lo observa Cuauthémoc Medina: "Uno de los principales debates acerca de la dimensión del genocidio ha girado en torno a la evidencia de residuos azules en algunas instalaciones de campos de exterminio. En casos como los campos de Majdanek y Sututthof, Polonia, las manchas de azul de Prusia en las paredes de las cámaras son palpables hasta nuestros días. Mientras los denegacionistas han pretendido apoyarse en la ausencia de residuos azules en Birkenau para cuestionar la función de las cámaras en ese complejo (Informe Leuchter, 1988), la investigación científica e histórica ha demostrado en múltiples formas la presencia de residuo de cianuro en ellas". Dossier de la serie *Azul de Prusia*, MUAC-UNAM, agosto-diciembre de 2016, p. 5.

meros recursos formales, sino condiciones estructurales de las potencias estético-políticas de esta serie. El punto de eclosión de la memoria en la materia define la pertinencia de la pregunta por el lugar de la pintura ante la aporía de la solución final. Pintura radical, la serie *Azul de Prusia* es una exploración sobre la aporía de la representación en tanto problema de la pintura; sin evadir la impotencia del medio, pero tampoco produciendo un simulacro de lo representado ni hiperbolizando el momento traumático de la violencia; la recuperación de la memoria como vestigio en la materia es sobre todo una data de la historia material de la aniquilación. Esta condición permite que la pintura afirme su carácter estético específico, pero sobre todo en alguna medida devuelve a la memoria su registro material e histórico. El hecho de que el azul de Prusia resulte como pigmento en los muros de las cámaras de gas hace que el registro plástico funcione como materia, memoria e historia; aquí sin duda la metáfora como estrategia de la representación se cancela por una metonimia donde el carácter singular de la materialidad aparece como rasgo y fragmento de un tiempo histórico bien determinado.

Un último registro se desprende de la condición histórico-material del azul de Prusia. En una suerte de pliegue de la aporía de la representación sobre las determinaciones genealógicas, el color azul de Prusia produce un quiasmo *en* la superficie, un quiasmo en la materia que propongo pensar como colisión. En la superficie se produce el choque de dos fuerzas; la de la violencia del exterminio y la de la materia en tanto tal, al punto que aquí la pintura produce lo que los medios de reproductibilidad técnica sólo han podido "mostrar" como imposibilidad. Así, mientras el instante y tiempo traicionan, por decirlo de alguna manera, la imagen en el cine y la fotografía, estas pinturas retrotraen el imaginario del terror al vestigio para volver a hacer presente, es decir, *representar* la aporía de Auschwitz.

Así, la *grisaille* como *subjectil* del azul de Prusia es algo más que un mero recurso técnico del artista, es el medio material donde se anuda la historia, la materia en el presente de la imagen como soporte y pantalla sobre las que se sostiene, no la representación, sino su aporía.

Es sobre esta aporía plástica, para decirlo de una vez, que Jusidman problematiza el estatuto de la materia en la pintura. Es sobre esta condición que se habrán de abordar los otros dos materiales sobre los que se despliega la serie *Azul de Prusia:* el color "rosa carne" y la piedra pómez. De la segunda baste decir que es utilizada como índice histórico y como determinante de las texturas en las pinturas. La piedra pómez, según lo refiere el artista, fue usada como conductor del gas letal en las cámaras. Plásticamente, este material produce un efecto "poroso" en las pinturas.

El rosa carne hace referencia implícita, según palabras del mismo Jusidman, "a los miles de hombres, mujeres y niños que fueron victimados en las cámaras" de gas: aquí el rosa carne es una especie de vestigio de los cuerpos y una metonimia de la carne, un resto que interpela la ausencia de la muerte como producción de cadáveres.[26]

Si algo ha obsesionado a la historia de la pintura es cómo hacer que uno de los principios materiales de la vida se exprese en la pintura misma. Cuando se habla de rosa carne, más bien tendríamos que pensar en una suerte, como lo enuncia Didi-Huberman, de hiperfísica de la mímesis: "la mímesis aparece aquí pensada [...] como una materia, una 'sustancia madre'..., un *tejido de entrañas*. Es por lo tanto una hipefísica del pliegue y de la vibración, como una *diaphanés* generalizada, casi orgánica".[27] Y es que la piel no es un color; antes bien, en lo ontológico es un quiasmo, quizá, el más radical entre el mundo y el cuerpo a través de la carne como vida; en lo orgánico, una compleja retícula de laminillas a través de las cuales corre la sangre. Apenas perceptible en las pinturas que conforman la serie *Azul de Prusia*, el rosa carne queda como impronta, como trazo callado de los cuerpos a través del azul, como una latencia, como un resto que testimonia la Shoah *en* pintura.

Es entonces a través de vestigios, trazos, porosidades, transparencias —para decirlo pronto—; es *en* pintura como Yishai Jusidman lleva al límite la aporía de Auschwitz. Pensada como una dramaturgia, la trama de esta serie se urde

—

26— En la medida en que el exterminio produce cadáveres lo que se hace imposible es la muerte. En un sentido radical un cadáver jamás es la muerte. Véase: José Luis Barrios, "Invisible e irrepresentable: el despojo no es la muerte. Notas sobre la aporética de la imagen en el mundo contemporáneo", en *Tópicos del seminario*, vol. 18, Puebla, BUAP, 2007.

27— Didi-Huberman, *op. cit.*, p. 43.

en el color como memoria material, de la cual emerge la figura como huella-fuerza, tal es lo que sucede en *Cámaras de gas*; transita por una citación del silencio a la manera de Lanzmann, en *Paisaje*; y hace de los materiales de origen alemán el *Memorial* de lo impresentable como geopolítica del exterminio. Desemboca (y esto habrá que entenderlo casi en el sentido literal del término) en *Manchas* como el gesto que el artista *deja ser* en su despojo, para dar cuenta de la condición mimética del terror: la indefinición del cuerpo ante la muerte en las cámaras de gas.

Trapo #19—Rag #19, 2013-2015 [Cat. 39]

On the Imminence of the Senseless, or, Painting as Annihilation. Memory, Matter and History

JOSÉ LUIS BARRIOS

Treblinka, 2012 [Cat. 3]

0. The unknown work of art

> [...] the painter's Hell, to the depths of which he must descend in order to bring life back with him, the *movere*, is first and foremost a color.
>
> GEORGES DIDI-HUBERMAN, *La peinture incarnée*[1]

> For in death the visibility of the tomb would have been able to reappropriate the foreigner, it would have been able to signify a sort of repatriation for him.
>
> JACQUES DERRIDA, *On Hospitality*[2]

In his short novel *The Unknown Masterpiece*, Balzac reconsiders what seems to have defined the relationship between drive [*pulsión*], gaze and representation in the heart of the history of Western art. It is well known that this relationship is also in large part what, in its time, would have led Paris to decide on the most beautiful goddess on Olympus, Aphrodite. In both cases, what is at play is the relationship between eroticism, beauty and the gaze. Apart from the theme—or even the canon—that defines the meaning and value of the beautiful in painting, the history of painting knots together a certain intrigue in which eye, thing and representation find a "comfortable position," or, if one prefers, their condition of possibility in the image as "speculum,"[3] as "phantasm." By contrast with sculpture, especially any sculpture that fits *life* into an instant—a crystallization that would perhaps be the figure that defines the ontologico-aesthetic status of the idol, idolatry

—

1— "[...] l'enfer du peintre, ce au fond de quoi il a à descendre pour en ramener la vie, le movere, c'est d'abord une couleur." Georges Didi-Huberman. *La peinture incarnée.* p. 69.

2— Jacques Derrida and Anne Dufourmantelle, *On Hospitality*, translated by Rachel Bowlby, Stanford, Stanford University Press, 2000, p. 133.

3— That is, as reflection, as specter. In any case, the mechanical definition of a speculum offers a good description of its ocular function: "a surgical instrument of various forms, used for dilating orifices of the body so as to facilitate examination or operations." *OED Online*. June 2016. Oxford University Press. http://www.oed.com/view/Entry/186126 (accessed June 23, 2016). [The Real Academia Española's definition of the Spanish equivalent, *espéculo*, translates as: "Instrument used to examine certain body cavities by means of luminous reflection." *Diccionario de la Real Academia Española*. June 2016. http://dle.rae.es/?id=GX-gjH1m (accessed June 23, 2016).

and its consequent prohibition in monotheistic religions—it is in painting and poetry that one encounters problems with the relationships between representation and truth. To be sure, Plato's condemnation of these two arts declared their equivocal character: deception in the former case, delirium in the latter. This is perhaps why Plato's condemnation also signifies a radical index on the basis of which painting and poetry have attempted to escape from the delirium and deception with which they have been thought, perhaps in spite of themselves, throughout Western history.

What is certain is that, at first blush, something appears on the "scene" at the moment of thinking painting as a *surface* where the play between gaze (desire + thing = object = *phantasm*) and representation (delirium + deception = deceit) is pulled taut. The phantasm always deceives us because, so it would seem, it is a knotting together of thing and desire that tends to obscure the truth. This assertion, maximalist as it is, opens one of the perspectives from which I would like to address my considerations of Yishai Jusidman's series *Azul de Prusia* [*Prussian Blue*].

The other general consideration I would like to bring up—apart from the thematics of the extermination camps and their obscene core, the gas chamber, which I address below—is the equivocal figure that has inspired in many commentators a certain sacrificial and sacred reading of the fact that the "final solution"[4] should be interpreted in accordance with the biblical proscription of images. As I suggested just a few lines above: the context of the biblical prohibition refers to idols as the real bodies of the gods, therefore to the idolatry of sculpture.[5] This is not the space to expand on this

—

4— *Endlösung der Judenfrage* (final solution to the Jewish question) is how Nazi leaders referred to the extermination of the Jews during World War II.

5— "Let us first recall that the commandment forbids the making of images 'of anything that is in heaven above, or that is in the earth beneath, or that is in the water under the earth,' that is, of anything at all. Above all, however, it forbids the making of *sculpted* images [...]. The commandment therefore concerns the production of forms that are solid, whole, and autonomous, as a statue is, and that are thus destined for use as an idol. The question here concerns idolatry and not the image as such or 'representation.' The idol is a fabricated god, not the representation of one, and the contemptible and false character of its divinity derives from the fact it is fabricated." Jean-Luc Nancy, "Forbidden Representation," in *The Ground of the Image*, translated by Jeff Fort, New York, Fordham University Press, 2005, p. 30.

discussion; suffice it to note, as Georges Didi-Huberman rightly observes, that if we lose sight of the fact that the referent of this prohibition has to do with an interrelation between volume, stone and force as a field of aesthetic immanence of the relationships between life, figure and form, then what we lose is the idol's character of ontological totality itself, and with it the religious, political and historical implications of sculpture or the sculptural for classical antiquity,[6] something which, furthermore, is fundamental to bear in mind in order likewise to understand the temper and aesthetic character of Nazi art, an art conceived in terms of a production of idolatry, as demonstrated by the sculpture and architecture of the German national-socialist regime.

In this context, it is likely that the first problematic to which we should attend, as Jean-Luc Nancy rightly observes, is a certain confusion in the history of discussions of the representation of the moment: the final solution; namely, the confusion between prohibition and impossibility. Put briefly, the final solution is unrepresentable because it is prohibited—the status of the victim is sacrosanct—or, alternatively, it is unrepresentable because it is impossible to do so, because it has the status of horror and has to do with the aesthetics and politics of extermination. According to Nancy:

> The question of the representation of *Auschwitz*—supposing that it must be maintained in these terms as a question—cannot be resolved (if, indeed, it can be at all) through a reference, be it negative or positive, either to an extreme horror or to an extreme sanctity. Rather, this question must pass through the following one: What became of representation itself at Auschwitz? How was it brought into play there?[7]

From this perspective, the question of the representation of the camps and the obscene—and, as we will see below, perverse—core of the prohibition of representation is related more to a certain imposed limit at the nexus of politics,

—

6— See Georges Didi-Huberman, *La peinture incarnée*, Paris, Minuit, 1985, pp. 102-103.

7— Nancy, op. cit., p. 34. I have emphasized the word Auschwitz in order to stress the paradigmatic character of this camp in particular in the history of the exterminations that took place during World War II.

aesthetics and representation, than to a certain religious character associated with it. This is no minor question. Among other things, it raises the possibility of considering the meaning, function and potentiality [*potencia*] of painting with regard to this discussion, which, to be sure, has also traversed photography, cinema, the novel, and even poetry throughout the history of the image and the word in the last seventy years.

It is not, then, a genealogical problem of the causes that either prohibit the representation of the Shoah or make it impossible, but rather one that has to do with a question leveled at its limits —and that no doubt directly or indirectly touches the duty of painting in the political and ethical history of the West. This question would seem to make the work of painting relevant once more, enabling us to rethink its meaning in accordance with Derrida in *The Truth in Painting*. In order to formulate this in terms of the series *Azul de Prusia*, I draw on this observation of Nancy's: in terms of the impossibility of the representation of the final solution, the question does not consist in knowing whether it is impossible to represent the fatal "instant" of annihilation, which, in fact, it is. Rather, it has to do with making present (representing) the absence (*absens*, that which is unrepresentable insofar as it is not there) *in* the thing. But what does this mean, that which is unrepresentable *in* the thing? This returns us to painting in the history of the image as our history; it makes the question of its fundamental potentiality —that is, representation— relevant once more. I will have to insist on this throughout the pages that follow. For now, suffice it to understand that asking ourselves about the unrepresentable *in* the thing supposes an unimpeachable interpellation of painting, and even more of the *surface*, not to say of the canvas. Canvas has always meant "extension of a body lengthwise and widthwise," or, if one prefers, the chunk of a plane...

To be sure, the problem of representation is painting's fundamental "issue," and even that of what is perhaps the most debated concept of its history of representation: mimesis. To re-present means to make present the presence of something that is no longer there. Merely being present does not require being presented again, that is, being *re*-presented. By contrast, *presence* is re-presented insofar as what is absent from the *present* returns to presence through the representation.

Another issue is knowing whether making something present again has to do with figuration or abstraction. I cannot deal with this issue here, but it matters for the purposes of this analysis insofar as a good portion of the discussion about the status of the representation or non-representation of the terror of extermination was resolved in the binomial of figuration-expression (with Bacon) or abstraction-expression (with Rothko and de Kooning). In any case, it is important to use painting, and particularly the series *Azul de Prusia*, to consider what mimesis means at the point where the Nazi regime postulated an aesthetics of super-representation as being proper to its art:

> "I propose," writes Nancy, that we call this regime "super-representation" to emphasize that it is not simply a matter of representing triumphant humanity as a type [...], but of a nature or an essence (the Aryan body). It is in this body that the presence of a self-creating humanity would truly consist (a humanity that is, in this sense, divine, but with no separation of the divine, that is, with no "sanctity"). The Aryan body is an idea identical to a presence, or it is the presence of an idea without remainder: precisely what the West has, for centuries, thought of as the idol. [...] By contrast, for Hitler the Jew is the representative of representation in its ordinary, pejorative sense: the only art in which the Jew succeeds is that of an actor or, rather, a charlatan [...].[8]

Perhaps this observation by Jean-Luc Nancy might give us some clue as to how to understand this phrase that Celan drops into his poem "Death Fugue": "He calls out jab deeper into the earth you lot you others sing now and play / he grabs at the iron in his belt he waves it his eyes are blue."[9] And perhaps that is why Celan then writes, "jab deeper you lot with your spades you others play on for the dance."[10]

—

8— Ibid, pp. 38-39.

9— Paul Celan, "Death Fugue," in *Selected Poems*, translated by Michael Hamburger, New York, Penguin, 1990, p. 61.

10— Ibid.

I. Medium, history and representation

> Death makes its promises to us through cinematography.
> JEAN-LUC GODARD, *Histoire(s) du cinéma*[11]

> Within *unitary* community [*communauté une*] there is nothing but death, and not the sort of death found in the cemetery, which is a place of spacing or distinctness, but the death found in the ashes of crematorium ovens or in the accumulations of charnel-houses.
> JEAN-LUC NANCY, *Being Singular Plural*[12]

There can be no doubt that the so-called crisis of painting not only has to do with the supposed limit to representation that may have been posed by the final solution, but is also a history whose genealogy goes back to the historical moment of national socialism. It is a history that is quite familiar to everyone and known to the point of exhaustion. It begins with the appearance of photography and the subsequent development of the technologies of technical reproducibility, which raised problematics that were unprecedented, although not unknown, in the tradition of Western visuality. But, from my perspective, aside from this consideration, there is a more complex knot of relationships between technics, history and representation that, for my purposes here, enables us to delve into the problem posed by these relationships to painting's place in the aesthetics of terror in the twentieth century.

In this context we might perhaps venture a provisional affirmation—namely, that the truth is not an issue for painting—or at least consider whether the truth *in* painting[13]

—

11— "La mort nous fait ses promesses par cinématographie." Jean-Luc Godard,. *Histoire (s) du cinéma. Toutes les histoires une seule histoire seule, 1*, Paris, Gallimard, 1998, p. 68.

12— Nancy, op. cit., pp. 154-155.

13— [The author is alluding to the title of a book by Derrida, *La vérité en peinture*, Paris, Flammarion, 1978, published in English as *The Truth in Painting*, translated by Geoff Bennington and Ian McLeod, Chicago, University of Chicago Press, 1987. Both the French *peinture* and the Spanish *pintura* can refer to the activity of painting as well as the physical substance of painting—that is, paint. The author makes use of this double meaning throughout the text. I have added the word "paint" in brackets as a reminder whenever this sense of *pintura* seems to take precedence.—Trans.]

responds to other conditions of possibility from the ones that are determined in the relationships between representation and reproducibility. This assertion enables me to pose a question that I will not address more fully, but that functions as a frame of reference for the analyses elaborated here. Thinking about the truth of the arts or considering the regimes of the image supposes that we think truth *in* the arts: that is, that we think their techniques, their physical media, their materiality, but also that we think the historico-material character of these media. With regard to the first issue—having to do with everything that relates directly to painting, to which I will return below—I would like to bring up a problematic that pertains to the historico-material character of the mechanical means of technical reproducibility with respect to the problem of representing the final solution, of the (im)possibility of showing, of capturing the fatal instant of the gas chamber.

In his *Histoire(s) du cinéma* (1988–1998), Jean-Luc Godard asserts that the political vocation of film failed historically. He means this in at least two senses, the first having to do with the equivocal character of film and photography, and the second having to do with montage as an ideological operation. The context of these assertions has to do with the fact that during World War II, and particularly with respect to the extermination camps, film was compelled to give an account of the atrocities of the operation and administration of death carried out by the Nazis during those years. Nevertheless, for this Swiss-French director, film did not give such an account of the Nazis' necropolitical operation: it showed up late to history and against its own political power [*potencia*] of representation. Film wasn't there; it didn't bear witness to the administration of extermination. The constative aspect of this assertion is true, but it is also true that part of the logic of the final solution involved the erasure and closure of representation. In this context, film did not give an account of the extermination because it was precluded from doing so. This is perhaps why, in its political failure at being unable to observe the instant of extermination, it produces the aporia of representation.

Even aside from Godard's observations, one would have to consider the empty point in the image of terror seen in the photographs taken by the *Sonderkommandos* at the

Birkenau gas chambers (1944). It was impossible for the photographic camera—at least for the cameras that were available in the 1940s—to extend their exposure times long enough to capture the blind spot where the gas was sprayed over the prisoners in the "bathrooms" of the extermination camps. In this context, Nancy's question about the fact that representation became impossible at Auschwitz seems to be not only relevant, but necessary. The final solution poses the question of the conditions of possibility of representation.

There are many ways of approaching this problematic, and I will not treat them all exhaustively here, but it is worth mentioning them in order to specify what Yishai Jusidman's series *Azul de Prusia* puts into operation.

Circumscribed around the media of technical reproducibility, and with the aim of posing the dialectical tension in the different visual practices that have tackled the aporia of the representation of the final solution, *Nuit et brouillard* [*Night and Fog*] (1955) by Alain Resnais (1922–2014), *Shoah* (1985) by Claude Lanzmann (1925) and *Histoire(s) du cinéma* [*History(s) of the Cinema*] by Godard are films that in one way or another have addressed the contradiction between the representation and unrepresentability of the "instant" of extermination. By contrast to many others, in these films the point where death, time and impossibility coincide is the emptiness *of* representation, or emptiness *as* representation.

Away from the contexts for and in which these films were shot, here I can do no more than work with what these materials show us. Unlike such feature films as *La vita è bella* [*Life Is Beautiful*] (1997), *Schindler's List* (1993) or more recently *Saul fia* [*Son of Saul*] (2015), each of which, in its own way, attempts to suture the relationship between impossibility, death and emptiness (whether through the fable as a narrative resource in the first, through the hyperrealism of the second, or through the play between foreground and rite in the third), the films of Resnais, Godard and Lanzmann have something in common: filming the aftermath of the fatal event. None of these films encompasses the evental moment (*site événementiel*) of the final solution; none of them seeks to show the fatal moment of the gas chambers. It is impossible to do so insofar as that locus only functions as an emptiness that signals a final operation; impossible because the fatal event that *is located there* can only produce witnesses in the second person and victims. Perhaps it is an objectivation of death in its extreme sense, where the I and Me of death, as Heidegger would have thought of them, find the extreme point of their alienation in the impossibility of mourning, perhaps the extreme form of terror. In sum, what each of these films carries out is a sort of staging of the impossibility of death. Here impossibility of death means the impossibility of *my/ their* death. In other words, by making the blind spot of the gaze coincide with the closure of the camera, these directors turn the unrepresentable into the condition of possibility of radical evil, the obscene in Nietzsche's sense; not the violence of the living [*lo vivo*, that which is alive] but the violence of terror. This is no minor question, since these cinematic strategies herald the fundamental aporia of Auschwitz: absolute absence as a condition of possibility of the image. Emptiness *vis-à-vis* the camera thus appears not as prohibition, but as the very condition of the representation of horror.

In this light, the question is not whether or not to represent the obscene core of terror—the gas chamber. Rather, insofar as it is unshowable, the gas chamber is the point of the nullification, of the techno-political nihilization of bodies. To take responsibility for this foreclosure—at the point where emptiness, nothingness, and deprivation involve a radical question to the sense and meaning of mimesis in Western culture—means a sort of return of the real (in the Lacanian sense).

At this point it would thus seem that the aporia around the representation/unrepresentability of the final solution is produced not only in terms of the visual as such, but also and especially in the condition of technical reproducibility in itself. If we must agree with Godard's assertion about the historical failure of film and photography, it is on the condition of accepting—in a Benjaminian turn—that this failure cannot be alien to the historico-political character that pertains to its historico-material condition: namely, the relationship between instant, truth and representation. In keeping with the above, there can be no doubt about the truth of the assertion that art—qua material medium of representation—determines the historical conditions of mimesis. To this extent there can be no doubt that photography and film are the material media of the historico-political existence of the image since the late nineteenth century. Furthermore, this condition—as problematized since the nineteenth century in impressionism—determines the meaning and function of painting in the history of twentieth-century visuality and representation.

This issue takes on a particular meaning when considering the place of painting in the horizon, the aporia of representation signified by Auschwitz. Maybe, as Jusidman observes, painting has actually been absent with respect to the problem of the representation of the Shoah. And this is true in some sense as long as the instant, the document, the witnessing and the transformation of reproducibility in representation are not matters that historically belong to painting. It seems shaky in this context, given the frivolousness of the question of painting's function in the face of the Shoah as a radical index of terror in the twentieth century. Nevertheless, it is feasible to reformulate this in another way, from the standpoint of painting: how could painting supplement the aporia of representation? Or better yet, what problems does the aporia of Auschwitz pose to painting and representation?

To formulate this in pictorial terms: what are the conditions of possibility, no longer of the image—something that has been posed fundamentally in the history of film and photography—but rather of the pictorial [*lo pictórico*] in the face of the radical aporia at the point where emptiness and deprivation coincide and shape the conditions of representation of annihilation?

II. The aporia of poetry and the silence *of/in* painting

> So white your hair, night wind, like snow!
> White what I have left and white what I've lost!
> She counts the hours and I count the years.
> We drank rain. Rain drank we.
>
> PAUL CELAN, from *Poppy and Memory*[14]

—

14— "So schneeig weiß sind, Nachtwind, deine Haare!
Weiß, was mir bleibt, und weiß, was ich verlier!
Sie zählt die Stunden, und ich zähl die Jahre.
Wir tranken Regen. Regen tranken wir." Paul Celan, "So Schlafe" in *Mohn und Gedächtnis: Vorstufen—Textgenese—Endfassung*, edited by Jürgen Wertheimer, Frankfurt am Main: Suhrkamp Verlag, 2004, p. 89.

Is the dreamer not in the process of *converting* this painting, others might say perverting it, into a religious painting, into a sacrament of some Jewish memory, elsewhere interpreted freely? Is he not in the process of making it talk, of giving it a voice, of forcing its voice out, there where the painting goes quiet? And even there where it would be a matter of making Yahweh go quiet?

JACQUES DERRIDA, *De la couleur à la lettre*[15]

NO MORE SAND ART, no sand book, no masters.

Nothing won by dicing. How many
dumb ones?
Seventeen.

Your question — your answer.
Your song, what does it know?

Deepinsnow,
Eepinnnow,
Ee—i—o.

PAUL CELAN, *Breathturn*[16]

It is commonplace to refer to the horror of the extermination camps with the assertion that Theodor W. Adorno would make with respect to poetry being impossible after Auschwitz. One need not let this assertion pass too lightly, nor subsume it to the discourses surrounding the problem of the unrepresentability of the final solution that has taken place in the visual arts, film and photography. From my perspective, Adorno's assertion is closer to the considerations that Walter Benjamin would make regarding the relationships between experience, narration and silencing

—

15—"Le rêveur n'est-il pas en train de convertir cette peinture, d'autres diraient de la pervertir en peinture religieuse, en sacrement de quelque mémoire juive, d'ailleurs librement interprétée? N'est-il pas en train de la faire parler, de lui donner une voix, de lui forcer la voix, arbitrairement, là où la peinture se tait? Et même là où il s'agirait de faire taire Iahwé?" in Derrida, "De la couleur à la lettre," in *Atlan, grand format: De la couleur à la lettre*, Paris, Gallimard, 2001, p. 15.

16— Celan, *Selected Poems*, translated by Michael Hamburger, New York, Penguin Books, 1990, p. 232.

that he observed in the soldiers who participated in World War I.

According to Benjamin, the silencing of the soldiers is not to be explained by the fact of their inability to narrate their experience on the warfront, but rather by the fact that being on the warfront meant a lack of experience. For this philosopher, the soldiers' silence meant an impossibility of experience: there was nothing to tell.[17] At issue is an impossibility of narrating by virtue of which that which deserves to be narrated is related to a sort of magic of memory and tradition, in which mutes are made out of the experience of that which was endured [*lo vivido*]. By contrast, there where violence is inscribed upon the body, a certain amnesia, forgetfulness and the suture define a condition of the plotline that has to be negotiated by recollection from out of a certain perturbation of the present of that which was endured [*lo vivido*].

Whatever the case may be, for the European "consciousness," World War I meant something unimaginable: barbarism reached its extreme degree of violence with the development of industrial technology at the very heart of modern civilization. Modernity then gets perverted in the extermination industry that Nazism produced in the process of annihilating the Jews. An account of this can no doubt be found in the narrative of Primo Levi, especially in the stories that concern the silence of the "*Muselmann*" [Muslim]: those subjects who were submerged in the shock of the almost dead, of the upright shock and the gesture/facial expression of what "still remains" and that, for him, represented the closest point at which the narrative of the Shoah could be approached. There can be no doubt about the importance of Levi's stories about life in the concentration and extermination camps. His literature introduces one of the most radical ethico-juridical paradoxes of the Nazi extermination industry: the paradox between the witness and the survivor who is "incarnated" in the figure of the *Muselmann*. What this "remnant of humanity" shows is that:

—

17— Walter Benjamin, "Experience and Poverty," in *Selected Writings, vol. 2, part 2 (1931–1934)*, edited by Michael W. Jennings, Howard Eiland and Gary Smith, translated by Rodney Livingstone, Cambridge, Mass., The Belknap Press, 1999, pp. 731-732.

> [...] there is an inseparable division and non-coincidence between the inhuman and the human, the living being and the speaking being, the *Muselmann* and the survivor. Precisely insofar as it [i.e., testimony] inheres in language as such, precisely insofar as it bears witness to the taking place of a potentiality of speaking through an impotentiality alone, its authority depends not on a factual truth, a conformity between something said and a fact or between memory and what happened, but rather on the immemorial relation between the unsayable and the sayable, between the outside and the inside of language. [...] It is because there is testimony only where there is an impossibility of speaking, because there is a witness only where has been desubjectification, that the *Muselmann* is the complete witness and that the survivor and the *Muselmann* cannot be split apart.[18]

Here the immemorial will thus has to be understood in the sense of life —mere life, bare life— as that which testifies in spite of language, in spite of the subject, he who wounds language.

If, as Adorno argued, poetry was no longer possible after Auschwitz, could it be that this collapse of language and body of which Primo Levi gives an account is the flight that reconfigures the political function of the story after Auschwitz? This is true to an extent, but nevertheless, as Levi himself would recognize, this was what emerged from the "obscure darkness," from a language that was neither living nor dead that the author of *If This Is a Man* recognized in Paul Celan's "Death Fugue."

Language emerges wounded from his poetry; that is, there is the imprint of a wound in language and of language as wound, a politics of the poem as material critique of history. A politics of the poem, not of language nor of just poetry. Here the politics of the poem, in Celan's francés, has to do with at least two things: with the poem as a kind of

—

18— Agamben, *Remnants of Auschwitz: The Witness and the Archive* (*Homo sacer III*), translated by Daniel Heller-Roazen, New York, Zone Books, 1999), pp. 157-158. Agamben postulates the aporia of Levi's witnessing in the following way: "the *Muselmann* is the complete witness." It implies two contradictory propositions: 1) 'the *Muselmann* is the non-human, the one who could never bear witness,' and 2) 'the one who cannot bear witness is the true witness, the absolute witness.'" Ibid, p. 150.

dating or date-stamp [*data*] and with poetry as a political critique of modernity. Although I cannot address it here, suffice it to say that the dialectical tension between these two terms has to do with language as material event of the poem and with this as potentiality of memory as irrevocable dating of history.[19] This is perhaps why, the poem as dating or date-stamp emerges from "So Schafe" [*To Sleep So*], along with the merely present character of the memory of the past as wound: "So white your hair, night wind, like snow!/ White what I have left and white what I've lost!/ She counts the hours and I count the years." But the critique of modernity also emerges from the poem—"NO MORE SAND ART, no sand book, no masters./ Nothing won by dicing."—at the point where all poems are a dating of the memory of the past in the present as loss and evanescence, and poetry is an event that is not explained by chance. So perhaps Celan laid down the guidelines for a way of thinking the aporia of representation right at the point where there is no metaphor, but rather metonym: a remnant of something that takes poetry away from metaphor, takes it away from mythology and puts it in the place, not of the poetics of the event, but of the event as poem and of this as politics, even if it is a politics of flight [*fuga*].

Right at this tension between a politics of the poem and of poetry as critique of modernity, it is possible to think about the aesthetic condition of representation. It seems to me that this is where painting's conditions of possibility are drawn with respect to the aporia of representation produced by the final solution. In this light, the question is not for the final solution to be resolved only by a certain iconographic, figurative, abstract or thematic program encompassed by the history of painting after World War II, nor is it about a poetics of form or of the formless which, vis-à-vis the aporia of representation, would find a way of bringing the horror of extermination to presence in the expressionist qualities of matter and the trace.[20] Rather, it is an issue of turning the closure

—

19— On this consideration of Paul Celan, see Pablo Oyarzún Robles, *Entre Celan y Heidegger*, Santiago de Chile, Ediciones Metales Pesados, 2013.

20— Rather, perhaps the representation of the dialectics of the terror of World War II is materialized in the early work of Francis Bacon, where the relationship between facial expression, terror and head prefigures the forms of violence of representation into an aesthetic condition of painting; that is, of rethinking the conditions of pictorial mimesis at the moment of confronting it with the problem of having to redefine, as I joined Nancy in asserting above, what happened with representation itself after Auschwitz.

As I have tried to argue, the truth *in* painting and *in* film rests on their mere indication of that which is absent [*lo ausente*], put in the interstice between the instant, time and the thing. Thus, photography's dictum defines truth purely in the trace that it succeeds in impressing qua instant-of-the-event; while film, although it distends the instant into the duration of a shot, does so on the condition of attempting to replace the movement and time of the thing with that of the image. These considerations are fundamental because, by contrast to what tends, perhaps too easily, to be thought, these technologies of the gaze are determined by their potentiality of falseness, which makes them radically different with respect to the sense and meaning of the truth in painting. Placed within the dialectical content of these analyses, one would thus have to understand what the truth *in* painting means.

At the beginning of this essay I advanced an assertion regarding what the truth *in* the thing could mean. To finish up with the referent of what now will have to be understood as thing, here *thing* means painting—not just any *painting*, but rather a painting that takes charge of the aporia of representation of which I have aimed to give an account throughout these pages; that is, a painting that takes charge of the history of representation according to a certain *politics of painting*.

Politics of painting: this assertion, bold though it may be, results from a complex consideration regarding the dialectical tension proper to the reproducibility of the image and poetry, as materialized by Paul Celan.

Of course many things have happened: there are Atlan's paintings, the films of Resnais and Lanzmann, even, as I stated in passing, Godard's political critique / montage [*montaje*] out of dismantling [*desmontaje*]. But in all this, at least in painting, there had only been a certain silence and a certain absence at the moment of addressing the closure of

—

that would be produced by the extermination camps: a sort of subtraction of the human toward the animal.

the representation of horror as one of the constant features of the visual regimes of the twentieth century, and even of the twenty-first century. In any case, it is within this complexity that Jusidman addresses the problem of representation, of mimesis in painting.

To be sure, an initial discomfort could arise in these considerations, one that has to do with the question of why an artist would have to address the problem of the conditions of the representation of the final solution sixty years after we saw the first images of the extermination camps, of the piles of corpses and even of the gas chambers. Further still, why is a Mexican artist associated with the generation of the neoconceptualisms of the 1990s in Mexico the one addressing this theme, which has already been so worked over by the historical, artistic and aesthetic conscience of hegemonic sites of art?

I could try out an immediate reply and say that, in addition to being a Mexican artist, Jusidman is Jewish, which places him in a certain condition of debt with respect to the mandate to safeguard the memory of the extermination as a Talmudic mandate to preserve the community through "narration," that is, as a sort of Mishnaic[21] figure that takes charge of absence and testifies to it in a specific artistic program. Even if this were the case, it seems to me that it does not account for the entirety of the problem that the artist addresses in starting out from the aporia of Auschwitz. On the contrary: in my view, the specificity of his work is defined by taking charge of the history of this aporia in order to reconsider the place of painting in contemporary art. In this light, it is an issue of understanding what questions are posed to painting by the complexity of the final solution as a questioning wherein the historico-material conditions of the lack of correspondence between event and representation are produced, a problem that photography and film no doubt and in principle tried resolve, and that painting seeks to address with its own means.

Returning to painting from a remove of sixty years and starting off from a certain distancing, if not from history,

—

21— The Mishnah is a part of the Talmud that requires the Talmud to be reinterpreted according to the historical present.

at least from the memory of history, *Azul de Prusia* is an investigation into the conditions of memory and matter as mimetic potentialities on the basis of which to resignify the relationship between the archive and history of the final solution. In a mating of archival materials and ways of circulating the images of the extermination camps, Jusidman reconsiders painting's conditions of aesthetic possibility in the face of the extreme event of Jewish extermination by the Nazis. In what functions as a declaration of principle, the artist explores the "issue" of representation as something that belongs to painting, an exploration that takes charge not only of what painting could or could not do with it, but rather of what it means to paint a radical event that in good measure has been over-exposed to the point of having been emptied out.

The series unfolds on several registers. Constructed through dialectical montage, it unfolds atop the tension of contexts and affects within which images function according to a strategy that belongs more to photography and film than to painting. Bringing together "wide shots" (*Haus der Kunst* [*Art House*], 2012) and "extreme close-ups" (*Birkenau*, 2012), the first two canvases in the series were conceived as a prologue to the narrative of the work as a whole, a narrative that, in the first instance, is constructed out of four thematic, pictorial motifs: *"Gas Chambers"*, *"Landscapes"*, *"Memorial"* and *"Stains"*. Nevertheless, this resource exceeds its own strategy, entering more complex zones of aesthetic signification such that it is not an issue of a mere thematic or formal ordering present in the paintings. Without disqualifying these, we would have to pay more attention to the format, the placement in space, and the haptic quality of the pieces. At issue is a montage that is constructed at the intersections of figure and abstraction, of scale and affection, of depth and atmosphere. Thus, the four moments that make it up move upon a certain history of the "plastic aporia" of representation: from hyperreal images of the camps to the minimal gesture of the residue of the working canvases or the impression of the traces of pigment on the walls of the artist's studio; in the tension between figure and "residual expression," what gets put into operation is a certain affective feature in which the historical imprint of extermination is inscribed on the corporality of the spectator, in a double play of memory and affect. At issue is a certain fold of the document on the canvas/surface as present memory of the historical past in *re*presentation.

If *Azul de Prusia* is conceived as the relationship between series and montage, it is feasible to regard its placement as a form of spacing: that is, it is feasible to regard it as a totality of memory and history extended out into "space." At the same time that it is a date with the history of painting, it is a chiasmus between the memory and history of the atrocities of the Shoah on the materiality of the pictorial. Perhaps this is one of the fundamental differences of the series. In contrast to other painting practices—and even in contrast to the etchings of David Olère (1902–1985)—Jusidman takes on the photographic and documentary matrix as a moment in the same aporia of the representation of Auschwitz. He does this in two senses: first, in these kinds of visual documents, as I argued above, there is a delay with respect to the fatal instant of the gas chamber. Secondly, starting off from this condition, the paintings in this series attempt neither to suture nor to clarify this aporia. Rather, they embrace the delay as a condition of historical possibility with which such documents get shaped. At issue is a breaking of the absence and emptiness of those images from the standpoint of painting. In other words, here painting takes charge of showing the closure of representation not as a function of time, whether as memory or as history, but rather by re-mounting it [in the sense of montage] in space as a trace or imprint, as an imprint of terror upon a surface. Embracing the aporia of representation, then, signifies not the unrepresentable, but rather a sort of search through painting for that which, in one way or another, film and photography—as the material media that defined the character of the image and the imaginary of the Shoah—could not give an account. In the latter, the event (temporality and instant) was taken away as an ontological condition of their representation.

At this point, the series *Azul de Prusia* is not a mere pictorial exercise about just any theme or event. Rather, it is an aesthetic, ethical, political and historical position-taking with respect to the final solution on the part of the artist, and on the basis of his own medium. If the historico-material conditions of film and photography configured a particular way of addressing the aporia of representation, if Celan's poetry is taken away from the foundational relationships between myth and metaphor as that which is proper to poetry and instead turns the materiality of the pictorial image into a dating in which to play with the political character of language, and likewise, the poetic image as political memory of history, then Jusidman's work problematizes the historico-political task of painting after Auschwitz in these same terms.

Prussian blue or ferric ferrocyanide is an artificial color that has accompanied the material memory of Austria since the eighteenth century. As Cuauhtémoc Medina has noted, "Ferrocyanide was the color chosen for Prussian military uniforms in the eighteenth and nineteenth centuries: among other things, it was the distinguishing feature of the soldiers who confronted Napoleon's armies. In a more sinister way, Prussian blue has been tied to the extermination of the Jews in Europe."[22] The appropriation of this historico-material index is the point of departure that first defines the series *Azul de Prusia* as a dating in the sense in which Celan does the same with his poetry. The fact that this artificial pigment is the raw material on which Yishai Jusidman works in principle involves a reconsideration of the grisaille[23] as subjectile.[24] One can guess immediately that the Prussian blue in Yishai Jusidman's "quiet paintings" is what supports and envelops at the same time, in a sort of action and passion of materiality.

One would have to understand this subjectile-grisaille in various senses: first, as an indeterminate ground through which the elements of the painting emerge; it is a sort of drive [*pulsión*] that permeates the conditions of possibility of figuration on the canvas; secondly, as a material, and only material, imprint of the final solution qua vestige and delay; finally, as the emergence of the event in the material production of the closure and aporia of representation. Let us consider these one by one.

As base, ground, atmosphere and transparency, Prussian blue defines the way in which foreground and

—

22— Dossier of the *Azul de Prusia* series, MUAC-UNAM, August-December 2016, p. 4.

23— Grisaille is a pictorial technique in which different tones of gray, white and black are used, imitating sculptural reliefs or recreating architectural spaces.

24— I am referring here to Derrida's understanding of the subjectile as that which underlies (*subjectum*) and supports, which in painting would mean that which subjects and envelopes the representation, or, more precisely, *what lies underneath*.

background, chromatic changes, forms and figures show up in the paintings. In this sense, blue underlies and supports the "temper" of whatever it represented in the paintings. But not only this: in both its artificiality and the patronymic that qualifies it (Prussia), right away Prussian blue involves a certain historical index from which it is not impossible to be taken away. At issue is not a mere "natural" color; rather, the genealogy of Prussian blue inscribes it within a certain history of science (that of eighteenth-century chemistry) where the accident can be articulated in terms of knowledge and power according to the well-known formula postulated by Foucault, which, taken to the extreme, gives an account of one of modernity's forms of necropolitics: the death industry.[25]

Regardless, the blue imprint in the gas chambers is a result of the use of Zyklon B gas. At issue is the vestige of a chemical that produces a material inscription of history in space, which in other terms means a sort of memory of matter that in its own process of reaction vis-à-vis the medium, functions as a material proof of a fact, in this case the gassing inside the chambers. Does this have a character of forensic proof? Here the closure of the material residue acquires its political potentiality: at the same time that it defines a failure in the strategy of erasure of any vestige as a condition of the final solution, it has a character of material memory of history. Although it could never be a resounding proof of the lethal use of the gas, in its ruling Prussian blue coloring makes evident something that was a constant feature in other gas chambers where the vestige is erased: the use of cyanide.[26] In any case, here Prussian blue "hitches"

—

25— Without a doubt, it is easy to deduce from Foucault's arguments the consideration that in modernity there are no accidents but only variations of probability of the truth value and knowledge according to the scientistic a priori that defines the meaning of knowledge in modernity. In accordance with this, to produce Prussian blue by accident is really determined by a minimal variation of the eighteenth-century model of chemistry. Within a range of experimentation the accident is recognized as a variable of the model, never as an eruption of chaos or the force of matter.

26— Perhaps, as Cuauhtémoc Medina observes, "One of the main debates around the scale of genocide has hinged around the evidence of blue residues in some buildings in extermination camps. In cases such as the camps of Majdanek and Sututthof, in Poland, the Prussian blue stains on the walls of the chambers are still palpable to this day. While the deniers have attempted to support themselves on the absence of blue residues at Birkenau in order to question the function of the chambers in that complex (Leuchter Report, 1988), scientific and historical research has representation to the facticity of history; it ties the signified to matter. In sum, it evades the signifier as excess, impossibility and prohibition of the representation or impossibility of the Shoah, and instead assumes a certain materiality of the fact, which is where silence vibrates in matter. Jusidman points to this relationship between matter and memory as the element that enables the reintroduction of painting into the history of representing the Shoah. This series of paintings cannot be read as just one version, as yet one more story to be added to the history of representations of the atrocity of the extermination of the Jews. Rather, here color defines an objective condition of a certain material history of horror, to the point that the relationship between matter and form is radically reconfigured in Jusidman's work. Seen against the grain of the material conditions of representation of film and photography (the instant and the event), the appropriation carried out in these paintings reintroduces two fundamental qualities that are proper to this medium, and in doing so—at least from my perspective—achieves a dialectical tension between the vestige and the delay. To affirm a tension between the vestige and the delay involves a relationship, not of causality of the time of the trace that is supported on Prussian blue, but rather of the collision of the two on the pictorial plane as such. The way in which figuration emerges from form, form from the plane, and the plane from color, makes it such that the documentary matrix of the images from which the paintings' motifs originate gets reconfigured qua paintings, rather than just getting used according to the pretention of objectivity that they are supposed to possess. Perhaps this is why the haptic qualities of these paintings, that is to say their vibration and porosity, are not mere formal resources, but rather structural conditions of the aesthetico-political potentialities of this series. The point where memory emerges in matter defines the relevance of the question of the place of painting vis-à-vis the aporia of the final solution. As a radical form of painting, the series *Azul de Prusia* is an exploration of the aporia of representation as a problem of painting that does not elide the impotence of the medium, produce a simulacrum

—

demonstrated the presence of cyanide residue in them in many ways." Dossier from the *Azul de Prusia* series, MUAC-UNAM, August-December 2016, p. 5.

of what it represents, or hyperbolize the traumatic moment of violence. The recuperation of memory as a vestige in matter is above all a dating of the material history of the annihilation. This condition enables painting to affirm its specific aesthetic character, but above all in some measure it returns memory's material and historical register to it. The fact that Prussian blue results as a pigment on the walls of the gas chambers makes it such that the plastic document functions as matter, memory and history. Here, no doubt, metaphor as a strategy of representation is canceled out by a metonym in which the singular character of materiality appears as a feature and fragment of well-determined historical time.

A final register emerges from the historico-material condition of Prussian blue. In a sort of folding of the aporia of representation on top of genealogical determinations, Prussian blue produces a chiasmus *on* the surface, a chiasmus in the matter that I envision as a collision. A clash between two forces is produced on the surface; between the force of the violence of extermination and that of matter as such, to the point that here painting *produces* what the media of technical reproducibility have only been able to "show" as impossibility. Thus, while the instant and time betray the image, as it were, in film and photography, these paintings carry back the imaginary of terror at the vestige in order to make the aporia of Auschwitz present once more, that is, to *represent* it.

Thus, the *grisaille* as subjectile of Prussian blue is something more than merely one of the artist's technical resources; it is the material medium where history and matter are knotted together in the present of the image as physical support system and screen upon which not representation but its aporia is sustained.

It is upon this plastic aporia, to say it at once, that Jusidman problematizes the status of matter in painting. It is on this condition that one would have to address the other two materials upon which the series *Azul de Prusia* unfolds: the color "flesh pink" and the pumice stone. On the second suffice it to say that it is used as a historical index and as a determinant of the textures in the paintings. According to the artist, pumice stone was used as a conductor of the lethal gas in the chambers. Plastically, this material produces a "porous" effect in the paintings.

The flesh pink color makes implicit reference, according to Jusidman himself, "to the thousands of men, women and children who were victimized in the [gas] chambers." Here, flesh pink is a sort of vestige of the bodies and a metonym of flesh, a remnant that interpellates the absence of death as a production of corpses.[27]

If anything has obsessed the history of painting, it is how to make one of the material principles of life be expressed in painting itself. When one speaks of flesh pink, we would rather have to think of a sort of hyperphysics of mimesis, as Didi-Huberman puts it: "mimesis is thought here as matter [...], a 'mother substance' [...], a *fabric of entrails*. It is therefore a hyperphysics of the fold and of vibration, like a generalized, almost organic *diaphanés*."[28] Skin is not a color. Rather, in the ontological realm it is a chiasmus, perhaps the most radical one there is, between the world and the body through the flesh qua life. In the organic realm, it is a complex reticulum of thin films through which blood runs. Scarcely perceptible in the paintings that make up the series *Azul de Prusia*, flesh pink remains as an imprint, as a quiet trace of bodies through the blue, as a latency, a remnant that testifies to the Shoah *in* paint and painting.

It is thus through vestiges, traces, porosities, transparencies—or, to put it briefly—it is *in* paint and painting that Yishai Jusidman carries the aporia of Auschwitz to the limit. Considered as a kind of dramaturgy, the plotline of this series is concocted in color as material memory from which the figure emerges as a force-trace, as happens in *Cámaras de gas* [Gas Chambers]; it travels through a citation of silence in the manner of Lanzmann in *Paisaje* [Landscape]; and it turns German-origin materials into the *Memorial* of the unpresentable as a geopolitics of extermination. It empties out or debouches (in an almost literal sense of the term) into *Manchas* [Stains] as the gesture that the artist *lets be* in their residuality, in order to give an account of the mimetic condition of terror: the indefinition of the body vis-à-vis death in the gas chambers.

—

27— Insofar as extermination produces corpses what is made impossible is death. In a radical sense a corpse is never death. See José Luis Barrios, "Invisible e irrepresentable: el despojo no es la muerte. Notas sobre la aporética de la imagen en el mundo contemporáneo," in *Tópicos del seminario*, vol. 18, Puebla, Benemérita Universidad Autónoma de Puebla, 2007.

28— Didi-Huberman, op. cit., p. 43.

Sobibor, 2013. Detalle—Detail [Cat. 21]

 Haus der Kunst [*Casa del arte—House of Art*] [Cat. 2]

Birkenau, 2012 [Cat. 1]

 Mauthausen, 2011–2012 [Cat. 11]

Majdanek, 2011 [Cat. 9]

 Majdanek, 2012 [Cat. 10]

Auschwitz, 2010 [Cat.4]

 Dachau, 2010–2012 [Cat. 6]

Puerta de gas—Gas Door, 2011 [Cat. 12]

 Stutthof, 2011 [Cat. 15]

Auschwitz, 2011 [Cat. 5]

 Van, 2010 [Cat. 16]

Majdanek, 2010 [Cat. 8]

 Sobibor, 2013 [Cat. 21]

Birkenau, 2013 [Cat. 17]

 Mauthausen, 2013 [Cat. 20]

Birkenau, 2014 [Cat. 18]

 Azul de Prusia—Prussian Blue, 2014–2015 [Cat. 22]

Azul de Prusia/Tierra verde bohemia—Prussian Blue/Bohemian Green Earth, 2014–2015 [Cat. 25]

 Azul de Prusia/Tierra de Cassel—Prussian Blue/Kassel Earth, 2014–2015 [Cat. 24]

Azul de Prusia/Negro vid alemán—Prussian Blue/German Vine Black, 2014–2015 [Cat. 23]

 Delantal—Apron, 2011-2016 [Cat. 26]

Trapo #6—Rag #6, 2013–2014 [Cat. 30]

 Trapo #13—Rag #13, 2013–2015 [Cat. 36]

Trapo #12—Rag #12, 2013–2015 [Cat. 35]

 Trapo #18—Rag #18, 2013–2015 [Cat. 38]

Trapo #24—Rag #24, 2013–2016 [Cat. 41]

 Trapo #27—Rag #27, 2013–2016 [Cat. 42]

Trapo #28—Rag #28, 2013–2016 [Cat. 43]

 Trapo #1—Rag #1, 2011–2014 [Cat. 27]

Trapo #3—Rag #3, 2012–2014 [Cat. 29]

 Trapo #8—Rag #8, 2013–2015 [Cat. 32]

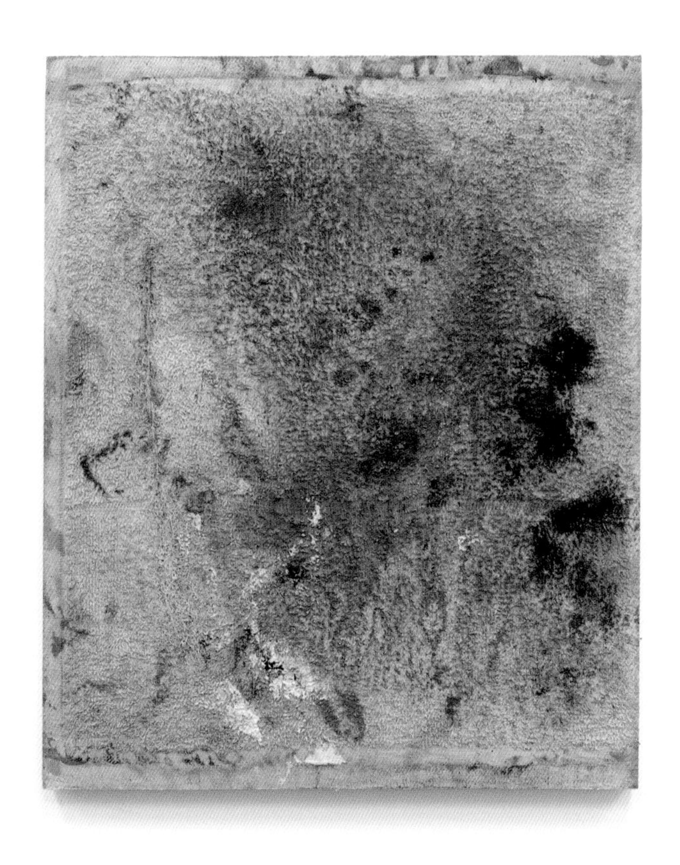

Trapo #23—Rag #23, 2013–2016 [Cat. 40]

 Trapo #7—Rag #7, 2013–2014 [Cat. 31]

Trapo #16—Rag #16, 2013–2015 [Cat. 37]

 Trapo #9—Rag #9, 2013–2015 [Cat. 33]

Manchas (AP+TVB)—Stains (PB+BGE), 2015 [Cat. 44]

 Manchas (AP+TC)—Stains (PB+CE), 2015 [Cat. 45]

Manchas (AP+NVA)—Stains (PB+GVB), 2015 [Cat. 46]

Sobibor, 2013 Detalle—Detail [Cat. 21]

Bitácora de viaje*

YISHAI JUSIDMAN

* Esta carta fue escrita por Yishai Jusidman para Gabriela Rangel en ocasión de la exposición *Prussian Blue—Memory after Representation: Yishai Jusidman* en el Americas Society, N.Y. (23 de enero a 23 de marzo de 2013), y presentada en el panel de discusión *Painting and Representation* el 5 de marzo de 2013.

Ruinas de barracas en Birkenau—Remnants of barracks at Birkenau. Foto—Photo: Yishai Jusidman, 2012

Querida Gabriela:

Por fin estoy de vuelta en Los Ángeles después de dos semanas de viaje por Alemania y Polonia. No entablé conversación con nadie mientras estuve allí (ni tuve deseos de hacerlo). Aun así, y como me esperaba, mi visita a los campos de concentración y de exterminio fue significativa en lo personal, aparte del hecho de que éste es el tema de mi obra actual.

Tú y yo estamos conscientes de que casi todo el mundo reconoce la historia del Holocausto, al igual de que el dolor derivado de su memoria es compartido, en mayor o menor medida, por todos. Sin embargo, aunque la narrativa del Holocausto se ha vuelto común, siempre seguirá siendo un desafío reflexionar seriamente los hechos materiales del genocidio —y las ramificaciones morales de tales hechos. Para algunos, dichas consideraciones pueden conducirnos a veces a un laberinto de terror crudo, rabia, asco, desprecio, desolación y vergüenza. Sin embargo, nuestro instinto de supervivencia no nos permitirá quedar atrapados en paroxismos, y recurrimos a todos los medios desplegados desde la guerra con el propósito específico de facilitar la sublimación emocional.

Tomemos, por ejemplo, el peso de la vergüenza, que fue ampliamente compartido cuando las primeras imágenes de los campos comenzaron a circular, y pensemos en cómo esta vergüenza fue finalmente reafirmada por el impulso de superar distintos racismos, así como la más mínima pretensión de supremacía nacionalista. Gracias a estos esfuerzos, un progreso social lento pero constante se ha afianzado desde los años sesenta. O tomemos la rabia y la desolación, y seamos testigos de cómo estas emociones han sido domesticadas por el protocolo homogeneizante que enmarca el legado conmemorativo del Holocausto. Y cuando se trata de nuestra capacidad para enfrentar y digerir el horror, melodramas pasteurizados, tales como *La lista de Schindler* (1993) y *El pianista* (2002), nos han permitido enfrentar el Holocausto mientras nos relajamos en nuestros asientos reclinables de las cómodas salas de cine.

Si bien el activismo social, la institucionalización y la mediatización nos ayudan a domesticar nuestras emociones frente al Holocausto, me temo que nuestro éxito reiterado en sublimar estas emociones ha allanado el camino para la auto-complacencia actual. Una inquietante indolencia hacia el Holocausto yace detrás de las cómicas provocaciones de Mel Brooks, Roberto Benigni y Quentin Tarantino. Si estos bromistas deben preocuparnos, Gabriela, es porque cuando Hollywood acoge algo considerado extremo —como ha sido el caso de la violencia, el sexo y el arte contemporáneo—, tú y yo hemos sido testigos de lo que hace con ello: lo extremo pronto se vuelve convencional, y lo convencional finalmente se vuelve ridículo. El Holocausto no es, evidentemente, inmune a tales transmutaciones en la imaginación del público.

Mira a tu alrededor y verás cómo la juventud de hoy, distante y orgullosa, ya no consigue entender la bestialidad de los nazis, el mezquino oportunismo de sus colaboradores, incluso la resignación de tantas de sus víctimas. Nuestros propios hijos nos dirán que el Holocausto fue una pesadilla que ya no pertenece al mundo en que vivimos, y confían plenamente en que nuestra lucidez poshistórica protegerá a este mundo de repetir la maldad urdida en el pasado. Uno podría leer en tal optimismo la benevolencia de una especie humana mejorada. Sin embargo, esta misma convicción desafía también la evidencia irrefutable de que el suelo que nutrió el humanismo ejemplar de Kant, Beethoven, Rilke y Thomas Mann fue el mismo suelo que nutrió el antisemitismo cotidiano —que creció, a su vez, hasta convertirse en la masacre más brutal y a sangre fría que la humanidad podría haber ideado. En todo caso, creo que la disposición a desvanecer el Holocausto en la densa niebla del pasado subraya una vez más lo animal sobre lo racional en nuestra especie.

Gabriela, uno tendrá que extender la mano y aferrarse a lo que sea que se mantenga sólido y tangible para evitar que la percepción del Holocausto sea sublimada hasta la inconsecuencia. Permíteme añadir mi granito de arena en la materia, ahora que mi viaje a Polonia y Alemania me provocó las siguientes reflexiones:

Los supervivientes del Holocausto han sido el más poderoso instrumento de la continuidad histórica que afianza la conciencia comunitaria del genocidio nazi. Su presencia corporal y moral ha eximido a nuestra generación, en parte, de la necesidad imperiosa de cultivar tal conciencia como individuos. Aun así, el privilegio de esta licencia es sólo temporal, en la medida en que la muerte de los últimos supervivientes es inminente. Y cuando sus historias adquieran la pátina de cierta leyenda épica —como es obligado que suceda— el testimonio más convincente del genocidio tendrá lugar en las ruinas de los campos que se han conservado como sitios conmemorativos. Estos sitios serán nuestro instrumento más sólido para repeler la indiferencia y la mitificación. Desafortunadamente, en vista de lo que encontré en mi viaje, la preservación de estos lugares será más difícil de lo que parecería. Para empezar, se han presentado algunos argumentos a favor de permitir que las ruinas de los campos se pudran y desaparezcan. Esto es lo que el intelectual español y antiguo prisionero en Buchenwald Jorge Semprún sugirió en su novela autobiográfica *El largo viaje* (1963). Semprún argumentó que una vez que el último superviviente del Holocausto haya fallecido —"... cuando ya no quede ningún recuerdo real de todo esto, sino sólo recuerdos de recuerdos, relatos de recuerdos narrados por quienes ya nunca sabrán verdaderamente... lo que todo esto, en realidad, ha sido..."— entonces se debe permitir a la hierba, las raíces y las zarzas invadir Buchenwald y borrar "este campo construido por los hombres".

Semprún tiene todo el derecho a reclamar el título moral de los supervivientes por las ruinas de los campos. Pero poner en práctica esta visión de los campos que desaparecen sería imperdonablemente coherente con el propio deseo de Himmler de erradicarlos, como lo hizo con los campos de exterminio de Treblinka, Belzec y Sobibor, una vez cumplido su propósito. Esto debería ser suficiente para sostener que, cuando el último superviviente muera, la única opción moral para nosotros será la de evitar el desvanecimiento de las ruinas de los campos. El reto de nuestra generación no radica en alcanzar el conocimiento de *lo que realmente sucedió* [en el Holocausto] —en el sentido de la experiencia en la descripción de Semprún—, sino más bien en no olvidar *que sucedió* realmente. Y más adelante, en hacer hincapié que sucedió *realmente*.

Las dificultades en preservar los campos como sitios testimoniales están claramente ejemplificadas por las ruinas del campo de Majdanek en Polonia oriental. Este campo fue evacuado a toda prisa por los alemanes poco antes de la llegada de las tropas soviéticas en julio de 1944, por lo que los edificios se mantuvieron entonces más o menos intactos. Apenas cuatro meses más tarde, se estableció un museo en algunas de las barracas, mientras que el resto del campamento fue tomado por las tropas rusas y polacas. En el transcurso de un año, sin embargo, el 80% del campo había sido desmantelado, saqueado, asignado o vendido como materiales reciclables. Ya en 1949, los terrenos del campo, o por lo menos cerca de la mitad del sitio original, fueron acordonados para conservarse como monumento. Las cámaras de gas aún en pie quedaron protegidas y el crematorio fue reconstruido, al igual que las cercas y torres. Algunos almacenes y talleres se convirtieron en pabellones de exposición. El material recuperado se utilizó para reconstruir dos hileras de barracas de prisioneros, que son las que hoy se pueden ver allí. Por otra parte, los terrenos despejados fueron plantados con árboles con el fin de crear un parque conmemorativo. Diez años más tarde, las autoridades de Majdanek consideraron que convertir el lugar en un parque no había sido después de todo una buena idea, por lo que eliminaron los árboles y sólo entonces instituyeron un plan para mantener el campo lo más "auténtico" posible. En 1969, un gran monumento escultórico brutalista, una cúpula memorial para un enorme montículo de cenizas, y un edificio para recibir a los visitantes se añadieron a las afueras del perímetro del campo. La configuración del memorial de Majdanek se ha mantenido igual desde entonces, a excepción de un cementerio civil que se estableció a su lado en la década de 1970, ahora lleno, y el crecimiento urbano de la ciudad de Lublin, que hoy bordea el campo.

De haber prevalecido el deseo de Semprún de modo que al paisaje circundante se le hubiera permitido engullir los restos del campo, Majdanek habría quedado enterrado bajo anodinas viviendas comunistas. En cambio, los terrenos conmemorativos evolucionaron a lo largo de los años como respuesta a las distintas voluntades de cómo deben ser presentados y mantenidos los campos.

Sin duda alguna, todo el mundo tiene derecho a visitar las ruinas de los campos. Estos sitios se han convertido en destinos turísticos obligados; durante la última década, se han transformado gradualmente en respuesta a la multitud de visitantes que, de una u otra manera, deben atenderse.

Durante mis viajes, sin embargo, he notado con preocupación las intervenciones que muchos edificios originales han sufrido al servicio del creciente número de visitantes. Lo que me parece alarmante es la idea de que los sitios deben ser modificados con el fin de ofrecer a los turistas alguna forma de entretenimiento sano y enriquecedor para hacerles sentir que su visita ha valido la pena.

En Dachau, cerca de Múnich, los edificios que quedaron en pie son los que fueron de uso común, y estas estructuras han sido recientemente equipadas con una exposición de vanguardia que narra la historia nefasta del campo. El elaborado montaje recurre a proyecciones, grabaciones, monitores, fotomurales y pantallas interactivas —incluso hay una sala dedicada a proyecciones recurrentes de cortometraje documental. La exposición resulta tan eficaz en capturar la atención que los artefactos originales intercalados en vitrinas se convierten en meros accesorios para la narración, mientras que el edificio en sí se convierte en poco más que un escenario que provee un ambiente inquietante a la exposición. Los diseñadores de esta museografía protagónica quisieron dar al visitante una valiosa lección de historia, pero lo hicieron a expensas de conservar la integridad testimonial del lugar. Creo que el costo por brindar esta lección fue innecesariamente elevado: podrían haberse salvaguardado los intereses pedagógicos y testimoniales si la exposición hubiera sido alojada en alguna nueva construcción adyacente al campo, de la misma forma que se coloca una cédula al lado de una pintura.

Sea como sea, la integridad del sitio ya había quedado comprometida décadas atrás, con el añadido en 1968 de un monumento escultórico que se apoderó del patio central. La imposición de este monumento por decreto pretendía señalar la erradicación del mal ocurrido allí. Sin embargo, las nobles intenciones de los autores de este acto de soberbia (artistas y burócratas por igual) no pudieron redimir el orgullo que les llevó a profanar el recinto con un ídolo inepto y torpe, un fetiche que revela las promesas impuestas injustamente en las obras de arte. A fin de cuentas, las intervenciones artísticas y didácticas en Dachau diluyen la fuerza de nuestro encuentro con sus ruinas.

En el campo de Mauthausen, cerca de Linz, en Austria, me encontré con que los variados monumentos conmemorativos se encuentran, como en Majdanek, fuera del perímetro del campo, dentro de un área designada en 1949 como un "parque conmemorativo". Este parque conmemorativo congrega más de veinte monumentos, financiados a lo largo de los años por los diferentes grupos nacionales que fueron víctimas de Mauthausen. La diversidad de estos monumentos y sus respectivos estilos nos permiten establecer una relación empática con la voluntad de recordar.

Las placas conmemorativas en Mauthausen se vuelven más personales cuando uno entra en la fortaleza que una vez conformó el campo. Durante décadas, las familias y amigos de las víctimas han colocado placas y memoriales dedicados a prisioneros individuales; su acumulación progresiva insinúa en proporción la magnitud de la operación asesina que tuvo lugar allí. Gracias a este recordatorio fragmentado y compartimentado, somos más capaces de sopesar el peso de la tragedia. Lamentablemente, sin embargo, también he encontrado que los administradores actuales de Mauthausen están en vías de adaptar sus edificios originales para introducir exposiciones didácticas actualizadas como en Dachau —a pesar del hecho de que justo fuera hay un nuevo edifico de recepción de visitantes que podría haber albergado las nuevas exposiciones.

La idea de adaptar los edificios originales de los campos para propósitos educativos se remonta al ejemplo establecido inicialmente en Auschwitz, que es hoy día el principal "atractivo" turístico en Polonia, con más de un millón y medio de visitantes anuales. La visita guiada por Auschwitz I es un ejercicio de estricto decoro, con algunos desafortunados destellos de oportunismo, artificio e, incluso, franca impertinencia. Esta peculiar confusión se hace evidente en cuanto uno pasa de la zona de estacionamiento al edificio de recepción de visitantes —que en realidad es el edificio original de la administración del campo de concentración y que ha sido reacondicionado para recibir a la masa de visitantes, entregarles audioguías y dividirlos en grupos, así como para comprar un aperitivo o una comida completa antes de comenzar el recorrido por las instalaciones. Por extraño que resulte, hay que tener en cuenta que la redistribución de los edificios de Auschwitz en la posguerra no fue producto de un "plan maestro", como sí fue el caso de Dachau, sino más bien una evolución que respondió a las circunstancias políticas particulares del momento.

Auschwitz I fue construido enteramente de ladrillo y mortero. A diferencia de la mayoría de los otros campos, el conjunto no fue desmantelado ni antes ni después de la liberación, y hoy conserva un cierto aire de, digamos, campus universitario —es decir, si hacemos caso omiso de las cercas electrificadas y de nuestra conciencia de lo ocurrido en su interior. Y tal vez fue gracias a su arquitectura extrañamente sobria que la autoridad que se hizo cargo del campo liberado consideró que serviría para albergar, en un par de los edificios vacíos, el instituto encargado de recopilar, archivar y custodiar la memoria de los crímenes nazis. Entre 1947 y 1955, a medida que los visitantes al infame sitio se hicieron frecuentes, cinco estructuras vacías más fueron adaptadas para exposiciones que representaban las condiciones de vida en el campo, y que incorporaron muebles y artefactos que habían sido recuperados. Incluso si las peticiones de poner énfasis en la masacre del pueblo judío fueron subestimadas en ese momento, el memorial parece haber conservado cierta congruencia teniendo en cuenta las complicaciones materiales de los años de la posguerra. La configuración actual de estas exposiciones no ha cambiado mucho. Con la guerra fría en pleno a principios de los años sesenta, los nuevos montajes fueron secuestrados ideológicamente. Muchos edificios todavía vacíos fueron asignados a diferentes países con el fin de establecer exposiciones que conmemoraran a poblaciones nacionales específicas que fueron víctimas de los nazis. La política silenció a todas las otras consideraciones, por lo que la mayoría de estos espacios se asignaron a los miembros del bloque soviético, ¡uno incluso fue dedicado a los alemanes orientales y otro a los austriacos! No debería sorprendernos que estas exposiciones fueron desmanteladas rápidamente poco después de la caída de la URSS. El único pabellón pre-perestroika que sigue abierto hoy es, de hecho, el de Austria, que ostenta el descarado título: “11 de marzo de 1938: Austria, primera víctima del nacionalsocialismo”.

La mayoría de los demás pabellones nacionales se han renovado desde el cambio de siglo. De los nueve pabellones nacionales hoy en funcionamiento en Auschwitz, cinco —Eslovaquia, Hungría, Francia, Bélgica y los Países

Bajos— están en su mayoría dedicados a la masacre de sus poblaciones judías. Estas exposiciones fueron montadas entre 2002 y 2006, durante una especie de carrera armamentista museográfica, en la que cada país parece haber hecho todo lo posible para eclipsar la espectacularidad de los otros. Al igual que en los cada vez más numerosos museos del Holocausto y la tolerancia, los guiones museográficos se sostienen en las llamadas "historias de interés humano". Mi aprehensión aquí se refiere menos al contenido de estos guiones que a los extraños entornos creados por sus diseñadores, ambiciosos pero equivocados, y sus supervisores políticos. Consideremos, por ejemplo, el pabellón de Hungría, que está patentemente empeñado en convertir el argumento condenatorio del antisemitismo húngaro en una especie de sueño surrealista, todo mediante un ambiente saturado de proyecciones, efectos de luz y la bravuconería escenográfica gratuita que recuerda el escenario de una película de ciencia ficción distópica. O podríamos considerar el pabellón francés, que aborda la tragedia de la deportación de los judíos en un entorno de inmaculada blancura, cemento pulido e iluminación sofisticada —un ambiente post-minimalista que recuerda las boutiques y galerías más elegantes de la *rive-droit* en París. Me siento incapaz de imaginar un uso del buen gusto más imprudente que éste.

Y si bien las elaboradas escenografías que capturan la atención de los turistas en los campos también permiten al crítico escudarse detrás de una actitud sentenciosa (como, evidentemente, yo mismo lo hice), cuando uno se acerca a los terrenos de Birkenau es imposible no quedar atónito ante la extensión de la producción más asesina de los alemanes. Este predio de 350 acres (140 hectáreas), totalmente rodeado por vallas electrificadas infranqueables, podría contener más de 100 000 prisioneros a la vez, el 90% de los cuales perecería de una u otra forma, y operaba hasta seis cámaras de gas que podían matar y procesar hasta a 6 000 personas al día. Se estima que entre un millón y un millón y medio de personas murieron en Birkenau. El complejo fue dinamitado parcialmente por los alemanes en su retirada, en parte destruido en los combates siguientes, y en parte desmantelado por la población local que necesitaba combustibles y materiales reciclables después de la guerra. Hoy día, Birkenau asemeja un enorme sitio arqueológico de una civilización perdida, o la devastación producida por un enorme desastre natural. La escala es una categoría estética que no requiere mediación, y aquí la magnitud del sitio convertiría automáticamente cualquier intervención didáctica en una maña pomposa. Al menos hasta ahora Birkenau se ha mantenido más o menos en crudo, como, en mi opinión, todos los demás restos de los campos de concentración y exterminio deberían haberse conservado.

Termino aquí interviniendo las palabras de Jorge Semprún, con la esperanza de que Birkenau, este campamento construido y destruido por hombres, no desaparezca bajo la hierba, las raíces y las zarzas, o, para el caso, bajo diseñadores, museógrafos y políticos ambiciosos.

Travel Log*

YISHAI JUSIDMAN

*This letter was written by Yishai Jusidman to Gabriela Rangel on the occasion of his exhibition *Prussian Blue—Memory after Representation: Yishai Jusidman* at the Americas Society, NY (January 23-March 23, 2013), and delivered there at the panel discussion *Painting and Representation* on March 5, 2013.

Excavación forense en Sobibor—Forensic exavation at Sobibor. Foto—Photo: Yishai Jusidman, 2012

Dear Gabriela,

I'm finally back in Los Angeles after two weeks of travel through Germany and Poland. I didn't engage in conversation with anyone while I was there (nor did I feel like it). Still, and as expected, my visit to the labor and extermination camps was of personal significance, aside from the fact that this is the subject of my current artwork.

You and I are both aware that pretty much everyone recognizes the story of the Holocaust, just as the grief derived from its memory is shared, to a greater or lesser degree, by all. Still, while the Holocaust narrative has become familiar, it will always remain a challenge to seriously ponder the material facts of genocide—and the moral ramifications of those facts. For some of us, such considerations can lead at times into a maze of crude horror, rage, disgust, disdain, desolation, and shame. But our instinct for self-preservation won't allow us to become trapped in paroxysms, and we resort to every possible means deployed since the war for the specific purpose of facilitating emotional sublimation.

Take, for instance, the burden of shame that was widely shared when the first images of the camps began circulating, and think of how this shame was eventually underwritten into the drive to overcome assorted racisms, as well as even the slightest pretense of nationalistic supremacy. Thanks to these efforts, a slow but steady social progress has taken hold since the sixties. Or take rage and desolation, and witness how these emotions are tamed by the homogenizing etiquette that frames the commemorative legacy of the Holocaust. And when it comes to our ability to confront and digest the horror, pasteurized melodramas such as *Schindler's List* (1993) and *The Pianist* (2002) have allowed us to engage with the Holocaust while relaxing in our reclining seats at the Multiplex.

While social activism, institutionalization, and mediatization assist us in taming our emotions vis-à-vis the Holocaust, I fear our repeated success in sublimating these emotions has now paved the way for self-complacency. A disturbing ease with the Holocaust lies behind the comedic provocations of Mel Brooks, Roberto Benigni, and Quentin Tarantino. If these pranksters should worry us, Gabriela, it's because when Hollywood embraces something that is considered hard-core—as it's been the case with violence, sex, and contemporary art—you and I have witnessed what becomes of it: hard-core soon turns into soft-core, and soft-core eventually becomes plain silly. The Holocaust is evidently not immune to such transmutations in the public imagination.

Look around and you'll see how today's youth, aloof and proud, no longer fathom the Nazis' bestiality, the petty opportunism of their collaborators, even the resignation of so many of their victims. Our own children will tell us that the Holocaust was a nightmare that no longer belongs in the world we live in, and they fully trust that our post-historical lucidity will protect this world from ever repeating the wickedness concocted in the past. One might read into such optimism the benevolence of a self-improved human-species. However, this very conviction also defies the irrefutable evidence that the soil that nurtured the exemplary humanism of Kant, Beethoven, Rilke, and Thomas Mann was the same soil that nurtured mundane anti-Semitism—which grew, in turn, into the most brutal and cold-blooded slaughter humankind could have devised. If anything, I believe that the inclination to fade the Holocaust away in the dense fog of the past once again emphasizes the animal over the rational in our species.

Gabriela, one will need to reach out and hold on to whatever remains solid and tangible in order to prevent the perception of the Holocaust from being sublimated into inconsequence. Allow me to add my two cents on the matter now that my trip to Poland and Germany brought about the following thoughts:

Holocaust survivors have been the most powerful affidavit of the historical continuity that secures communal awareness of the Nazi genocide. Their corporeal and moral presence has somewhat exempted our generation from the imperative to cultivate such awareness as individuals. Still, this comfortable license is only temporary, insofar as the last survivors' passing is imminent. And when their stories take on the patina of some epic legend—as is bound to happen—the most compelling testimony of the genocide will be embodied by the ruins of the camps that have been preserved as commemorative sites. These sites will be our most solid instrument for repelling indifference and mythification. Unfortunately, given the developments I witnessed, preserving these places will be more challenging than it would seem. For starters, some arguments have been put forth in favor of allowing the ruins of the camps to rot and disappear. This is what the Spanish intellectual and former Buchenwald inmate Jorge Semprún suggested in his autobiographical novel *The Long Voyage* (1963). Semprún argued that once the last Holocaust survivor has passed away—"...when there will no longer be any real memory of this, only the memory of memories told by those who will never know ... what all this really was...."—then grass, roots and brambles should be allowed to encroach on Buchenwald and efface "this camp constructed by men."

Semprún has every right to claim the survivors' moral title to the ruins of the camps. But to implement this vision of disappearing camps would be unforgivably consistent with Himmler's own desire to eradicate them, as he did with the extermination camps of Treblinka, Belzec, and Sobibor once their purpose was fulfilled. This much should be enough to maintain that, when the last survivor dies, the only moral option for us will be to prevent the effacement of the camps' ruins. Our generation's challenge lies not in attaining the knowledge of *what* [the Holocaust] *really was*—in the experiential sense of Semprún's description—but rather, in never forgetting *that* it really was. And, further down the line, in emphasizing that it *really* was.

The difficulties in preserving the camps as testimonial sites are clearly exemplified by the ruins of the Majdanek camp in Eastern Poland. This camp was hurriedly evacuated by the Germans soon before the Soviet troops arrived in July 1944, so the buildings remained then pretty much intact. Just four months later, a museum was established in a few of the barracks, while the rest of the camp was taken over by Russian and Polish troops. Within a year, however, 80% of the camp had been dismantled, stolen, allotted, or sold as recyclables. As early as 1949, the grounds of the camp, or at least about half of the original site, were cordoned off as a memorial. The still-standing gas chambers were protected and the crematorium was rebuilt, as were fences and towers. Some warehouses and workshops became exhibition pavilions. Salvaged material was used to reconstruct two rows of prisoner barracks, which are the ones that can be seen there today. Furthermore, the cleared prisoner grounds were planted with trees in order to create a park of remembrance.

Ten years later, the Majdanek authorities figured that turning the grounds into a park had not been a good idea after all, so they uprooted the trees and only then instituted a plan for keeping the camp as "authentic" as possible. In 1969 a large Brutalist sculptural monument, a memorial dome for a mound of ashes, and a visitor reception building were added just outside the perimeter of the camp. The configuration of the Majdanek memorial has remained the same ever since, apart from a civil cemetery that was set up right next to it in the 1970s, now full, and the encroaching outskirts of the city of Lublin, now bordering the camp.

Had Semprún's wish prevailed and the surrounding landscape been allowed to swallow the remnants of the camp, Majdanek would have been buried under communist tenements. Instead, the memorial grounds evolved throughout the years in response to conflicting perceptions of how the camps should be presented and maintained.

Surely everyone has a right to visit the ruins of the camps. These sites have become must-see destinations; over the past decade, they have gradually morphed in response to the crowds of visitors who, one way or another, must be accommodated. During my travels, however, I noticed with concern the interventions that many original buildings have undergone in the service of the proliferating visitors. What I find disturbing is the notion that the sites need to be modified in order to offer tourists some form of healthy and enlightening entertainment to make them feel their time there has been worthwhile.

At Dachau, near Munich, the remaining buildings were those of common use, and these structures have recently been fitted with a state-of-the-art exhibition narrating the nefarious story of the camp. The elaborate display resorts to projections, recordings, monitors, photomurals, and interactive screens—there is even a theater dedicated to ongoing screenings of a 20-minute film. The display's attention grabbing is so effective that the original artifacts interspersed in showcases become mere accessories to the narration, while the building itself becomes hardly more than a set to provide the exhibition with an eerie ambience. The designers of this encompassing museographic arrangement aimed to teach the visitor a valuable lesson in history, but they did so at the expense of upholding the site's testimonial integrity. I believe the cost of dispensing such knowledge was unnecessarily steep: pedagogical and testimonial interests could have been safeguarded if the exhibition had been housed at some newly built facility adjacent to the camp, just as a museum label is placed adjacent to a painting.

Be that as it may, the site's integrity had already been compromised decades ago, with the insertion in 1968 of a sculptural monument that took over the central courtyard. This monument's imposition by decree was meant to mark the eradication of the evil that occurred there. However, the noble intentions of the authors of this conceit (both artists and bureaucrats) can't redeem the pride that drove them to desecrate the grounds with an inept and clunky idol, a fetish revealing promises that were unfairly delegated to works of art. At the end of the day, the artistic and didactic interventions at Dachau dilute the force of our encounter with its ruins.

At the Mauthausen camp, near Linz in Austria, I found that the assorted commemorative monuments were located, as in Majdanek, outside the camp's perimeter, within an area designated in 1949 as a "memorial park." This memorial park contains over twenty monuments, funded over the years by the different national groups that were victimized at Mauthausen. The diversity of these monuments and their respective styles makes for an empathetic rapport with the will to memorialize.

The memorial plaques at Mauthausen become more personal as one steps into the fortress that once was the camp proper. For decades, the families and friends of its victims have been placing plaques and mementoes dedicated to individual prisoners; their progressive accumulation is only suggestively proportional to the scale of the murderous operation that took place there. Thanks to this fractured and compartmentalized memorializing, we are better able to consider the weight of the tragedy. Regrettably, though, I also found that Mauthausen's current administrators are in the process of retrofitting its original buildings to introduce updated didactic exhibitions such as those at Dachau—despite the fact that there is a newly built "visitors' center" nearby that could have hosted the new exhibits.

The idea of adapting the camps' original buildings for educational purposes goes back to the example initially established at Auschwitz, which is nowadays the biggest tourist "attraction" in Poland, with over 1.5 million visitors yearly. The guided walk through Auschwitz I is an exercise in obligatory decorum, with some unfortunate flashes of expediency, artifice, and even flat-out impertinence. This peculiar muddle becomes evident as soon as one steps from the parking area into the visitors' reception building—which is actually the original administration building of the concentration camp—and has been reconditioned to receive the mass of visitors, hand them audio-guides, and divide them into groups, as well as for buying a snack or a full lunch before starting the tour of the grounds. Odd as this is, one should bear in mind that the post-war redeployment of Auschwitz's buildings was not the product of a "master plan," as was the case in Dachau, but rather an evolving transformation that responded to the particular political circumstances of the times.

Auschwitz I was built entirely out of brick and mortar. Unlike most other camps, the ensemble was not dismantled before or after liberation, and today it retains a certain air of, say, a university campus—that is, if we disregard the electrified fences and our awareness of what went on inside. And maybe it was thanks to its unexpectedly sober architecture that the authority that took over the liberated camp considered it sensible to house, in a couple of the empty buildings, the institute charged with compiling, archiving, and protecting the memory of Nazi crimes. Between 1947 and 1955, as visitors to the infamous site became frequent, five more of the empty structures were adapted for exhibitions depicting the living conditions at the camp, incorporating furnishings and artifacts that had been recovered. Even if requests to emphasize the massacre of the Jewish people were underplayed at the time, the memorial seems to have retained some sort of reasonable balance given the material complications of the post-war years. The current configuration of these exhibits for present visitors has not changed much. With the Cold War at full throttle in the early 1960s, newer exhibits were ideologically hijacked. Many still-empty buildings were consigned to different countries in order to set up memorial exhibitions commemorating the specific national populations that were victimized by the Nazis. Politics trumped all other concerns, so most of these spaces were allotted to members of the Soviet Bloc; one was even dedicated to the East Germans and another to the Austrians! It should come as no surprise that these exhibits were swiftly dismantled soon after the fall of the USSR. The sole pre-Perestroika pavilion still open to this day is, indeed, the Austrian one, which parades the shameless title *March 11, 1938: Austria—The First Victim of National Socialism.*

Most other national pavilions have been redone in the past decade or so. Of the nine national pavilions in operation at Auschwitz today, five—Slovakia, Hungary, France, Belgium, and the Netherlands—are mostly dedicated to the slaughter of their Jewish populations. These exhibitions were mounted between 2002 and 2006 during a sort of museographic arms race where each country seems to have made every effort to outshine the others' showmanship. As in the recently proliferating museums focused on issues related to Judaism, the Holocaust, and tolerance, the museographic scripts are now guided by so-called "human-interest" stories. My apprehension here is less about the content of these scripts than about the bizarre environments created by their ambitious but misguided designers and politician overseers. Consider, for instance, the Hungarian pavilion, which is heavily invested in turning the case against Hungarian anti-Semitism into something of a surrealist dream, all by way of an environment saturated with projections, light effects, and gratuitous scenographic bravado reminiscent of a dystopian science fiction movie set. Or we might consider the French pavilion, which tackles the tragedy of the Jews' deportation against a backdrop of immaculate whiteness, polished cement, and sophisticated lighting design—a post-minimal ambiance reminiscent of the fanciest boutiques and galleries of the Rive-Droit in Paris. I find myself failing to imagine how good taste could ever be more impudent than here.

While the elaborate displays that secure tourists' attention at the camps may also allow the critic to shield him or herself behind a judgmental attitude (as I evidently did myself), when one approaches the grounds of Birkenau it becomes impossible not to be mesmerized by the expanse of the Germans' most murderous production. These 350 acres (140 hectares) of otherwise open terrain, entirely enclosed by impassable electrified fences, could hold over 100,000 inmates at a time, 90% of whom would perish one way or another, and operated up to six gas chambers that could kill and process up to 6,000 people a day. It is estimated that between one and 1.5 million people died at Birkenau. The complex was partly dynamited by the Germans as they retreated, partly destroyed in the ensuing skirmishes, and partly dismantled by locals who needed combustibles and recyclables following the war. Today, Birkenau resembles an enormous archeological site of some long-lost civilization, or the devastation left by an enormous natural disaster. Scale is an aesthetic category that does not require mediation, and here the sheer scale of the site would automatically turn any ostentatious didactic intervention into a pompous conceit. At least until now, Birkenau has been kept pretty much in the raw, as, in my view, every other remnant of the concentration and extermination camps should have been.

I finish here by twisting Jorge Semprún's words, hoping that Birkenau, this camp constructed and destroyed by men, shall *not* be overtaken by grass, roots, and brambles—or, for that matter, by ambitious designers, museographers, and politicians.

Mauthausen. Foto—Photo: Yishai Jusidman, 2012

De lo sublime a lo abyecto: seis décadas de arte*

ANDREW WEINSTEIN

* Publicado originalmente en Stephen C. Feinstein, ed. *Absence/Presence: Critical Essays on the Artistic Memory of the Holocaust*, Siracusa, Syracuse UP, 2005, pp. 70-92.

Fig. 6: **Arie A. Galles**, *Fourteen Stations/Hey Yud Dalet Suite. Station #3 Buchenwald* [*Catorce estaciones/ Hey Yud Dalet Suite. Estación #3 Buchenwald*] 2001; carbón sobre papel Arches Conte blanco en marco de hierro forjado—Charcoal on arches, white conte, wrought iron frame, 44.5 × 72 in. Reproducido con autorización del artista—Reproduced with permission of the artist. Foto—Photo: Tim Volk

Es un lugar común hoy en día decir que las representaciones artísticas del Holocausto son más poderosas cuando incorporan fotografías, documentos u otros materiales hallados hoy día. Pero esta idea era ajena inmediatamente después de la segunda guerra mundial. En ese momento, los artistas de la corriente principal se esforzaban por representar la muerte y la destrucción masivas, junto con la consecuente visión de la experiencia humana, a través de medios universalizantes inventados por ellos mismos. Los lienzos expresionistas abstractos de artistas tales como Mark Rothko y Barnett Newman —amplios campos de color como paisajes vacíos para la introspección y la meditación, en los que varios estudiosos han detectado recientemente una reacción específica al Holocausto—[1] aparecieron en las décadas de 1940 y 1950 envueltos por una retórica de lo sublime existencial, donde la blancura proyecta una maravilla o un terror demasiado poderosos para ser enfrentados directamente. Durante el mismo periodo, un desarrollo artístico relacionado sucedió en la forma de las expresionistas "nuevas imágenes del hombre". Eran distorsionadas y, a menudo, grotescas, y, de acuerdo con el curador de una importante exposición de 1959 en el Museo de Arte Moderno, respondían a los horrores de la segunda guerra mundial, mientras anticipaban horrores aún peores por venir.[2] Pero no incluyeron ninguna huella del Holocausto y sólo muy rara vez hicieron referencia específica a él. A falta de números tatuados, de uniformes a rayas o de estrellas amarillas, las figuras esqueléticas, atenuadas, de Alberto Giacometti, que se disolvían en la enormidad del espacio, mostraron la condición existencial, a pesar de que el propio Jean-Paul Sartre los describió como los "mártires descarnados de Buchenwald".[3] De los pocos

—

1— Ziva Amishai-Maisels, *Depiction and Interpretation: The Influence of the Holocaust on the Visual Arts,* Nueva York, Pergamon Press, 1993, pp. 268, 303–304; Matthew Baigell, *Jewish-American Artists and the Holocaust*, New Brunswick, Rutgers University Press, 1997, pp. 29-30. Steven Zucker trata el tema de forma más sutil en "Confrontations with Radical Evil, The Ambiguity of Myth and the Inadequacy of Representation", *Art History* 24 (2001), pp. 379–400.

2— Peter Selz, *New Images of Man*, Nueva York, The Museum of Modern Art, 1959, p. 12.

3— Jean-Paul Sartre, "The Search for the Absolute", *Art in Theory, 1900-2000*, eds. Charles Harrison y Paul Wood, Oxford, Blackwell, 2003, p. 616. Sartre artistas que representaron específicamente las atrocidades nazis, el más destacado fue Rico Lebrun [Fig. 1], con *Fosa de Buchenwald* (1955), *Estudio para la cámara de Dachau* (1958) y otros lienzos inspirados en Picasso.

Dentro de este contexto, es fácil entender por qué, en 1975, Lawrence Langer rechazaría la posibilidad de que "meras verdades fácticas" pudieran servir algún día como base de la representación del Holocausto en el arte.[4] En su lugar, Langer defendía una especie de expresionismo, ejemplificada para él por el *Guernica*, de 1937, el gran lienzo cubo-surrealista de Picasso en protesta por las atrocidades fascistas en España. [Fig. 2] Durante el Holocausto, según el argumento de Langer, los antiguos supuestos sobre el comportamiento humano y la interacción social habían quedado suspendidos, y fueron suplantados por una realidad alterna antes sólo imaginada en fantasías morbosas. Era tan ajena esta realidad hasta ahora imposible (*l'univers concentrationnaire*, el universo concentracionario, en términos de David Rousset, superviviente y novelista) que un espectador tenía que depender de una figura intermediaria, de un visionario artístico, para aclarar las características oscuras de su paisaje de pesadilla. El papel del artista parecía claro.

Dado todo lo anterior, puede resultar sorprendente que el novelista Leslie Epstein anulara tan resueltamente el argumento perfectamente razonable de Langer en una reseña un año más tarde. Al rechazar la premisa del argumento de Langer, Epstein insistió en que el universo en el que el Holocausto había ocurrido compartía las mismas leyes físicas y psicológicas que el nuestro y que fingir lo contrario, invariablemente, distanciaba el acontecimiento de las preocupaciones actuales hasta el punto de la irrelevancia, con la consecuencia de que sus lecciones podrían quedar sin respuesta.[5] Epstein reconoció el poder de una

—

escribió sus comentarios para el catálogo de la exposición *Alberto Giacometti. Sculptures, Paintings, Drawings* en la Pierre Matisse Gallery, Nueva York, enero-febrero de 1948.

4— Lawrence L. Langer, *The Holocaust and the Literary Imagination*, New Haven, Yale University Press, 1975, p. 8. Langer toma la frase citada de Richard Gilman, "Nat Turner Revisited", *New Republic* (27 de abril de 1968), p. 24.

5— Epstein le pregunta: "¿el 'arte como éste' nos acerca más a lo que ocurrió con los judíos, o es, como creo, una especie de *grand guignol*, un espectáculo de estrategia artística de representación basada en hechos. A miles de kilómetros de distancia, casi al mismo tiempo (1974), el periodista francés Claude Lanzmann comenzó a filmar *Shoah*, una epopeya de los hechos y evidencias por excelencia. En 1980, Art Spiegelman comenzó la publicación en serie de *Maus*, un cómic de no ficción que cuenta la experiencia del Holocausto del padre del artista, basado en entrevistas grabadas, en el que los representa a ellos mismos en el texto. Las compuertas se habían abierto a un nuevo enfoque de representación basado en los hechos.

Lo que me parece curioso de este cambio es que en general traza un paralelismo con la reorientación en el arte contemporáneo sucedida unos veinte años antes, que desafió rotundamente el expresionismo abstracto y sus tendencias contemporáneas, por razones que aparentemente no tienen nada que ver con el Holocausto. ¿Qué vamos a hacer con este desarrollo paralelo? Los artistas que tomaban el Holocausto como tema, ¿simplemente siguieron los movimientos del mundo del arte más amplio? ¿Se hallaban tales artistas, tal vez, respondiendo a otras condiciones culturales que aún estaban (y están) activas fuera del mundo del arte, a las que la mayoría de los artistas contemporáneos reaccionaron de manera similar? Ambas situaciones parecen ser el caso.

***

Al igual que la historia de la representación del Holocausto, la historia del arte contemporáneo impresiona al observador con su movimiento hacia ideales que habían sido por completo desconocidos en los años de la posguerra: el desapego emocional y la facticidad. Nadie puede negar que el expresionismo abstracto ejerció una enorme influencia en los artistas que surgieron entre mediados de la década de 1950 y principios de la de 1960, pero estos artistas reaccionaron a los patriarcas del expresionismo abstracto en gran

—

horror sustituto, destinado a distraernos de lo que fue la atrocidad real —más insoportable tal vez en su monotonía, su tranquilidad, en la manera en la que encaja discretamente en nuestro mundo?". Leslie Epstein, "The Reality of Evil", *Partisan Review* 43, 1976, p. 639.

medida parodiándolos. Sobre todo, la celebración del yo del expresionista abstracto estaba ya desgastada, junto con lo que la generación más joven consideró como la inflada vanidad de lo espiritual y lo sublime.

Apareció lo que algunos críticos llamaron el neo-dada, ejemplificado por Robert Rauschenberg y Jasper Johns. Ambos se inspiraron en Marcel Duchamp por sus obras de arte encontrado, o *ready-mades*, como su *Portabotellas* de 1914, así como en John Cage, cuya apertura zen al mundo motivó composiciones como *4'33"* (1952), un silencio cronometrado que anima a los oyentes a centrarse en los sonidos ambientales. En sus obras, Rauschenberg y Johns se apropiaron de todo, desde colchas de cama hasta latas de cerveza, mientras extinguían la emoción asociada con el expresionismo abstracto. Sus goteos y pinceladas, inspirados por Jackson Pollock y Willem de Kooning, son fríamente irónicos, una actitud que se verá un poco más tarde en las apropiaciones, al parecer sin prejuicios, de la cultura de masas del arte pop de Andy Warhol y los movimientos relacionados.

Junto al neo-dada, se desarrolló una escuela formalista, que vio en el expresionismo abstracto lo que el crítico Clement Greenberg y sus compinches habían reconocido desde su creación: un hincapié en la materialidad. Para Greenberg, no había ni lo sublime ni un yo en los grandes lienzos gestuales y de campos de color del expresionismo abstracto. Sólo había pintura, aplicada como plano más de lo que nadie lo había hecho antes. El crítico de arte preeminente de su tiempo, Greenberg propuso una teoría de la modernidad como un avance ineludible desde la mitad del siglo XIX, cuando Courbet y Manet evitaron los elementos narrativos y abrazaron la planitud del plano pictórico, hasta los años de la posguerra con la destilación de la pintura a su esencia como pintura pura.[6] Helen Franktha-

—

6— El formalismo apolítico de Greenberg tuvo su origen en una posición marxista de la preguerra. En ese momento, Greenberg argumentó que los artistas, decididos a conservar su autonomía cultural, se retiraron cada vez más al refugio enrarecido del formalismo en un intento por escapar de las implacables cooptaciones de la cultura popular. Presenta este argumento en su ensayo de 1939 "Avant-Garde and Kitsch", *Art and Culture: Critical Essays*, Boston, Beacon Press, 1961, pp. 3–21 ["Vanguardia y kitsch" en *La pintura moderna y otros ensayos*, Madrid, Siruela, 2006, pp. 23–44]. A partir de 1948, en el contexto ler, Morris Louis y otros siguieron fielmente los dictados de Greenberg por "ir más allá" de Jackson Pollock con sus propios lienzos no imprimados incluso más planos que los goteos de Pollock, ya que para ellos la pintura sólo manchaba la superficie, preservando el tejido en general. Después de eso, durante la década de 1960, una generación de escultores minimalistas aplicó la idea de Greenberg de la pureza formal a su propio medio y lo llevó a su conclusión lógica (a pesar de la desaprobación de Greenberg). Eliminaron la mano del artista a favor de la pura materialidad; las hojas de plomo y los bloques de acero hechos en fábrica de Richard Serra eran todos palpablemente pesados, las placas metálicas de Carl Andre eran tan planas en su significado como los pisos en los que yacían.

A mediados de la década de 1970, la tradición moderna finalmente sucumbió a la nueva hegemonía del mundo del arte, la del giro textual. Esta actitud ascendente privilegió las preocupaciones extra-estéticas, extra-materiales, como el lenguaje, típico del arte conceptual. Y fomentó la idea de que la historia era un depósito de imágenes y estilos disponibles para la manipulación contemporánea, como lo demuestran movimientos *revival* como el neo-expresionismo y, una década más tarde, el neo-geo. Del mismo modo, el desconocimiento de las posiciones tradicionales del sujeto y el objeto ("espectador", "artista" y "obra") llevó al arte a través de un ámbito cultural ampliado. En ocasiones, esta expansión supuso la eliminación física de la galería, como sucede con el *earth art* y buena parte del performance y el arte corporal. Otras veces supuso la remoción ideológica, por ejemplo, borrando la distinción entre las llamadas alta y baja culturas durante la década de 1980, como en los cachorros de cerámica kitsch de Jeff Koons y los *comix* de Art Spiegelman.

—

de la guerra fría, Greenberg abandonó esta historia social del arte por una teoría de la pintura autocrítica, expresada con mayor claridad en su ensayo de 1960 "Modernist Painting", *Art in Theory, 1900-2000*, 773–779 ["La pintura moderna", en *La pintura moderna y otros ensayos*, Madrid, Siruela, 2006, pp. 111–120]. Margaret Olin ubica el formalismo de Greenberg en un contexto socio-histórico fascinante en "C[lement] Hardesh [Greenberg] and Company: Formal Criticism and Jewish Identity", en *Too Jewish?: Challenging Traditional Identities*, ed. Norman L. Kleeblatt, Nueva York, The Jewish Museum; New Brunswick, Rutgers University Press, 1996, pp. 39–59.

Hal Foster caracteriza este giro textual en términos de dos posiciones ideológicas surgidas a finales de la década de 1970 y que todavía se mantienen. Una es paralela a un neoconservadurismo mayor que fomentó un retorno acrítico de la memoria cultural.[7] Sus promotores políticos (Ronald Reagan, Margaret Thatcher, Helmut Kohl) son más fáciles de nombrar que sus representantes en las artes. Algunos críticos sugieren a Koons como un ejemplo de conservadurismo por abrazar, al parecer de manera cínica, las prácticas comerciales tradicionales, incluida la producción masiva de mercancía barata y el violento sobreprecio por ella. Otros mencionan a Eric Fischl y David Salle (un crítico los llama "pubistas analíticos"[8]) por sus representaciones sexualizadas de mujeres desde puntos de vista tradicionalmente masculinos, representaciones que parecen la reacción de un chico malo contra el feminismo.

Este marco histórico admite cómodamente la representación del Holocausto; uno está tentado a colocar a Anselm Kiefer entre tales neoconservadores por la manera en que resucita la memoria histórica. A primera vista, sus *Ocupaciones* (1969) —una colección de fotografías de Kiefer actuando, haciendo solo el saludo de Hitler en espacios públicos vacíos en Francia, Suiza e Italia [Fig. 3]— puede parecer progresista porque se burla de los nazis y resucita el espectro de una historia que toda una generación de alemanes había preferido ignorar. Pero como Andreas Huyssen ha observado, al tratar ese pasado feroz con un humor paródico, la pieza de Kiefer trivializa el nazismo en formas que en última instancia podrían alentar el hacer caso omiso de sus crímenes.[9] Más tarde, en unas enormes pinturas grandilocuentes llamadas *Sulamita* (1983), lo que parece ser la

—

7— Hal Foster, *The Return of the Real: The Avant-Garde at the End of the Century,* Cambridge, MIT Press, 1996, p. 71 [*El retorno de lo real. La vanguardia a finales de siglo,* Madrid, Akal, 2001, p. 74.]. Los capítulos 3 y 5 de este brillante libro sobre el arte contemporáneo proveen gran parte del marco para mi propio acercamiento a la representación del Holocausto desde mediados de la década de 1970.

8— Robert Pincus-Witten, "Entries: Analytical Pubism", *Postminimalism into Maximalism: American Art, 1966–1986*, Ann Arbor, UMI Research Press, 1987, pp. 313–320.

9— Andreas Huyssen, *Twilight Memories: Marking Time in a Culture of Amnesia,* Nueva York, Routledge, 1995, p. 215.

representación de un monumento funerario para los muertos judíos es, de hecho, una adaptación pintada de una fotografía propagandística de época de la *Sala funeraria para los grandes soldados alemanes* (1939) de Wilhelm Kreis. Para quienes reconocen esta alusión problemática, Kiefer revela su identidad en conflicto tanto con la víctima como con el perpetrador: promueve una estética nazi no sólo al crear lo que parece ser un escenario para una gran ópera de la forma en que los propios nazis habían orquestado sus mítines del partido, etc., sino también mediante el empleo de la poderosa simetría y la perspectiva del punto de vista elegido por Kreis. “Tengo que recrear un poco lo que hicieron con el fin de comprender su locura”, ha dicho Kiefer, “Es por eso que hago estos falsos intentos por convertirme en un fascista.”[10] Sin embargo, al retener el hecho del origen nazi de su escenario elegido, Kiefer ofusca el estigma asociado a esta forma particular de retorno histórico, permitiendo de esta manera una revitalización revisionista de esa estética cuestionable.

La segunda manifestación ideológica del giro textual, según Foster, era una crítica principalmente de izquierda y postestructuralista, que tiene sus raíces en el arte de los sesenta. La crítica institucional, por ejemplo, inspiró a una generación de artistas posterior a 1968, incluyendo a Hans Haacke, cuya *Encuesta-MoMA* (1970) invitó a los espectadores en el Museo de Arte Moderno de Nueva York a votar su opinión respecto al apoyo tácito a la guerra de Vietnam del gobernador del estado de Nueva York Nelson Rockefeller, consejero y antiguo presidente y miembro de la junta del museo. *Cowboy with Cigarette* [*Vaquero con cigarrillo*] (1990), una pieza más reciente de Haacke [Fig. 4], recrea un famoso collage de Picasso (*Hombre con sombrero*, 1912) para una exposición patrocinada por Philip Morris —excepto que los recortes de papel de periódico y otros papeles de la versión de Haacke presentan citas condenatorias hacia la estrategia de la compañía tabacalera de cooptar la cultura en pro de las relaciones públicas, al tiempo que financiaba a Jesse Helms, el senador a favor del tabaco que también resultó ser la némesis del patrocinio

—

10— Amishai-Maisels, *op. cit.*, p. 363.

federal de las artes. Con un énfasis similar en las preocupaciones sociales, una serie de artistas llevó la conciencia feminista, étnica y homosexual, así como respecto al sida, a las artes.

Desde el ámbito de la representación del Holocausto, Susan Silas encaja en este grupo progresista con su obra sin título de 1989. [Fig. 5] Con la forma de una nota de rescate, en su collage de papel periódico se lee "Anselm Kiefer, ¿dónde estaba tu padre durante la guerra?" Silas aborda un aspecto preocupante de la biografía de Kiefer; a saber, que no es franco respecto a su propia historia familiar incluso cuando manipula materiales de la historia nazi y del Holocausto en formas que han vuelto su arte famoso e inmensamente lucrativo. Silas insinúa que un deseo de fama y fortuna puede motivar el proyecto de Kiefer, no el valor o una búsqueda de la verdad. Al llamar la atención hacia este problema, la elección de papel de periódico de Silas evoca el propio material de la historia (en el collage su palabra "The" evidentemente proviene de la cabeza del periódico de referencia, *The New York Times*), de la misma forma que sus recortes y la elaboración del collage manifiestan su desfiguración y re-presentación, distorsiones que las propias presentaciones de Kiefer logran ocultar.

***

A pesar de que parecen estar en oposición directa, tanto el impulso neoconservador como el impulso postestructuralista son, de acuerdo con Fredric Jameson, ejemplos de "la lógica cultural del capitalismo tardío". Para explicar su similitud, Jameson examina la dinámica evolutiva del capitalismo en términos de la emergencia y la transformación del signo.

En el recuento de Jameson, la industria y la ciencia, a mediados del siglo XIX, habían exorcizado la magia y la superstición, para reemplazarlos con un punto de vista materialista. Esta actitud materialista quedó reificada en su propia "realidad" y dio lugar a la aparición de los signos en el lenguaje. Cada uno constaba de un significante (palabra), junto con su significado (sobre el cual una comunidad de hablantes está de acuerdo). Los signos funcionaban de una manera positivista, entendida como que describían con precisión los referentes en el mundo real. Esta visión del mundo inspiró el realismo de Courbet y Manet y, posiblemente, el impresionismo de los pintores que les siguieron.

A medida que el capitalismo dominó la vida ordinaria, el mismo proceso de reificación que había erradicado la magia se dedicó entonces a la transformación del propio signo. Fenómenos abstractos que tenían escasa conexión con el mundo real asumieron su propia realidad; una fluctuación del mercado de valores basada en un rumor podría expulsar a miles de sus puestos de trabajo. De esta forma, el mero signo se convirtió en una fuerza potente, con poca o ninguna conexión con un referente en el mundo real. Éste fue el momento de la alta modernidad: el collage cubista de un hombre con un sombrero de Picasso de 1912 se relaciona sólo de manera tenue con un hombre y un sombrero de verdad, ya que la representación apenas se parece a la realidad. A través de su forma enrarecida, la cultura entró en un período de relativa autonomía, por lo que representaba o "redobla[ba] el mundo sin ser del todo parte de él".[11]

En el capitalismo tardío hoy, la reificación esquila el significante de un significado estable. Sin relación con ningún referente en lo absoluto, el significante *Star Wars*, despojado de su significado hollywoodense, reaparecería como el nombre de un escudo antimisiles del espacio exterior promovido por el actor convertido en presidente Ronald Reagan contra un enemigo recientemente designado como el Imperio del Mal. Mientras tanto, las pinturas de Marilyn Monroe de Andy Warhol presentan un significante básicamente vacío, creado en la mente de los agentes y productores de Hollywood, un significante cuyo significado desestabilizado puede ser el glamour, el atractivo sexual, la tragedia de tabloide o la nostalgia de los años cincuenta. Al perder su significado, en última instancia, los significantes se connotan sólo a sí mismos y a los períodos históricos que los crearon, por lo que "nos quedamos con

—

11— Fredric Jameson, *Postmodernism, or, The Cultural Logic of Late Capitalism*, Durham, Duke University Press, 1991, p. 96 [*El posmodernismo o la lógica cultural del capitalismo avanzado*, Buenos Aires-Barcelona-México, Paidós, 1991.]

ese juego puro y aleatorio de los significantes que llamamos posmodernidad".[12]

Durante los años setenta y ochenta, la mayoría de los artistas que se ocuparon por primera vez de la representación del Holocausto rechazaron las viejas estrategias estéticas que habían retratado el crimen nazi (como el expresionismo de Langer) o que habían denotado ese horror escondiéndolo detrás de una pantalla (el expresionismo abstracto). Creo que lo hicieron así porque, en parte, los diferentes estilos habían comenzado a significar conceptos tales como "arte del Holocausto", conmemoración y educación más que la historia del Holocausto en sí; las pinturas y esculturas que con imaginación retrataron chimeneas, vías férreas o cuerpos demacrados, como las de Rico Lebrun, pueden haber resonado entre los espectadores diez años después de la guerra, cuando el recuerdo de los noticiarios seguía siendo traumatizante y fresco,[13] pero a mediados de los años setenta, ya empezaban a aparecer como rancias y santurronas, mientras que las obras de estilo expresionista abstracto parecían decir más acerca de las preocupaciones estéticas de las décadas de 1940 y 1950 que de las atrocidades de los años de la guerra. En conjunto, las estrategias y motivos artísticos que el público podía considerar trillados o anticuados parecían, a los versados en semiótica, detritos de una visión moderna en un mundo posmoderno, meros significantes que habían sido despojados de sus significados originales, con el referente Holocausto perdido en la confusión. Parecía que la signalización había fracasado.

***

La desestabilización del signo como la he definido engendró las condiciones para el surgimiento de un arte ya no basado en la visión o el estilo de un artista, sino en objetos y documentos, material que parecía reafirmar una conexión con

—

12—*Ibíd.*

13— En relación con cesto, puede argumentarse que lo sublime de Newman trabajó más eficazmente en los primeros años de la posguerra, precisamente porque los espectadores contemporáneos podían intuir los problemas existenciales tanto en sentido literal como figurado detrás de las pinturas.

un referente en el mundo real. Rosalind Krauss analiza esta transformación en el arte contemporáneo de la década de 1970 como un vaciado rápido de la convención a favor del signo indicial, ese tipo de signo que toma su referente en la forma en que un efecto alude a una causa, por ejemplo la acción de una veleta en el viento. Con su preocupación por lo particular, en lugar de lo general, la indexicalidad ofrece un medio de representación, escribe Krauss, en el que "se entiende la verdad como una cuestión de evidencias en lugar de una función de la lógica".[14] Al igual que Lanzmann y Spiegelman, una gran cantidad de artistas contemporáneos incorporaron índices en su obra, especialmente fotografías.[15] En *Fourteen Stations* [*Catorce estaciones*] (1993–2002) [Fig. 6], Arie A. Galles dibujó minuciosamente a mano reproducciones de fotos aéreas de época de los campos de exterminio nazis; en su serie de 1991 *The Jews of Lodz and Krakow* [*Los judíos de Lodz y Cracovia*], Susan Erony utilizó sus propias fotos de lápidas cubiertas por la maleza. [Fig. 7]

Tarde o temprano, casi todos los análisis de la representación del Holocausto en el arte invocan el nombre de Theodor W. Adorno, quien asimismo tiene un lugar aquí, pues Adorno también exaltó lo particular. Pero él llegó a esta postura por su propio análisis del capitalismo y el positivismo de la Ilustración en la ciencia y la industria. Un bastión de la tradición materialista es el pensamiento en términos de identidad, una forma esencialmente reductiva de reflexión en la que un pensador presume entender totalmente el significado o valor de un objeto. En términos filosóficos, el concepto subsume el objeto, sin dejar ningún residuo. En términos semióticos, se supone que el signo tiene una relación no problemática y literal con su referente. En la práctica, pensar en términos de identidad deshumaniza a los trabajadores al equipararlos con su valor

—

14— Rosalind E. Krauss, "Notes on the Index: Part 2", *The Originality of the Avant-Garde and Other Modernist Myths*, Cambridge, MIT Press, 1985, p. 218 ["Notas sobre el índice: parte 2", en *La originalidad de la vanguardia y otros mitos modernos*, Madrid, Alianza, 2006, p. 233].

15— El propio uso que Spiegelman da a tres fotografías familiares de época en *Maus* es analizado por Marianne Hirsch en *Family Frames: Photography, Narrative, and Postmemory*, Cambridge y Londres, Harvard University Press, 1997.

de uso y nada más. Del mismo modo, desparticulariza los objetos al juzgarlos sólo con respecto a su valor monetario o de intercambio. Los obreros se vuelven intercambiables, y lo mismo sucede con los objetos fabricados. En la mente de quien piensa en términos de identidad, nada mágico o misterioso permanece con el objeto, sea humano o inanimado. Con el tiempo, esta forma de pensar infiltró todos los aspectos de la sociedad y, según sostiene Adorno, condujo a la identificación racial nazi de las personas como valiosas o sin valor, una identificación que culminó en el genocidio. Esta consideración se ilumina en la famosa cita de Adorno de 1949, "escribir poesía después de Auschwitz es un acto de barbarie", pues la poesía sobre el Holocausto hablaría ostensiblemente en nombre de la totalidad de esa horrible historia en unas pocas líneas tersas, identificándolo así de manera reductiva. Es cierto que Adorno más tarde calificó su declaración acerca de la poesía al admitir que "el sufrimiento perenne tiene tanto derecho de expresión como el que un hombre torturado tiene de gritar".[16] Pero su advertencia es clara: el arte sobre el Holocausto podría perpetuar el tipo de pensamiento que había hecho posible el genocidio en el primer lugar.

El antídoto de Adorno al pensamiento de identidad es complicado y sutil, la sustancia de un sistema filosófico descrito en su *Dialéctica negativa*. Su esencia radica en negar el positivismo abogando por el pensamiento de *no*-identidad, es decir, por considerar un objeto en su particularidad única y a la vez rechazar la posibilidad de entenderlo alguna vez por completo. Adorno imagina al pensador concienzudo como una especie de chamán, un individuo que reconoce el misterio y la magia de un objeto en particular, al mismo tiempo que trata de desentrañar su acertijo y llamarlo por su verdadero nombre. Desentrañar un acertijo supone la "fantasía exacta": presentar los hechos históricos precisos para una investigación intelectual asequible gracias a una llave metodológica actual (es decir, el marxismo, el feminismo, el psicoanálisis, etc.) a partir de un número infinito de posibles llaves —con el

—

16— Theodor W. Adorno, *Negative Dialectics*, trad. E. B. Ashton, Nueva York, Continuum, 1973, p. 362 [*Dialéctica negativa. La jerga de la autenticidad*, Madrid, Akal, 2005, p. 332].

fin de desbloquear "la verdad no intencional" del objeto, la cual es su verdadero nombre. Pero inmediatamente después del destello de la verdad epifánica —ese atisbo de Utopía en el que el lenguaje existe en su estado pre-torre de Babel— el nombre puede llegar a ser una etiqueta reductora, un ejemplo del pensamiento de la identidad. Esta situación impulsa al pensador diligente a buscar otros nombres de un fondo inagotable, pues la naturaleza del objeto nunca puede ser conocida del todo.[17]

Al parecer, una meticulosidad similar motiva a muchos artistas que trabajan el tema del Holocausto a abstenerse de hacer declaraciones temerarias o categóricas.[18] La incorporación del signo indicial, lo que Krauss llama "la muda presencia de un acontecimiento sin codificar", permite una rendición respetuosa del control autoral, un evitar aparente del pensamiento de la identidad.[19] En *Catorce estaciones*, Galles empleó imágenes fotográficas por primera vez en su trayectoria, ya que sentía que los documentos son más poderosos para conectar con la realidad histórica que cualquier cosa que un artista pueda inventar.

Dicha confrontación con la historia puede dar lugar a algunos efectos contradictorios. Galles representa a una comunidad de artistas relacionados con el Holocausto al informar de una respuesta en dos sentidos. Habla de llorar en su caballete cuando toma en cuenta a los parientes perdidos y de la rabia hacia la indiferencia de Dios. Por otra parte, habla de la dureza, de la insensibilidad necesarias para proseguir la obra.[20]

—

17— El opaco texto de Adorno, aparentemente creado para entablar una conversación sólo con los pensadores más importantes, y anticiparse a la cooptación por parte de los pensadores de la identidad, es aclarado hermosamente por Susan Buck-Morss, *The Origin of Negative Dialectics: Theodor W. Adorno, Walter Benjamin, and the Frankfurt Institute*, Nueva York, The Free Press, 1977 [*Origen de la dialéctica negativa. Theodor W. Adorno, Walter Benjamin y el Instituto de Frankfurt*, México, Siglo XXI, 1981].

18— Para un análisis de los paralelismos entre las representaciones artísticas del Holocausto y la filosofía de Adorno, véase mi ensayo "Art after Auschwitz and the Necessity of a Postmodern Modernism", *Contemporary Portrayals of Auschwitz: Philosophical Challenges*, eds. Alan Rosenberg, R. James Watson y Detlef Linke, Amherst, Nueva York, Humanity Books, 2000, pp.151–167.

19— Krauss, *op. cit.*, p. 212 [227].

20— Arie A. Galles, entrevista personal, 2 de mayo de 1998.

No sólo en el arte, sino también en el ámbito académico, el encuentro desalentador con documentos del Holocausto —una confrontación potencialmente traumatizante con la memoria histórica (y, a veces, personal)— da pie a las dos respuestas alternativas que Galles describe. Equilibrarse entre ese entumecimiento que proporciona un escudo protector que hace posible la obra y la emoción que de vez en cuando rompe el escudo es, de hecho, el principal desafío para el historiador del Holocausto, según Saul Friedlander, quien sugiere que el reconocimiento de ambas tendencias es una forma de aceptar un pasado traumático.[21]

Curiosamente, este doble enfoque también pasa a ser la estrategia que Hal Foster ve en las pinturas de 1963–1964 de Andy Warhol tituladas *Disaster* [*Desastre*], de disturbios raciales, linchamientos, accidentes automovilísticos, la silla eléctrica y el asesinato de Kennedy, serigrafías que presentan múltiples reproducciones de una sola fotografía inquietante. [Fig. 8] En estas obras, Warhol no sólo aborda lo real, sino que lo aleja. "Cuando ves una imagen morbosa una y otra vez, en realidad no tiene ningún efecto", explicó Warhol en 1963.[22] En términos freudianos, la repetición se convierte en una manera de vencer un trauma. Sin embargo, los múltiples de Warhol no son, de hecho, idénticos: las variaciones en la pintura hacen única cada reproducción de una horrible imagen, recuperando inesperadamente su poder traumático. Foster da a este encuentro contradictorio con lo horrible el nombre de "realismo traumático".[23]

La diferencia del realismo traumático con el realismo decimonónico, se encuentra en su relación con la vida y la muerte. El realismo tradicional, especialmente en su forma literaria, aspira a recrear el mundo de forma mimética. Incluso después de que el mundo real desaparece, perdura de manera ficticia. Pero el realismo traumático

—

21— Saul Friedlander, "Trauma and Transference", *Memory, History, and the Extermination of the Jews of Europe*, Bloomington-Indianápolis, Indiana University Press, 1993, p. 130.

22— Foster, 131 [134]. Foster toma la cita de Warhol de Gene Swenson, "What is Pop Art? Answers from 8 Painters, Part I", *ArtNews* (noviembre de 1963, p. 60. Reproducido en *Art in Theory, 1900-2000*, pp. 747–749.

23— Foster, *op. cit.*, pp 130-36 [133–140].

apunta a la realidad de una ausencia, que deja al lector o al espectador con un agudo sentido de carencia.[24]

***

La diferencia entre el realismo literario y el realismo traumático recuerda la distinción entre el cine y la fotografía fija. Mientras que la película cinematográfica imita el mundo real al recrear su sentido del flujo del tiempo y la expansión espacial acompañante más allá del marco de cualquier imagen momentánea, las fotografías fijas, como momentos congelados, según observa Susan Sontag, funcionan de la misma forma que los *memento mori*.[25] En ellos, el mundo más allá del marco "muere absolutamente", escribe Roland Barthes, al aislar y capturar la imagen en la foto, que evoca un sentido de la vida ya vivida: "Observo con horror un futuro anterior que la muerte tutela... Esté o no el sujeto ya muerto, cada fotografía es esta catástrofe."[26] En este sentido, la fotografía tipifica la sensibilidad de realismo traumático. Resulta profundamente significativo la manera en que un artista que trabaja con fotografías, y en particular con fotografías del Holocausto, opta por negociar ese encuentro nominalmente traumático con la pérdida y la muerte.

En un extremo, dicho artista puede abrazar la perspectiva de Adorno, esforzándose por promover un punto de vista del índice fotográfico en su particularidad histórica, reinscribiéndolo tanto como sea posible dentro de una comprensión de su contexto original —intentando revivir el mundo muerto más allá del marco de la foto. En el otro extremo, el artista puede posicionar intencionalmente el índice fotográfico como un *memento mori* y sacrificar o

—

24— Michael Rothberg ofrece esta distinción en *Traumatic Realism: The Demands of Holocaust Representation*, Minneapolis, University of Minnesota Press, 2000, p. 99.

25— Susan Sontag, *On Photography*, 1977; Nueva York, Penguin, 1979, pp. 15, 17 [*Sobre la fotografía*, México, Alfaguara, 2006, pp. 31-35].

26— Roland Barthes, *Camera Lucida*, 1981; Londres, Fontana Paperbacks, 1984, pp. 57, 96 [*La cámara lúcida. Nota sobre la fotografía*, Barcelona, Paidós, 1989, pp. 96, 147].

someter el contexto histórico para promover el sentido de la muerte y la pérdida intrínseca al medio. Sacralizado, el índice se asemeja a una reliquia.[27]

En la práctica religiosa, es tradición considerar que las reliquias participan en o se conectan con la figura a la que se refieren de manera veraz. Mucho antes de la llegada de la fotografía o de los supuestos positivistas de la Ilustración que fomentarían su invención, la distinción entre la reliquia y el icono, o entre el índice y la imagen, era vaga. Un ejemplo: la Verónica (o *vera icona*),[28] la tela que supuestamente capturó la imagen de Jesús cuando se secó la cara con ella en las estaciones de la cruz y que por lo tanto poseía poderes milagrosos, funcionaba en el siglo XIII como un registro indicial del rostro, un modelo que los artistas copiaron, con el resultado de que el retrato del busto icónico se hizo popular entre los diseños para pinturas devocionales.[29] Sin embargo, versiones anteriores de la historia de la Verónica no mencionan nada de un índice sino que hablan más bien de una mujer llamada Verónica que pintó una imagen de Cristo que poseía poderes curativos.[30]

La religión no es, por supuesto, la fuerza operante que era en los tiempos pre-modernos, por lo que no es posible afirmar que los índices del Holocausto y las obras de arte que los incorporan ofrezcan alguna conexión con los temas representados como lo harían una reliquia o un icono hecho por el hombre. Despojados de lo numinoso, hablan de la pérdida.

Entonces, ¿qué significa sacralizar la memoria del Holocausto? Al escribir una "teología" de Auschwitz, Jacob

—

27— Un factor que problematiza la recepción de una obra de arte que represente el Holocausto como sagrado es la realidad de que los espectadores probablemente se encuentren en un museo o una galería —lo que Sontag llama "una situación social, llena de distracciones". Susan Sontag, *Regarding the Pain of Others*, 2003, Nueva York, Picador, 2004, p. 121 [*Ante el dolor de los demás*, Buenos Aires, Alfaguara, 2003].

28— Hans Belting, *Likeness and Presence: A History of the Image before the Era of Art*, trad. Edmund Jephcott, Chicago y Londres, University of Chicago Press, 1994, p. 208 [*Imagen y culto. Una historia de la imagen anterior a la edad del arte*, Madrid, Akal, 2009, p. 277].

29— Belting, *op. cit.*, p. 220 [294].

30— Belting, *op. cit.*, p. 218 [292].

Neusner sugiere que la memoria del Holocausto en los Estados Unidos se ha convertido en parte integrante de una identidad religiosa judía ligada a las nociones de redención (el nacimiento de Israel) y la determinación general de sobrevivir como pueblo y como tradición: "El hecho irónico es que el Holocausto, que debería haber desanimado y desmoralizado a los judíos, hizo que una generación sin rumbo se diera cuenta que debía ser fiel a su condición judía."[31] Una comprensión más crítica de la función de la memoria del Holocausto en la vida judía contemporánea proviene de Jack Kugelmass. Por medio de la sacralización de esa memoria, escribe, una población de judíos esencialmente privilegiados (norteamericanos) y opresivos (israelíes) "revierten simbólicamente la realidad" mediante la reivindicación de la identidad de la victimización experimentada por los judíos de Europa bajo Hitler. A través de gestos performáticos, como visitar los sitios de la atrocidad en Europa del Este, los judíos contemporáneos reafirman su martirio no sólo para sí mismos, sino también para un público de no-judíos.[32] Además, al ofrecer una identidad común, la memoria del Holocausto unifica a una comunidad de judíos que se ha vuelto tan diversa que sus distintas facciones podrían llegar de otro modo al desacuerdo político. En resumen, sacralizar la memoria del Holocausto la desparticulariza al grado que puede ser cooptada para conveniencias ideológicas, tanto dentro de las comunidades judías contemporáneas como fuera de ellas.

Para muchos artistas, resistir la sacralización es una preocupación primordial. Al trabajar no con fotos, sino más bien con textos de diarios de la época, cartas y testimonios, Ruth Liberman elabora lo que podría llamarse anti-reliquias. Reescribe sus palabras de propia mano o las remecanografía en una máquina de escribir eléctrica. Al superponer las palabras hasta que desaparecen en palimpsestos entintados o entre tachones y correcciones

—

31— Jacob Neusner, *American Judaism: Adventure in Modernity*, Englewood Cliffs, N.J., Prentice-Hall, 1972, p. 137.

32— Jack Kugelmass, "The Rites of the Tribe: American Jewish Tourism in Poland", *Museums and Communities: The Politics of Public Culture*, eds. Ivan Karp, Christine Mullen Kreamer y Steven D. Lavine, Washington y Londres, Smithsonian Institution Press, 1992, p. 411.

mecanografiados, hace que los textos parezcan de nuevo inconclusos, como si regresaran a los momentos históricos de su concepción. [Fig. 9]

Otros artistas gravitan hacia el material patentemente repugnante, creando obras de arte ofensivas que parecerían imposibles de sacralizar y que muy improbablemente alguien pudiera cooptar. Entre los artistas contemporáneos pertenecientes al *mainstream*, Mike Kelley echa por tierra las representaciones mediáticas sentimentales de los niños mediante la confrontación de lo que ve como sus verdaderos comportamientos y deseos, en *Representación nostálgica de la inocencia de la infancia*, un performance de 1990 en el que adultos parecieran defecar y masturbarse en animales de peluche. Damien Hirst cae aún más bajo en la abyección con su *Esperando la inspiración, rojo* (1994), una cabeza de vaca putrefacta, infestada de gusanos, dentro de una vitrina de plexiglás. En la obra de Hirst, la "vaca sagrada" de la vitrina desinfectada del supermercado, con su negación de la muerte, se sustituye por la materialidad de la descomposición, estremeciendo al espectador hacia la conciencia básica. La inmundicia corporal y la decadencia son abyectas, escribe Julia Kristeva, porque esos estados perturban las barreras de un ser, destruyendo la integridad de un cuerpo así como su distinción del entorno circundante. Además de su repulsión física, lo que hace que el Holocausto sea abyecto, sugiere, es precisamente que rompió la integridad de "los límites, las posiciones, las reglas", sacrificando "al asesino que afirma ser un salvador" y revelando la "fragilidad de la ley"[33]

Durante los años noventa, algunos artistas que abordaron el tema del Holocausto comenzaron a desacralizar agresivamente el significante del Holocausto, ya sea éste indicial o no. Entre estos artistas, varios desviaron la atención primaria lejos de la historia del Holocausto y se centraron en cambio en la crítica de los valores culturales actuales. *Self-Portrait at Buchenwald: It's the Real Thing* [*Lo auténtico. Autorretrato en Buchenwald*] (1993) de Alan Schechner no es para nada lo auténtico, sino más bien una

—

33— Julia Kristeva, *Powers of Horror: An Essay on Abjection*, trad. Leon S. Roudiez, Nueva York, Columbia University Press, 1982, p. 4 [*Poderes de la perversión: ensayo sobre Louis-Ferdinand Céline*, México, Siglo XXI, 1988, p. 11].

imagen fabricada, una foto fija digital que crea a la perfección una ficción visual que recuerda los fotomontajes de John Heartfield. En una de las fotos canónicas de Margaret Bourke-White de los hombres recién liberados, dentro de una barraca del campo de concentración de Buchenwald, el artista, nacido en 1962, superpuso una imagen en blanco y negro de sí mismo vistiendo el uniforme a rayas del campo con una lata de Diet Coke, el único elemento que aparece en color. Un "icono de los occidentales preocupados por su peso", al lado de los supervivientes demacrados, el refresco perturbó en particular a una crítica, quien llegó tan lejos como para condenar lo que vio como "antisemitismo latente" de este artista de doble nacionalidad israelí-inglesa.[34] Schechner defiende su pieza como un esfuerzo para llamar la atención hacia la manipulación de la memoria del Holocausto por lo que llama "objetivos ideológicos y políticos" de Israel con respecto a los palestinos.[35]

***

Las imágenes del Holocausto, continúa, están impregnadas de una especie de falsa religiosidad; se convierten en sagradas... Al colocar a mi ser bien alimentado con una Diet Coke entre los supervivientes demacrados de Buchenwald no sólo estaba atacando a la sociedad israelí con su

—

34— Valerie Reardon, "A Reply: Whose Image is it Anyway?", *Art Monthly*, (abril de 1996), p. 45. También disponible en línea: Alan Schechner, "How Many of My People Does It Take to Screw In a Lightbulb? On the Ownership of Experience, or, Who Can Say What to Whom, When", *Work By Alan Schechner*, vers. 22 de julio de 2003, Alan Schechner, 20 de marzo de 2004: <http://dottycommies.com/art_paper.html>

35— En respuesta al ataque de Reardon, Schechner explica, "A lo largo de mi estancia en Israel me hice muy consciente de cómo se utilizó el Holocausto para justificar algunos de los aspectos más desagradables de la política israelí. Me dijeron más de una vez cómo: 'Lo que les hagamos [a los palestinos] nunca será tan malo como lo que [los alemanes] nos hicieron'. La primera parada de todos los diplomáticos extranjeros a su llegada a Israel es el Yad Vashem; antes de la diplomacia, antes de las cenas de estado y de las visitas, estas imágenes se utilizan para servir agendas políticas estrechas." Alan Schechner, citado en "How Many of My People Does It Take to Screw In a Lightbulb? On the Ownership of Experience, or, Who Can Say What to Whom, When", *Art Papers* (marzo-abril de 1997), p. 34; y <http://dottycommies.com/art_paper.html>

fascinación fetichista por todas las modas estadounidenses, sino también, y lo que es más importante, diciendo que nosotros [el pueblo judío] necesitamos ponernos de nuevo en la piel de los supervivientes.[36]

***

La experiencia de ver la conocida foto de Bourke-White en la forma modificada de Schechner, escribe Joanna Lindenbaum, trae una sensación de terror a los espectadores porque se les pide que imaginen al artista —y a sí mismos— entre las víctimas. Entonces, "el terror se transforma en vergüenza" cuando los espectadores reconocen su propia "desensibilización a la sobreexposición de imágenes del Holocausto" como la de Bourke-White.[37] El efecto de esta sobreexposición se aproxima a la experiencia de la repetición discutida por Hal Foster en sus observaciones a los *Desastres* de Andy Warhol. Sin embargo, Foster también señala que las variaciones añadidas por Warhol a cada una de las imágenes repetidas en serigrafía llevan al espectador a estudiar cada reproducción de la foto como si fuera única, superando de esta manera el efecto adormecedor de la repetición. Del mismo modo, la estrategia de Schechner de modificar un índice cuya repetición en la sociedad lo ha vuelto banal pretende provocar en el espectador una visión de su obra con otros ojos, en consecuencia, restaurar hasta cierto punto su horror inicial.

Yo sugeriría que la pieza de Schechner es abyecta, también, por romper la barrera temporal entre la época del Holocausto y la nuestra, confundiendo conceptualmente quién pertenece dónde. En vez de permanecer a salvo donde pertenece, el Holocausto irrumpe en el presente y, al mismo tiempo, el autorretrato de Schechner se transporta al pasado. De esta manera, tanto el realismo traumático como la abyección se combinan para confrontar al espectador con un

—

36— Schechner; <http://dottycommies.com/art_paper.html>

37— Joanna Lindenbaum, "Alan Schechner", en *Mirroring Evil: Nazi Imagery/ Recent Art* ed. Norman L. Kleeblatt, New Brunswick, Rutgers University Press; Nueva York, The Jewish Museum, 2001, p. 115.

inesperado retorno de lo real del Holocausto bajo la apariencia de los supervivientes del Holocausto, "No son imágenes de los muertos y desaparecidos", Schechner insiste, "sino de personas, algunas de las cuales todavía están vivas y de ellas aún podemos y tenemos que aprender" con el fin de re-inscribir los significantes del Holocausto en su contexto original.[38]

Elke Krystufek, una artista austriaca nacida en 1970, aborda la cultura nazi y su glorificación en los medios de entretenimiento como una forma de explorar las cuestiones de género de una manera indiscutiblemente abyecta. Una serie de collages fotográficos de 1998 llamada Economical Love [*Amor económico*] incluye una foto recortada y pegada de su propio cuerpo desnudo, con los muslos abiertos, junto con representaciones pintadas del mismo tema manchadas con gotas de pintura. Junto a ellas hay fotos de actores masculinos en uniforme nazi, y fragmentos de textos recortados de diversas fuentes, entre ellas la siguiente cita: "No puedes escandalizarnos, Damien. Y es que no has basado toda una exposición en imágenes de los nazis."[39] La línea se refiere a Damien Hirst, cuya propia abyección aparentemente Krystufek aspira a superar.

Al utilizar sólo medios e imágenes actuales, Krystufek explora las relaciones entre hombres y mujeres y, en última instancia, entre nazis y judíos, como se manifiestan en el poder controlador de la mirada masculina. Con los temas de la dominación y la sumisión sexual, revela lo que Norman Kleeblatt llama "la auto-victimización... en sí misma y en otras mujeres de su generación", y al mismo tiempo utiliza su desnudez para reflejar las fantasías masculinas de regreso hacia los "criminales en potencia —los hombres que miran a las mujeres o fantasean acerca de ellas con violencia".[40] En cuanto a los papeles de género en la histo-

—

38— Schechner, *op. cit.*.

39— Krystufek recortó esta cita de una reseña británica de la instalación de Piotr Uklaski de 1998 *Los nazis*. La pieza se compone de 166 fotos de las estrellas de Hollywood en uniforme nazi. A cinco de ellos Krystufek los incorpora en tres obras de la serie *Amor económico*: *Amor económico (Control de coño)*, *Amor económico (Peinado de Hitler)* y *Amor económico (Expresionismo abstracto)*.

40— Norman L. Kleeblatt, "Elke Krystufek", en *Mirroring Evil: Nazi Imagery/ Recent Art*, ed. Norman L. Kleeblatt, New Brunswick, Rutgers University Press; Nueva York, The Jewish Museum, 2001, p. 112. Kleeblatt ve la exploración de

ria del arte, Krystufek condena lo estereotípico masculino con un fragmento de texto pegado en otra obra de la serie, *Amor económico (Expresionismo abstracto)*: “Creer en el poder trascendental de la imagen y en su belleza es como querer ser un expresionista abstracto o un vaquero.”

Krystufek desestabiliza la autoridad de la mirada masculina al complicar las posiciones de sujeto y objeto. No sólo su cuerpo femenino, sino también las estrellas de cine están en cierto sentido feminizadas, puesta en escena, objetificadas por su apego a los tropos o de la sexualidad o del glamour, que la pornografía y el entretenimiento popular perpetúan en la sociedad. Al mismo tiempo, Krystufek, como la mayoría de los rostros masculinos, también nos enfrenta con su propia atención penetrante, dramatizada por la cámara con la que apunta al espectador.[41] Krystufek, al parecer, se identifica con los opresores nazis —una implicación de su figurado alarde de superar a Hirst en su propio juego. Él no puede escandalizar*nos*, leemos en la cita que se lee a través de su torso, lo que implica una comunidad con los hombres retratados. Si, efectivamente, ella misma ha “basado toda una exposición en imágenes de los nazis”, como la cita sugiere, entonces la artista, tal como se representa en las obras, pareciera contarse a sí misma entre ellos.[42] Al actuar el papel de un nazi, como hizo Kiefer en sus *Ocupaciones*, puede decirse que Krystufek explora la atracción del poder nazi, junto con su perpetuación en los medios de entretenimiento, con el fin de comprender mejor su atractivo y su amenaza contemporáneos.

Tal vez no es de extrañar que esta amplia transformación en la conciencia artística del Holocausto comenzó

—

la artista en relación con las *Male Fantasies* de Klaus Theweleit, un importante estudio del tema en la historia de Alemania.

41— Las figuras femeninas en cuclillas de Krystufek asumen un aire similar a una gorgona, que no expresa sumisión, sino la potencia sexual arquetípica. Carol Duncan considera el tema en relación con obras de Picasso y Willem de Kooning, en “The MoMA’s Hot Mamas”, *Art Journal* 14.2 (1989), pp. 171-178.

42— En *Amor económico (Expresionismo abstracto)*, una representación de Krystufek que no sólo comparte la mirada de dominación de los nazis, sino también la carne. Superpuesta sobre la pierna izquierda doblada de la artista, los hombros de un actor (Hardy Krüger) en uniforme nazi sustituyen visualmente las porciones cubiertas de su muslo y pantorrilla, convirtiendo su cabeza en algo así como una erupción de la rodilla.

precisamente cuando la cultura corporativa descubrió el potencial éxito de taquilla de la memoria del Holocausto. *La lista de Schindler*, de Steven Spielberg, apareció en 1993, el llamado "año del Holocausto" por ser el de la preponderancia de la memoria del Holocausto en la conciencia pública, particularmente en los Estados Unidos.

El valor de *La lista de Schindler* como herramienta educativa ha sido debatido por la academia, que señala que la película está plagada de distorsiones de los hechos históricos.[43] Desde su creación, han proliferado malas representaciones cinematográficas, entre las que destaca como ejemplo *La vida es bella* (1998) de Roberto Benigni, pues mejora el horror de la verdad histórica al representar un campo de concentración como un ambiente limpio donde un niño puede por meses. Por el contrario, las obras de arte de la abyección que comenzaron a aparecer durante la década de los noventa no niegan la brutalidad del Holocausto. Si bien tales obras de arte son ofensivas para muchos, no distorsionan el registro histórico.[44] Ya que la historia del Holocausto no es, de hecho, su tema, sino que se centran más bien en la forma de su representación actual. Al exagerar tales representaciones en la política, el entretenimiento popular, los papeles de género, etc., de hoy día, hasta el punto en que en realidad pueden ofender a los espectadores, las obras de arte llaman la atención hacia aquello de lo que esas representaciones carecen: una conexión con el referente del mundo real, con la propia historia del Holocausto.[45]

—

43— Véase Yosefa Loshitzky, ed., *Spielberg's Holocaust: Critical Perspectives of Schindler's List,* Bloomington e Indianápolis: Indiana University Press, 1997.

44— Entre los comentaristas sobre la notable exposición de 2002 "Mirroring Evil: Nazi Imagery/Recent Art" ("Reflejo del mal: Imágenes nazi / arte reciente") en el Museo Judío de Nueva York, que incluía tanto a Schechner como a Krystufek, solamente Walter Reich, ex director del Museo Memorial del Holocausto de Estados Unidos, señala este hecho. Reich dirige su oprobio a los gobiernos y los grupos de interés que distorsionan la memoria del Holocausto para promover sus propias agendas, y a los medios de comunicación como el cine popular que presentan falsas interpretaciones de la historia del Holocausto. Walter Reich, "Appropriating the Holocaust", en *New York Times*, 15 de marzo de 2002, ed. vespertina, p. A23.

45— En su reseña de "Mirroring Evil", el crítico Michael Kimmelman da en el clavo en lo que creo que es el punto esencial, a pesar de que el espíritu de sus palabras era de broma: "En un mundo inundado por imágenes comerciales que nos anestesian y sustituyen la verdad con la ficción, el arte que causa dolor nos

Posdata: la serie *Azul de Prusia* de Yishai Jusidman en el Museo Universitario Arte Contemporáneo

Escribí "De lo sublime a lo abyecto: seis décadas de arte" en 2005. Desde entonces, muchos artistas relacionados con el Holocausto se han desplazado hacia otros temas o han regresado a los temas y asuntos de su obra anterior. Mientras que el Holocausto sigue presente en la cultura popular, la obsesión ha pasado. En esta relativa calma, Yishai Jusidman ha indagado en la historia y la memoria del Holocausto para crear lo que veo como una valoración de la eficacia de ese arte anterior relacionado con el Holocausto. Su serie *Azul de Prusia* (2010–2015) explora y pone a prueba lo sublime, lo documental, lo abyecto y otras estrategias formales. Como lo expresa el artista: "Mis pinturas no abordan el Holocausto, sino más bien la posibilidad de su representación."[46]

Como introducción a la serie *Azul de Prusia*, la pintura *Haus der Kunst* [*Casa del arte*] (2012) retrata a la manera nazi la sala de exposiciones de Múnich diseñada por los nazis, con escala monumental, simetría y una poderosa perspectiva lineal. La pintura, basada en una foto que el propio Jusidman tomó, recuerda los coqueteos de Anselm Kiefer con el fascismo en obras como *Interior* (1981), una representación de la Cancillería del Nuevo Reich de Hitler, y *Sulamita* (1983), una representación de un monumento de guerra nazi, excepto que la decisión de Jusidman de representar una galería de arte vacía establece su enfoque en el arte mismo.

Junto con esta obra, como parte del "Prólogo" de Jusidman, hay una recreación pictórica del infame legado del nazismo. *Birkenau* (2012) reproduce una rarísima fotografía histórica hecha fuera de una cámara de gas en funcionamiento. La fuente fotográfica elegida por Jusidman no representa atrocidades evidentes, sólo extrañas distorsiones a través de la lente de la cámara; árboles borrosos

—

hace volver la atención a lo real." Michael Kimmelman, "Evil, the Nazis and Shock Value", reseña de "Mirroring Evil: Nazi Imagery/Recent Art", The Jewish Museum, Nueva York, *New York Times*, 15 de marzo de 2002, ed. vespertina, p. E33.

46— Alexander Neta, "Painting the Nazi Gas Chambers With Defiant Realism", *Haaretz* (22 de enero de 2013); consultado en línea el 20 de marzo de 2016.

que se doblan y atenúan, perdiendo su rigidez en un despliegue de lo *informe* (en francés, "carente de forma"). Lo *informe* es un concepto que trata de la transgresión de los límites fijos y fue teorizado por primera vez por Georges Bataille en 1929 junto con ideas sobre la abyección. Inspiró a Salvador Dalí para concebir imágenes de huesos de goma y relojes derretidos. Mientras que algunos artistas contemporáneos durante la reciente moda sobre el Holocausto emplearon materiales más abyectos para tratar de llevar la atención de nuevo a su referente histórico, el involucramiento de Jusidman con estas ideas tiene un propósito diferente. Sugiere que las violaciones dentro de la cámara de gas invisible han desestabilizado literalmente el mundo más allá de sus paredes.

A pesar de que estas dos primeras obras del "Prólogo" están, de hecho, basadas en fotografías, no es sino hasta que dirigimos la atención a las pinturas de tamaño más pequeño de Jusidman en la segunda y tercera secciones de su serie *Azul de Prusia*, "Cámaras de gas" y "Paisajes", que la noción de lo documental ocupa un lugar central. Fotos de la posguerra y contemporáneas proporcionan las fuentes para los sitios inhóspitos, despoblados, de las atrocidades que Jusidman cataloga en pintura acrílica. Estas escenas desoladas de las secuelas de la guerra proporcionan evidencia del genocidio, pero se niegan a ofrecer su comprensión. En un sentido, son monumentos: las representaciones de Jusidman en azul de Prusia, un color producido por la misma reacción química que se produjo entre el gas venenoso Zyklon B y algunas paredes de la cámara de gas, y su uso de tonos de piel en estas obras para representar a los asesinados, recuerdan la utilización simbólicamente cargada que Arie A. Galles dio al carbón vegetal, que él llama ceniza, en sus reproducciones de fotos de los campos. Las pinturas de Jusidman conservan las diferentes dimensiones y perspectivas de sus fotografías de la fuente original, e incluso poseen diferentes tonalidades de azul de Prusia, lo que hace de ellas un grupo heterogéneo. Esta sensibilidad contrasta con el tipo de totalización estética moderna defendida por los nazis que habría impuesto una uniformidad estandarizada en ellas.

Jusidman presenta grandes pinturas monocromáticas en su cuarta sección, "Memorial". Mostradas después de las representaciones de las cámaras de gas y de los paisajes de la atrocidad, estas obras abstractas manifiestan el poder duradero del expresionismo abstracto para reflexionar sobre el Holocausto. Como los grandes lienzos de Mark Rothko en la Capilla Rothko en Houston, las pinturas revelan sutiles variaciones en la densidad de la superficie para las que toma tiempo darse cuenta, y una modulación del color en el borde inferior que sugiere un paisaje bajo una noche impenetrable o un cielo oscurecido por el humo. Entre estas obras, la llamada simplemente *Azul de Prusia* (2014–2015) presenta una superficie como de espejo que insinúa la larga reflexión del espectador en su vasto espacio pictórico.

Jusidman termina su serie con "Epílogo: Manchas", que incluye los trapos que utilizó para limpiar, y fotos de las paredes que se ensuciaron mientras pintó sus imágenes conmemorativas en en los lienzos colgados de ellas. El arte sigue siendo un tema primordial en este caso, sus prácticas y aspectos prácticos. Pero junto con las representaciones de los sitios de la atrocidad, estas obras, al igual que los cuadros conmemorativos, evocan la memoria del Holocausto. Ensuciados con manchas de forma indeterminada, los trapos personifican la abyección, y sugieren no sólo el residuo del gas venenoso, sino también la suciedad de los campos y el humo y la ceniza en que se convirtieron tantos seres humanos. Las fotos de las paredes manchadas ofrecen una conclusión conmovedora. Muestran marcos pintados vacíos, huecos que nada denotan pero que sugieren tanto: la ausencia de las víctimas asesinadas por el nazismo; la multitud de testimonios nunca dichos; el conocimiento imposible de la depravación humana; y, quizá con mayor fuerza en este contexto, la incapacidad última de cualquier representación artística para dar definición —o cierre, si se quiere— al Holocausto.

Fig. 1: **Rico Lebrun**, *Study for Dachau Chamber* [*Estudio para cámara de Dachau*], 1958. Óleo sobre tela—Oil on canvas, 79 × 85 in. The Jewish Museum, N.Y.; Cortesía de—Courtesy of Koplin Del Rio Gallery, Los Angeles, y el legado de—and the estate of Rico Lebrun. D.R. © Rico Lebrun/ BILDKUNST/SOMAAP/México/2016. Foto—Photo: Jewish Museum/Art Resource, NY/ADGAP, Paris

Fig. 3: **Anselm Kiefer**, *Occupations* [*Ocupaciones*], 1969. Publicado en—Published in *Interfunktionen* (1975) Cologne, photo 9. Cortesía de—Courtesy of Gagosian Gallery, New York. D.R. © Anselm Kiefer/BILDKUNST/SOMAAP/México/2016

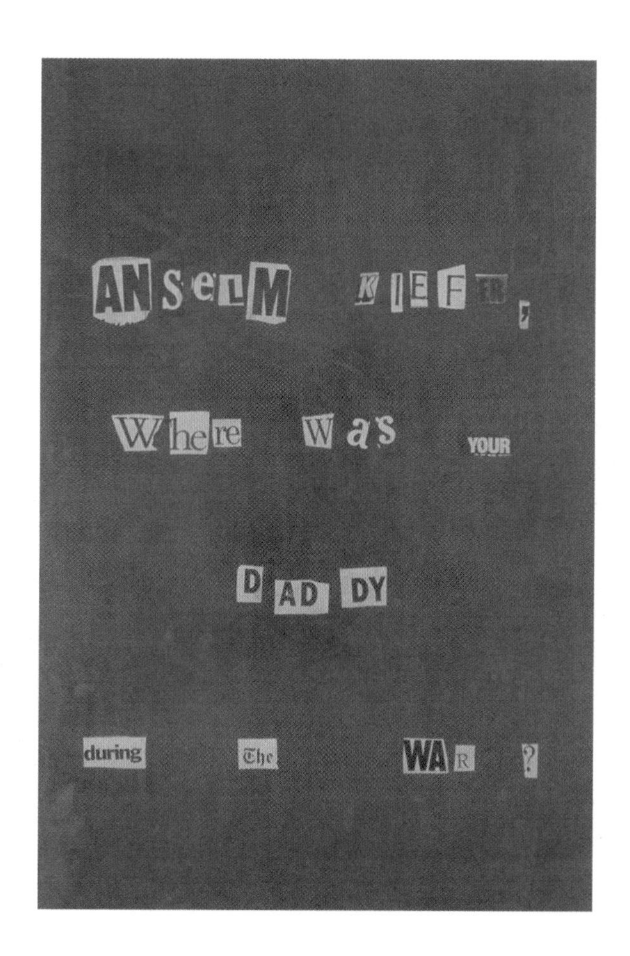

Fig 5: **Susan Silas**, *ohne titel* [*Sin título—Untitled*], 1989. Recortes de periódico sobre plomo en madera, acero y vidrio—Newsprint on lead-on wood, steel, and glass, 40 × 30 in. Reproducido con permiso del artista—Reproduced with permission of the artist

Fig. 4: **Hans Haacke**, *Cowboy with Cigarette* [*Vaquero con cigarro*], 1990. Collage, carbón, tinta y sobre papel—Collage, charcoal and ink on paper, 37 × 31 × 2.25 in. (con marco—including frame). Reproducido con permiso del artista—Reproduced with permission of the artist. Foto—Photo: Hans Haacke. © Hans Haacke/BILDKUNST/SOMAAP/México/2016

Fig. 9: **Ruth Liberman**, *January 20, 1942 [20 de enero, 1942]*, 1999. Película de carbón para máquina de escribir, y lápiz sobre vidalón, tela y uñas—Typewriter film carbon and pencil on vidalon, cloth, nails. Dimensiones al instalar—dimensions when installed: 90 × 137 in. Cortesía de la artista—Courtesy of the artist

Fig 7: **Susan Erony**, *The Jews of Lodz and Krakow #13* [*Los judíos de Lodz y Cracovia #13*], 1991. Fotografías y técnica mixta sobre tela—Photos, mixed media on canvas, 10 × 8 in.
Reproducido con autorización del artista—Reproduced with permission of the artist

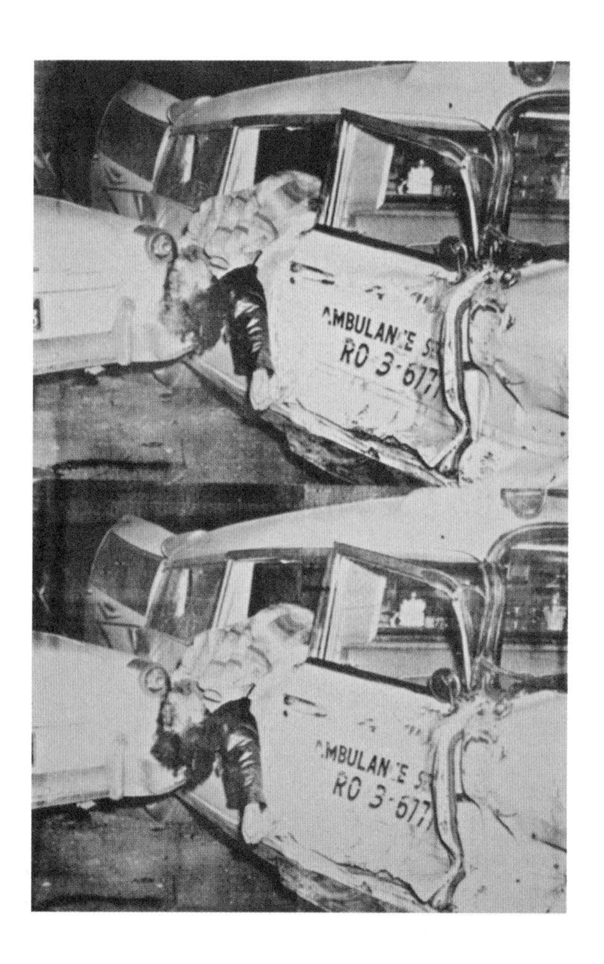

Fig. 8: **Andy Warhol,** *Ambulance Disaster*, 1963; Serigrafía con tinta acrílica sobre tela—silkscreen ink/acrylic on canvas, 10 ft. 4 × 6 ft. 8 in. Stiftung Sammlung Marx, Hamburger Banhof-Museum fur Gegenwart, Berlin. Photo: author. © Andy Warhol/The Andy Warhol Foundation for the Visual Arts/Artists Rights Society (ARS)/SOMAAP/México/2016

From the Sublime to the Abject: Six Decades of Art*

ANDREW WEINSTEIN

* Originally published in Stephen C. Feinstein, ed. *Absence/Presence: Critical Essays on the Artistic Memory of the Holocaust*, Syracuse, Syracuse UP, 2005, pp. 70-92.

Fig. 2: **Pablo Picasso,** *Guernica*, 1937; óleo sobre tela—oil on canvas, 138 × 25 ft. 8 in. El Museo Nacional. Centro de Arte Reina Sofia, Madrid; © Pablo Picasso/Estate of Pablo Picasso/Artist Rights Management (ARS), New York/SOMAAP/México/2016. Foto—Photo: John Bigelow, Taylor/Art Resource, N.Y.

That artistic representations of the Holocaust are most powerful when they incorporate photographs, documents, or other found materials is a truism today. But this idea was alien immediately after World War II. At that time, mainstream artists struggled to represent mass death and destruction, together with the consequent view of the human experience, through universalizing means of their own invention. The Abstract Expressionist canvases of such artists as Mark Rothko and Barnett Newman—vast fields of color like empty landscapes for introspection and meditation, in which several scholars have recently detected a reaction specifically to the Holocaust—[1]appeared in the late 1940s and '50s enveloped by a rhetoric of the existential sublime, where blankness screens a wonder or terror too powerful to directly confront. During the same period, a related artistic development occurred in the form of expressionistic "new images of man." These were distorted and often grotesque, and, according to the curator of an important 1959 exhibition at the Museum of Modern Art, they responded to the horrors of World War II while anticipating worse ones to come.[2] But they incorporated no traces of the Holocaust and only very rarely made specific reference to it. Lacking tattooed numbers, striped uniforms, or yellow stars, Alberto Giacometti's skeletal, attenuated figures dissolving into the enormity of space evinced the existential condition, notwithstanding the fact that Jean-Paul Sartre himself described them as the "fleshless martyrs of Buchenwald."[3] Of those few artists who depicted specifically Nazi atrocity, Rico Lebrun was the most prominent, with *Buchenwald Pit*,

—

1— Ziva Amishai-Maisels, *Depiction and Interpretation: The Influence of the Holocaust on the Visual Arts*, New York, Pergamon Press, 1993, pp. 268, 303–304. Matthew Baigell, *Jewish-American Artists and the Holocaust*, New Brunswick, Rutgers UP, 1997, pp. 29-30. Steven Zucker treats the issue most subtly in "Confrontations with Radical Evil: The Ambiguity of Myth and the Inadequacy of Representation" in *Art History, num.* 24, 2001, pp. 379-400.

2— Peter Selz, *New Images of Man*, New York, The Museum of Modern Art, 1959, p. 12.

3— Jean-Paul Sartre, "The Search for the Absolute" in *Art in Theory, 1900-2000*, eds. Charles Harrison and Paul Wood, Oxford, Blackwell, 2003, p. 616. Sartre wrote his comments for the catalogue of the exhibition *Alberto Giacometti. Sculptures, Paintings, Drawings* at the Pierre Matisse Gallery, New York, January-February 1948.

(1955), *Study for Dachau Chamber*, (1958) and his other Picasso-inspired canvases.

Within this context it's easy to appreciate why, back in 1975, Lawrence Langer would reject the possibility that "mere factual truths" could ever serve as a basis of Holocaust representation in art.[4] Instead, Langer advocated a kind of expressionism, exemplified for him by *Guernica*, Picasso's great 1937 statement of protest against fascist atrocities in Spain. [Fig. 2] During the Holocaust, argued Langer, age-old assumptions about human behavior and social interaction had been suspended, supplanted by an alternate reality previously only imagined in ghoulish fantasies. So alien was this heretofore impossible reality (*l'univers concentrationnaire*, the concentrationary universe, a term from survivor and novelist David Rousset) that a viewer had to depend on an intermediary figure, an artistic visionary, to clarify the shadowy features of its nightmare landscape. The role of the artist seemed clear.

Given all this, it might be surprising that novelist Leslie Epstein so resolutely struck down Langer's perfectly reasonable argument in a review essay the following year. Rejecting the premise of Langer's argument, Epstein insisted that the universe in which the Holocaust had occurred shared the same physical and psychological laws as our own and that to pretend otherwise invariably distanced the event from present-day concerns to the point of irrelevance, with the consequence that its lessons might go unheeded.[5] Epstein recognized the power of an artistic strategy of representation based on facts. Thousands of miles away, at just about that time (1974), French journalist Claude Lanzmann began filming *Shoah*, an epic of facts and traces par excellence. In 1980, Art Spiegelman started serially publishing *Maus*, a non-fiction comic book that

—

4— Lawrence L. Langer, *The Holocaust and the Literary Imagination*, New Haven, Yale UP, 1975, p. 8. Langer borrows the quoted phrase from Richard Gilman, "Nat Turner Revisited" in *New Republic*, April 27, 1968, p. 24.

5— Epstein asks, "does 'art such as this' take us closer to what happened to the Jews, or is it, as I believe, a kind of *grand guignol*, a substitute horror show, meant to divert us from what the actual atrocity—most unbearable perhaps in its monotony, its calmness, the way in which it fit unobtrusively into our world—was like?" Leslie Epstein, "The Reality of Evil" in *Partisan Review*, num. 43, 1976, p. 639.

tells the Holocaust experience of the artist's father, based on tape-recorded interviews that are themselves depicted in the text. The floodgates had been thrown open to a new fact-based representational approach.

What strikes me as curious about this shift is that it generally parallels a reorientation in contemporary art some twenty years earlier, one that resoundingly challenged Abstract Expressionism and its contemporary trends for reasons which ostensibly have nothing to do with the Holocaust. What are we to make of this parallel development? Did artists of Holocaust subject matter simply follow the movements of the larger art world? Were, perhaps, such artists responding to still other cultural conditions that were (and are) active outside of the art world, to which most contemporary artists similarly reacted? Both appear to be the case.

***

Like the history of Holocaust representation, the history of contemporary art impresses the observer with its move toward ideals that had been entirely unfamiliar in the immediate postwar years: emotional detachment and facticity. No one can deny that Abstract Expressionism exerted enormous influence on artists who emerged between the mid-1950s and early 1960s, but these artists reacted to the Abstract Expressionist patriarchs largely by parodying them. Out, above all, was the Abstract Expressionist celebration of the self, together with what the younger generation regarded as the bloated self-importance of the spiritual and the sublime.

What some critics called Neo-Dada appeared, exemplified by Robert Rauschenberg and Jasper Johns. Those two drew inspiration from Marcel Duchamp for his found, or "readymade," artworks like the *Bottle Rack* (1914), as well as from John Cage, whose Zen openness to the world motivated such compositions as *4' 33"* (1952), a timed silence that encourages listeners to focus on ambient sounds. Rauschenberg and Johns appropriated anything from bed quilts to beer cans in their art while extinguishing the emotion associated with Abstract Expressionism. Their drips and brushwork, inspired by Jackson Pollock and Willem de

Kooning, are coolly ironic, an attitude one sees slightly later in the apparently non-judgmental appropriations from mass culture of Andy Warhol's Pop Art and related movements.

Alongside Neo-Dada, a formalist school developed which saw in Abstract Expressionism what the critic Clement Greenberg and his cronies had recognized since its inception: a focus on materiality. For Greenberg, there was no sublime, no self in the big gestural and color-field canvases of Abstract Expressionism. There was only paint, applied more flatly than anyone had ever done before. The preeminent art critic of his time, Greenberg propounded a theory of modernism as an ineluctable advance from the middle of the nineteenth century, when Courbet and Manet eschewed narrative elements and embraced the flatness of the picture plane, toward the postwar years with the distillation of painting to its essence as pure paint.[6] Helen Frankenthaler, Morris Louis, and others loyally followed Greenberg's dictates by "advancing" beyond Jackson Pollock with their own unprimed canvases even flatter than his drips because in theirs the paint merely stained the surface, preserving the overall weave. After that, during the 1960s, a generation of Minimalist sculptors applied Greenberg's idea of formal purity to their own medium and took it to its logical conclusion (despite Greenberg's disapproval). They eliminated the artist's touch in favor of pure materiality; Richard Serra's factory-made sheets of lead and blocks of steel were all so palpably heavy, and Carl Andre's metal tiles were as flat in meaning as the floors on which they lay.

By the mid-1970s, the modernist tradition finally succumbed to a new art-world hegemony of the textual turn.

—

6— Greenberg's apolitical formalism had its origins in a pre-war Marxist position. At that time, Greenberg argued that artists, determined to preserve their cultural autonomy, retreated farther and farther into the rarefied haven of formalism in an attempt to escape the relentless co-optations of popular culture. He presents this argument in his 1939 essay, "Avant-Garde and Kitsch" in *Art and Culture: Critical Essays*, Boston, Beacon Press, 1961, pp. 3-21. Beginning in 1948, against the backdrop of the Cold War, Greenberg abandoned this social history of art for a theory of self-critical painting, most clearly expressed in his 1960 essay "Modernist Painting" in *Art in Theory, 1900-2000*, pp. 773-79. Margaret Olin puts Greenberg's formalism into a fascinating socio-historical context in "C[lement] Hardesh [Greenberg] and Company: Formal Criticism and Jewish Identity" in *Too Jewish?: Challenging Traditional Identities* ed. Norman L. Kleeblatt., New York, The Jewish Museum; New Brunswick, Rutgers UP, 1996, pp. 39-59.

This ascendant attitude privileged extra-aesthetic, extra-material concerns such as language, typical of Conceptual Art. And it advanced a notion that history was a reservoir of images and styles available for contemporary manipulation, as witnessed by such revivalist movements as Neo-Expressionism and (a decade later) Neo-Geo. Likewise, a disregard of traditional subject and object positions ("viewer," "artist" and "artwork") led to art across an expanded cultural field. Sometimes this expansion involved physical removal from the gallery, as with Earth Art and much Body and Performance Art. Other times it involved ideological removal by, for example, blurring the distinction between so-called low and high culture during the 1980s, as in the kitsch ceramic puppies of Jeff Koons and the comix of Art Spiegelman.

Hal Foster characterizes this textual turn in terms of two ideological positions, both of which had emerged by the late 1970s and continue still. One parallels a larger neo-conservatism that advanced an uncritical return of cultural memory.[7] Its political promoters (Ronald Reagan, Margaret Thatcher, Helmut Kohl) are easier to name than its representatives in the arts. Some critics suggest Koons as an example of conservatism for his apparently cynical embrace of traditional business practices, even mass-producing cheap merchandise and wildly overcharging for it. Others mention Eric Fischl and David Salle ("analytical pubists", one critic calls them[8]) for their sexualized depictions of women from traditionally male points of view, depictions which look like a bad-boy backlash against feminism.

This historical framework comfortably accommodates Holocaust representation; one is tempted to position Anselm Kiefer among such neoconservatives for the manner in which he resuscitates historical memory. At first glance, his *Occupations* (1969)—a collection of photographs of Kiefer in performance, standing alone with a Hitler salute in empty

—

7— Hal Foster, *The Return of the Real: The Avant-Garde at the End of the Century*, Cambridge, MIT Press, 1996, p. 71. Chapters 3 and 5 of this brilliant book on contemporary art provide much of the framework for my own approach to Holocaust representation since the mid-1970s.

8— Robert Pincus-Witten, "Entries: Analytical Pubism" in *Postminimalism into Maximalism: American Art, 1966–1986*, Ann Arbor, UMI Research Press, 1987, pp. 313-20.

public spaces in France, Switzerland, and Italy [Fig. 3]—may seem progressive because it mocks the Nazis and raises the specter of a history that an entire generation of Germans had preferred to ignore. But as Andreas Huyssen has observed, by treating that ferocious past with parodic humor Kiefer's piece trivializes Nazism in ways that could ultimately encourage ignoring its crimes.[9] Later, in a huge bombastic paintings called *Shulamite* (1983) what seems to be the depiction of a funerary monument to the Jewish dead is, in fact, a painted adaptation of a vintage propaganda photograph of Wilhelm Kreis' *Funeral Hall for the Great German Soldiers* (1939). To those who recognize this problematic allusion, Kiefer reveals his conflicted identity with both victim and perpetrator—he promotes a Nazi aesthetic not only by creating what looks like a stage set for a grand opera the way the Nazis themselves had orchestrated their party meetings, etc., but also by employing the powerful symmetry and perspective of Kreis's chosen point of view. "I have to reenact what they did just a little bit in order to understand their madness," Kiefer has said, "That is why I make these false attempts to become a Fascist."[10] Yet by withholding the fact of the Nazi origin of his chosen scene, Kiefer obfuscates the stigma attached to this particular form of historical return, thereby allowing for a revisionist revitalization of that suspect aesthetic.

A second ideological manifestation of the textual turn, says Foster, was a chiefly leftist, poststructuralist critique which had roots in 1960s art. Institutional critique, for example, inspired a post-1968 generation of artists, including Hans Haacke, whose *MOMA-Poll* (1970) invited viewers in the Museum of Modern Art in New York to vote their opinion on the tacit support of the Vietnam War by New York State Governor Nelson Rockefeller, a trustee and former president and chairman of the board of the museum. Haacke's more recent *Cowboy with Cigarette* (1990) [Fig. 4] recreates a famous Picasso collage, *Hombre con sombrero* [*Man with a Hat*] (1912), from an exhibition sponsored by Philip

—

9— Andreas Huyssen, *Twilight Memories: Marking Time in a Culture of Amnesia*, New York, Routledge, 1995, p. 215.

10— Amishai-Maisels, op. cit., p. 363.

Morris—except that the newsprint and other paper components of Haacke's version present damning quotes about the tobacco company's strategy of co-opting culture for the sake of public relations even as it bankrolled Jesse Helms, the pro-tobacco senator who also happened to be the nemesis of federal funding for the arts. With a similar emphasis on social concern, a range of artists brought feminist, ethnic, and gay identity as well as AIDS awareness into the arts.

From the realm of Holocaust representation, Susan Silas fits into this progressive group with her *ohne titel* (1989) [Fig. 5] In the form of a ransom note, her newsprint collage reads "Anselm Kiefer, where was your daddy during the war?" Silas engages a troubling aspect of Kiefer's biography; namely, that he is not forthcoming about his own family history even as he manipulates the materials of Nazi and Holocaust history in ways that have made his art famous and immensely lucrative. Silas implies that a desire for fame and wealth may motivate Kiefer's project, not courage or a quest for truth. In calling attention to this problem, Silas's choice of newsprint evokes the very material of history (her collaged word "The" evidently hails from the masthead of the newspaper of record, *The New York Times*), just as her cutting and collaging manifests its disfigurement and re-presentation, distortions which Kiefer's own presentations manage to hide.

***

Although they appear to be directly opposed, the neoconservative and the poststructuralist impulses are both, according to Fredric Jameson, examples of "the cultural logic of late capitalism." Toward explaining their similarity, Jameson examines the evolutionary dynamic of capitalism in terms of the emergence and transformation of the sign.

In Jameson's account, industry and science had, by the mid-nineteenth century, exorcised magic and superstition and replaced them with a materialist point of view. This materialist attitude became reified into its own "reality" and led to the emergence of signs in language. Each comprised of a signifier (word) together with its signified (meaning upon which a community of speakers agree), signs functioned in a positivist way, understood as accurately describing referents in the real world. This world view inspired the Realism of Courbet and Manet and, arguably, the Impressionism of the painters who followed them.

As capitalism dominated ordinary life, the same process of reification that had eradicated magic then set about transforming the sign itself. Abstract phenomena that had scant connection to the real world assumed their own reality; a stock market fluctuation based on a rumor could cast thousands out of their jobs. In this way, the sign alone became a potent force, with little or no connection to a real-world referent. This was the moment of high modernism: a Cubist collage by Picasso of a man with a hat relates to a real man and hat only tenuously, since the depiction hardly looks like the reality. Through its rarified form, culture entered a period of relative autonomy, so that it represented or "redouble[d] the world without being altogether of it."[11]

In late capitalism today, reification shears the signifier from a stable signified. Without a relation to any referents whatsoever, the signifier *Star Wars*, stripped of its Hollywood signified, would reappear as the name for an outer space missile shield promoted by actor-cum-President Ronald Reagan against an enemy newly designated as the Evil Empire. Meanwhile, Andy Warhol's paintings of Marilyn Monroe present a basically empty signifier, created in the minds of Hollywood agents and producers, a signifier whose destabilized signified may be glamour or sex appeal or tabloid tragedy or 1950s nostalgia. Losing their meaning, signifiers ultimately connote only themselves and the historical periods that created them, so that "we are left with that pure and random play of signifiers that we call postmodernism."[12]

During the 1970s and '80s, most artists who were newly concerned with Holocaust representation rejected older aesthetic strategies which had either depicted Nazi crime (such as Langer's expressionism) or had denoted that horror by hiding it behind a screen (Abstract Expressionism). I believe that they did so because, in part, the different

—

11— Fredric Jameson, *Postmodernism, or, The Cultural Logic of Late Capitalism*, Durham, Duke UP, 1991, p. 96.

12— Ibid. p. 96.

styles had begun to signify such concepts as "Holocaust art," memorialization, and education rather than Holocaust history itself; paintings and sculptures that imaginatively portrayed chimneys, train tracks, or emaciated bodies like Rico Lebrun's may have resonated with viewers ten years after the war, when memory of the newsreels remained traumatizing and fresh,[13] but by the mid 1970s, they had begun to appear both stale and sanctimonious, while Abstract-Expressionist-style works seemed to say more about the aesthetic concerns of the late 1940s and '50s than about the atrocities of the war years. Altogether, art strategies and motifs that the general public might consider hackneyed or old-fashioned looked, to those schooled in semiotics, like the detritus of a modernist vision in a postmodern world, mere signifiers which had been shorn from their original signifieds, with the Holocaust referent lost in the shuffle. It appeared that signage had failed.

***

The destabilization of the sign as I have defined it engendered the conditions for the emergence of an art that was based no longer on an artist's vision or style but rather on artifacts and documents, material which seemed to reaffirm a connection to a real-world referent. Rosalind Krauss discusses this transformation in contemporary art of the 1970s as a jettisoning of convention in favor of the indexical sign, that type of sign which relates to its referent the way an effect relates to a cause, the action of a weather vane in the wind, for example. With its concern for the particular instead of the general, indexicality offers a means of representation, writes Krauss, in which "truth is understood as a matter of evidence, rather than a function of logic."[14] Like Lanzmann and Spiegelman, a host of contemporary artists

—

13— A related argument can be made that Newman's sublime worked most effectively in the immediate postwar years precisely because contemporary viewers could intuit the existential issues literally and figuratively behind the paintings.

14— Rosalind E. Krauss, "Notes on the Index: Part 2" in *The Originality of the Avant-Garde and Other Modernist Myths,* Cambridge, MIT Press, 1985, p. 218.

incorporated indices in their art, most often photographs.[15] In *Fourteen Stations* (1993–2002) [Fig. 6], Arie A. Galles painstakingly hand-drew reproductions of vintage aerial photos of Nazi death camps; in her series *The Jews of Lodz and Krakow* (1991), Susan Erony utilized her own recent photos of overgrown cemetery headstones [Fig. 7]

Sooner or later, nearly every discussion of Holocaust representation in art marshals the name of Theodor W. Adorno, and he belongs here too, for Adorno also exalted the particular. But he arrived at this position through his own analysis of capitalism and Enlightenment positivism in science and industry. A bulwark of that materialist tradition is identity thinking, an essentially reductive way of thinking in which a thinker presumes to understand the meaning, or value, of an object totally. In philosophical terms, the concept subsumes the object, leaving no remainder. In semiotic terms, the sign is assumed to have a literal, unproblematic relationship to its referent. In practice, identity thinking dehumanizes workers by equating them with their use value, nothing more. Likewise, it departicularizes objects by judging them only with regard to monetary or exchange value. Factory workers become interchangeable, and so do factory-made objects. In the mind of the identity thinker, nothing magical or mysterious remains with the object, whether human or inanimate. With time, this way of thinking infiltrated all aspects of society and, Adorno contends, led to the Nazis' racial identification of people as either valuable or valueless, an identification that culminated in genocide. This consideration illuminates Adorno's famous 1949 quote, "to write poetry after Auschwitz is barbaric," for poetry about the Holocaust would ostensibly speak for the whole of that horrible history in a few terse lines, thereby reductively identifying it. It is true that Adorno later qualified his statement about poetry by admitting that "perennial suffering has as much right to expression as a tortured man has to scream."[16] But his admonition is clear: art about the Holo-

—

15— Spiegelman's own use of three vintage family photographs in *Maus* is discussed by Marianne Hirsch in *Family Frames: Photography, Narrative, and Postmemory*, Cambridge and London, Harvard UP, 1997.

16— Theodor W. Adorno, *Negative Dialectics*, trans. E. B. Ashton, New York, Continuum, 1973, p. 362.

caust might perpetuate the kind of thinking that had made genocide possible in the first place.

Adorno's antidote to identity thinking is complicated and subtle, the substance of a philosophical system described in his *Negative Dialectics*. Its essence lies in negating positivism by advocating *non*-identity thinking, that is, by regarding an object in its unique particularity while rejecting the possibility of ever totally understanding it. Adorno imagines the conscientious thinker as a kind of shaman, one who acknowledges the mystery and magic of a particular object at the same time as s/he seeks to unriddle its riddle and call it by its true name. Unriddling involves "exact fantasy"—submitting the precise historical facts to an intellectual inquiry afforded by a present-day methodological key (i.e. Marxism, feminism, psychoanalysis, etc.) from an infinite number of possible keys—in order to unlock the object's "unintentional truth," which is its true name. But immediately after that flash of epiphanic truth—that glimpse of Utopia where language exists in its pre-Tower of Babel state—the name may become a reductive label, an example of identity thinking. This situation impels the dutiful thinker to seek other names from a pool which is inexhaustible, for the nature of the object can never totally be known.[17]

It appears that a similar conscientiousness motivates many artists of Holocaust subject matter to refrain from making brash or categorical statements.[18] Incorporating the indexical sign, what Krauss calls "the mute presence of an uncoded event," allows a respectful surrender of authorial control, an apparent avoidance of identity thinking.[19] With *Fourteen Stations* Galles employed photographic imagery for the first time in his career because he felt that documents are more

—

17— Adorno's opaque text, ostensibly crafted to engage only serious thinkers while forestalling co-optation by identity thinkers, is clarified most beautifully by Susan Buck-Morss, *The Origin of Negative Dialectics: Theodor W. Adorno, Walter Benjamin, and the Frankfurt Institute*, New York, The Free Press, 1977.

18— For a consideration of the parallels between artistic representations of the Holocaust and Adorno's philosophy see my essay "Art after Auschwitz and the Necessity of a Postmodern Modernism" in *Contemporary Portrayals of Auschwitz: Philosophical Challenges*, eds. Alan Rosenberg, James R. Watson and Detlef Linke, Amherst, NY, Humanity Books, 2000, pp. 151-67.

19— Krauss, op. cit., p. 212.

powerful in connecting to historical reality than anything an artist can invent.

Such a confrontation with history can lead to some contradictory effects. Galles represents a community of Holocaust-related artists when he reports a two-sided response. He speaks of weeping at his easel as he considers lost relatives and raging at God's disregard. Alternatively, he talks of the toughness, the callousness required to go on with the work.[20]

Not only in art, but also in scholarship, the sobering encounter with Holocaust documents—a potentially traumatizing confrontation with historical (and sometimes personal) memory—prompts the two alternative responses which Galles describes. Balancing between that numbness which provides a protective shield that makes work possible and the emotion that occasionally breaks through the shield is, in fact, the primary challenge to the Holocaust historian, according to Saul Friedlander. Acknowledgement of both tendencies, he suggests, is a form of coming to terms with a traumatic past.[21]

Curiously enough, this dual approach also happens to be the strategy that Hal Foster sees at work in Andy Warhol's *Disaster* (1963–64) paintings of race riots, lynchings, automobile accidents, the electric chair, and the Kennedy assassination, silk-screen paintings each of which features multiple reproductions of a single disturbing photograph. [Fig. 8] In these works, Warhol not only engages the real, but actually distances it. "When you see a gruesome picture over and over again, it doesn't really have any effect," Warhol explained in 1963.[22] In Freudian terms, repetition becomes a means of mastering a trauma. Yet Warhol's multiples are not, in fact, identical: variations in the paint make each reproduction of a horrible image unique, unexpectedly restoring its traumatic

—

20— Arie A. Galles, personal interview, May 2, 1998.

21— Saul Friedlander, "Trauma and Transference" in *Memory, History, and the Extermination of the Jews of Europe*, Bloomington & Indianapolis, Indiana UP, 1993, p. 130.

22— Foster, op. cit., p. 131. Foster takes Warhol's quote from Gene Swenson, "What is Pop Art? Answers from 8 Painters, Part I" in *ArtNews*, Nov. 1963, p. 60. Reprinted in *Art in Theory*, 1900-2000, pp. 747-49.

power. Foster calls this contradictory encounter with the horrible "traumatic realism."[23]

Where traumatic realism differs from older, nineteenth-century realism is in its relation to life and death. Traditional realism, especially in its literary form, aspires to mimetically recreate the world. Even after that real world disappears, it fictively endures. But traumatic realism points to the reality of an absence, one which leaves the reader or viewer with a keen sense of lack.[24]

***

The difference between literary realism and traumatic realism recalls the distinction between cinema and still photography. Whereas cinematic film mimics the real world by re-creating its sense of the flow of time and the incumbent spatial expansion beyond the frame of any momentary image, still photographs, as frozen moments, Susan Sontag observes, function in the way that memento mori do.[25] In them, the world beyond the frame "dies absolutely," writes Roland Barthes, isolating and trapping the image in the photo, which becomes redolent of a sense of life already lived: "I observe with horror an anterior future of which death is the stake. [...] Whether or not the subject is already dead, every photograph is this catastrophe."[26] In this regard, still photography epitomizes the sensibility of traumatic realism. How an artist who works with photographs, in particular Holocaust photographs, chooses to negotiate that nominally traumatic encounter with loss and death is profoundly significant.

On the one extreme, such an artist can embrace an Adornian perspective by striving to promote a view of the photographic index in its historical particularity, reinscribing

—

23— Ibid. pp. 130-36.

24— Michael Rothberg offers this distinction in *Traumatic Realism: The Demands of Holocaust Representation*, Minneapolis, University of Minnesota Press, 2000, p. 99.

25— Susan Sontag, *On Photography*, New York, Penguin, 1979, pp. 15, 17.

26— Roland Barthes, *Camera Lucida*, London, Fontana Paperbacks, 1984, pp. 57, 96.

it as much as possible within an understanding of its original context—attempting to revive the dead world beyond the frame of the photo. On the other extreme, the artist may intentionally position the photographic index as a memento mori, sacrificing or subjugating historical context in the promotion of the sense of death and loss intrinsic to the medium. Sacralized, the index resembles a relic.[27]

In religious practice, relics have traditionally been conceived as truthfully partaking in or connecting to the figure to which they refer. Long before the advent of photography or of the Enlightenment positivist assumptions that would foster its invention, the distinction between relic and icon, or index and image, was vague. One example: the Veronica (or *vera icona*[28]), the cloth which had purportedly captured Jesus's image when he wiped his face with it on the Stations of the Cross and consequently possessed miraculous powers, functioned in the thirteenth century as an indexical record of the face, a model which artists copied, with the result that the iconic bust portrait became popular among designs for devotional paintings.[29] Yet earlier versions of the story of the Veronica mention nothing of an index and tell instead of the woman named Veronica who had painted an image of Christ which possessed healing powers.[30]

Religion is not, of course, the operant force that it was in pre-modern times, so Holocaust indices and the artworks that incorporate them cannot be claimed to offer any connection to the depicted subjects in the manner of a relic or man-made icon. Stripped of the numinous, they speak of loss.

What, then, does it mean for Holocaust memory to become sacralized? In writing of a "theology" of Auschwitz, Jacob Neusner suggests that Holocaust memory in the

—

27— A factor that problematizes the reception of an artwork of Holocaust representation as sacred is the reality that viewers are likely to encounter it in a museum or gallery —what Sontag calls "a social situation, riddled with distractions." Susan Sontag, *Regarding the Pain of Others*, New York, Picador, 2004, p. 121.

28— Hans Belting, *Likeness and Presence: A History of the Image before the Era of Art*, trans. Edmund Jephcott, Chicago and London, University of Chicago Press, 1994, p. 208.

29— Ibid, p. 220.

30— Ibid, p. 218.

United States has become part and parcel of a Jewish religious identity wrapped up with notions of redemption (the birth of Israel) and the general determination to endure as a people and a tradition: "The ironic fact has been that the Holocaust, which should have dispirited and demoralized the Jews, made an aimless generation realize it must be true to its Jewishness."[31] A more critical understanding of the role of Holocaust memory in contemporary Jewish life comes from Jack Kugelmass. Through the sacralization of that memory, he writes, a population of essentially privileged (American) Jews and oppressive (Israeli) Jews "symbolically revers[e] reality" by reclaiming the identity of victimization experienced by European Jews under Hitler. Through performative gestures, such as visiting the sites of atrocity in Eastern Europe, contemporary Jews reaffirm their martyrdom not only for themselves but for an audience of non-Jews.[32] Furthermore, by offering a common identity, Holocaust memory unifies a community of Jews that has grown so diverse that its distinct factions might otherwise come to political loggerheads. In short, sacralizing Holocaust memory de-particularizes it to the extent that it may be co-opted for ideological expediencies both within contemporary Jewish communities and without.

For many artists, resisting sacralization is a primary concern. Working not with photos but rather with the texts of period diaries, letters, and testimony, Ruth Liberman crafts what might be called anti-relics. She rewrites their words in her own hand or retypes them on an electric typewriter. By overlaying words until they disappear in inky palimpsests or including typed cross-outs and corrections, she makes texts seem inchoate again, as if returned to their historical moments of conception. [Fig. 9]

Other artists gravitate toward patently disgusting material, creating offensive artworks which would seem impossible to sacralize and improbable for anyone to co-opt.

—

31— Jacob Neusner, *American Judaism: Adventure in Modernity*, Englewood Cliffs, NJ, Prentice-Hall, 1972, p. 137.

32— Jack Kugelmass, "The Rites of the Tribe: American Jewish Tourism in Poland" in *Museums and Communities: The Politics of Public Culture*, eds., Ivan Karp, Christine Mullen Kreamer and Steven D. Lavine, Washington and London, Smithsonian Institution Press, 1992, p. 411.

Among contemporary artists in the mainstream, Mike Kelley debunks sentimental media representations of children by confronting what he sees as their true behavior and desires, in *Nostalgic Depiction of the Innocence of Childhood* (1990), a performance of adults appearing to defecate and masturbate on stuffed animals. Damien Hirst plumbs even lower into abjection with his *Waiting for Inspiration, Red* (1994), a putrefied cow head infested with maggots inside a Plexiglas vitrine. In Hirst's artwork the "sacred cow" of sanitized supermarket display, with its denial of death, is replaced by the materiality of decay, shocking a viewer toward base awareness. Bodily defilement and decay are abject, writes Julia Kristeva, because those states disturb the barriers of a being, destroying the integrity of a body as distinct from its surrounding environment. In addition to its physical revulsion, what makes the Holocaust abject, she suggests, is precisely that it ruptured the integrity of "borders, positions, rules," offering "the killer who claims he is a savior" and revealing the "fragility of the law."[33]

During the 1990s, some artists of Holocaust subject matter began aggressively de-sacralizing the Holocaust signifier, indexical and otherwise. Among these artists, several shift primary attention away from Holocaust history and focus instead on critiquing present-day cultural values. Alan Schechner's *It's the Real Thing—Self-Portrait at Buchenwald* (1993) is not the real thing at all, but rather a fabricated image, a digital still that seamlessly creates a visual fiction reminiscent of John Heartfield photomontages [Fig. 4] It incorporates one of Margaret Bourke-White's canonical photos of just-liberated men in a Buchenwald concentration camp barracks into which the artist, born in 1962, superimposed a black-and-white image of himself in a striped camp uniform with a can of Diet Coke that alone appears in color. An "icon of weight-conscious Westerners" alongside the gaunt survivors, the soda can particularly disturbed one critic, who went so far as to decry what she saw as "latent anti-Semitism" in this artist of dual Israeli-English

—

33— Julia Kristeva, *Powers of Horror: An Essay on Abjection*, trans. Leon S. Roudiez, New York, Columbia UP, 1982, p. 4.

citizenship.[34] Schechner defends his piece as an effort to draw attention to the manipulation of Holocaust memory for what he calls Israel's "ideological and political aims" vis-a-vis the Palestinians.[35]

Holocaust images, he continues, are imbued with a sort of false religiosity; they become sacred. [...] By placing my well-fed self with a Diet Coke amongst the emaciated survivors of Buchenwald I was not only attacking Israeli society with its fetishistic fascination with all fads American, but also more importantly, saying that we (the Jewish people) need to put ourselves back in the shoes of those survivors.[36]

The experience of seeing the familiar Bourke-White photo in Schechner's modified form, writes Joanna Lindenbaum, brings a feeling of terror to viewers because they are prompted to imagine the artist—and themselves—among the sufferers. Then "the terror transforms into shame" as viewers recognize their own prior "desensitization to the overexposure of Holocaust images" like Bourke-White's.[37] The effect of this overexposure approximates the experience of repetition discussed by Hal Foster in his remarks on Andy Warhol's *Disasters*. Yet Foster also notes that variations added by Warhol to each of the repeated images in a silk-screen painting prompt a viewer to study every reproduction of the photo as if it were unique, thereby overcoming the

—

34— Valerie Reardon, "A Reply: Whose Image is it Anyway?" in *Art Monthly*, Apr. 1996, p. 45. Also posted online: Alan Schechner, "How Many of My People Does It Take to Screw In a Lightbulb? On the Ownership of Experience, or, Who Can Say What to Whom, When" in *Work By Alan Schechner*, vers. July 22, 2003. <http://dottycommies.com/art_paper.html>

35— Responding to Reardon's attack, Schechner explains, "Throughout my time in Israel I became acutely aware of how the Holocaust was used to justify some of the more unsavory aspects of Israeli policy. I was told more than once how: 'Whatever we do to them (the Palestinians) can never be as bad as what they (the Germans) did to us.' The first stop of all foreign diplomats on arrival in Israel is Yad Vashem, before the diplomacy, before the state dinners and the visits these images are being used to serve narrow political agendas." Alan Schechner, quoted in "How Many of My People Does It Take to Screw In a Lightbulb? On the Ownership of Experience, or, Who Can Say What to Whom, When" in *Art Papers*, Mar.-Apr. 1997, p. 34; and <http://dottycommies.com/art_paper.html>

36—Ibid, <http://dottycommies.com/art_paper.html>

37— Joanna Lindenbaum, "Alan Schechner," in *Mirroring Evil: Nazi Imagery/ Recent Art*, ed. Norman L. Kleeblatt, New Brunswick, Rutgers UP; New York, The Jewish Museum, 2001, p. 115.

numbing effect of the repetition. Similarly, Schechner's strategy of modifying an index whose repetition in society has turned it banal is intended to lead a viewer toward seeing it in his work with fresh eyes, consequently restoring a measure of its original horror.

I would suggest that Schechner's piece is abject, too, by rupturing the temporal barrier between Holocaust time and our own time, conceptually confusing who belongs where. Rather than staying safely where it belongs, the Holocaust erupts into the present at the same time that Schechner's self-portrait is transported into the past. In this way, both traumatic realism and abjection combine to confront a viewer with an unexpected return of the Holocaust real in the guise of Holocaust survivors, "not images of the dead and lost," Schechner insists, "but of people, some of whom are still alive from whom we can and must still learn" in order to re-inscribe Holocaust signifiers into their original contexts.[38]

Elke Krystufek, an Austrian artist born in 1970, engages Nazi culture and its glamorization in the entertainment media as a means of exploring gender issues in an indisputably abject manner. A series of photographed collages called *Economical Love (1998)* includes a cut and collaged photo of her own naked body, thighs spread, along with painted renditions of the same subject defiled with paint drips [Fig. 5] Joining these are photos of male actors in Nazi uniform, and fragments of texts clipped from various sources, including the following quote: "You can't shock us, Damien. That's because you haven't based an entire exhibition on pictures of Nazis".[39] The line refers to Damien Hirst, whose own abjection Krystufek apparently aspires to outdo.

Using media and present-day images only, Krystufek explores the relations between men and women and, ultimately, Nazi and Jew, as they are manifest in the controlling power of the male gaze. With the themes of sexual domination and submission, she reveals what

—

38— Schechner, op. cit.

39— Krystufek snipped this quote from a British art review of Piotr Uklaski's 1998 installation, *The Nazis*. The piece is composed of 166 photos of Hollywood stars in Nazi costume, five of which Krystufek incorporates in three works in the *Economical Love* series: *Economical Love (Pussy Control), Economical Love (Hitler Hairdo), and Economical Love (Abstract Expressionism).*

Norman Kleeblatt calls "the self-victimization... in herself and in other women of her generation" at the same time that she also uses her nakedness to mirror male fantasies back onto "potential perpetrators —men who might gaze at women or fantasize violently about them."[40] Regarding gender roles in art history, Krystufek indicts the stereotypically masculine with a portion of collaged text in another work in the series, *Economical Love (Abstract Expressionism)* "Believing in the transcendental power of the image and it's [sic] Beauty is like wanting to be an Abstract Expressionist or a Cowboy."

Krystufek destabilizes the authority of the male gaze by complicating subject and object positions. Not only her female body but also the film stars are in a sense feminized, on display, objectified by their adherence to tropes of either sexuality or glamour, which are perpetuated in society by pornography and popular entertainment. Simultaneously, Krystufek, like most of the male faces, also confronts us with her own penetrating attention, dramatized by the camera that she aims at the viewer.[41] Krystufek, it appears, identifies with the Nazi oppressors—an implication of her apparent boast of outdoing Hirst at his own game. He can't shock "us," the quote across her torso reads, implying community with the depicted men. If she herself has, as the quote implies, indeed "based an entire exhibition on pictures of Nazis," then the artist, as depicted in the works, apparently counts herself among them.[42] By acting out the role of a Nazi much as Kiefer did in his *Occupations*, Krystufek may be said to explore the attraction of Nazi power, along with its

—

40— Norman L. Kleeblatt, "Elke Krystufek" in *Mirroring Evil: Nazi Imagery/Recent Art*, ed. Norman L. Kleeblatt, New Brunswick, Rutgers UP; New York, The Jewish Museum, 2001, p. 112. Kleeblatt sees the artist's exploration in relation to Klaus Theweleit's *Male Fantasies*, an important study of the topic in German history.

41— Krystufek's squatting female figures assume a gorgon-like mien that expresses not submission but archetypal sexual power. The theme is discussed in relation to works of Picasso and Willem de Kooning by Carol Duncan, "The MoMA's Hot Mamas" in *Art Journal*, num.14.2, 1989, pp. 171-78.

42— In *Economical Love (Abstract Expressionism)*, a representation of Krystufek shares not only the Nazis' gaze of domination, but flesh, as well. Superimposed over the artist's crouching left leg, the shoulders of an actor (Hardy Krüger) in Nazi uniform visually substitute for the covered portions of her thigh and calf, turning his head into something like an eruption from her knee.

perpetuation in entertainment media, so as to better understand its appeal and its contemporary menace.

Perhaps it is no wonder that this broad transformation in artistic consciousness of the Holocaust began at just the time when corporate culture discovered the blockbuster potential of Holocaust memory. Steven Spielberg's *Schindler's List* appeared in 1993, the so-called "year of the Holocaust" for the preponderance of Holocaust history and memory in public consciousness, particularly in the United States.

The value of *Schindler's List* as an educational tool has been debated by scholars, who note that the film is rife with distortions of historical fact.[43] Since its creation, cinematic misrepresentations have proliferated, a prominent example being Roberto Benigni's *Life is Beautiful* (1998), which ameliorates the horror of the historical truth by depicting a concentration camp as a clean environment where a child could hide for months. By contrast, the artworks of abjection which began to appear during the 1990s do not deny the brutality of the Holocaust; even if such artworks are offensive to many, they do not distort the historical record.[44] Because Holocaust history is not, in fact, their subject, they focus instead on the manner of its current representation. By exaggerating such representations in present-day politics, popular entertainment, gender roles, etc., to such an extent they may actually offend viewers, the artworks call attention to what those representations lack, a connection to the real-world referent, to Holocaust history itself.[45]

—

43— See Yosefa Loshitzky, ed., *Spielberg's Holocaust: Critical Perspectives of Schindler's List*, Bloomington and Indianapolis, Indiana UP, 1997.

44— Among commentators about the notorious 2002 exhibition "Mirroring Evil: Nazi Imagery/Recent Art," which included both Schechner and Krystufek at the Jewish Museum in New York, only Walter Reich, a former director of the United States Holocaust Memorial Museum, notes this fact. He targets his opprobrium at governments and interest groups who distort Holocaust memory to advance their own agendas, and at media like popular film that present false renderings of Holocaust history. Walter Reich, "Appropriating the Holocaust" in *New York Times*, March 15, 2002, p. A23.

45— In his review of "Mirroring Evil," critic Michael Kimmelman hit on what I believe is the essential point—even though the spirit of his words was facetious: "In a world inundated by commercial images that anesthetize us and replace truth with fiction, art that causes you pain returns your attention to the real." Michael Kimmelman, "Evil, the Nazis and Shock Value," rev. of "Mirroring Evil: Nazi Imagery/Recent Art," The Jewish Museum, New York, in *New York Times*, March 15, 2002, p. E33.

Postscript: Yishai Jusidman's *Prussian Blue* series at the Museo Universitario Arte Contemporáneo

I wrote "From the Sublime to the Abject: Six Decades of Art" in 2005. Since that time, many artists of Holocaust-related art have moved on to other subjects or returned to the themes and issues of earlier work. While the Holocaust remains present in popular culture, the obsession has passed. In this relative quiet, Yishai Jusidman has engaged with Holocaust history and memory to provide what I see as an appraisal of the efficacy of that earlier Holocaust-related art. His *Prussian Blue* series (2010–15), explores and tests the sublime, the documentary, the abject and other formal strategies. As the artist puts it, "my paintings do not deal with the Holocaust but rather with the possibility of its representation."[46]

Introducing the *Prussian Blue* series, the painting *Haus der Kunst* (2012) [*House of Art* in German] portrays the Nazi-designed Munich exhibition hall in a Nazi manner, with monumental scale, symmetry and powerful linear perspective. The painting, based on a photo Jusidman shot himself, recalls Anselm Kiefer's flirtations with fascism in such works as *Interior* (1981), a depiction of Hitler's New Reich Chancellery, and *Shulamite* (1983), a rendering of a Nazi war memorial, except that Jusidman's decision to depict an empty art gallery establishes his focus on art itself.

Paired with this work as part of Jusidman's "Prologue" is a painted re-creation of the inglorious legacy of Nazism. *Birkenau* (2012) reproduces a rare historical photograph made outside a functioning gas chamber. Jusidman's chosen photographic source depicts no evident atrocities, only wild distortions through the camera lens; blurred trees bend and attenuate, losing their wooden rigidity in a display of the *informe* [French for "lacking in form"]. The informe is a concept concerned with the transgression of fixed boundaries first theorized by Georges Bataille in 1929 in conjunction with ideas about abjection. It inspired Salvador Dalí to conceive images of rubbery bones and melting clocks. While some contemporary artists during the recent fad about the

—

46— Alexander, Neta. "Painting the Nazi Gas Chambers With Defiant Realism." in *Haaretz*, January 22, 2013, Web, March 20, 2016.

Holocaust employed abject material to try to jolt attention back to its historical referent, Jusidman's engagement with these ideas serves a different purpose. He suggests that the violations inside the unseen gas chamber have literally destabilized the world beyond its walls.

Even though these first two "Prologue" works are, in fact, based on photographs, it isn't until we turn attention to Jusidman's smaller-size paintings in the second and third sections of his *Prussian Blue* series, "Gas Chambers" and "Landscapes," that the notion of the documentary takes center stage. Postwar and contemporary photos provide the sources for the bleak, unpeopled sites of atrocity Jusidman catalogues in acrylic paint. These desolate scenes of the aftermath provide evidence of genocide but refuse to offer understandings. In a sense they are memorials: Jusidman's renderings in Prussian blue, a color produced by the same chemical reaction that occurred between Zyklon B poison gas and some gas chamber walls, and his use in these works of skin tones to represent the murdered, recall Arie A. Galles's symbolically charged use of charcoal, which he calls ash, in his reproductions of camp photos. That Jusidman's paintings preserve the different dimensions and perspectives of their original source photographs, and even possess different tonalities of Prussian blue, makes them a heterogeneous group. This sensibility contrasts with the kind of totalizing modernist aesthetic championed by the Nazis that would have imposed a standardized uniformity on them.

Jusidman presents large monochrome paintings in his fourth section: "Memorial." Shown alongside representations of gas chambers and landscapes of atrocity, these abstract works manifest the lasting power of Abstract Expressionism for reflection about the Holocaust. Rather like Mark Rothko's large canvases in the Rothko Chapel in Houston, the paintings reveal subtle variations in surface density that take time to notice, and a modulation of color at the bottom edge that suggests a landscape below an impenetrable night- and/or smoke-darkened sky. Among these works, the one called simply *Prussian Blue* (2014–15) presents a mirror-like surface that insinuates the viewer's full-length reflection into its vast painterly space.

Jusidman ends his series with "Epilogue: Stains," which comprises the rags that he used for cleaning up, and photos of the walls that were dirtied when he painted his memorial pictures on linen pinned to them. Art remains a primary subject here, its practices and practicalities. But together with representations of sites of atrocity, these works, like the memorial paintings, conjure Holocaust memory. Defiled with stains of indeterminate form, the rags epitomize abjection, and suggest not only the residue of gaseous poison but also the filth of the camps and the smoke and ash that so many human beings became. The photos of the stained walls offer a poignant conclusion. They feature empty painted frames, voids that denote nothing while suggesting so much: the absence of the murdered victims of Nazism; the multitude of testimonies never told; the impossible knowledge of human depravity; and, perhaps most powerfully in this context, the ultimate inability of any artistic representation to provide definition—closure, if you will—to the Holocaust.

 Foto—Photo: Edward Duarte

SEMBLANZA

—

YISHAI JUSIDMAN

(Ciudad de México, 1963) mantiene una práctica estrechamente ligada a un amplio rango de inquietudes inherentes a la tradición pictórica, mismas que rearticula en nuevos marcos para insertarlas en el entorno contemporáneo. Entre sus exposiciones de la última década destacan *Prussian Blue* (The Americas Society, Nueva York, 2013); *Pintura en obra* (Museo de Arte Moderno, Ciudad de México, 2009); *The Economist Shuffle* (Yvon Lambert, Nueva York, 2007); *Mutatis mutandis & Working Painters* (SMAK, Gante, Bélgica; MEIAC, Badajoz, España; Marco, Monterrey, 2002–2003). Su pintura ha sido seleccionada para importantes muestras internacionales, tales como SITE Santa Fe, 2014; la Biennale di Venezia, 2001; Ultra Baroque: Aspects of Post Latin American Art (MCASD, San Diego; SFMOMA, San Francisco; Walker Art Center, Mineápolis; MAM, Miami, 2000–2003) y ARS 01 (Kiasma, Helsinki, 2001). La obra de Jusidman ha estado presente en las grandes exposiciones panorámicas de arte contemporáneo mexicano que han itinerado internacionalmente, como *La era de la discrepancia: arte y cultura visual en México, 1968–1997* (MUCA C.U., Ciudad de México; MALBA, Buenos Aires; Pinacoteca do Estado de São Paulo, Sao Paulo, 2007–2008), *Eco: Arte contemporáneo de México* (Museo Nacional Centro de Arte Reina Sofía, Madrid, 2005), *Soleils mexicains* (Petit Palais, París 2000). Su bibliografía incluye publicaciones como *Vitamin P: New Perspectives in Painting* (Phaidon Press, 2003) y *100 artistas latinoamericanos* (Exit Press, 2007). Sus exposiciones han sido comentadas en los más prestigiados medios especializados del arte contemporáneo.

BIOGRAPHICAL SKETCH

—

YISHAI JUSIDMAN

(Mexico City, 1963). His practice is closely associated with a wide range of themes intrinsic to the pictorial tradition, which he rearticulates within new frameworks for the contemporary context. His exhibitions over the last decade include *Prussian Blue* (The Americas Society, New York, 2013); *Pintura en obra* (Paintworks, Museo de Arte Moderno, Mexico City, 2009); *The Economist Shuffle* (Yvon Lambert, New York, 2007); *Mutatis Mutandis and Working Painters* (SMAK, Ghent, Belgium; MEIAC, Badajoz, Spain; Marco, Monterrey, 2002–2003). His paintings have been selected for important international exhibitions, such as SITE Santa Fe, 2014; the Venice Biennale, 2001; Ultra Baroque: Aspects of Post Latin American Art (MCASD, San Diego; SFMOMA, San Francisco; Walker Art Center, Minneapolis; MAM, Miami, 2000–2003); and ARS 01 (Kiasma, Helsinki, 2001). Jusidman's work has appeared in major panoramic exhibitions of contemporary Mexican art that have traveled internationally, like *La era de la discrepancia: arte y cultura visual en México, 1968–1997* (The Age of Discrepancies: Art and Visual Culture in Mexico, 1968–1997, MUCA C.U., Mexico City; MALBA, Buenos Aires; Pinacoteca do Estado de São Paulo, São Paulo, 2007–2008), *Eco: Arte contemporáneo mexicano* (Echo: Mexican Contemporary Art, Museo Nacional Centro de Arte Reina Sofía, Madrid, 2005); and *Soleils mexicains* (Petit Palais, Paris 2000). His work is featured in surveys such as *Vitamin P: New Perspectives in Painting* (Phaidon Press, 2003) and *100 artistas latinoamericanos* (*100 Latin American Artists*, Exit Press, 2007). His exhibitions have been reviewed in the most prestigious contemporary art publications.

CATÁLOGO
—
CATALOGUE

I. PRÓLOGO—PROLOGUE

1. *Birkenau*, 2012
Acrílico sobre lienzo montado en tabla—
Acrylic on linen mounted on wood
203 × 203 cm

2. *Haus der Kunst—[Casa del arte—House of Art]*, 2012
Acrílico sobre lienzo montado en tabla—
Acrylic on linen mounted on wood
203 × 203 cm

3. *Treblinka*, 2012
Acrílico sobre tabla, marco del artista—
Acrylic on wood, artist's frame
81 × 111 cm

II. CÁMARAS DE GAS—GAS CHAMBERS

4. *Auschwitz*, 2010
Acrílico sobre tabla, marco del artista—
Acrylic on wood, artist's frame
111 × 79 cm

5. *Auschwitz*, 2011
Acrílico sobre tabla, marco del artista—
Acrylic on wood, artist's frame
108 × 82 cm

6. *Dachau*, 2010–2012
Acrílico sobre tabla, marco del artista—
Acrylic on wood, artist's frame
176 × 117 cm

7. *Auschwitz*, 2011
Acrílico sobre tabla, marco del artista—
Acrylic on wood, artist's frame
81 × 109 cm

8. *Majdanek*, 2010
Acrílico sobre tabla, marco del artista—
Acrylic on wood, artist's frame
84 × 104 cm

9. *Majdanek*, 2011
Acrílico sobre tabla, marco del artista—
Acrylic on wood, artist's frame
104 × 87 cm

10. *Majdanek*, 2012
Acrílico sobre tabla, marco del artista—
Acrylic on wood, artist's frame
84 × 107 cm

11. *Mauthausen*, 2011–2012
Acrílico sobre tabla, marco del artista—
Acrylic on wood, artist's frame
114 × 76 cm

12. *Puerta de gas—Gas Door,* 2011
Acrílico sobre tabla, marco del artista—
Acrylic on wood, artist's frame
76 × 70 cm

13. *Puerta de gas—Gas Door*, 2011
Acrílico sobre tabla, marco del artista—
Acrylic on wood, artist's frame
76 × 66 cm

14. *Stuthof*, 2010
Acrílico sobre tabla, marco del artista—
Acrylic on wood, artist's frame
76 × 114 cm

15. *Stuthof*, 2011
Acrílico sobre tabla, marco del artista—
Acrylic on wood, artist's frame
82 × 110 cm

16. *Van*, 2010
Acrílico sobre tabla, marco del artista—
Acrylic on wood, artist's frame
105 × 85 cm

III. PAISAJES—LANDSCAPES

17. *Birkenau*, 2013
Acrílico sobre lienzo montado en tabla—
Acrylic on linen mounted on wood
89 × 152 cm

18. *Birkenau*, 2014
Acrílico sobre lienzo montado en tabla—
Acrylic on linen mounted on wood
89 × 152 cm

19. *Dachau*, 2014
Acrílico sobre lienzo montado en tabla—
Acrylic on linen mounted on wood
86 × 140 cm

20. *Mauthausen*, 2013
Acrílico sobre lienzo montado en tabla—
Acrylic on linen mounted on wood
89 × 152 cm

21. *Sobibor*, 2013
Acrílico sobre lienzo montado en tabla—
Acrylic on linen mounted on wood
86 × 140 cm

IV. MEMORIAL

22. *Azul de Prusia—Prussian Blue*, 2014–2015
Óleo y acrílico sobre lienzo, montado en tabla—
Oil and acrylic on linen mounted on wood
236 × 203 cm

23. *Azul de Prusia / Negro vid alemán—Prussian Blue / German Vine Black*, 2014–2015
Óleo y acrílico sobre lienzo, montado en tabla—
Oil and acrylic on linen mounted on wood
236 × 203 cm

24. *Azul de Prusia / Tierra de Cassel—Prussian Blue / Kassel Earth*, 2014–2015
Óleo y acrílico sobre lienzo, montado en tabla—
Oil and acrylic on linen mounted on wood
236 × 203 cm

25. *Azul de Prusia / Tierra verde bohemia—Prussian Blue / Bohemian Green Earth*, 2014–2015
Óleo y acrílico sobre lienzo, montado en tabla—
Oil and acrylic on linen mounted on wood
236 × 203 cm

V. EPÍLOGO: MANCHAS—EPILOGUE: STAINS

26. *Delantal—Apron*, 2011–2016
Acrílico sobre algodón montado en tabla—
Acrylic on cotton mounted on wood
51 × 76 cm

27. *Trapo #1—Rag #1*, 2011–2014
Acrílico sobre algodón montado en tabla—
Acrylic on cotton mounted on wood
46 × 37 cm

28. *Trapo #2—Rag #2*, 2011–2014
Acrílico sobre algodón montado en tabla—
Acrylic on cotton mounted on wood
46 × 37 cm

29. *Trapo #3—Rag #3*, 2012–2014
Acrílico sobre algodón montado en tabla—
Acrylic on cotton mounted on wood
48 × 36 cm

30. *Trapo #6—Rag #6*, 2013–2014
Acrílico sobre algodón montado en tabla—
Acrylic on cotton mounted on wood
44 × 37 cm

31. *Trapo #7—Rag #7*, 2013–2014
Óleo sobre algodón montado en tabla—
Oil on cotton mounted on wood
52 × 42 cm

32. *Trapo #8—Rag #8*, 2013–2015
Acrílico y óleo sobre algodón montado en tabla—
Acrylic and oil on cotton mounted on wood
50 × 40 cm

33. *Trapo #9—Rag #9*, 2013–2015
Acrílico y óleo sobre algodón montado en tabla—
Acrylic and oil on cotton mounted on wood
48 × 40 cm

34. *Trapo #10—Rag #10*, 2013–2015
Acrílico y óleo sobre algodón montado en tabla—
Acrylic and oil on cotton mounted on wood
48 × 40 cm

35. *Trapo #12—Rag #12*, 2013–2015
Acrílico y óleo sobre algodón montado en tabla—
Acrylic and oil on cotton mounted on wood
47 × 38 cm

36. *Trapo #13—Rag #13*, 2013–2015
Acrílico y óleo sobre algodón montado en tabla—
Acrylic and oil on cotton mounted on wood
50 × 41 cm

37. *Trapo #16—Rag #16*, 2013–2015
Óleo sobre algodón montado en tabla—
Oil on cotton mounted on wood
45 × 37 cm

38. *Trapo #18—Rag #18*, 2013–2015
Óleo sobre algodón montado en tabla—
Oil on cotton mounted on wood
49 × 41 cm

39. *Trapo #19—Rag #19*, 2013–2015
Óleo y acrílico sobre algodón montado en tabla—
Oil and acrylic on cotton mounted on wood
67 × 50 cm

40. *Trapo #23—Rag #23*, 2013–2016
Óleo y acrílico sobre algodón montado en tabla—
Oil and acrylic on cotton mounted on wood
45 × 37 cm

41. *Trapo #24—Rag #24*, 2013–2016
Óleo y acrílico sobre algodón montado en tabla—
Oil and acrylic on cotton mounted on wood
51 × 39 cm

42. *Trapo #27—Rag #27*, 2013–2016
Óleo sobre algodón montado en tabla—
Oil on cotton mounted on wood
51 × 46 cm

43. *Trapo #28—Rag #28*, 2013–2016
Óleo sobre algodón montado en tabla—
Oil on cotton mounted on wood
45 × 39 cm

VI.

44. *Manchas (AP+TVB)—Stains (PB+BGE)*, 2015
Impresión de pigmento sobre acrílico—Pigment print on acrylic
142 × 123 cm

45. *Manchas (AP+TC)—Stains (PB + CE)*, 2015
Impresión de pigmento sobre acrílico—Pigment print on acrylic
142 × 123 cm

46. *Manchas (AP+NVA)—Stains (PB+GVB)*, 2015
Impresión de pigmento sobre acrílico—Pigment print on acrylic
142 × 123 cm

200 ml
6.75 US fl oz

CRÉDITOS DE EXPOSICIÓN
—
EXHIBITION CREDITS

Curaduría—Curatorship
Cuauhtémoc Medina
Virginia Roy

Producción museográfica—
Installation Design
Joel Aguilar

Salvador Ávila Velazquillo
Benedeta Monteverde
Cecilia Pardo

Programa pedagógico—Teaching Program
Pilar Ortega
Muna Cann
Ignacio Plá
Luis Vargas Santiago

Coordinación de colecciones
—Collections Coordination
Julia Molinar

Juan Cortés
Claudio Hernández
Elizabeth Herrera

Procuración de fondos—Fundraising
Gabriela Fong

María Teresa de la Concha
Josefina Granados
Alexandra Peeters

Comunicación—Media
Carmen Ruíz

Ekaterina Álvarez
Francisco Domínguez
Ana Cristina Sol

Servicio social—Interns
Adrián Martínez Caballero

Curador en jefe—Chief Curator
Cuauhtémoc Medina

AGRADECIMIENTOS
—
ACKNOWLEDGEMENTS

El Museo Universitario Arte Contemporáneo, MUAC, agradece a las personas e instituciones cuya generosa colaboración hizo posible la muestra de la exposición *Azul de Prusia*.
—
The Museo Universitario Arte Contemporáneo, MUAC, wishes to thank the people and institutions whose generous assistance made possible the exhibition *Prussian Blue*.

Yishai Jusidman agradece la confianza, el apoyo y el buen consejo de los integrantes del equipo del MUAC, quienes han trabajado de manera profesional y diligente para que este proyecto salga adelante.
—
Yishai Jusidman expresses his gratitude for the support, the trust and good counsel of the members of the team at MUAC, all of whom have striven, professionally and diligently, to make this project happen.

Simón Nissan

YISHAI JUSIDMAN. AZUL DE PRUSIA se terminó de imprimir y encuadernar el 26 de agosto de 2016 en los talleres de Offset Rebosán S.A. de C.V., Acueducto 115, col. Huipulco, Tlalpan, Ciudad de México. Para su composición se utilizó la familia tipográfica Linotype Centennial, diseñada por Adrian Frutiger. Impreso en Domtar Lynx de 216 g, Bond blanco de 120 g y Couché mate 150 g. Diseño y supervisión de producción Periferia. El tiraje consta de 1000 ejemplares.

—

YISHAI JUSIDMAN. PRUSSIAN BLUE was printed and bound in August 26, 2016 in Offset Rebosán S.A. de C.V., Acueducto 115, col. Huipulco, Tlalpan, Mexico City. Typeset in Linotype Centennial, designed by Adrian Frutiger. Printed on 216 g Domtar Lynx, 120 g Bond white and 150 g Couche matte paper. Design and production supervision by Periferia. This edition is limited to 1000 copies.

—

—

FOLIO MUAC 047